# THE ECOLOGY OF SOIL BACTERIA

GRAY, T. R. G. and D. Parkinson, eds. The Ecology of Soil Bacteria, an International Symposium. Toronto, 1968. 681p il tab bibl. 21.75 68-101074

CHOICE OCT. '68
Biology

NUC 68

A high-pitched collection of 47 invitational papers given by *the* outstanding international soil microbiologists. Subject areas covered include isolation and taxonomy of soil bacteria, effects of factors on the development of bacteria in soil, growth and physiology, and interrelations between bacteria and other organisms. Nearly all the papers deal with soil bacteria and are evenly divided between research summations of the authors and review-type articles. The majority are interesting and well written. The titles of the papers in this volume differ considerably from *Microbial Ecology — Seventh Symposium of the Society for General Microbiology* (1957), and as a result there is little overlap in subject matter. However, format and organization are nearly identical. *Microbial Ecology* does consider a wider variety of microorganisms. Brock's *Principles of Microbial Ecology* (CHOICE, June 1967) overlaps both of the above books in a very general way, but its presentation is strictly synthesis with the aim of elaborating principles concerning population dynamics and interactions, ecosystems, and other microbial relationships. *Principles* should be in

263

Continued
GRAY, T. R. G.

CHOICE OCT. '68
Biology

libraries wishing information on a wide and general range with a textbook approach. *Soil Bacteria* is for research libraries and those desiring to update and supplement *Microbial Ecology*.

264

# THE ECOLOGY OF
# Soil Bacteria



AN INTERNATIONAL SYMPOSIUM

*Edited by*

T. R. G. GRAY

AND

D. PARKINSON

UNIVERSITY OF TORONTO PRESS
1968

PUBLISHED IN GREAT BRITAIN BY
LIVERPOOL UNIVERSITY PRESS

PUBLISHED IN CANADA BY
UNIVERSITY OF TORONTO PRESS





PRINTED IN GREAT BRITAIN BY
HAZELL WATSON & VINEY LTD
AYLESBURY, BUCKS

# CONTRIBUTORS

ALEXANDER, M., Department of Agronomy, Cornell University, Ithaca, New York, USA.

BACON, J. S. D., Department of Biochemistry, Macaulay Institute, Craigiebuckler, Aberdeen, UK.

BAXBY, PAMELA, Hartley Botanical Laboratories, The University, Liverpool, UK.

BRISBANE, P. G., CSIRO, Division of Soils, Glen Osmond, Adelaide, Australia.

BROWN, MARGARET E., Department of Soil Microbiology, Rothamsted Experimental Station, Harpenden, UK.

BURLINGHAM, SUSAN K., Department of Soil Microbiology, Rothamsted Experimental Station, Harpenden, UK.

CASIDA, L. E., Jr., 204, Patterson Building, Pennsylvania State University, Pennsylvania, USA.

CHASE, F. E., Department of Microbiology, University of Guelph, Guelph, Ontario, Canada.

CLARK, F. E., Agricultural Research Service, Fort Collins, Colorado, USA.

CORKE, C. T., Department of Microbiology, University of Guelph, Guelph, Ontario, Canada.

CROSSE, J. E., East Malling Research Station, Maidstone, Kent, UK.

FÅHRAEUS, G., Department of Microbiology, College of Agriculture, Uppsala, Sweden.

GOODFELLOW, M., Hartley Botanical Laboratories, The University, Liverpool, UK.

GORDON, RUTH E., Institute of Microbiology, Rutgers, The State University, New Brunswick, New Jersey, USA.

GRAY, T. R. G., Hartley Botanical Laboratories, The University, Liverpool, UK.

GREENWOOD, D. J., National Vegetable Research Station, Wellesbourne, Warwick, UK.

GYLLENBERG, H. G., Department of Microbiology, University of Helsinki, Helsinki, Finland.

HARMSEN, G. W., Institute for Soil Fertility, Groningen, The Netherlands.

HILL, I. R., Hartley Botanical Laboratories, The University, Liverpool, UK.

HOLDING, A. J., School of Agriculture, West Mains Rd., Edinburgh, UK.

IMSHENETSKY, A. A., Institute of Microbiology, Academy of Sciences, Moscow, USSR.

JACKSON, R. M., Department of Soil Microbiology, Rothamsted Experimental Station, Harpenden, UK.

JEFFREY, A. J., School of Agriculture, West Mains Rd., Edinburgh, UK.

JENSEN, V., Royal Veterinary and Agricultural College, Copenhagen, Denmark.

KRASILNIKOV, N. A., Institute of Microbiology, Academy of Sciences, Moscow, USSR.

KÜSTER, E., Department of Industrial Microbiology, University College, Dublin, Ireland.

LJUNGGREN, H., Department of Microbiology, College of Agriculture, Uppsala, Sweden.

LOCKWOOD, J. L., Department of Botany and Plant Pathology, Michigan State University, East Lansing, Michigan, USA.

MACFADYEN, A., Department of Zoology, University College, Swansea, UK.

MCLAREN, A. D., College of Agriculture, University of California, Berkeley, California, USA.

MACURA, J., Institute of Microbiology, Prague, Czechoslovakia.

MIRSOEVA, V. A., Institute of Microbiology, Academy of Sciences, Moscow, USSR.

MISHUSTIN, E. N., Institute of Microbiology, Academy of Sciences, Moscow, USSR.

POCHON, J., Institut Pasteur, Paris, France.

PRAMER, D., Department of Biochemistry and Microbiology, Rutgers, The State University, New Brunswick, New Jersey, USA.

ROBINSON, J. B., Department of Microbiology, University of Guelph, Guelph, Ontario, Canada.

ROUATT, J. W., Microbiology Research Institute, Canadian Experimental Farm, Ottawa, Ontario, Canada.

ROVIRA, A. D., CSIRO, Division of Soils, Glen Osmond, Adelaide, Australia.

RUSSELL, E. W., Department of Soil Science, The University, Reading, UK.

SCHLEGEL, H. G., Institute of Microbiology, The University, Göttingen, Germany.

SCHREVEN, D. A. van, Rijksdienst voor de Ijsselmeerpolders, Kampen, The Netherlands.

SKINNER, F. A., Department of Soil Microbiology, Rothamsted Experimental Station, Harpenden, UK.

SKUJINS, J., College of Agriculture, University of California, Berkeley, California, USA.

STARKEY, R. L., Department of Biochemistry and Microbiology, Rutgers, The State University, New Brunswick, New Jersey, USA.

TARDIEUX, P., Institut Pasteur, Paris, France.

VELDKAMP, H., Department of Microbiology, The University, Groningen, The Netherlands.

ZAVARZIN, G. A., Institute of Microbiology, Academy of Sciences, Moscow, USSR.

## CHAIRMAN OF SESSIONS

ALEXANDER, M., Department of Agronomy, Cornell University, Ithaca, New York, USA.

BURGES, N. A., New University of Ulster, Coleraine, Northern Ireland.

COWAN, S. T., Central Public Health Laboratories, Colindale, London, UK.

HARMSEN, G. W., Institute of Soil Fertility, Groningen, The Netherlands.

JENSEN, H. L., Statens Planteavls-Laboratarium, Lyngby, Denmark.

PARKINSON, D., Department of Biology, The University, Waterloo, Ontario, Canada.

SCHMIDT, E. L., Department of Soil Science and Microbiology, University of Minnesota, Minneapolis, Minnesota, USA.

## WELCOME TO PARTICIPANTS

DOWNIE, A. W., Department of Bacteriology, The University, Liverpool, UK.

# PREFACE

On many occasions, the late Dr. Marjory Stephenson stressed that when micro-organisms were being studied, they must be examined at all levels of complexity. She referred to five different levels, comprising the investigation of the behaviour of cell-free enzyme systems, the growth of pure cultures in highly purified media, the reactions of non-proliferating cells in pure cultures on chemically defined media, the growth of pure cultures on laboratory media and the growth of mixed cultures in natural environments. In the first and fifth Marjory Stephenson Memorial Lectures, D. D. Woods (*J. gen. Microbiol.*, **9**, 151) and B. C. J. G. Knight (*J. gen. Microbiol.*, **27**, 357), rendered biologists in general a very great service by putting many of Dr. Stephenson's ideas together in a way which made them available to a very wide audience.

During the great upsurge of interest in microbiology since the last war, the major effort has been in investigating either the organisms in pure culture or the behaviour of their enzyme systems. If the present volume appears to pay less attention to enzymes and subcellular particles than many microbiologists might think appropriate, it is because the symposium which is recorded here was deliberately framed to concentrate on the ecological aspects of bacteria in their natural environment.

No matter how much we may learn about the biochemical tricks which bacteria can play, such knowledge falls short of its true meaning unless we can relate it to the behaviour of the organism in nature. As in all ecology, one cannot investigate one group of organisms without considering the other species which occur in the environment studied, and perhaps one of the many interesting points which arose out of the discussions was the deficiency of our knowledge on the interaction between soil bacteria and other members of the soil population.

Clearly, in any symposium such as the one reported here, it is impossible to cover all aspects of the subject. In inviting speakers, it was the hope of the organizers that the contributions would be framed so as to indicate approaches to further study, at least as much as to report achieved results.

The earlier symposium in this series, *The Ecology of Soil Fungi*, edited by Dr. D. Parkinson and Dr. J. S. Waid, gave very great stimulus to workers in that field. In the present symposium, Dr. Parkinson has again played a major part in the organization and he and Dr. Gray are to be congratulated, not only on a most successful symposium, but on seeing the present work through from the initial invitations to the final publication.

ALAN BURGES

*Liverpool, 1966*

# ACKNOWLEDGEMENTS

Any value that this book possesses is due to those who presented papers and participated in the discussions. In addition to them, we wish to thank the United Nations Educational, Scientific and Cultural Organization for their generous support; without their help many of the contributors and participants could not have attended the meeting. We also wish to record our gratitude to the Agricultural Research Council who made it possible for Dr. R. L. Starkey to come to Liverpool.

We owe particular thanks to Professor N. A. Burges and Dr. S. T. Williams who took a very considerable part in the organization of the meeting, and the Lord Mayor and City of Liverpool and the University of Liverpool for their warm-hearted hospitality.

Countless people have helped us in an enormous variety of ways, but it gives us special pleasure to thank our colleagues, the members of our graduate and undergraduate schools and our technical staff, who prepared a series of demonstrations of the work in progress in the Hartley Botanical Laboratories and who helped with the administrative work. These included Mrs. P. Baxby, Mr. F. L. Davies, Mr. M. Goodfellow, Mr. I. R. Hill, Dr. H. M. Hurst, Miss C. E. Jones, Miss A. P. Kerrigan, Miss R. A. Kibble, Mr. B. Ledger (who recorded all the discussions), Mr. W. E. Lowe, Mr. C. Mayfield, Mr. S. Ruddick, Mr. M. Shameemullah, Mr. R. E. Smith, Mr. C. Stewart, Dr. J. H. Walsh, and Miss J. Watson.

During the preparation of the papers for publication we received much invaluable advice and assistance from Mr. J. G. O'Kane and Mr. D. Stockwell of the University Press. Their advice, the written papers, and the contributions of all the speakers in the discussions have been translated into print through the untiring efforts of a bevy of typists, including Mrs. M. Holledge, Miss E. A. Durkin, Miss G. M. Arthur and Miss W. E. Anderson.

T. R. G. GRAY
D. PARKINSON

# CONTENTS

## THE PHYSIOLOGY OF SOIL BACTERIA



## THE TAXONOMY OF SOIL BACTERIA



## BACTERIA IN THE ROOT REGION OF PLANTS

## THE GROWTH OF BACTERIA IN SOIL



## SUMMARY

# THE ENVIRONMENT OF SOIL BACTERIA

# THE PHYSICAL ENVIRONMENT OF MICRO-ORGANISMS IN SOIL[1]

A. D. McLAREN AND J. SKUJINS

*College of Agriculture, University of California, Berkeley*

## *INTRODUCTION*

For the present purpose we define soil as the loose surface layer of earth which supports the various organisms dwelling within. The soil is formed by various physical, chemical, climatic and biological factors and may be represented as a matrix of colloidal systems. The inert solid particles are complexes of minerals and organic polymeric substances

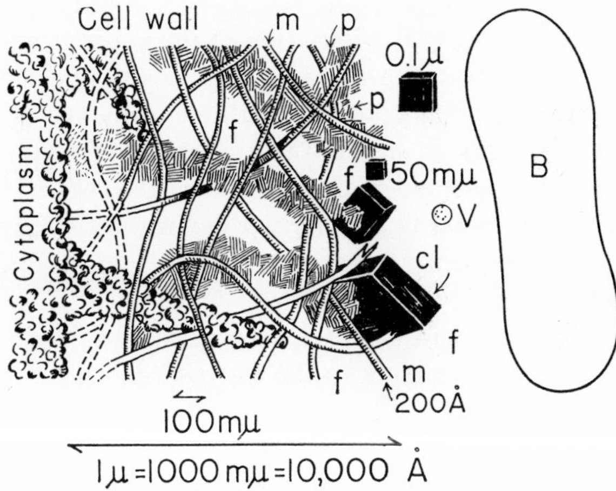


Fig. 1. Micro-environments of soil-plant root-microbe relationships. Modified figure from Lopez-Gonzales, J. de D. and Jenny, H. (1958). Modes of entry of strontium into plant roots. *Science*, **128**, 90. (m) cellulose microfibrils; (p) pectic substances; (f) free space; (C1) clay particles of various sizes; (v) virus particle; (B) bacterium. The molecular environments are made up of surface-soil solution concentration gradients one order of magnitude smaller than illustrated (McLaren and Babcock, 1959).

(humus), in which are dispersed organic molecules, inorganic salts and ions, water and gases. Within the soil matrix are found micro- and macro-organisms in vast numbers and of many kinds, together with dead roots and excrements of soil fauna in all stages of disintegration

[1] Prepared under N.A.S.A. Grant NsG 704/05 and U.S.A.E.C. Contract No. AT(11-1)-34; Project 50.

(Fig. 1). Since micro-organisms may number $10^9$ per gram of soil in a typical field soil, the soil may be regarded as a living tissue (Quastel, 1946). However, the physiological and biochemical activities of micro-organisms in such a heterogeneous system must differ drastically from those in classical bacteriological media. In soil there is a point-to-point variation in concentration of all solutes and further, the microbe may usually be thought to be on the verge of starvation.

It is not the purpose of this discussion to describe the many ecological niches of the micro-organisms resulting from the various chemical and nutritional aspects of the soil environment, but rather to consider some of the conditions pertaining in the soil environment which affect biological processes in soil. Incidentally, the physiological and biochemical relationships and activities of micro-organisms in soil environments have been reviewed recently (Alexander, 1964).

## *THE MICRO-ENVIRONMENT*

Since there is a point-to-point variation in the concentration of solutes and gases in a soil matrix we may speak of soil *micro-environments*. These micro-environments consist of volume elements which are commensurate in size with an organism in question. Furthermore, at the surface of a soil particle and at the surfaces of the cells of micro-organisms themselves there exists a *molecular* environment characterized by gradations in ion concentrations, including the pH and the reduction-oxidation potential.

Micro-environments in the soil are discussed in terms of the diverse ecological conditions available to the micro-organisms.

### *Soil porosity*

All biological activities and interactions are dependent on water, which in turn is dependent in part on the soil structure, and especially on the soil porosity. The ultimate solid particles in soil tend to aggregate, which gives a soil a texture. Thus, soil may exist in a finely dispersed, dusty state or in the form of soil aggregates of various sizes. Physically the structure may be characterized by two interdependent systems—a labyrinth of interconnecting pores and a matrix of contiguous solid particles.

Depending on the composition of the mineral fraction of the soils, its organic matter characteristics and on various external factors, such as climate and vegetation, the soil may consist of aggregates from the submicroscopic size to 20 mm. and more in diameter. Theoretical considerations show that in a cubic type geometrical packing of equal size spheres the pore space is close to 50 per cent of the total volume. Similarly, a hexagonal type packing gives a porosity of only about 25 per cent. However, soil is not packed in a geometrically homogeneous manner and it contains particles of various sizes and shapes. In view of what follows, however, it is instructive to subdivide soil porosity into intra-aggregate and inter-aggregate porosity. In the intra-aggregate pores, gas concentrations can differ drastically from that between soil particles. In a permanent pasture the percentage pore space between particles was found to be c.15 (in a young ley it was only one-fourth as much) (Gadgil, 1963). Total pore space may be as high as 30–45 per cent.

*Soil water*

Examination of the physical structure of soil shows that water exists in the soil in several forms with respect to its retention. The soil-water relationship with respect to biological activities in soil and plant growth has been lately reviewed by several authors (Black, 1957; Marshall, 1959; Russell, 1961; Krasilnikov, 1961).

Gravitational water moves downwards in the soil under the pull of gravitational forces until it reaches subsoil or is retained in soil by forces counteracting gravitation. The ability of soil to drain water is called soil permeability. Gravitational water is available to soil organisms and it plays a major role in the transport of solutes in soil.

The capillary water moves in soil by means of capillary forces in the soil pores. The smaller the diameter of a pore the higher the water rises against the gravitational force. Pores in soil are of various dimensions and shapes and the soil structure greatly influences the water movements. In soils with large aggregates, water penetrates easily, whereas in soils without aggregates the pores are small and the water moves through capillaries slowly but it can rise quite high. Keen (1922), for example, has calculated that in a fine silt (0·01–0·002 mm.), water can rise to a theoretical height of 45 metres. The upward movement of the capillary water is enhanced by the surface evaporation. The capillary water is available to organisms and it also transports soil solutes.

Following removal of capillary water from soil, some water remains on and in the soil particles. This water is held to the clays by osmotic reduction of vapour pressure, by adsorption and by solution in polymeric humus. Part of this water may move as a liquid of higher viscosity and lower freezing point than bulk water. According to Low (1961), who has examined extensively the properties of this osmotically held water at clay surfaces, the viscosity is increased at distances up to 60 to 100 Å from clay surfaces, depending on the clay type. This water comprises about 1 per cent of sandy soils and reaches about 10 per cent in humus-rich soils. According to data collected by Low (1961), it freezes at temperatures of −7 to −17°; such water held by quartz and montmorillonite freezes even below −25°.

The layer of adsorbed water, corresponding to a film up to perhaps 15 Å in thickness remains unfrozen at very low temperatures. Such tightly bound hygroscopic water can be mostly removed from soil by heating to 105°. All such bound water can be in equilibrium with water vapour over a range of relative humidities extending down to 1 to 5 per cent, which is far below the range of biological interest.

In biological studies the moisture regime has often been described in terms of moisture content of soils; however, such data give us little information related to the ability of an organism to absorb and utilize soil water. In order to utilize water, a growing organism must expend the energy required to remove water from soil and this depends on the types and sizes of the soil particles, the characteristics of the aggregates (soil structure), and on the concentration of the ions in the water phase. This energy may be expressed logarithmically by the pF scale (Schofield, 1935); that is,

$$pF = \log \left( \frac{RT}{Mg} \times \ln \frac{p}{p_0} \right)$$

where R = gas constant, T = absolute temperature, M = molecular weight of liquid, g = gravitational constant, and $p/p_0$ = relative vapour pressure. In order to remove water from a 1·5 μ diameter

TABLE 1

*Approximate relation between water suction and relative humidity*

| Relative humidity | pF | Relative humidity | pF |
|---|---|---|---|
| 99·9 | 3·10 | 85·0 | 5·36 |
| 99·5 | 3·84 | 80·0 | 5·50 |
| 99·0 | 4·16 | 75·0 | 5·62 |
| 98·0 | 4·45 | 70·0 | 5·71 |
| 97·0 | 4·63 | 65·0 | 5·78 |
| 95·0 | 4·86 | 50·0 | 6·00 |
| 90·0 | 5·17 | | |

capillary, commensurate with the diameter of bacteria, a suction of one atmosphere is required. This is equivalent to 1000 cm. water (pF 3), and a relative humidity of 99·9 per cent (Table 1, Griffin, 1963). In other words, for the organism to obtain water from such a capillary, a free energy of about a half calorie per mole of water must be expended; the organism can easily compete with a plant root system. Conversely, plants show a permanent wilt at or below about 99 per cent relative humidity and it will be of interest to compare the extent to which some soil microbes can withstand drought.

Actually, the mechanisms by which the water is held in soil (capillary, osmotic and hygroscopic water) operate simultaneously. These mechanisms may be distinguished by the energy of the negative suction pressure that the water in any particular region exerts, e.g. gravitational water (not a true water holding mechanism by a strict definition), 0 to 0·3 atmospheres; capillary water, 0·3 to about 15 atmospheres; osmotic water, approximately 15 to 150 atmospheres (this value is strongly influenced by the solutes present); hygroscopic water, above 150 atmospheres. For a comparison, it may be noted that 143 atmospheres of water suction is equivalent to 90 per cent relative humidity.

In the studies of biological activity in drying and remoistened soils, it should be noted that the soils exhibit a so-called hysteresis phenomenon. If a wet soil is dried at a certain relative humidity A, the soil will equilibrate with a certain soil moisture content $B_1$; however, if the soil is dried further and then subjected to the relative humidity A, the equilibrated soil moisture content $B_2$ will be less than $B_1$. In some soils, the difference in moisture content might be considerable, depending on the treatment (Schofield, 1935).

### *Microbial response to soil water content*

Generally, the additive effects of tensiometer and osmotic components of soil water have been taken to constitute the total stress against which an organism must do work to absorb water (Richards and Wadleigh, 1952); however, other hydraulic factors also appear to be important (Gingrich and Russell, 1957). The bacterial activity in soil with respect to moisture content has been widely studied on an empirical level, and generally, a good correlation has been found; microbial activity increases with increasing water content to about 60 to 80 per cent of the water-holding capacity and decreases in waterlogged soils (Seifert, 1960, 1961; Gondo, 1961).

The maximum activities of micro-organisms may depend on the thickness of the water film surrounding the solid soil particles. Rahn

(1913), found the optimum thickness of the film to be 20 to 40 $\mu$ for *Bacillus mycoides*; this corresponds to a pF of a little less than 2. Some soil micro-organisms may develop at relative humidities down to 85 per cent or less. Dommergues (1959) studied microbial activities at low moisture levels and showed that the minimal moisture content in soil for cellulolytic organisms was 1·5 per cent and glucose-utilizing organisms 0·7 per cent, which was considerably below the wilting point (1·7 per cent). Cell division of *Pleurococcus vulgaris* occurs at a relative humidity of 48 per cent at 20° (Zeuch, 1934). This is extreme: at this relative humidity a typical protein contains only about 8 per cent water, at a partial molar-free energy of about 500 calories (McLaren and Rowen, 1951). If the cell is also at such a low water content, enzyme reactions must take place in the absence of a liquid water phase and at very low velocities (Ruchti and McLaren, 1964).

Available data for the minimal relative humidity requirements for growth of soil fungi have been collected by Griffin (1963). Minima for most of the fungi lie between 85 and 95 per cent relative humidity, but *Aspergillus amstelodami*, *A. glaucus* and *A. repens* have minimal relative humidity requirements of 70 to 72 per cent and *Penicillium glaucum* 78 per cent. For most fungi, however, growth decreases by half at 94 to 97 per cent, as compared with growth at 100 per cent relative humidity.

Excellent survival of some micro-organisms in air-dry soil is a well-known phenomenon. The maintenance of stock microbiological cultures in dried soil suspensions is an accepted method for preserving bacteria. Non spore-formers, such as *Nitrosomonas*, may be recovered from air-dry soils after several years. Preservation of these organisms on other bacteriological maintenance media for the same period of time would fail.

A study of the survival of some 50 fungal isolates in five-year-old dried soil cultures showed a wide range of ability to survive. *Rhizopus nigricans*, for example, showed an extremely high survival capacity, whereas *Fusarium oxysporum* showed the least viability (Atkinson, 1954). Studies on survival of algae in Rothamsted soils, kept hermetically sealed in an air-dry state for 26 to 73 years, showed that a number of Cyanophyceae, Chlorophyceae and one species of diatom could be recovered (Bristol, 1919). We have shown that after 10 years of storage, however, the general population of soil micro-organisms decrease about 100-fold, i.e. from about $10^{-7}$ organisms to $10^{-5}$ organisms per gram of soil (unpublished results). Nevertheless, the survival of the remaining organisms may be due to the osmotic and hygroscopic water present in the soils stored air-dry.

*Soil solution*

The water phase in soil carries dissolved compounds of various types and forms: inorganic ions, including the nutrient minerals for micro-organisms, and organic compounds—the metabolic products of the living organisms in soil. It has been shown that the soil solution contains also dispersed colloidal material, comprising 5 to 20 per cent of the dry weight of the solution residue; the major constituents of the colloidal fraction are of organic nature, but there are also iron and aluminium hydroxides and silicic acid.

The amounts and ratios of the compounds in the soil solution fluctuate with respect to the characteristics of the soil type and the climate. Upon drying the salt concentration increases and the salts precipitate according to their solubilities.

The soil solution is the liquid nutrient medium for the soil micro-organisms. In connection with Quastel's notion of the soil as a living tissue, it is interesting to note that already in 1902 Visotskii had compared the soil solution to the blood of animals. The nutrients found in the extracted soil solutions of specific soils greatly influence the make-up of microflora found in any particular soil (Krasilnikov, 1961).

Decrease of soil moisture not only limits the available water to micro-organisms, but also increases the salt content in the soil solution. In solute-rich soils specific halophytic populations become established, but the effects of an increase in ionic concentrations due to soil drying on micro-organisms in regular soils has been little studied. Johnson and Guenzi (1963), have pointed out that increasing osmotic tension with increasing salt concentration causes a decrease in nitrifying activity, but the total microbial activity is less affected, and that microbial populations show greater salt tolerance in calcareous than in noncalcareous soils. It should be noted than many individual species of bacteria can tolerate relatively large changes in the salt concentration.

*Soil atmosphere*

The pore space in soil is either filled with air, as in dried soils, or filled with water, as in waterlogged soils. In the first case all life processes practically cease, in the latter case anaerobic processes predominate. The air-water ratio in the pore space is of utmost importance for determining the types of biological processes in soil. Most of the soil micro-organisms require a certain air-water ratio for their maximal proliferation as already noted (Rahn, 1913).

Gases in soil exist in three states: (1) a free state, filling the otherwise empty soil pores, (2) dissolved in the water phase and (3) adsorbed on the solid phase.

The adsorption of the atmospheric components by the solid soil matter is of importance only in very dry soils. With an increase of moisture the sites for hygroscopic adsorption of water become occupied, and generally, the water molecules are adsorbed by the soil particles more tenaciously than gases.

The solubility of gases in the water phase depends on the type of gas, temperature, the salt concentration in the water phase, and on their partial pressures in the atmosphere. The most soluble are gases which become ionized in water solution, as $CO_2$, $NH_3$ and $H_2S$. Oxygen is less soluble (0·31 cm.$^3$ per litre of water at 10°, 760 mm. Hg.), and nitrogen the least soluble (0·15 cm.$^3$ per litre at 10°, 760 mm. Hg.). Because of dissolved electrolytes the solubility of gases in the soil water is less than in pure water. The total amount of air in soil fluctuates widely and it is dependent on the soil porosity and moisture content, as well as on microbial and root activity. Penman (1940*a*, 1940*b*), and Currie (1962), among others have discussed the problem of gas diffusion in soil. Generally, oxygen continuously diffuses into the soil and $CO_2$ diffuses out; for porosities greater than 10 per cent by volume of soil the rate of exchange of oxygen and carbon dioxide with the surface atmosphere comes to equilibrium down to a depth of 30 cm. in about an hour. The ratio of $CO_2/O_2$ increases with increasing depth and with a decrease in the available porosity. The sum of the partial pressures of $CO_2$ and $O_2$ remains nearly constant at 21 per cent of the total pressure. When the water content in soil is increased and the available air pore volume is less than 10 per cent, the above relationship does not apply, the physical shape of the pores becomes more important for diffusion rates, and eventually $O_2$ concentration approaches zero in waterlogged soils.

It should be emphasized that the equilibrium conditions between water—water vapour—oxygen and $CO_2$ in the soil pores are greatly influenced by temperature fluctuations, including the diurnal changes. The effects of temperature changes on the equilibria in the soil liquid and gaseous phases with respect to soil organisms have been described by Collis-George (1959).

Generally, the soil atmosphere differs from the surface atmosphere by its higher $CO_2$ content, which is formed at the expense of $O_2$. Nitrogen is almost constant. Besides the atmospheric gases, there are also metabolically formed gases, e.g. $NH_3$, $CH_4$, $H_2S$, and also many biologically formed volatiles, e.g. organic acids, esters, hydrocarbons, etc.

Although nitrogen is of prime importance for nitrogen-fixing organisms, the nitrogen availability for microbes in soil has been but little studied (Shields and Durrell, 1964).

It has been suggested that the regime of $CO_2$ in soil is important not only because it affects the metabolism of autotrophic organisms and influences the pH at the microsites in soil, but also because of its potential role as a differential inhibitor for heterotrophs (Alexander, 1964). Papavizas and Davey (1962) have shown that the saprophytic growth of *Rhizoctonia* in soil was reduced at 10 to 20 per cent $CO_2$ concentration and drastically inhibited at 30 per cent concentration. Blair (1943) found that forced aeration of the soil increased the growth rate of *Rhizoctonia solani* and that the growth rate was also increased when $CO_2$ from soil was absorbed by chemical means. Newcombe (1960) reported that under an atmosphere of $CO_2$ conidia of *Fusarium oxysporum* germinated freely but failed to form chlamydospores.

The various combined effects of soil structure, water availability and aeration of fungal growth was critically examined and reviewed by Griffin (1963) who used artificial soil (aluminium oxide grits) of known pore size. Growth was inhibited in waterlogged conditions, but normal growth appeared if sufficient suction was applied to drain pores within limits of 16 to 550 μ diameters, irrespective of particle size. The sporulation did not seem to be affected by the suctions used, but its intensity was greatly reduced when the pore diameter was reduced less than 23 μ.

Scott and Evans (1955) have shown that oxygen rapidly disappears not only in completely waterlogged soils but also in well-structured and aerated soils under conditions where waterlogged crumbs are present. Winogradsky (1924) determined depths to which an aerobe, *Azotobacter*, and an anaerobe, *Clostridium*, could grow in wet soils; at a moisture content of 23 per cent the former was limited to the extreme surface and the latter was found throughout the soil. In view of the high concentration of $CO_2$ found in soil after rain (3·5 to 9·2 per cent), $CO_2$ content rather than low $O_2$ content may determine the vertical distribution of soil fungi (Burges and Fenton, 1953).

Recently, from a study of widely different soils, it has become evident that the changeover from aerobic to anaerobic metabolism takes place at an oxygen concentration of less than about $3 \times 10^{-6}$M (Greenwood, 1961; Greenwood and Berry, 1962). It appears that water-saturated soil crumbs larger than about 3 mm. in radius have no oxygen at their centres and, since crumbs of this size are present in most soils, it means that microsites having anaerobic conditions are ubiquitous, and this provides an explanation for the universality of strict anaerobes. Oxidative processes, however, abound in relatively warm, well-aerated soils. In relatively wet soils organic matter content increases with increasing rainfall (Jenny, Bingham and Padilla-Saravia, 1948).

A delay in nitrification processes, due to anaerobic metabolism taking place in soil, has been observed (Brandt, Wolcott and Erickson, 1964). The rate of nitrification is enhanced if the crumb diameters are below 1 mm. (Seifert, 1962) and an improved soil crumb dispersion with soil conditioners can increase the rate of nitrification. A similar study (Hagin, 1955) showed that in soils where aggregates were stabilized with a soil conditioner, the nitrification rate was doubled at the crumb size range of 0·5 to 5 mm. diameter, whereas ammonia accumulation occurred in soils with crumb sizes $< 0{\cdot}5$ mm. in diameter.

The existence of appreciable differences in population sizes at microsites within the soil was demonstrated by the study of Tyagnii-Ryadno (1958), who showed that considerably larger numbers of bacteria proliferate on the crumb surfaces as compared with the interior of aggregates.

The lack of oxygen in anaerobic (waterlogged) conditions is not the only parameter determining the type of microflora. With anaerobic conditions several chemical changes can take place which potentially influence the composition of the microflora. These include increases in soluble Ca, Mg, Fe, Ni, Mn, and Co compounds, accumulation of $Fe^{++}$, and decrease of $NO_3^-$ and of available phosphorus. Fatty acids and other oxidizable organic compounds accumulate in this reduced state, and the reduction-oxidation potential decreases (Siuta, 1962; Ng and Bloomfield, 1962; Grechin, 1963).

Soluble plant and animal residues and products of microbial metabolism may be translocated and adsorbed on the soil particles in micropores physically inaccessible to micro-organisms. Rovira and Graecen (1957) showed that the decomposition of soil organic matter was accelerated when the micro-pores of the aggregates in certain soil types were disrupted. A burst of microbial activity in freshly moistened air-dried soils is a well-known phenomenon and in part such an increase in activity has been ascribed to the effect of drying on the organic matter which renders some of the organic matter more soluble (Griffiths and Birch, 1961). However, a disruption of aggregates upon drying, thereby making the organic substrates accessible to micro-organisms when rewetted, may also be a contributing factor.

The oxygen concentration directly affects the red-ox potential ($E_h$); in the absence of oxygen the negativity of the soil increases. Environmental limits of $E_h$ (correlated with pH) for a large number of different micro-organisms in natural environments have been established by Baas-Becking, Kaplan and Moore (1960). However, it is not yet clear whether the red-ox potential *per se* is important for microbial activity or if it is only a reflection of the oxygen availability and the influence of reducing or oxidizing compounds on micro-organisms.

It is of interest to note that the soil organic matter, especially the soil humic acids, contain stable-free radicals in a range of about $10^{18}$ radicals per gram of humic acid (Steelink and Tollin, 1962; Tollin, Reid and Steelink, 1963). The free radicals appear to be an integral part of the humic acid molecular structure. They may consist of a mixture of semi-quinone-type radicals and electron-transfer complexes of quinhydrone type. Any influence of free radicals on microbial growth in soil is unknown.

## *THE MOLECULAR ENVIRONMENT*

As mentioned earlier, micro-organisms live in a complex soil matrix, where the solid phase is characterized by discrete solid particles having a spectrum of size. A full understanding of microbial behaviour in the micro-environment requires an examination of certain colloidal properties of the organic and inorganic solids. These properties include adsorption of solutes and exchange of cations and anions, Donnan equilibrium behaviour and others. Considering the scope of the subject-matter, only some topics of importance for microbial biology will be considered here; the reader's attention is directed to several excellent review articles regarding the physical chemistry of soil, namely by Toth (1964), Wiklander (1964) and Babcock (1963), among others.

### *Effect of electrokinetic charges at interfaces*

The colloidal fraction of soil is made up of inorganic crystalline clay particles, organic decomposed residues, organic matter-clay complexes and organic macromolecules. Any of the colloidal particles, especially the clay particles, may be coated with iron, aluminium, or manganese hydroxide gels. These colloidal particles in soil have electric charges which are of prime importance for nutrient cation and anion retention and availability. Soil colloids have negative charges. The clay particles are very strongly electro-negative; organic soil colloids and the hydroxide-coated colloids are more or less amphoteric. In an aqueous phase the negative charge requires a cloud of cations for an overall state of neutrality. This cloud includes the biologically important $H_3O^+$ ion.

Hartley and Roe (1940) derived an equation for the difference between the pH at a charged interface, $pH_s$, and that of an adjacent bulk phase, $pH_b$, by an application of the theory of Debye and Hückel. They pointed out that the electrokinetic potential (zeta potential, $\zeta$) can be identified with the potential $\psi$ in the neighbourhood of a simple ion at the distance of the closest approach of another ion, as considered by Debye and Hückel. In this sense the zeta potential determines the local concentration of ions near the surface of a particle, and the hydrogen ion concentration near the surface will be $e^{-\varepsilon\zeta/kT}$ times the $H^+$ concentration in bulk. The effective dissociation constant becomes

$$K_s + K_b e^{-\varepsilon\zeta/kT} = K_b e^{-F\zeta/RT}$$

where $K_b$ = thermodynamic dissociation constant in bulk, $\varepsilon$ = electronic charge, F = faraday, T = absolute temperature, and k = Boltzmann constant.

At 25° this equation may be rewritten as

$$pK_s = pK_b - \zeta/60$$

or

$$pH_s = pH_b + \zeta/60$$

where pH is in terms of $H^+$ concentration, not activities. No distinction between concentration and activity of $H^+$ is needed in bulk under physiological conditions near neutrality. That an enzyme acting at a charged surface responds to hydrogen ion concentration rather than activity has been shown elsewhere (McLaren and Babcock, 1959). The last equation can be evaluated via electrophoretic measurements by substituting, for large particles, the Smoluchowski relationship

$$u = \frac{\zeta D}{4\pi\eta}$$

We thereby arrive at the experimentally useful equation

$$pH_s = pH_b + 0{\cdot}217\,\mu$$

For small particles, Hartley and Roe give at 25°,

$$pH_s = pH_b + 0{\cdot}325\,\mu$$

The mobility of a particle $\mu$ is reckoned negative for motion toward an anode, in microns/sec./volt/cm.; D is the dielectric constant and $\eta$ is the viscosity of the disperse medium at the same temperature. The effect of the zeta potential in practice extends from the interface of the colloidal particle to 50–150 Å into the liquid phase. Several consequences of the existence of Δ pH (equal to $pH_b - pH_s$), in biological systems have been further considered by McLaren (1960). Here we concern ourselves with soil enzymes and bacteria.

A wide variety of enzymatic activities exist in soil, some of which has been attributed to extracellular enzymes (Skujins, 1966). Although the precise physical state of the extracellular enzymes in soil is poorly understood, it is apparent that some of the enzyme protein molecules are adsorbed on surfaces of the colloidal soil particles; they may also exist in some type of covalently bound form with the organic macromolecular components. Incidentally, catalytically active enzyme derivatives, covalently bound to organic polyelectrolyte copolymers, have been prepared by Riesel and Katchalski (1964) and Levin *et al.* (1964).

In studies with adsorbed chymotrypsin (McLaren and Estermann, 1957), phosphatase (McLaren and Ramirez-Martinez, unpublished results) and urease (Durand, 1964*a*) on clay particles, or with the trypsin-polyelectrolyte copolymer (Goldstein, Levin and Katchalski, 1964), it is clear that because of the ionic double-layer surrounding the clay particles, the observed pH maxima of the respective enzymatic activities were several units higher than in liquid solutions.

In context with the foregoing concepts the micro-organisms themselves should be considered as colloidal soil particles exerting their own field of zeta potential around the cells. Attempts to explain the apparent pH activity shifts of bacteria adsorbed on soil particles solely on the basis of the $H^+$ ion concentration in the double-layers of the soil particles have given conflicting results. Doubtless, the interplay of electrokinetic potentials of the adsorbing clay particle, and that of the bacterial cell should be considered, i.e. a cloud of a higher $H^+$ concentration exists not only around the clay particle, but also around the microbial cell of a distinct but different magnitude. Also, the distinction between the adsorbed and the adsorbing particles becomes semantic. Lahav (1962), for example, has studied the adsorption of small clay particles by bacterial cells.

Nitrification in soil takes place at a hydrogen ion concentration as high as pH 4. However, in solutions there is no nitrification below pH 6 (Weber and Gainey, 1962). McLaren and Skujins (1963) have shown that optimum nitrification by organisms in soil and adsorbed on cation exchange resins, irrespective of surface change, takes place at a pH greater than in solution.

Hattori and Furusaka (1960) have studied the biochemical activities of *Escherichia coli* and of *Azotobacter agilis* (Hattori and Furusaka, 1961) adsorbed on an anion exchange resin. In both cases the peak activity of the adsorbed cells was at a pH greater than that of the cells in suspension.

To resolve the question of the effect of ionic environment at the molecular level on the activities of micro-organisms more experimental data are needed. It should be emphasized that not only the $H^+$ and $OH^-$ equilibrium around the charged particles is of importance, but that those ions may be replaced by others, including anionic and cationic species of the bacterial substrates. These other ions may be present in quite an excess over the $H^+/OH^-$ species and exert an inhibitory or stimulatory effect on the micro-organisms. In these cases, correlations with the pH might be only coincidental.

The acidity ($pH_b$) of soils has been very extensively studied and very good empirical correlations with microbial activities, ecology and pH have been found. Such information, however, does not tell us very much about the influence of the hydrogen ion concentration on the bacterial cell within its micro-environment. The effects of the anionic part of an ionized acid molecule on micro-organisms has been studied in general bacteriology, but there is no information relating these effects to the soil microflora (Eno, 1957). Obviously, $H^+$ exerts a direct effect on a bacterial cell, but at the same time, changes in the hydrogen ion concentration in the soil markedly change the availability of various inorganic and organic nutrients. Again, only meagre data exist in the literature pertaining to the separation of these two hydrogen ion effects.

*Sorbtive phenomena in soil*

Typical colloidal particles in soil exhibit strong sorbtive properties. Several types of interactions are of importance in the microbial soil micro-environment, sorption of micro-organisms on soil particles, sorption of colloidal and monomolecular organic nutrients and microbial metabolic products on solid soil particles; and the activities of adsorbed extracellular enzymes at liquid-solid interfaces.

The adsorption of micro-organisms by soil and similar solid particles has been extensively studied in the 1920s and 1930s, as reviewed by Estermann and McLaren (1959). Some later studies have shed some light on the mechanisms involved in the adsorption processes. Tschapek and Garbosky (1950), made an extensive study of *Azotobacter* adsorption by surface-neutral quartz sand, and of the various factors affecting it. Zvyagintsev (1962), has presented an enlightening study of adsorption of various soil micro-organisms by cation and anion exchange resins. Micro-organisms of various species were adsorbed on an anion exchange resin, especially at pH values below pH 6. There was no adsorption at an alkaline pH. Selective adsorption with respect to species occured on cation exchange resin and the ions saturating the resin exhibited a striking effect: adsorption took place if the cation exchange resin was saturated with divalent and trivalent ions or $H_3O^+$, but there was no adsorption on the resin saturated with monovalent ions. Thus, the adsorption was dependent on the initial surface charge on the solid particles, the cations present in the solution and on the pH, correlating nicely the adsorption phenomena with our present understanding of the surface charge effects of solid particles (including microbes), and with the double-layer theory.

It is interesting to note that Lahav studied adsorption of colloidal clay particles to *Bacillus subtilis* cells and noted the presence of two distinct cell types: the adsorbing and the non-adsorbing *B. subtilis* cells (Lahav, 1962). Zvyagintsev (1959) found that the adsorption of bacteria on glass surfaces is strongly dependent on the taxonomic characteristics of the organisms and that the adsorption is not an 'all or none' phenomena but varies in a range from none to very strong.

It has been rather difficult to establish and to distinguish the numbers, ratios and types of adsorbed and non-adsorbed bacteria in soils. A recent study of Aristovskaya (1963) indicates that the bacterial flora of the soil particles consists mainly of attaching and creeping species, the majority of which form micro-colonies. The non-adsorbed inhabitants of the soil solution are mostly individual, single-cell organisms. The adsorption of viruses by soil particles was noted by Miyamoto (1959), among others.

Although it is generally recognized that soil particles might adsorb a great variety of organic compounds, the literature contains rather meagre specific data in this respect. Apart from the important function of the adsorbed organic metabolites as nutrients for micro-organisms, adsorption of the organic matter by mineral particles might be the first step in the formation of the biologically resistant humus fractions.

The adsorption of small organic molecules by clay particles, such as antibiotics (Krasilnikov, 1961), purines and pyrimidines (Durand, 1964*b*) and amino acids (Putnam and Schmidt, 1959; Greenwood and Lees, 1960), is of interest; the adsorption of large colloidal polymers (proteins, carbohydrates, etc.) also must play a large role in soil processes.

Protein molecules, released in soil by microbes, soil fauna or plant roots, are polyelectrolytes; i.e. water-soluble, ionized polymers. The chemical and physical behaviour of these polymer molecules is determined by the composition of the polymer chain, ionization and van der Waal's forces. The adsorption of macromolecules on solid surfaces has been reviewed by Silberberg (1962*a*, 1962*b*), and by McLaren and Peterson (1965). Some examples of the influence of adsorption on soil metabolism are now discussed. Goldberg and Gainey (1955) reported that the availability of ammonia to nitrifying bacteria proliferating on different soil minerals was directly related to the quantity of unadsorbed ammonia or to the quantity of $NH_4^+$ released from the soil minerals by the cation exchange mechanism. Ammonium fixed by illite and bentonite is nitrified very slowly. Incidentally, the process of nitrification is further reduced by additional increase in $K^+$ (Welch and Scott, 1960).

It appears that about 35 to 45 per cent of the total nitrogen in soil is in the form of polymers containing amino acid residues (Bremner 1949, 1955). Although the actual chemical composition of these polymers is unknown much of it may be adsorbed by clay particles. The adsorption of proteins on clays has been studied by Ensminger and Gieseking (1939, 1941) and by McLaren (1954*a*). Generally, proteins are adsorbed on clays in a wide pH range because of the amphoteric nature of the proteins and the relatively strongly, negatively charged clay particles. Proteolytic enzymes may be adsorbed on the clay-protein complexes and hydrolyse adsorbed proteins. An entirely new form of the chemical kinetic equations is required to handle enzyme reactions on insoluble substrates (McLaren, 1963). The enzymes may be desorbed from the complexes with a minimal loss of activity (McLaren, 1954*b*; McLaren and Estermann, 1956). Depending on the type of protein and on the experimental conditions, a single monolayer (McLaren, Peterson, and Barshad, 1958) or several layers (Talibudeen, 1950) of protein may be adsorbed on clays. Upon adsorption of protein the clays expand as the protein enters the interlayer space of the crystal lattices (McLaren, Peterson, and Barshad, 1958; Armstrong and Chesters, 1964).

Studies have shown that not only the protein adsorbed on the outside surfaces of clay particles but also the protein present in the interlayer space is utilized by micro-organisms, suggesting that extracellular proteolytic enzymes have access to the interlayer space (Estermann, Peterson and McLaren, 1959). Both stimulatory and retarding effects of adsorbents on the metabolic rates of bacteria have been observed (Estermann and McLaren, 1959). For example, *Bacillus subtilis* adsorbed on clays respire slower than in the free state. Lahav and Keynan (1962), however, have shown that under certain conditions the respiration of *B. subtilis* is enhanced. Macura and Pavel (1959) demonstrated that the adsorption of *Azotobacter* on clays increased the rate of nitrogen fixation.

A study of the bentonite-adsorbed urease by Durand (1964*a*), mentioned above, showed that in the presence of bentonite, $Cu^{++}$ was considerably less effective as an inhibitor. A very striking stimulation of uricase activity on uric acid was evident when the enzyme was adsorbed on bentonite (Durand, 1964*b*). On the other hand, another recent study on the retardation of the proteolytic activity in presence of clays (Aomine and Kobayashi, 1964) showed that the type of clay used for adsorption had a drastic influence on the activity: allophanic clays inhibited the protease activity to a much greater extent than montmorillonite or halloysitic clays.

A very striking and interesting interaction between clay minerals and soil fungi was examined by Stotzky and Martin (1963). The spread of the pathogenic *Fusarium oxysporum* f. *cubense* was completely correlated with the presence of a certain specific clay mineral in the soil. The mechanism of this clay-fungus interaction is not understood.

Apart from clays, other colloidal material in the soils, e.g. water-soluble constituents of plant residues (Handley, 1961), may significantly influence the availability of proteins to micro-organisms.

Although, with few exceptions, proteinases are almost the only enzymes which have been studied in relation to their activities on adsorbed substrates, it should be noted that other extracellular enzymes may act in the soil environment in an adsorbed state. In a study associated with the lysis of fungal walls by the enzymes of soil *Streptomyces* spp. (Skujins, Potgieter and Alexander, 1965), it was noted that the extracellular streptomycete chitinase was rapidly adsorbed by the fungal wall constituent chitin which is degraded (Skujins, unpublished data).

When considering enzyme reactions in soil, one should be aware of the changes that the molecular environment in the soil imposes on enzyme kinetics. Terms used in traditional enzyme chemistry, such as 'moles per litre' are meaningless in such structurally restricted systems (McLaren and Babcock, 1959) and equations using mole fractions instead of concentrations have been developed (McLaren, 1962). Enzymatic kinetics expressed in terms of mole fractions are useful in structures of low water content and reaction rates on surfaces and in gels may be meaningfully examined.

## REFERENCES

ALEXANDER, M. (1964). Biochemical ecology of soil microorganisms. *A. Rev. Microbiol.*, **18**, 217.

AOMINE, S. & KOBAYASHI, Y. (1964). Effects of allophane on the enzymatic activity of a protease. *Soil Pl. Fd, Tokyo*, **10**, 28.

ARISTOVSKAYA, T. V. (1963). Natural forms of existence of soil bacteria. *Mikrobiologiya*, **32**, 663.

ARMSTRONG, D. E. & CHESTERS, G. (1964). Properties of protein-bentonite complexes as influenced by equilibration conditions. *Soil Sci.*, **98**, 39.

ATKINSON, R. G. (1954). Quantitative studies on the survival of fungi in five-year-old dried soil cultures. *Can. J. Bot.*, **32**, 673.

BAAS-BECKING, L. G. M., KAPLAN, I. R. & MOORE, D. (1960). Limits of the natural environment in terms of pH and oxidation-reduction potentials. *J. Geol.*, **68**, 243.

BABCOCK, K. L. (1963). Theory of the chemical properties of soil colloidal systems at equilibrium. *Hilgardia*, **34**, 417.

BLACK, C. A. (1957). *Soil-Plant Relationships*. New York. Wiley.

BLAIR, I. D. (1943). Behaviour of the fungus *Rhizoctonia solani* Kühn in the soil. *Ann. appl. Biol.*, **30**, 118.

BRANDT, G. M., WOLCOTT, A. R. & ERICKSON, A. E. (1964). Nitrogen transformations in soil as related to structure, moisture and oxygen diffusion rate. *Proc. Soil Sci. Soc. Am.*, **28**, 71.

BREMNER, J. M. (1949). Studies on soil organic matter. I. *J. Agric. Sci.*, **39**, 181.

BREMNER, J. M. (1955). Studies on soil humic acids. I. *J. Agric. Sci.*, **46**, 247.

BRISTOL, B. M. (1919). On the retention of vitality by algae from old stored soils. *New Phytol.*, **18**, 92.

BURGES, A. & FENTON, E. (1953). The effect of carbon dioxide on the growth of certain soil fungi. *Trans. Br. mycol. Soc.*, **36**, 105.

COLLIS-GEORGE, N. (1959). The physical environment of soil animals. *Ecology*, **40**, 550.

CURRIE, J. A. (1962). The importance of aeration in providing the right conditions for plant growth. *J. Sci. Food Agric.*, **13**, 380.

DOMMERGUES, Y. (1959). L'activité de la microflore tellurique aux faibles humidités. *C. r. Acad. Sci. Paris*, **248**, 487.

DURAND, G. (1964*a*). Modifications de l'activité de l'uréase en présence de bentonite. *C. r. Acad. Sci., Paris*, **259**, 3397.

DURAND, G. (1964*b*). Influence des minéraux argileaux sur la decomposition de quelques dérivés nucléiques. *Annls Inst. Pasteur*, **107**, 136.

ENO, C. F. (1957). The relationship of soil reaction to the activities of soil micro-organisms. *Proc. Soil Crop Sci. Soc. Fla.*, **17**, 34.

ENSMINGER, L. E. & GIESEKING, J. E. (1939). The adsorption of proteins by montmorillonitic clays. *Soil Sci.*, **48**, 467.

ENSMINGER, L. E. & GIESEKING, J. E. (1941). The adsorption of proteins by montmorillonite and its effect on base-exchange capacity. *Soil Sci.*, **51**, 125.

ESTERMANN, E. F. & MCLAREN, A. D. (1959). Stimulation of bacterial proteolysis by adsorbents. *J. Soil Sci.*, **10**, 64.

ESTERMANN, E. F., PETERSON, G. H. & MCLAREN, A. D. (1959). Digestion of clay-protein, lignin-protein, and silica-protein complexes by enzymes and bacteria. *Proc. Soil Sci. Soc. Am.*, **23**, 31.

GADGIL, P. D. (1963). Soil sections of grassland. In *Soil Organisms*. Ed. Doeksen, J. & van der Drift J., Amsterdam. North-Holland Publ. Co.

GINGRICH, J. R. & RUSSELL, M. B. (1957). A comparison of effects of soil moisture tension and osmotic stress on root growth. *Soil Sci.*, **84**, 185.

GOLDBERG, S. S. & GAINEY, P. L. (1955). Role of surface phenomena in nitrification. *Soil Sci.*, **80**, 43.

GOLDSTEIN, L., LEVIN, Y. & KATCHALSKI, E. (1964). A water-insoluble polyanionic derivative of trypsin. II. Effect of the poly-electrolyte carrier on the kinetic behaviour of the bound trypsin. *Biochemistry, N.Y.*, **3**, 1913.

GONDO, M. (1961). Soil-ecological studies on soil pathogens. 5. Effect of various soil factors on the growth of *Agrobacterium tumefaciens*. *Bull. Fac. Agric. Kagoshima Univ.*, **10**, 28.

GRECHIN, I. P. (1963). Oxygen deficiency in soils and its effect on soil properties. *Agrokém. Talajt.*, **12**, 45.

GREENWOOD, D. J. (1961). The effect of oxygen concentration on the decomposition of organic materials in soil. *Pl. Soil*, **14**, 360.

GREENWOOD, D. J., & BERRY, G. (1962). Aerobic respiration in soil crumbs. *Nature, Lond.*, **195**, 161.

GREENWOOD, D. J. & LEES, H. (1960). Studies of the decomposition of amino acids in soils. II. The anaerobic metabolism. *Pl. Soil*, **12**, 69.

GRIFFIN, D. M. (1963). Soil moisture and the ecology of soil fungi. *Biol. Rev.*, **38**, 141.

GRIFFITHS, E. & BIRCH, H. F. (1961). Microbiological changes in freshly moistened soil. *Nature, Lond.*, **189**, 424.

HAGIN, J. (1955). Rates of nitrification in natural and 'conditioner'-formed soil aggregates of various sizes. *Bull. Res. Coun. Israel*, **5**, 98.

HANDLEY, W. R. C. (1961). Further evidence for the importance of residual leaf protein complexes in litter decomposition and the supply of nitrogen for plant growth. *Pl. Soil*, **15**, 37.

HARTLEY, G. S. & ROE, J. W. (1940). Ionic concentrations at surfaces. *Trans. Faraday Soc.*, **36**, 101.

HATTORI, T. & FURUSAKA, C. (1960). Chemical activities of *E. coli* adsorbed on a resin. *J. Biochem., Tokyo*, **48**, 831.

HATTORI, T. & FURUSAKA, C. (1961). Chemical activities of *Azotobacter agile* adsorbed on a resin. *J. Biochem., Tokyo*, **50**, 312.

JENNY, H., BINGHAM, F. & PADILLA-SARAVIA, B. (1948). Nitrogen and organic matter contents of equatorial soils of Colombia, South America. *Soil Sci.*, **66**, 173.

JOHNSON, D. D. & GUENZI, W. D. (1963). Influence of salts on ammonium oxidation and carbon dioxide evolution from soil. *Proc. Soil Sci. Soc. Am.*, **27**, 663.

KEEN, N. A. (1922). The system soil-soil moisture. *Trans. Faraday Soc.*, **17**, 228.

KRASILNIKOV, N. A. (1961). *Soil micro-organisms and higher plants*. OTS, Washington. U.S. Department of Commerce, (English transl. of Acad. Sci., U.S.S.R., 1958).

LAHAV, N. (1962). Adsorption of sodium bentonite particles on *Bacillus subtilis*. *Pl. Soil*, **17**, 191.

LAHAV, N. & KEYNAN, A. (1962). The influence of bentonite and attapulgite on the respiration of *Bacillus subtilis*. *Can. J. Microbiol.*, **8**, 565.

LEVIN, Y., PECHT, M., GOLDSTEIN, L. & KATCHALSKI, E. (1964). A water-insoluble polyanionic derivative of trypsin. I. Preparation and properties. *Biochemistry, N.Y.*, **3**, 1905.

LOW, P. F. (1961). Physical chemistry of clay-water interaction. *Adv. Agron.*, **13**, 269.

MCLAREN, A. D. (1954*a*). The adsorption and reactions of enzymes and proteins on kaolinite, I. *J. Phys. Chem., Ithaca*, **58**, 129.

MCLAREN, A. D. (1954*b*). The adsorption and reactions of enzymes and proteins on kaolinite, II. The action of chymotrypsin on lysozyme. *Proc. Soil Sci. Soc. Am.*, **18**, 170.

McLaren, A. D. (1960). Enzyme action in structurally restricted systems. *Enzymologia*, **21**, 356.

McLaren, A. D. (1962). Use of mole fractions in enzyme kinetics. *Archs Biochem. Biophys.*, **97**, 1.

McLaren, A. D. (1963). Enzyme reactions in structurally restricted systems, IV. The digestion of insoluble substrates by hydrolytic enzymes. *Enzymologia*, **26**, 237.

McLaren, A. D. & Babcock, K. L. (1959). Some characteristics of enzyme reactions at surfaces. In *Subcellular particles*. Ed. Hayashi, T. New York. Ronald Press.

McLaren, A. D. & Estermann, E. F. (1956). The adsorption and reactions of enzymes and proteins on kaolinite III. The isolation of enzyme-substrate complexes. *Archs Biochem. Biophys.*, **61**, 158.

McLaren, A. D. & Estermann, E. F. (1957). Influence of pH on the activity of chymotrypsin at a solid-liquid interface. *Archs Biochem. Biophys.*, **68**, 157.

McLaren, A. D. & Peterson, G. (1965). Physical chemistry and biological chemistry of clay mineral-organic nitrogen complexes. In *Soil Nitrogen*. Ed. Bartholomew, W. V. & Clark, F. E. *Am. Soc. Agron., Monograph*, **10**.

McLaren, A. D., Peterson, G. H. & Barshad, I. (1958). The adsorption and reactions of enzymes and proteins on clay minerals, IV. Kaolinite and montmorillonite. *Proc. Soil Sci. Soc. Am.*, **22**, 239.

McLaren, A. D. & Rowan, J. (1951). Sorption of water vapor by proteins and polymers. *J. Polym. Sci.*, **7**, 289.

McLaren, A. D. & Skujins, J. J. (1963). Nitrification by *Nitrobacter agilis* on surfaces and in soil with respect to hydrogen ion concentration. *Can. J. Microbiol.*, **9**, 729.

Macura, J. & Pavel, L. (1959). The influence of montmorillonite on nitrogen fixation by *Azotobacter*. *Folia microbiol., Praha*, **4**, 82.

Marshall, T. J. (1959). Relations between water and soil. *Tech. Communs Common. Bur. Soils*, **50**.

Miyamoto, Y. (1959). Further evidence for the longevity of soil-borne plant viruses adsorbed on soil particles. *Virology*, **9**, 290.

Newcombe, M. (1960). Some effects of water and anaerobic conditions of *F. oxysporum* f. *cubense* in soil. *Trans. Br. mycol. Soc.*, **43**, 51.

Ng, S. K. & Bloomfield, C. (1962). The effect of flooding and aeration on the mobility of certain trace elements in soils. *Pl. Soil*, **16**, 108.

Papavizas, G. C. & Davey, C. B. (1962). Activity of *Rhizoctonia* in soil as affected by carbon dioxide. *Phytopathology*, **52**, 759.

Penman, H. L. (1940*a*). Gas and vapour movements in the soil. I. The diffusion of vapours through porous solids. *J. agric. Sci.*, **30**, 437.

Penman, H. L. (1940*b*). Gas and vapour movements in the soil. II. The diffusion of carbon dioxide through porous solids. *J. agric. Sci.*, **30**, 570.

Putnam, H. D. & Schmidt, E. L. (1959). Studies on the free amino acid fraction of soils. *Soil Sci.*, **87**, 22.

Quastel, J. H. (1946). *Soil metabolism*. A lecture before the Royal Institute of Chemistry of Great Britain and Ireland, London.

Rahn, O. (1913). Die Bakterientätigkeit in Boden als Funktion der Nahrungskonzentration und der unlöslichen organischen Substanz. *Zentbl. Bakt. Parasitkde., Abt. II*, **38**, 484.

Richards, L. A. & Wadleigh, C. H. (1952). Soil water and plant growths. In *Soil physical conditions and plant growth*. Ed. Shaw, B. T. New York. Academic Press.

RIESEL, E. & KATCHALSKI, E. (1964). Preparation and properties of water-insoluble derivatives of urease. *J. biol. Chem.*, **239**, 1521.

ROVIRA, A. D. & GREACEN, E. L. (1957). The effect of aggregate disruption on the activity of microorganisms in the soil. *Aust. J. agric. Res.*, **8**, 659.

RUCHTI, J. & MCLAREN, A. D. (1964). Enzyme reactions in structurally restricted systems. *Enzymologia*, **27**, 185.

RUSSELL, Sir E. J. & RUSSELL, E. W. (1961). *Soil conditions and plant growth*. 9th edition. New York. Wiley.

SCHOFIELD, R. K. (1935). The pF of the water in soil. *Trans. 3rd. int. Congr. Soil Sci.*, **2**, 37.

SCOTT, A. D. & EVANS, D. D. (1955). Dissolved oxygen in saturated soils. *Proc. Soil Sci. Soc. Am.*, **19**, 7.

SEIFERT, J. (1960). The influence of moisture and temperature on the number of microorganisms in the soil. *Folia microbiol., Praha*, **5**, 176.

SEIFERT, J. (1961). The influence of moisture and temperature on the number of bacteria in the soil. *Folia microbiol., Praha*, **6**, 268.

SEIFERT, J. (1962). The influence of soil structure and moisture content on the number of bacteria and the degree of nitrification. *Folia microbiol., Praha.*, **7**, 234.

SHIELDS, L. M. & DURRELL, L. W. (1964). Algae in relation to soil fertility. *Bot. Rev.*, **30**, 92.

SILBERBERG, A. (1962*a*). The adsorption of flexible macromolecules. Part I. The isolated macromolecule at a plane interface. *J. phys. Chem., Ithaca*, **66**, 1872.

SILBERBERG, A. (1962*b*). The adsorption of flexible macromolecules. Part II. The shape of the adsorbed molecule; the adsorption isotherm, surface tension and pressure. *J. phys. Chem., Ithaca*, **66**, 1884.

SIUTA, J. (1962). Influence of reduction processes and acidification on the solubility of mineral soil compounds. *Soviet Soil Sci.*, 500.

SKUJINS, J. J. (1966. In preparation). Soil enzymes. In *Soil Biochemistry*. Ed. McLaren, A. D. & Peterson, G. H. New York. Marcel Dekker.

SKUJINS, J. J., POTGIETER, H. J. & ALEXANDER, M. (1965). Dissolution of fungal cell walls by a streptomycete chitinase and β-(1-3)-glucanase. *Archs Biochem. Biophys.*, **111**, 358.

STEELINK, C. & TOLLIN, G. (1962). Stable free radicals in soil humic acid. *Biochim. Biophys. Acta*, **59**, 25.

STOTZKY, G. & MARTIN, R. T. (1963). Soil mineralogy in relation to the spread of *Fusarium* wilt of banana in Central America. *Pl. Soil*, **18**, 317.

TALIBUDEEN, O. (1950). Interlamellar adsorption of protein monolayers on pure montmorillonoid clays. *Nature, Lond.*, **166**, 236.

TOLLIN, G., REID, T. & STEELINK, C. (1963). Structure of humic acid. IV. Electron-paramagnetic-resonance studies. *Biochim. biophys. Acta*, **66**, 444.

TOTH, S. J. (1964). The physical chemistry of soils. In *Chemistry of the soil*. Ed. Bear, F. E. 2nd edition. New York. Reinhold.

TSCHAPEK, M. & GARBOSKY, A. J. (1950). Adsorcion del *Azotobacter* y su importancia agronomica. *Minist. Agric. Ganad., Argentina*, Publ. **14**, 5.

TYAGNII-RYADNO, M. G. (1958). Biophysical and chemical analysis of soil aggregates. *Soviet Soil Sci.*, 1378.

VISOTSKII, G. N. (1902). Mycorrhiza of oak and pine saplings. *Lêsoprom. Vêst.*, **29**, 504.

WEBER, D. F. & GAINEY, P. L. (1962). Relative sensitivity of nitrifying organisms to hydrogen ions in soils and in solutions. *Soil Sci.*, **94**, 138.

WELCH, L. F. & SCOTT, A. D. (1960). Nitrification of fixed ammonium in clay minerals as affected by added potassium. *Soil Sci.*, **90**, 79.

WIKLANDER, L. (1964). Cation and anion exchange phenomena. In *Chemistry of the soil.* Ed. Bear, F. E. 2nd edition. New York. Reinhold.

WINOGRADSKY, S. (1924). Sur l'etude de l'anaerobiose dans la terre arable. *C. r. Acad. Sci., Paris*, **179**, 861.

ZEUCH, L. (1934). Untersuchungen zum Wasserhaushalt von *Pleurococcus vulgaris. Planta*, **22**, 614.

ZVYAGINTSEV, D. G. (1959). Adsorption of microorganisms by glass surfaces. *Mikrobiologiya*, **28**, 112.

ZVYAGINTSEV, D. G. (1962). Some regularities of adsorption of microorganisms on ion exchange resins. *Mikrobiologiya*, **31**, 339.

# THE CHEMICAL ENVIRONMENT OF BACTERIA IN SOIL

J. S. D. BACON

*Department of Biochemistry, Macaulay Institute for Soil Research, Aberdeen, Scotland*

## *INTRODUCTION*

A simple way to begin would be to ask whether soil is a good or bad environment for bacteria. The answer must be in terms of abundance of bacterial life, and it is really the duty of other speakers to give it, but I suspect I shall not be very wrong if I say that the question should not be put like this. Depending upon many outside influences, soil can support a desert or a tropical forest, and we can guess that its bacterial population can vary in a similar fashion.

Another simple question to ask would be for a definition of soil, but this is better avoided. Like other virtually indefinable biological phenomena, in its more typical forms it can be recognized by most people. It differs characteristically from mere finely-divided minerals in carrying a growth of plants when season and climate are favourable, and unless special steps have been taken to kill them, its existence is inseparable from the presence of various forms of life. The chemical environment of any particular bacterial species is to a small degree created by itself, and to a much larger degree by the activities of other micro-organisms, of animals and particularly of the dominant plant species.

A brief glance at the use which other organisms make of the resources in the soil may help us to put the activities of bacteria into perspective. At first sight, from a gross analysis, one would expect that all requirements for inorganic nutrients would be met. This is not necessarily the case. The occurrence of mineral deficiency diseases in plants and animals living in dependence on certain soils shows that functional deficiencies of certain elements may occur, and there may occasionally be absolute deficiencies that arise from a lack of these elements in the parent rock, or from subsequent losses by leaching. There may also be toxic quantities of some elements, and we have no reason to suppose that bacteria as a group are any more or less resistant than higher organisms.

From the quantitative point of view, though, it is certain that the availability of organic constituents, however derived, is the factor most likely to limit bacterial growth. During a single season plants growing in the same soil may reach ten to twenty times the weight of the soil bacteria, despite the intense metabolic activity of which many of the latter are capable. Plants achieve this much greater growth with a supply of inorganic elements which are no less available to the bacteria, and despite the fact that some plants are subject to self-imposed limitations of their nitrogen supply, which has to be in the form of nitrate. The main reason for the discrepancy would seem to be that plants can acquire the necessary energy and carbon from sources outside the soil. On the other hand it must be admitted that the organic matter in a soil usually greatly exceeds the bacterial mass (and may exceed the plant cover), and in certain conditions (e.g. the formation of peat in cold regions of high rainfall), large quantities of organic matter accumulate faster than microbial action can remove it.

Soil bacteria must for the most part utilize the excretions and dead tissues of plants and animals. Much of this material is already second-hand by the time it enters the soil. Other bacteria have been at work on it, and fungi especially attack dead leaves even before they become detached from the plant (Webster, 1957; Hudson and Webster, 1958). Autumn leaf fall and the wholesale death of plants from frost bring sudden increases in these contributions, so that the nature of the organic constituents is subject to seasonal variations.

This organic material is naturally accompanied by inorganic nutrients, but the leaching action of rain may soon transfer these to exchange sites in the soil colloids. So from the moment of entry of organic matter into the soil its contribution must be considered in relation to the mineral fractions.

### *Humification*

On the other hand there is equally no point at which organically derived material loses its identity completely; that is, not until its constituent elements have all entered new forms of combination. It is not difficult, however, to visualize convergent processes which give rise to substances more characteristic of soil than of their biological origins. Thus when bacteria spread through the soil they will find many large and small molecules which are directly derived from higher organisms or other microbes, but will also, it seems, encounter a class of substances which are typical of soils.

It is a truism, thermodynamically speaking, that what goes up must come down and this, applied to the synthesis of living matter, means that ultimately living and non-living processes will bring its constituent substances back to their starting point. Most of this return path is traced out in the metabolism of free-living sub-aerial organisms, but the final stages, which include the process called 'humification', are found in the soil and also in lakes and oceans. As each organism is demolished the useful parts are incorporated into new living matter, and the useless parts rejected. The economics of the process are such that a good living can be had even when much is discarded. Eventually, however, someone has to deal with the most intractable residues. By this time they have been subjected to enzymic degradations and to a variety of chemical reactions independent of living systems. Structures which once served precise functions have lost this reason for existence, and we can no longer hope to find much biochemical significance in what is left. For this reason complicated explanations of the humification process will always appear more plausible than simple ones.

### *Heterogeneity*

Consideration of the chemical nature of soil cannot proceed far without directing attention to its exceedingly heterogeneous character. As found in nature a soil has major structural features which are revealed in a vertical section as the *soil profile*. Soil-forming processes create differences of texture and chemical composition at different levels, and any full consideration of the environment created by a particular soil should take account of these differences with depth. But even if a sample is taken from a selected soil horizon and is milled and sieved in the laboratory it remains heterogeneous in character. A multitude of micro-environments is created by this heterogeneity, and, while it is easily recognized that the situation exists, the chemist does not find it any easier than the microbiologist to attempt an adequate description of how materials are distributed.

For agricultural purposes the soil needs to have a good tilth, and this is usually associated with the presence of stable aggregates ('crumbs') of 1 to 5 mm. diameter. Stable crumb structure is found under well-established grassland, where the organic matter content of the soil is high, and can be maintained in arable soils by frequent applications of organic manures, but the way in which organic substances act is not fully understood. Water-soluble polysaccharides may play a part in some soils (Greenland, Lindstrom and Quirk, 1962) but not in all

(Mehta, Streuli, Muller and Deuel, 1960). All that we need notice here is that agricultural practice continually seeks to impose further heterogeneity on the soil.

*Accessibility of Soil Constituents*

This heterogeneity permits the inclusion of substances like nitrate, which appears to be present only in solution, and at the other extreme substances so insoluble in water that they are not likely to be available to any of the soil organisms. It is not unexpected that some cations, such as ammonium and potassium, most of whose salts are readily soluble, nevertheless occur in part as insoluble complexes.

What is less expected is that a variety of organic substances should be rendered inaccessible to microbial (i.e. enzymic) attack by their association with the soil minerals. It is in this sense especially that soil becomes, chemically speaking, more than the sum of its parts, and we still have only the most elementary ideas of the part played by interactions between organic and inorganic constituents in directing the course of the humification process.

Lees and Quastel (1946) attempted 'to study the metabolism of a soil as though it were a living tissue', and there are obviously analogies to be drawn between the chemistry of soil and the chemistry of protoplasm, which once provoked such heated controversies between chemists and biologists (Hopkins, 1933). It is questionable whether the degree of order found in tissues and cells can be expected in soils, but a lesson might still be learned from the considerable advance in biochemistry which resulted from co-operation between microscopists and enzymologists; if studies of the fine structure of soils could be successfully extended to individual organic constituents new light might be thrown on the factors influencing their susceptibility to attack.

*Persistence of Organic Constituents*

In tropical soils organic matter is decomposed very rapidly and may practically disappear under cultivation. In temperate regions it reaches a fairly stable equilibrium level, the reason for this not being immediately apparent. Repeated additions of organic manures do not produce any permanent increase; on the other hand if the rate of disposal continued unchecked all the organic matter would quite soon disappear. Does the persisting fraction then consist of material that has been more or less completely converted to new forms? Is it, in fact, largely a microbial product as some assume (e.g. Barker, Finch, Hayes,

Simmonds and Stacey, 1965) and thus controlled in amount by factors limiting the microbial population, other than the total substrate available?

Other explanations are possible. The first stage of degradation of plant residues may have ended and a more intractable 'core' be left. This intractability could arise from complexity of structure: hemicelluloses on this argument would be more difficult to hydrolyse than starch or cellulose. Waxes and related lipids may resist decomposition because of their insolubility in water. A new microbial population has to be established, and will confer new characteristics on the final stages of degradation.

The chemistry of the soil might influence the equilibrium level; for example, by helping the formation of substances (? humic acids) which are not purely biological in origin and hence more resistant to enzymic attack, or by extending a limited amount of protection (Williams, Scott and McDonald, 1958) to humified or perhaps even to slightly degraded material (Greenland and Ford, 1964). In this connection most attention has been paid to complex formation between organic substances and clays.

Our present knowledge of the chemistry of soil does not permit us to distinguish between these possibilities. Further research will probably show that all are to some extent true, though to varying degrees for particular soils. It is important that we should not allow our thinking about this problem to be dominated by one explanation, to the exclusion of all others. In particular microbiologists should realize that chemists, although they have the advantage of dealing with simpler and more readily characterized entities than bacterial species, still understand relatively little of the complexities of chemical structure displayed by living organisms, or for that matter by many minerals. To give only one example, the suggestion that soil polysaccharides are of microbial origin because they contain fucose (Duff, 1952) was made at a time when it was not known that this sugar occurs commonly (perhaps universally?) in plant cell walls (Andrews and Hough, 1958; Bacon, unpublished observations).

We are faced by a vast disordered complexity. To describe it fully we shall need to employ a wide range of techniques, drawn from many branches of science. It follows that any hypothesis proposed to explain events taking place in soil must be criticized from every standpoint. To be valid any description of the chemistry of soil must satisfy the microbiologist as well as the chemist. It is the object of this survey to provoke just this kind of criticism.

## *MAIN CLASSES OF SOIL CONSTITUENTS*

From these general remarks let us pass to more specific considerations of the substances present in a typical soil, keeping in mind always their apparent availability to living organisms, of whatever kind. What follows is not intended to be comprehensive; those seeking more detailed information should consult books such as those by Russell (1961) and Bear (1964) and the many excellent reviews on individual topics, some of which are referred to below. References given to original work are intended as starting points for further reading, and do not imply that these are the first or the only contributions to the subject in question.

### *Oxygen and Carbon Dioxide*

These two gases occur in the air spaces of soils, and vary in concentration under the influence of the metabolic activity of roots and soil organisms. In the surface layers the composition of the air approaches that of the atmosphere, except that it is rather richer in carbon dioxide, but in heavy badly-drained soils the oxygen content may decrease (to 5 per cent or less), and the carbon dioxide content increase considerably (to 10 per cent).

Little is known about the amounts of these gases dissolved in the soil water, but it is evident that the potential supply of each is of more significance, and this will be controlled by many factors, in particular the porosity of the soil.

### *Ammonia*

The proportion of soil nitrogen liberated as ammonia by acid hydrolysis varies with depth, being highest (sometimes exceeding 50 per cent) in the lower layers of the soil profile (Stevenson, 1957). Some of this ammonia arises from inorganic compounds, and is released only by drastic means, e.g. by the action of hydrofluoric acid (Bremner, 1959). Tests of nitrification and plant growth (Allison, Doetsch and Roller, 1953) show that only a small proportion of ammonia fixed in this form can be utilized by living organisms.

### *Water*

The presence of water is important and the amount may vary very considerably and so influence the availability of other constituents. Plant physiologists use the concept of the 'soil solution', the composition of which will be dependent upon the nature of the soil and the time

TABLE 1

*Composition of some soil solutions obtained by various methods. Constituents expressed as me./1.*

| Method of extraction | Ca | Mg | K | Na | $NH_4$ | $PO_4$ | $HCO_3$ | $SO_4$ | Cl | $NO_3$ | |
|---|---|---|---|---|---|---|---|---|---|---|---|
| (*a*) Displacement by water | 9·4 | 0·4 | 0·2 | 0·3 | — | — | — | 1·2 | 0·2 | — | (also $SiO_2$, 29 mg./1.; organic matter, 38 mg./1.) |
| (*b*) Displacement by water | 12·1 | 3·3 | 0·5 | 1·8 | — | 0·03 | 1·4 | — | — | 2·4 | |
| (*c*) Pressed through ceramic cup | | | | | | | | | | | |
| (i) saturated with water | 10·6 | 2·5 | 2·7 | 0·6 | 0·4 | — | 1·7 | 3·6 | 1·6 | 9·6 | |
| (ii) with tenth-bar moisture | 17·4 | 3·9 | 3·7 | 1·0 | 0·5 | — | 2·3 | 6·0 | 1·9 | 16·9 | |
| (*d*) Pressure | 7·1 | 7·8 | — | — | — | — | — | 1·0 | 1·0 | | |
| Displacement by ethanol | 6·9 | 6·2 | — | — | — | — | — | 1·0 | 1·0 | | |

These analyses are given by (*a*) Th. Schloesing, quoted by Russell (1961), (*b*) Burd and Martin (1924), (*c*) Eaton, Harding and Ganje (1960), and (*d*) Kaurichev, Komarova, Skrynnikova and Shilova (1963). A method using filter paper tablets has been described by Schuffelen, Bolt and Koenigs (1964); it should have the advantage of simplicity, and of potential adaptation to use with small samples.

TABLE 2

*Some analyses of exchangeable cations in soils. Cations expressed as me./100 g. soil, other constituents as per cent of total*

| | Exchangeable cations | | | | | Other constituents | |
|---|---|---|---|---|---|---|---|
| | Ca | Mg | K | Na | $CaCO_3$ | Organic matter | Fine clay fraction |
| (*a*) Broadbalk, Rothamsted | 13·57 | 0·75 | 0·42 | — | 3 | 2–3 | 17·0 |
| (*b*) Elinelund, topsoil | 18·1 | 0·93 | 0·29 | 0·25 | 0·36 | 2·82 | 17·8 |
| subsoil | 10·2 | 0·67 | 0·10 | 0·16 | 0·17 | — | 14·2 |
| Lanna, topsoil | 7·9 | 2·82 | 0·30 | 0·13 | 0·00 | 3·52 | 40·0 |
| subsoil | 10·9 | 7·64 | 0·37 | 0·45 | 0·00 | — | 60·0 |
| Raskobil, topsoil | 11·2 | 2·03 | 0·25 | 0·36 | 0·00 | 5·00 | 33·5 |
| subsoil | 10·0 | 1·05 | 0·18 | 0·22 | 0·00 | 1·90 | 28·0 |

Analyses given by (*a*) Page and Williams (1925), (*b*) Wiklander and Koutler-Andersson (1963).

of year. In this solution one may find most of the commoner inorganic ions, but their relative concentrations will be influenced by short-term equilibration with the colloidal fraction (especially organic material and clays) and long-term contributions from the more insoluble materials. The pH of the solution can vary within fairly wide limits (4·5 to 8·5), but the full significance of a particular measurement can be appreciated only by taking into account the potential contribution of ions from insoluble fractions of the soils and from plant roots and members of the microbial population.

Typical analyses of soil solutions and of certain exchangeable cations are given in Tables 1 and 2.

*Mineral Constituents*

A question of some importance is the nature of the mechanisms by which further nutrients are made available from the mineral fraction. It was early realized that some plants were able to obtain more nourishment from the soil than others. The reasons for these differences are not yet wholly explained, but most certainly include the excretion of acidic products of metabolism by the roots or by micro-organisms associated with them. Many bacteria can produce acids from organic substrates and so should be capable of influencing conditions in their immediate vicinity. This has been supported by many *in vitro* experiments, but it is more difficult to establish the operation of this process *in situ*.

For example, the production of 2-ketogluconic acid has been shown by Duff and Webley (1959) to be responsible for the ability of certain soil bacteria to dissolve insoluble phosphates and silicates incorporated in agar plates. Duff, Webley and Scott (1963) tested its action on an extensive range of minerals by incorporating them in a liquid growth medium, and found that many were wholly or partly dissolved. When pellets containing glucose were buried in soil there was an abundant growth of bacteria round them, and small quantities of 2-ketogluconic acid were detected after a few days at 25° (Webley and Duff, 1962), but the acid was not normally detectable in the soils they examined.

The mineral constituents may be freed from organic matter by oxidation and then separated into fractions according to their particle size. The products range from coarse fractions derived mainly from the parent rock, to clay fractions of very small particle size (2 μ diameter or less), which are the ultimate products of the weathering process. The clay fractions often constitute a large proportion of the soil and confer on it the ability to bind anions, cations and water. The formation of complexes between clays and organic substances has already been referred to above. The most convincing demonstration of the existence of such complexes in soils would be to isolate them, but little progress has yet been made in this direction (Tyulin, 1938); evidence has been chiefly drawn from the results of extractions with mixtures of hydrofluoric and hydrochloric acids, which dissolve part of the clay fraction.

### *Organic Constituents*

Hydrofluoric acid is only one of the many reagents which have been tested as a means of separating organic material from inorganic. For many years chemists were satisfied with aqueous sodium hydroxide, which extracts a large part of the organic carbon of soils, but Bremner and Lees (1949) and others since that time (Tinsley and Salam, 1961; Whitehead and Tinsley, 1964) have experimented with less destructive reagents, each of which has some advantage, but none, as might be expected, has proved to be capable of extracting the whole of the organic matter in an undegraded form.

Our knowledge of the organic constituents of soil has accordingly been limited by the methods available for their extraction. It is perhaps best to begin by considering what recognizable 'conventional' substances are to be found in soil and to consider them from three points of view: (*a*) as sources of carbon compounds utilizable for energy production and synthetic processes, (*b*) as sources of nitrogenous compounds, and (*c*) as sources of other indispensable nutrients.

*Carbohydrates* (*see Mehta, Dubach and Deuel, 1961.*) Simple aqueous extractions of soils yields some free monosaccharides, but these represent a very small proportion of the total carbon (perhaps 0·1 per cent; Gupta and Sowden, 1963). The aqueous extract contains combined sugars, presumably mainly in the form of polysaccharide, but they represent only 1–2 per cent of the total carbon. It is difficult to measure the total carbonhydrate content because no satisfactory general reagent is known. The use of mineral acids at fairly high concentrations with suitable reagents (e.g. anthrone, orcinol, carbazole) gives figures for hexoses, pentoses and uronic acids, which together far exceed the water-soluble fraction, but are still well within the limits set by the carbon content.

Recent investigations by Sowden (Sowden and Ivarson, 1962) and unpublished work begun by the late Dr. R. B. Duff at the Macaulay Institute have made possible analyses of the constituent sugars of the carbohydrates not extractable by water. Extraction, involving inevitably some degradation, with 72 per cent sulphuric acid at room temperature

TABLE 3

*Sugars in hydrolysates of soils. Results of chromatographic analyses expressed as mg./g.—organic matter*

| | (*a*) Sassafras loam | (*a*) Cultivated Pokomoke | (*b*) Orthic grey wooded; O horizon | (*b*) Orthic podzol $B_2$ horizon | (*b*) Cultivated soil | (*c*) Soil under grass | (*c*) Fallow soil | (*c*) 1g. holo-cellulose from *Tilia* leaves |
|---|---|---|---|---|---|---|---|---|
| Galactose | 8 | 4 | 25 | 13 | 24 | 7 | 9 | 20 |
| Glucose | 7 | 6 | 72 | 28 | 49 | 19 | 34 | 142 |
| Mannose | 2 | 2 | 19 | 13 | 23 | 6 | 7 | 6 |
| Arabinose | 14 | 5 | 20 | 7 | 23 | 5 | 10 | 22 |
| Xylose | 9 | 3 | 14 | 7 | 17 | 6 | 8 | 31 |
| Ribose | — | — | }6 | }5 | }7 | 1 | — | — |
| Fucose | 11 | 4 | } | } | } | 1 | 2 | 3 |
| Rhamnose | 5 | 3 | 8 | 7 | 13 | 3 | 4 | 5 |
| % organic matter | 1·4 | 4·4 | 52·4 | 13·9 | 2·4 | 12·1 | 11·2 | — |

Analyses by (*a*) Lynch, Olney and Wright (1958), (*b*) Gupta, Sowden and Stobbe (1963), and (*c*) Dr. M. V. Cheshire and Mr. C. M. Mundie, Macaulay Institute (unpublished). Hydrolysis of the soil was effected with (*a*) 0·6 N-$H_2SO_4$ for 6 hr. at 85°, (*b*) 72% $H_2SO_4$ for 2 hr. at room temperature, followed by hydrolysis with N-$H_2SO_4$ overnight, (*c*) 72% $H_2SO_4$ for 16 hr. at room temperature, followed by 5 hr. hydrolysis with N-$H_2SO_4$ at 100°, the holocellulose sample being treated identically.

or prolonged hydrolysis of the soil with normal acid at 100° liberates a fraction in which many of the commoner sugars may be identified and estimated by suitable chromatographic techniques. Some typical results are shown in Table 3.

An interesting feature of these analyses is that the water-insoluble carbohydrate, which in amount far exceeds the water-soluble fraction, does not differ markedly from it in sugar composition. This suggests that insolubility in water may be partly the consequence of high molecular weight, or of intimate association with inorganic constituents, in which the uronic acid residues may well play a role. Earlier estimates of the uronic acid content of soil by the Tollens method were unbelievably high (Bremner, 1951); colorimetric procedures, which are more specific, give values of the same order as those for the other sugars, but are probably underestimates (Mehta *et al.*, 1961).

There is evidently an ample supply of energy here, in the form of carbohydrate, for any organism which can unlock the store. It should be noticed that the relatively low glucose content probably means that cellulose is one of the more readily degraded constituents of plant tissue; the sugar composition is reminiscent of the hemicellulose fractions of roots, stems and leaves.

Among the amino-sugars, glucosamine has been identified and may constitute an appreciable proportion (up to 20 per cent) of the organic nitrogen of soil, especially at lower levels in the profile (Bremner and Shaw, 1954; Stevenson, 1957; Sowden, 1959). Galactosamine is also present. Both are probably of microbial origin (and hence presumably in the form of chitin-like polymers) because glucosamine is not abundant in plant tissues, having been characterized only in certain seed glycoproteins (Pusztai, 1965).

*Amino acids.* A greater proportion of the organic nitrogen is always identifiable as amino acid nitrogen. Very little of this is in the form of free amino acids (Putnam and Schmidt, 1959) and these in any case may already be within the cells of the living microflora. Hydrolysis with hydrochloric acid under conditions capable of effecting complete hydrolysis of proteins yields up to half the soil nitrogen in a mixture of all the common amino acids, with the addition of $\gamma$-aminobutyric acid, $\beta$-alanine and diaminopimelic acid (the latter a characteristic bacterial product); some analyses are given in Table 4. There is evidently a good conventional source of organic nitrogen here, but it is not known to what extent these compounds are combined in a polypeptide structure. A proportion is liberated by the action of proteases.

*Organic phosphates.* About half the organic phosphate of soil has been

TABLE 4

*Amino acids in hydrolysates of soils. Results of analyses by ion-exchange chromatography (mg./100 g. soil)*

| | (*a*) Untreated silt loam | (*a*) Silt loam with organic and inorganic additions | (*b*) Podzol (Lennoxville) | (*b*) Black soil (Lacombe) | (*b*) Dark brown prairie soil (Scott) |
|---|---|---|---|---|---|
| Aspartic acid | 49 | 46 | 190 | 146 | 124 |
| Serine | 34 | 40 | 99 | 48 | 50 |
| Threonine | 39 | 48 | 157 | 79 | 87 |
| Glutamic acid | 62 | 63 | 281 | 117 | 143 |
| Proline | 17 | 21 | 35 | 40 | 52 |
| Glycine | 36 | 45 | 129 | 81 | 90 |
| Alanine | 51 | 64 | 114 | 46 | 85 |
| β-Alanine | 8 | 11 | — | — | — |
| γ-Aminobutyric acid | 6 | 11 | — | — | — |
| Valine | 27 | 32 | 110 | 58 | 75 |
| Isoleucine | 21 | 27 | 69 | 34 | 41 |
| Leucine | 23 | 27 | 126 | 39 | 62 |
| Tyrosine | 11 | 12 | 42 | 26 | 19 |
| Lysine | 32 | 39 | — | — | — |
| Histidine | 7 | 8 | — | — | — |
| Arginine | 11 | 12 | — | — | — |
| Phenylalanine | 6 | 7 | 45 | 36 | 28 |
| Cysteine | — | — | 12 | — | 12 |
| Methionine | — | — | 14 | 12 | 14 |
| % nitrogen in soil | 0·260 | 0·285 | 0·48 | 0·50 | 0·45 |

Analyses by (*a*) Stevenson (1954) and (*b*) Sowden (1955). Sowden calculates that 35%, 18% and 24% of the soil nitrogen (respectively for the Lennoxville, Lacombe and Scott soils) is accounted for by amino acids measured.

identified as esters of inositol and a much smaller proportion is present as phospholipid and nucleic acids (Anderson, 1961; Hance and Anderson, 1963). The nature of the remainder is unknown.

It is rather surprising that inositol phosphates should survive to this extent because many soil micro-organisms are known to be capable of hydrolysing them (Greaves, Anderson and Webley, 1961). These compounds can serve as sources of phosphate for plants growing in sand culture, but the addition of soil reduces the availability considerably, probably through the formation of insoluble salts (Anderson and Arlidge, 1962).

*Other compounds*. A large proportion of the sulphur of some soils is in organic forms, e.g. as methionine (Whitehead, 1964). There have been suggestions that soils may become deficient in sulphur for crops, but the needs of the microbial population are likely to be met under most circumstances.

The material extracted from soils by organic solvents includes straight-chain hydrocarbons ($C_{20}$ to $C_{34}$) and alcohols and acids related to them (Meinschein and Kenny, 1957; R. I. Morrison, unpublished observations).

Certain fractions of organic matter are able to bind polyvalent cations and may thus be imagined to constitute a reserve of trace elements for organisms which can metabolize the organic carrier or exert a greater affinity for the element in question.

### *Less well-defined constituents*

*Humic acids*. In addition to the constituents listed above, which are at once recognizable as food for bacteria, there are less well-defined substances which must ultimately be utilized when the right organism comes along. Such for example are the humic acids, which are typical soil constituents (Dubach and Mehta, 1963) and thus might be expected to attract a group of organisms adapted to utilize them.

Humic acids are precipitated when alkaline extracts of soil are acidified. They are intensely coloured as a result of their chemically unsaturated nature, and are largely responsible for the dark colours of soils and peats. By reduction they can be converted to almost colourless forms, which are spontaneously reoxidized by the atmosphere. Infrared spectra give indications of some aromatic rings and carboxyl groups, the former weakening and the latter strengthening as humification processes in the soil advance (Farmer and Morrison, 1960). Some of the amino acids are combined in the humic acid fraction, but do not account completely for their nitrogen content. Little can yet be said with conviction about the structure of a typical humic acid, although resemblances to lignin exist. Considerable interest centres round their ability to form complexes with inorganic cations, which is presumably the consequence of the presence of carboxyl and associated amino and hydroxyl groups. As usually prepared they contain rather large amounts of minerals, ash contents being as high as 5–7 per cent even after repeated re-precipitation, but the extent to which this results from the method of extraction is not yet clear. In studies of substances extracted from soils one must always concede that changes in physical state and in the extent of association with inorganic substances may be so great that results of experiments on their biological degradation *in vitro* may have little relevance to their behaviour in the soil.

*Other constituents.* While speaking of humic acids it is perhaps appropriate to mention the classical division of humus into (*a*) a fraction extractable with water, (*b*) fulvic acids and humic acids (both extractable with alkaline solutions, the former remaining in solution on acidification) and (*c*) humin (not extractable with alkali). This classification naturally cuts across our earlier division into carbohydrates, amino acids, etc.

## *LABILITY OF ORGANIC CONSTITUENTS*

When isotopes of carbon became available, particularly $^{14}C$, a number of research workers began to investigate the conversion of labelled whole plant residues into soil organic matter. The chief obstacle to interpretation here was once again the difficulty of isolating definable fractions from soils. The classical scheme just outlined is not discriminating enough. For example, even before its degradation has begun, labelled protein distributes itself between water-soluble, fulvic and humic fractions (Simonart, 1964). In the absence of soil, root residues are decomposed with relatively early production of material behaving like humic acid, but obviously not very much humified (Myśków and Morrison, 1963).

Experiments based on the classical methods of separation can therefore give only the broadest picture of events and have not helped much to elucidate the pathways of conversion. On the other hand they provide important quantitative information about the turn-over of organic materials and the basis for another kind of sub-division, viz. in terms of the rate of decomposition. Thus, part of the $^{14}C$ is quickly incorporated into the 'biomass' (the sum total of living organisms). This can be shown by heating the soil or exposing it to chloroform to kill these organisms; when a microbial population again develops there is a sudden increase in the evolution of labelled carbon dioxide as the dead bodies are utilized. Alternatively, selective extraction procedures can be shown to yield fractions of higher specific activity than the soil carbon considered as a whole (Jenkinson, 1963*a*).

Attempts can be made to assess the half-life of different fractions from an analysis of the progress curves for evolution of labelled $CO_2$. Experiments at Rothamsted gave a half-life of 95 days for uniformly labelled rye grass considered as a whole, but 10 per cent of it had a half-life greater than 5·8 years (Rayner, Jenkinson and Ross, 1964). Radiocarbon dating has given values as high as 50–200 years for the age of extractable soil organic matter, and even higher values for that which is not extractable (Talibudeen, 1964). It seems difficult to believe that differences as great as this can be attributed simply to differences in chemical composition. It seems more reasonable to expect that accessibility is also a factor.

Some controversy has surrounded attempts to draw from these experiments conclusions about the effect of freshly added organic matter on the progress of decomposition of organic matter already present. The earliest experiments seemed to show that new additions stimulated the oxidation of that already present (Hallam and Bartholomew, 1953), but some authors have not been able to detect any effect at all (Stotzky and Mortensen, 1958; Jenkinson, 1963*b*).

One can think of various explanations for a stimulatory effect of freshly added materials, but none of them demand that the effect shall occur irrespective of the soil type and of its previous history. There is certainly no easy answer here to a question that lies behind much thinking about the organic matter of soils. It is its persistence under certain circumstances which is more surprising than its disappearance, and inevitably one asks if this is because in the later stages of humification its chemical structure presents biochemical problems that few microorganisms can solve, or because early or late for a variety of reasons it becomes physically inaccessible to them.

If the first explanation were correct most of the organic matter in a fallow soil should be well humified; if the second, the organic fraction should contain material at all stages of decomposition. At present it is difficult to find information which distinguishes between these possibilities, but two observations may be pertinent. One is that if we accept the suggestion by Dubach and Mehta (1963) that humic substances 'which are produced in soils . . . and constitute over 50 per cent of the organic matter' contain no nitrogen, they must be accompanied by considerable quantities of non-humified substances in order to support a carbon to nitrogen ratio of 10 (the typical value for such soils). The other is that Greenland and Ford (1964) seem to have direct evidence that soils can somehow protect finely divided plant material from degradation.

Both observations lend support to our second alternative, and encourage the view that it is the accessibility of the substances present, rather than their lack of abundance or diversity, which limits the life of bacteria in soils.

## *ACKNOWLEDGEMENTS*

It is a pleasure to acknowledge the help of many colleagues, both in my initiation into the mysteries of soil science and more recently in the preparation of this paper. It is also appropriate to mention here Dr. W. G. C. Forsyth, sometime of this Institute, whose name, by mischance, does not appear in the list of references, but who was one of the pioneers of the application of modern techniques to the chemistry of soil organic matter.

## *REFERENCES*

ALLISON, F. E., DOETSCH, J. H. & ROLLER, E. M. (1953). Availability of fixed ammonium in soils containing different clay minerals. *Soil Sci.*, **75**, 373.

ANDERSON, G. (1961). A partial fractionation of alkali-soluble soil organic phosphate. *J. Soil Sci.*, **12**, 276.

ANDERSON, G. & ARLIDGE, E. Z. (1962). The adsorption of inositol phosphates and glycerophosphate by soil clays, clay minerals and hydrated sesquioxides in acid media. *J. Soil Sci.*, **13**, 216.

ANDREWS, P. & HOUGH, L. (1958). Biosynthesis of polysaccharides. I. Composition of plum leaf polysaccharides. *J. chem. Soc.*, 4476.

BARKER, S. A., FINCH, P., HAYES, M. H. B., SIMMONDS, P. G. & STACEY, M. (1965). Isolation and preliminary characterisation of soil polysaccharides. *Nature, Lond.*, **205**, 68.

BEAR, F. E. (1964). Chemistry of the soil. 2nd Edn. New York. Reinhold.

BREMNER, J. M. (1951). A review of recent work on soil organic matter. Part I. *J. Soil Sci.*, **2**, 67.

BREMNER, J. M. (1959). Determination of fixed ammonium in soil. *J. agric. Sci.*, **52**, 147.

BREMNER, J. M. & LEES, H. (1949). Studies on soil organic matter. Part II. The extraction of organic matter from soil by neutral reagents. *J. agric. Sci.*, **39**, 274.

BREMNER, J. M. & SHAW, K. (1954). The estimation and decomposition of amino sugars in soil. *J. agric. Sci.*, **44**, 152.

BURD, J. S. & MARTIN, J. C. (1924). Secular and seasonal changes in the soil solution. *Soil Sci.*, **18**, 151.

DUBACH, P. & MEHTA, N. C. (1963). The chemistry of soil humic substances. *Soils Fertil., Harpenden*, **26**, 293.

DUFF, R. B. (1952). The occurrence of L-fucose in soil, peat, and in a polysaccharide synthesized by soil bacteria. *Chemy Ind.*, 1104.

DUFF, R. B. & WEBLEY, D. M. (1959). 2-Ketogluconic acid as a natural chelator produced by soil bacteria. *Chemy Ind.*, 1376.

DUFF, R. B., WEBLEY, D. M. & SCOTT, R. O. (1963). Solubilization of minerals and related materials by 2-ketogluconic acid-producing bacteria. *Soil Sci.*, **95**, 105.

EATON, F. M., HARDING, R. B. & GANJE, T. J. (1960). Soil solution extractions at tenth-bar moisture percentages. *Soil Sci.*, **90**, 253.

FARMER, V. C. & MORRISON, R. I. (1960). Chemical and infrared studies on *Phragmites* peat and its humic acid. *Scient. Proc. R. Dubl. Soc., B*, **1**, 85.

GREAVES, M. P., ANDERSON, G. & WEBLEY, D. M. (1963). A rapid method for determining phytase activity of soil micro-organisms. *Nature, Lond.*, **200**, 1231.

GREENLAND, D. J. & FORD, G. W. (1964). Separation of partially humified materials from soils by ultrasonic dispersion. Abstracts of papers. II. Soil chemistry. *8th int. Congr. Soil Sci.*, 28.

GREENLAND, D. J., LINDSTROM, G. R. & QUIRK, J. P. (1962). Organic materials which stabilize natural soil aggregates. *Proc. Soil Sci. Soc. Am.*, **26**, 366.

GUPTA, U. C. & SOWDEN, F. J. (1963). Occurrence of free sugars in soil organic matter. *Soil Sci.*, **96**, 217.

GUPTA, U. C., SOWDEN, F. J. & STOBBE, P. C. (1963). The characterization of carbohydrate constituents from different soil profiles. *Proc. Soil Sci. Soc. Am.*, **27**, 380.

HALLAM, M. J. & BARTHOLOMEW, W. V. (1953). Influence of rate of plant residue addition in accelerating the decomposition of soil organic matter. *Proc. Soil Sci. Soc. Am.*, **17**, 365.

HANCE, R. J. & ANDERSON, G. (1963). Extraction and estimation of soil phospholipids. *Soil Sci.*, **96**, 94.

HOPKINS, F. G. (1933). Some chemical aspects of life. Reprinted in *Hopkins and Biochemistry, 1861–1947*. Ed. Needham, J. & Baldwin, E. Cambridge. Heffer. (1949).

HUDSON, H. J. & WEBSTER, J. (1958). Succession of fungi on decaying stems of *Agropyron repens. Trans. Br. mycol. Soc.*, **41**, 165.

JENKINSON, D. S. (1963*a*). *Rothamsted Experimental Station Report for 1962*, 44.

JENKINSON, D. S. (1963*b*). *The priming action*. Paper to F.A.O./I.A.E.A. Technical meeting on the use of isotopes in soil organic matter studies.

KAURICHEV, I. S., KOMAROVA, N. A., SKRYNNIKOVA, I. N. & SHILOVA, YE. I. (1963). Methods of investigating the chemical composition of the liquid soil phase (soil solution). *Pochvovedeniye*, 6, 35.

LEES, H. & QUASTEL, J. H. (1946). Biochemistry of nitrification in soil. 1. Kinetics of, and the effect of poisons on, soil nitrification, as studied by a soil perfusion technique. *Biochem. J.*, **40**, 803.

LYNCH, D. L., OLNEY, H. O. & WRIGHT, L. M. (1958). Some sugars and related carbohydrates found in Delaware soils. *J. Sci. Fd Agric.*, **9**, 56.

MEHTA, N. C., DUBACH, P. & DEUEL, H. (1961). Carbohydrates in the soil. *Adv. Carbohyd. Chem.*, **16**, 335.

MEINSCHEIN, W. G. & KENNY, G. S. (1957). Analyses of a chromatographic fraction of organic extracts of soils. *Analyt. Chem.*, **29**, 1153.

MYŚKÓW, W. & MORRISON, R. I. (1964). Decomposition of leguminous plant roots in sand. II. Humus formation. *J. Sci. Fd Agric.*, **15**, 162.

PAGE, H. J. & WILLIAMS, W. (1925). Studies on base exchange in Rothamsted soils. *Trans. Faraday Soc.*, **20**, 573.

PUSZTAI, A. (1965). The isolation and characterization of a glycoprotein from the seeds of kidney beans. *Biochem. J.*, **95**, 3.

PUTNAM, H. D. & SCHMIDT, E. L. (1959). Studies on the free amino acid fraction of soils. *Soil Sci.*, **87**, 22.

RAYNER, J. H., JENKINSON, D. S. & ROSS, G. J. S. (1964). *Rothamsted Experimental Station Report for 1963*, 68. (See also Jenkinson, D. S. (1965). *J. Soil Sci.*, **16**, 104).

RUSSELL, E. W. (1961). *Soil conditions and plant growth*. 9th Edn. London. Longmans.

SCHUFFELEN, A. C., BOLT, G. H. & KOENIGS, F. F. R. (1964). The isolation of the soil solution with the aid of filter paper tablets. Abstracts of papers. II. Soil chemistry. *8th int. Congr. Soil Sci.*, 89.

SIMONART, P. (1964). Microorganismes et humus. *Annls Inst. Pasteur, Paris*, **107**, 7.

SOWDEN, F. J. (1955). Estimation of amino acids in soil hydrolysates by the Moore and Stein methods. *Soil Sci.*, **80**, 181.

SOWDEN, F. J. (1959). Investigations on the amounts of hexosamines found in various soils and methods for their determination. *Soil Sci.*, **88**, 138.

SOWDEN, F. J. & IVARSON, K. C. (1962). Methods for the analysis of carbohydrate material in soil. 2. Use of cellulose column and paper chromatography for determination of the constituent sugars. *Soil Sci.*, **94**, 340.

STEVENSON, F. J. (1954). Ion exchange chromatography of amino acids in soil hydrolysates. *Proc. Soil Sci. Soc. Am.*, **18**, 373.

STEVENSON, F. J. (1957). Distribution of the forms of nitrogen in some soil profiles. *Proc. Soil Sci. Soc. Am.*, **21**, 283.

STOTZKY, G. & MORTENSEN, J. L. (1958). Effect of addition level and maturity of rye tissue on the decomposition of a muck soil. *Proc. Soil Sci. Soc. Am.*, **22**, 521.

TALIBUDEEN, O. (1964). Natural radioactivity in soils. *Soils Fertil., Harpenden*, **27**, 347.

TINSLEY, J. & SALAM, A. (1961). Extraction of soil organic matter with aqueous solvents. *Soils Fertil., Harpenden*, **24**, 81.

TYULIN, A. T. (1938). The composition and structure of soil organo-mineral gels and soil fertility. *Soil Sci.*, **45**, 343.

WEBLEY, D. M. & DUFF, R. B. (1962). A technique for investigating localized microbial development in soils. *Nature, Lond.*, **194**, 364.

WEBSTER, J. (1957). Succession of fungi on decaying cocksfoot culms. Part II. *J. Ecol.*, **45**, 1.

WHITEHEAD, D. C. (1964). Soil and plant-nutrition aspects of the sulphur cycle. *Soils Fertil., Harpenden*, **27**, 1.

WHITEHEAD, D. C. & TINSLEY, J. (1964). Extraction of soil organic matter with dimethylformamide. *Soil Sci.*, **97**, 34.

WIKLANDER, L. & KOUTLER-ANDERSSON, E. (1963). Influence of exchangeable ions on release of mineral-bound ions. *Soil Sci.*, **95**, 9.

WILLIAMS, E. G., SCOTT, N. M. & MCDONALD, M. J. (1958). Soil properties and phosphate sorption. *J. Sci. Fd Agric.*, **9**, 551.

# THE FUNGAL ENVIRONMENT OF SOIL BACTERIA

JOHN L. LOCKWOOD

*Department of Botany and Plant Pathology, Michigan State University*

## *INTRODUCTION*

Since the bacterial environment we are considering is the fungus, we should first try to place in perspective the occurrence of fungi in soil and the kinds of fungus structures which are available as micro-sites for bacterial development. According to current ecological concepts the soil is an impoverished medium in which microbial development is restricted to available nutrient substrates rather than occurring actively at all times throughout the soil mass (Alexander, 1961; Clark, 1965; Garrett, 1965). Prominent among potential substrates for fungi are dead plant or animal material, rhizospheres or root tissues of plants. A temporary fungal development may occur more generally when soluble nutrients become released or redistributed by such processes as alternate drying and wetting (Warcup, 1957) or evaporation from a surface (Kubiëna, 1938). As nutrients become exhausted, hyphae of many fungi are rapidly lysed in soil (Lloyd, 1965; Lockwood, 1960). Fungi must then survive as resting spores, sclerotia or resting mycelium or be extinguished. Thus, vegetative development of fungi is dispersed in time and space according to the availability of nutrients.

Unfortunately, knowledge of the fungal biomass in soil is only fragmentary. The general impression gained from direct microscopic examination of soils is that hyphal development therein is scant (Conn, 1922; Jensen, 1931; Kubiëna, 1938). On the other hand, some direct counts such as those of a Rothamsted arable soil made at intervals from January to June, revealed a mean of about a million pieces of mycelium with a total length of about 40 metres per g. of air-dry soil (Russell, 1961). Alexander (1961) gives estimates of the same order, ranging from 10–100 metres of mycelium per g. of soil. In these methods, however, the proportion of dead hyphae is unknown and is possibly quite high. However, based on values of these kinds, the total biomasses of fungi and bacteria in soil are calculated to be roughly equivalent—300 or more lbs. per acre on a dry weight basis (Alexander, 1961; Russell, 1961).

It is generally accepted that colony counts of fungi on dilution plates reflect numbers of fungus spores and values obtained with this method range from a few thousand to over a million per gram of soil (Alexander, 1961; Russell, 1961). Plate counts of the same Rothamsted soil mentioned above gave a mean value of around 200,000 colonies. Such estimates are no doubt low due to the well-known deficiencies of plating methods.

Besides the indigenous soil fungi, vast amounts of air-borne fungus spores come to rest on soil and these may also provide a significant substrate. Prominent among such spores might be basidiospores of hymenomycetes, uredospores of cereal rusts, teliospores of cereal smuts and conidia of common saprophytes such as *Cladosporium*.

In this context, this paper will attempt to describe the types of interactions which bacteria and actinomycetes enter into with fungi in soil, and to interpret the significance of such interactions to both partners.

## *THE FUNGI AS SUBSTRATES FOR SOIL BACTERIA AND ACTINOMYCETES*

Three kinds of evidence lend support to the concept that fungi serve as micro-substrates for bacteria and actinomycetes in soil: (*a*) physical colonization of fungal hyphae observed mainly on glass slides, (*b*) increased numbers and activity of bacteria and actinomycetes developing after amendment of soil with fungi, and (*c*) lysis of fungal structures in soil.

### *Physical colonization of fungal hyphae*

The most obvious evidence for a close relationship between fungi and bacteria or actinomycetes is from studies using buried glass slides after the method of Cholodny (1930) who first observed bacterial colonization of fungal hyphae. In Cholodny's method plain glass slides are buried in natural soil in the field or in containers in the laboratory, removed at designated time intervals (usually about 4 to 20 days) and examined microscopically. Characteristically, fungus mycelium is seen growing over the slides within 1 or a few days, followed rather quickly by the appearance of bacterial or actinomycete colonies growing on the hyphae (Cholodny, 1930; Conn, 1932*a*, *b*; Demeter and Mossel, 1933; Garrett, 1938; Glathe, 1955; King, Hope and Eaton, 1934; Jensen, 1934; Mitchell, Hooton and Clark, 1941; Starkey, 1938). Decomposition of the hyphae frequently, but not always, accompanies the development of bacteria or actinomycetes thereon.

Similar associations have been revealed on glass slides placed in partially sterilized soils (Rehm, 1959*a*; Winter, 1950*a*, *b*), in soil supplemented with various kinds of organic materials (Garrett, 1938; Glathe, 1955; Jensen, 1934; King *et al.*, 1934; Mitchell *et al.*, 1941; Rehm, 1959*a*, *b*; Sequeira, 1962; Subramanian, 1946, 1950), in rhizospheres (Glathe, 1955; Starkey, 1938), or in composts (Waksman, Umbreit and Cordon, 1939). Modifications of the Cholodny method include coating slides with nutrients prior to placement in soil (Mollenhoff, Smith and Brown, 1936; Ziemiecka, 1934–5), or introducing a selected fungus in a culture medium, usually agar, into the soil on the glass slide (Rehm, 1959*a*, *b*; Sequeira, 1962; Subramanian, 1946, 1950; Wallhäuser, 1951; Winter, 1950*a*, *b*). The associations developed with these modifications resemble those shown when plain glass slides are used.

Bacterial associations with fungi appear to predominate in most reports. Bacterial cells may occur along the hyphal strands in small aggregates or in rows one or more cells thick, or larger colonies may completely enclose the hypha in a sheath. Restricted or large areas of the hyphae may be colonized. Small cocci (Cholodny, 1930; Conn, 1932*a*, *b*; Demeter and Mossel, 1933; Starkey, 1938; Ziemiecka, 1934–5) or larger rods (Cholodny, 1930; Mollenhoff *et al.*, 1936; Starkey, 1938; Ziemiecka, 1934–5) were most commonly seen in association with fungal hyphae in various modifications of the Cholodny method. Glathe (1955) also mentioned short rods, Jensen (1934) Gram-negative rods, and Demeter and Mossel (1933) spore-forming rods and short rods, although Starkey (1938) seldom encountered spore-forming rods. Cholodny (1934) believed that several species were involved. Novogrudsky (1948) has listed several species of bacteria which he regards as adapted for colonization of fungal hyphae. These include *Pseudomonas fluorescens*, *Achromobacter denitrificans*, *Bacillus coli*, *Proteus vulgaris*, *Bacillus mesentericus*, and *Bacillus subtilis*, but I am unaware of the basis on which they were selected.

Photographs of bacteria colonizing fungal hyphae on glass slides are given in several references (Cholodny, 1930; Conn, 1932*a*, *b*; Demeter and Mossel, 1933; Glathe, 1955; King *et al.*, 1934; Sequeira, 1962; Starkey, 1938; Subramanian, 1946, 1950; Tribe, 1957; Waksman *et al.*, 1939; Winter, 1950*a*; Ziemiecka, 1934–5).

Actinomycete colonization of fungal hyphae on glass slides in soil also occurs frequently (Demeter and Mossel, 1933; Glathe, 1955; Rehm, 1959*a*, *b*; Thornton, 1953; Waksman *et al.*, 1939; Winter, 1950*a*, *b*; Ziemiecka, 1934–5), and in some instances fungal mycelium seemed more attractive to actinomycetes than to bacteria. Rhizoctonia-like hyphae developing on slides appeared to act as a pathway for the smaller epiphytic actinomycete hyphae whose branching followed that of the fungus (Thornton, 1953). This relationship was reproduced when *Rhizoctonia solani* and *Streptomyces scabies* were artificially introduced into (sterilized?) soil. A similar close association developed between naturally occurring actinomycetes and *Ophiobolus graminis* or *Fusarium* sp. introduced into soil on slides (Winter, 1950*a*, *b*). Actinomycetes grew along the fungal hyphae and were able to cross from one strand to another only when they lay close together. In partially sterilized soil hyphal disintegration occurred as a result of a greatly increased development of actinomycetes, whereas in natural soil the fungi were not damaged despite colonization of their hyphae. Winter (1950*a*) speculated that nutrients in the agar inoculum used for *O. graminis* may have enabled the fungus to resist destruction by the relatively fewer actinomycetes occurring in natural soil.

Rehm (1959*a*) compared the interaction occurring between *Streptomyces albus* and *Aspergillus niger* when both organisms were inoculated onto glass slides and placed either in natural soil, soil partially sterilized by 2 exposures to steam at 96° for 10 min. or 30 min. each, and sterilized soil. He was particularly interested in the relative degree of development of each member of the pair, and in the extent of parasitic penetration of the cells of the fungus by the streptomycete. In all 4 treatments *S. albus* colonized and penetrated the mycelium of *A. niger* which resulted in suppression of growth of the fungus and in its partial utilization by *S. albus*. With increasing non-sterility the intensity of development of both partners diminished, but the parasitic habit of the streptomycete permitted its relatively greater development, even in natural soil. In natural and in partially sterilized soils, actinomycetes other than the test organism and bacteria were seen colonizing hyphae of *A. niger* and of native fungi growing on the slide. When the soils were supplemented with nutrient solutions the balance changed to permit better fungal development despite active parasitic attack by *S. albus*, especially in sterilized soil. However, with increasing non-sterility the shift was minimal.

Parasitic development of a different strain of *Streptomyces albus* on *Aspergillus niger* and on *Fusarium culmorum* occurred when inoculated glass slides were placed in soil in the field (Rehm, 1959*b*). Here also, other organisms than the test organisms frequently grew on the glass and complicated interpretation of the interaction.

A similar close relation between *Streptomyces albus* and 10 different Fungi Imperfecti, including *Aspergillus niger*, was shown in liquid culture media (Rehm, 1954). Penetration of the hyphal cells of most fungi was observed, but it was not clear in most instances to what extent this development occurred before or after the death of the hyphae. In any case, partial destruction of the fungus mycelium eventually occurred. Definite parasitic penetration of mycelium of *Stemphylium alternaria* was established, however. A similar relation between *Streptomyces albidoflavus* and *Fusarium culmorum* in liquid and in sand cultures has been described by Skinner (1956*a*, *b*).

While 8 of 10 fungi studied by Rehm followed this pattern, 2 significant variations were noted. With *Trichothecium roseum* a tolerant relationship was established. Although the fungus mycelium became completely enmeshed by the streptomycete mycelium no penetration of the fungus was observed and it continued to grow unsuppressed. Despite some parasitic penetration of *Aspergillus niger* mycelium, the fungus flourished. The streptomycete developed relatively poorly, its growth being restricted to the hyphae of the fungus. Suppression of the streptomycete was thought to be due to the development of a strongly acidic reaction in the liquid culture medium. The relative balance between the 2 partners was subsequently found to be influenced by the nature of the medium (Rehm, 1958). Colonization and parasitism of *A. niger* by *S. albus* also took place in agar media (Rehm, 1956).

The ability to enter into a close relation of the kind described seems to be as non-specific for actinomycetes as it is for fungi. Of 33 isolates of various species of *Streptomyces* from 7 taxonomic series, 24 isolates representing 6 series were able to colonize and parasitize *Aspergillus niger* on glass slides in nutrient cultures or in sterilized soil (Rehm, 1959*c*).

Photographs of actinomycetes in association with fungal hyphae are given in the following references (Demeter and Mossel, 1933; Skinner, 1956*a*; Rehm, 1954, 1956, 1958, 1959*a*; Waksman *et al.*, 1939; Winter, 1950*a*, *b*; Ziemiecka, 1934–5).

Although studies in culture media provide useful insight into the specificity of the interactions for different organisms, the types of microbial interrelationships and the extent to which they occur, are best interpreted from studies made in the more restrictive conditions of natural soil.

Growth of bacteria and actinomycetes on fungal hyphae has also been observed with other methods. Waid and Woodman (1957) buried nylon mesh in soil. The meshes first became colonized by fungi whose hyphae later became colonized by bacteria. This kind of successional development was also observed on buried cellulose filter paper (Cholodny, 1930) and more recently with cellophane (Tribe, 1957). Hyphae of *Fusarium oxysporum* f. *cubense* (Stover, 1958) and of *Fusarium solani* f. *pisi* (Chacko and Lockwood, unpublished) were colonized by bacteria and actinomycetes in aqueous soil extracts.

Where external colonization of the fungus accompanies degradation of the mycelium, it is often difficult to determine if the parasite is the cause of death or whether it is subsisting on mycelium dead or dying from other causes. Many authors understandably are indefinite on this point (Cholodny, 1930; Conn, 1932*a*, *b*; Demeter and Mossel, 1933; Glathe, 1955; Jensen, 1934; Mollenhoff *et al.*, 1936; Starkey, 1938; Waid, 1960; Waksman *et al.*, 1939; Ziemiecka, 1934–5), but most seem to feel that there is a connection between colonization and destruction of dead or moribund mycelium. Some believe that the colonizing organisms caused both death and destruction of the living fungal hyphae (Garrett, 1938; King *et al.*, 1934; Mitchell *et al.*, 1941; Rehm, 1959*a*, *b*; Subramanian, 1946, 1950).

Despite the results discussed above, the concept that bacteria and actinomycetes proliferate extensively on the surface of living fungal mycelium in soil cannot be regarded as unequivocally established. Spores and mycelia of several kinds of fungi placed directly on soil surfaces and subsequently recovered by means of plastic films never were colonized by bacteria or actinomycetes until they were almost completely destroyed (Lloyd, 1965). This method uses no supporting materials or nutrients—only the fungus and the soil. While work with this technique has been done with only a few soils, the possibility should be considered that the presence of the glass slide or other such materials may somehow induce the more extensive development of bacteria and actinomycetes on fungal structures than naturally occurs in soil. It may be significant that Skinner (1956*b*) did not observe a direct connection between *Streptomyces albidoflavus* and *Fusarium culmorum* in sterilized soil though close association was seen in culture or in sand. Useful as the Cholodny method has been, it is well known that micro-organisms are stimulated to more extensive development on continuous solid surfaces than in the soil itself (Burges, 1958; Russell, 1961). While there is no *a priori* reason for doubting that hyphae could be colonized and parasitized by bacteria and actinomycetes in soil itself, perhaps some caution should be exercised in interpreting results with the Cholodny method until such colonization is seen by methods which do not utilize supporting materials of any kind. In connection with this, Kubiëna apparently did not report colonization of hyphae by other micro-organisms in soil with direct microscopic methods (Kubiëna, 1938; Kubiëna and Renn, 1934–5).

*Increased numbers and activity of micro-organisms in soil supplemented with fungi*

Heck (1929) was the first to show that total bacterial numbers increased following amendment of soil with a living fungus. He added washed live mycelium of *Aspergillus oryzae* to soil at the rate of 2 g. of dry mycelium to 1 kg. of soil. After 30 days bacterial counts in soil supplemented with mycelium were 8 times higher than those in non-supplemented soil.

More recent results also suggest that living fungus mycelium is rapidly utilized by other micro-organisms in soil. In our laboratory Lloyd (1965) added washed, live mycelium of *Glomerella cingulata* to moist, natural loam soil in an amount equivalent to 1 per cent of the soil weight. When soil dilutions were plated on soil extract agar bacterial numbers first increased 6-fold by the 2nd day and reached a maximum of 70-fold on the 7th day. Actinomycete numbers on chitin agar had doubled by the 4th day and increased 10 to 12-fold by the 9th day when the experiment ended. At 3 days the soil surface was covered with grey streptomycete colonies, and the soil had taken on the characteristic actinomycete odour. Lysis of the fungus began on the 2nd day and was complete by the 4th day.

Rapid increases in bacterial numbers also followed supplementation of soil with fungus spores. Uredospores of *Puccinia rubigo-vera* shaken from wheat plants, and conidia of *Neurospora* sp. shaken from the aerial mycelium produced in culture were used to supplement moist, loam soil at rates from 20–200 mg. dry weight (1–5 $\times$ $10^9$ spores) per g. of soil (Lingappa and Lockwood, 1964; unpublished). Increases in bacterial numbers after 8–16 hours ranged from 3–9-fold. Mitchell and Alexander (1963) showed a 7-fold increase of bacilli and pseudomonads counted together and a similar increase of actinomycetes on the 3rd day following addition of conidia of *Fusarium oxysporum* f. *cubense* (apparently unwashed) to soil. These increases were accompanied by a marked decline in numbers of viable *Fusarium* propagules. Bacterial numbers increased another 10-fold by the 7th day and sharply declined by the 14th day, by which time almost all the *Fusarium* was dead.

The initial rapid increases in microbial numbers seem to be due to soluble nutrients in or on the spores. A single brief aqueous washing of *Neurospora* conidia or rust uredospores extracted approximately 10 per cent of the spore dry weight of each (Lingappa and Lockwood, 1964). When soil was amended with 10 mg. dried extract from *Neurospora* conidia or 25 mg. dried extract from rust uredospores per g. of soil, 5- and 10-fold increases, respectively, in bacterial numbers occurred in 16 hrs.

From several experiments (Lingappa and Lockwood, 1964; unpublished) the number of bacteria formed in spore-supplemented soil can be roughly estimated. For *Neurospora* conidia and rust uredospores, values 16 hrs. after amendment range from 0·3–3 bacteria formed per spore. Data of Mitchell and Alexander (1963) suggest that somewhere between 4 and 12 *Bacillus* or pseudomonad cells may develop from a single propagule of *Fusarium oxysporum* f. *cubense* in 7 days. Rough estimates can also be made of the weight of bacteria formed per unit amount of fungus applied to the soil, taking fresh weight of 1 bacterial cell as $10^{-11}$ g. and dry weight as $10^{-12}$ g. (Oginsky and Umbreit, 1959). Based on these values and plate count estimates of bacterial numbers, 0·01–0·1 g. of bacteria was formed in 16 hours for each g. of *Neurospora* conidia or rust uredospores added to soil. From the data of Lloyd (1965), 0·14 g. of bacteria were formed in 7 days from 1 g. of washed hyphae of *Glomerella cingulata*. All of these values must be considered as underestimating the total amount of micro-organisms whose development could be supported by a single spore or hypha for several reasons. These include limitations inherent in the dilution plate method, and the fact that some days or weeks would be required for complete digestion of the fungus, and many of the experiments cited were of short duration.

Results obtained with soil dilution plates were supported by respirometric assays of spore-supplemented soil (Lingappa and Lockwood, 1964). When soil was supplemented with 7·5 mg. ($1{\cdot}6 \times 10^8$) washed conidia of *Fusarium solani* f. *pisi* or 3·6 mg. ($1{\cdot}5 \times 10^8$) *Neurospora* conidia per gram of soil, respective increases in oxygen uptake of 33- and 10-fold occurred within 30 min. as compared with rates in non-supplemented soil. These relatively higher values continued for 6 hrs. when the experiment ended. Similar increases occurred with conidia of *Helminthosporium victoriae* or *Glomerella cingulata*, but these conidia had not been washed and spore suspensions may have included nutrients from the agar medium. Although some portion of the increased respiration may have been due to endogenous fungal spore respiration, killed conidia and cell-free washings of conidia also induced similar rapid increases in oxygen uptake in soil.

*Lysis of fungal structures in soil*

The fact that mycelium, and also spores, of many fungi disappear rapidly when placed in contact with soil also provides evidence for their utilization by other soil micro-organisms. Live or killed mycelia of numerous plant parasitic and saprophytic fungi were partially or completely lysed by soil within a few days (Lloyd, 1965; Lockwood, 1959, 1960; Payen, 1962). Spore germination was followed by lysis of germ tubes within 4–8 days when glass slides containing spores of several fungi in thin films of agar were placed in soil supplemented with 2 per cent soybean meal (Chinn, 1953).

That soil micro-organisms cause lysis is indicated by the fact that sterilized soil is non-lytic and that mycolysis can be restored to sterilized soil by inoculating it with certain actinomycetes (Lloyd, 1965; Lockwood, 1959; Lockwood and Lingappa, 1963; Stevenson, 1956) or bacteria (Mitchell and Alexander, 1963; Park, 1956). Moreover, lytic micro-organisms will lyse fungi growing on weak agar media (Carter and Lockwood, 1957; Lloyd, 1965; Lockwood and Lingappa, 1963; Messiaen, 1962; Messiaen and Beyries, 1963) or in mixed liquid cultures (Carter and Lockwood, 1959; Mitchell and Alexander, 1963) in the absence of soil.

Although most lytic micro-organisms remain unidentified, virtually all lytic actinomycetes reported are members of the genus *Streptomyces*. A *Micromonospora*, however, was involved in destruction of a *Thermomyces* sp. in compost (Waksman *et al.*, 1939). Identified lytic bacteria include *Bacillus cereus*, *B. megaterium* and *Pseudomonas* sp. (Mitchell and Alexander, 1963) and *Bacillus macerans* (Park, 1956). Most of the fungi shown to be lysed by soil or by lytic micro-organisms are Fungi Imperfecti, but *Rhizoctonia* spp. and several Phycomycetes were also subject to lysis (Lloyd, 1965; Lockwood, 1959, 1960; Mitchell and Alexander, 1963).

In our observations in soil (Lloyd, 1965; Lockwood, 1960) and in culture (Carter and Lockwood, 1957; Lloyd, 1965), lysis is accomplished without direct colonization of the fungal mycelium. In agar, zones cleared of mycelium (often completely so) are developed surrounding the actinomycete colony streaked on the fungus culture. Plastic peelings of lysing mycelium taken from the surface of natural soil never showed any colonization until the mycelium was nearly decomposed, whereupon the few remains became colonized by both bacteria and actinomycetes. The course of mycolysis was similar in soil sterilized and inoculated with lytic streptomycetes.

In our own tests lytic actinomycetes were much more frequently encountered than were lytic bacteria (Lloyd, 1965; Lockwood, 1959; Lockwood and Lingappa, 1963). For example, 14 of 20 randomly selected streptomycete isolates lysed live mycelium of *Glomerella cingulata* in culture, but only 2 of 27 bacterial isolates did so. In soil the same 14 actinomycetes and none of the bacteria lysed the fungus (Lockwood and Lingappa, 1963). All 20 actinomycetes partially lysed dead mycelium of *G. cingulata* in soil but none of the bacteria did so. Messiaen and Beyries (1963) have shown that individual actinomycetes are capable of inducing a greater rate and extent of mycolysis than are bacteria, but combinations of certain spore-forming bacteria caused as much lysis as did actinomycetes.

The isolation of lytic bacteria from soil and rhizospheres has been of particular interest to Russian microbiologists who have reported incredible numbers occurring in some soils (Krasilnikov, 1958). One reference indicates that numbers of lytic bacteria may reach several millions per g. of soil. In another reference $10^5$–$10^8$ bacteria lytic to *Fusarium vasinfectum* occurred per g. of soil, the exact number depending on the type of vegetation.

Fungus structures other than hyphae are also lysed by microorganisms in natural soil. Lysis of conidia or sporangiospores of several fungi placed in contact with soil was seen on contact slides (Park, 1955) and soil smears (Lingappa and Lockwood, 1961). Even chlamydospores (Subramanian, 1946, 1950) and sclerotia (Mitchell *et al.*, 1941) were attacked and destroyed. It seems a safe generalization, however, that hyphae are most susceptible to lysis followed by conidia or sporangiospores and that chlamydospores or sclerotia are most resistant. This is nicely documented for *Fusarium vasinfectum* (Subramanian, 1946, 1950).

Some bacteria may escape the rigorous competition of the soil by temporarily emigrating to grow on rusts and smuts on the foliage of cereals. Stem and leaf rusts of wheat were destroyed by a *Bacillus* sp. which was reported to be common throughout the Mississippi Valley and East to Virginia and West to Oregon (Levine, Bamberg and Atkinson, 1936). In greenhouse tests it lysed pycnia, aecia and uredia of several cereal rusts. More recently another bacterium, *Xanthomonas uredovorus* was reported to parasitize and lyse uredia of stem rust on wheat, oats and rye, leaf rust on wheat and rye, and crown rust of oats (Pon, Townsend, Wessman, Schmidt and Kingsolver, 1954). This bacterium was said to be spread from soil to plants by splashing rain and from plant to plant by means of uredospores. The bacteria attacking smuts were isolated from contaminated cultures or from artificially inoculated corn plants (Bamberg, 1931; Johnson, 1931) and included a Gram-negative coccus, a small Gram-negative rod, a Gram-positive rod and a *Myxococcus* sp. (Johnson, 1931). These bacteria destroyed corn smut on inoculated plants, and several kinds of smuts in culture, but were non-parasitic on fungi other than smuts (Bamberg, 1931). Apparently little is known of their occurrence in the field.

Reduction in diseases caused by root-infecting fungi has been accomplished by direct inoculation of seed or soil with mycolytic organisms, or indirectly by enhancing microbial activity in soil through organic amendments. Russian workers have been particularly interested in the direct application of lytic bacteria for disease control. Much of their work was recently summarized by Krasilnikov (1958). Partial success has been claimed by soil application for a number of root diseases, including *Fusarium* wilt of potato (Nikitina, 1958), and of flax (Krasilnikov, 1958; Novogrudski, 1936), *Verticillium* wilt of cotton (Krasilnikov, 1958), a *Fusarium* disease of *Pinus sylvestris* seedlings (Krasilnikov, 1958; Krasilnikov and Raznitzyna, 1946) and *Fusarium gramineum* infecting wheat seedlings (Novogrudski, 1936). Treatment of seed with lytic bacteria is also said to have reduced the *Fusarium* disease of wheat (Khudiakov and Raznitzyna, 1939; Krasilnikov, 1958; Naumova, 1939) and *Fusarium* wilt of flax (Krasilnikov, 1958). Among the mycolytic bacteria used, strains of *Pseudomonas* and *Achromobacter* were most effective in reducing *Fusarium* disease of pine seedlings (Krasilnikov and Raznitzyna, 1946), and *Pseudomonas mycophaga* was used for *Fusarium* wilt of potatoes (Nikitina, 1958). Though most of these experiments were done in sterilized soils, some successes were reported with non-sterile soil.

Practical control of *Phymatotrichum* root rot of cotton (King *et al.*, 1934; Mitchell *et al.*, 1941) and of take-all of wheat (Garrett, 1965) has been achieved by supplementing soil with organic materials. Reduction in these diseases seems related, in part at least, to an increase in the numbers of micro-organisms whose activity appears to result in destruction of the causal fungi.

For example, only 30–35 per cent of sclerotia of *Phymatotrichum omnivorum* originally placed in samples of soil supplemented with 3 per cent barnyard manure, or chopped sorghum were subsequently recovered by screening and washing, whereas in non-supplemented soil 80–85 per cent were recovered (Mitchell *et al.*, 1941). These results were confirmed with sclerotia recovered from manured soil in the field and with sclerotia introduced into straw or manure-treated soil on glass slides. In all of these experiments large increases in microbial numbers accompanied decomposition of the sclerotia. Moreover, mycelium of *P. omnivorum* was parasitized on 19 of 53 glass slides placed in soil supplemented with stable manure or alfalfa hay, whereas in non-manured soil parasitized hyphae occurred in only 5 of 54 slides (King *et al.*, 1934). Further evidence for the involvement of soil micro-organisms in destruction of *P. omnivorum* sclerotia was their equally good survival in sterilized organic-amended and in sterilized non-amended soil, and the fact that in non-sterile, organic-supplemented soil, temperature and moisture levels most favourable for general microbial activity were most destructive to sclerotia (Clark and Mitchell, 1942).

The addition of plant residues to soil also hastened decomposition of *Ophiobolus graminis* as measured by the wheat straw method (Garrett, 1938). Cholodny slides revealed a concurrent increase in numbers of soil microbes, and increased colonization and destruction of fungal hyphae in general.

A similar increased rate of destruction of germ tubes of *Fusarium vasinfectum* was observed in agar on glass slides placed in soil supplemented with animal manure (Subramanian, 1946). With this fungus also, more rapid hyphal decomposition occurred at high soil moisture and temperature levels.

The selective augmentation of the lytic microbial population of soil by amendments has been suggested by Alexander and his colleagues as a possible means of control of root-infecting fungi. Amendment of soil with chitin caused an increase in total numbers of bacteria and actinomycetes, and of chitinase-producing organisms, and also gave some reduction of *Fusarium* root rot of bean in greenhouse tests (Mitchell and Alexander, 1962). However, a causal relation between an increased population of lytic microbes and disease reduction has not been established. *Fusarium* root rot of bean and *Fusarium* wilt of radish were also reduced in soil supplemented with an impure source of laminarin ($\beta$, 1-3 glucan), also a constituent of fungus cell walls, but this was accompanied by a temporary decrease in total bacteria and actinomycetes (Mitchell, 1963).

The addition of soluble nutrients to soil may delay the onset of mycolysis. When soil was supplemented with glucose or peptone at the rate of 0·2 per cent of the soil dry weight, fungi placed on the soil surface grew luxuriantly with bacteria and actinomycetes for 3 or 4 days before lysis began, whereas without nutrients the onset of visible lysis occurred within 2 days (Lloyd, 1965). Similar results were obtained in sterilized soil which had been inoculated with streptomycetes. However, when soil was supplemented with chitin, lysis was enhanced presumably because this compound is utilized by actinomycetes and some bacteria but not by the test fungi.

## *SIGNIFICANCE TO THE BACTERIA AND ACTINOMYCETES*

Whether bacteria and actinomycetes develop as epiphytes or parasites, either directly on or at a short distance from fungi, the fungus must be providing some stimulus for the establishment of the relationship. In the intimate associations this could be a contact stimulus as it is well known that bacterial development is enhanced in contact with inert surfaces (Russell, 1961). The extensive proliferation of bacterial and actinomycete cells which may occur in contact with the hyphae, however, strongly suggests that soluble nutrients from the mycelium or spores are utilized as food. Although some evidence has been presented that spores readily lose soluble nutrients (Lingappa *et al.*, 1961), direct evidence is lacking that the same is true for mycelium.

A nutritional basis for the development of bacteria and actinomycetes on or near fungal hyphae can be assumed, however, from numerous reports of exudation of nutrients from fungal mycelium in pure culture (Cochrane, 1958). Typically, following the linear phase of growth, some loss in dry weight of mycelium occurs, and is accompanied by a release into the medium of an array of substances which could serve as nutrients for other micro-organisms. These include various nitrogen-containing compounds such as ammonia, free amino acids, proteins, peptides and urea; free monosaccharides and polysaccharides; and organic acids including Krebs' cycle intermediates. Minerals released include phosphorus and sulphur. Vitamins synthesized by the fungus usually appear in the medium also. Though most exudation occurs after the onset of autolysis, movement into the medium of ammonium ions, amino acids and peptides during the growth phase is reported for many fungi (Cochrane, 1958; Morton and Broadbent, 1955). Presumably exudation of similar compounds would occur in soil and provide a food base for microbial growth.

For several reasons, it is impossible to ascertain with present information how significant the fungal substrate is to the beneficiaries. In the first place inadequate information is available as to the species involved, although the existing evidence indicates that a considerable number of diverse types both of bacteria and actinomycetes can enter into the interrelationships.

A second problem is lack of knowledge of the nutrient requirements of these organisms and of the specificity of the fungus as a substrate. Although the exudates from hyphae or spores of fungi are unlikely to be very selective, those fewer soil micro-organisms which are able to cause lysis of fungal cell walls may be selectively stimulated. The fact that *Azotobacter* increased to high levels in soil in which added fungal mycelium was lysed by mycolytic bacteria (Novogrudski and Mitrofanova, 1957) suggests that microbes other than the primary lysing micro-organisms may utilize the by-products of fungal decay.

A third factor is our almost complete ignorance of the amount of fungal protoplasm existing in soil at any given time, and the extent of this substrate in comparison with others.

Fourthly, it is difficult to get a clear view of the frequency with which the various interrelationships occur in soil. From results with Cholodny slides it is clear that not all hyphae become colonized by bacteria and actinomycetes, although words like 'common' and 'frequent' are often used to describe the frequency of the association (Cholodny, 1930; Conn, 1932*a*, *b*; Garrett, 1938; Jensen, 1934; Starkey, 1938; Thornton, 1953; Waksman *et al.*, 1939; Wallhäuser, 1951). Actinomycetes grew on *Rhizoctonia*-like hyphae in 1127 of 1765 microscope fields on glass slides (Thornton, 1953), and bacteria colonized fungal hyphae in every interstice of buried nylon mesh where fungi developed (Waid and Woodman, 1957). In neither case, however, do we know how many hyphae were colonized per slide or mesh. Starkey (1938) was so impressed with the extensive development of bacteria on fungal mycelium in rhizospheres of crop plants that he considered the fungi responsible for a considerable portion of the increase in numbers of bacteria in rhizospheres. In other reports in which glass slides were used (Glathe, 1955; Demeter and Mossel, 1933; Mollenhoff *et al.*, 1936; Ziemiecka, 1934–5), the writers give the impression that associations of bacteria or actinomycetes with fungi were not abundant. Winter (1950*a*) was more specific in stating that only a small proportion of the hyphae of *Ophiobolus graminis* were associated with microbes even after 18 weeks in natural soil. However, those actinomycetes which did appear were almost entirely associated with *O. graminis*. Free actinomycete hyphae were found only between closely lying fungal hyphae, connecting them. Fungi with pigmented mycelia seem to be relatively unattractive to bacteria and actinomycetes and more resistant to lysis as compared with those having hyaline mycelia (Starkey, 1938; Waid, 1960). This may, in part, explain Warcup's (1957) observations that most of the fungal hyphae isolated directly from soil were dark, whereas hyaline hyphae were rare.

In at least one instance the associations were sought but not found (Timonin, 1940). Fungi were seen growing on glass slides in the rhizosphere of flax but the hyphae remained free of micro-organisms. Uncertainties in evaluating data obtained with glass slides already discussed further complicate interpretations of the significance of the interactions.

Finally it should be mentioned that Thornton (1953) and Cholodny (1930, 1934) felt that fungal hyphae may influence the distribution of actinomycetes and bacteria, respectively, by providing a pathway for movement from place to place.

## *SIGNIFICANCE TO THE FUNGI*

The view has been expressed that fungus parasites of plants are more often influenced than influencing in their relationship with other micro-organisms (Park, 1963). This statement can be applied to the interactions discussed herein, and can be extended to fungi in general in the soil, with the possible exception of some dark mycelial types. While there is no evidence that filamentous fungi benefit nutritionally from these interrelationships, there is abundant evidence, except where the association is purely epiphytic and commensal, that microbial activity on or near fungi profoundly affects the survival of fungi in soil.

### *Soil fungistasis*

It is now well known that the germination of spores of most fungi is inhibited in almost any natural soil, and that this property is related to the presence of micro-organisms therein. In natural soil, fungal spore germination seems restricted to nutrient substrates such as root exudates or pieces of undecomposed organic debris. Soil fungistasis seems to be of survival value to the fungus spore by preventing germination in the absence of potentially colonizable substrates (Dobbs and Hinson, 1953).

Fungistasis can be restored to sterilized soil by re-inoculation with any of many unselected isolates of actinomycetes, bacteria or fungi (Griffin, 1962; Lockwood and Lingappa, 1963), suggesting a non-specific origin of this property. Although many workers believe that fungistatic substances in soil account for the inhibition, no clear evidence that such substances are widespread in soil and cause fungistasis has yet been presented, despite numerous attempts. As an alternative the possibility of an inhibitory interaction as a result of bacterial or actinomycete activity near the spore in soil has been suggested (Lingappa and Lockwood, 1961). Micro-organisms in soil are rapidly activated by the presence of added fungal spores and a connection may exist between the microbial utilization of nutrients from the spores and inhibition of their germination. For example, spores which would germinate in buffer solutions or on water agar were inhibited in the presence of washed cells of various bacteria or actinomycetes. That the inhibition resulted from a rapid interaction between spores and microbes was indicated by the strong inhibition of conidia of *Helminthosporium victoriae* which germinated within 1 to 2 hrs. in the absence of associated micro-organisms. It is not clear whether the inhibition was caused by antibiotic substances produced by bacteria and actinomycetes growing on spore exudates, or to competition for nutrients, but no antibiotic activity could be demonstrated in filtrates of the fungistatic micro-organisms or from mixtures of spores and these microbes. It would be difficult to account for long-term inhibition of fungus spores in soil by a mechanism of antibiotic production in the spore vicinity, since spore nutrients would soon be exhausted and any antibiotics produced would be unlikely to persist in soil. Attention has recently been drawn to the alternative possibility that absence of required exogenous nutrients may account for soil fungistasis (Lockwood, 1964). Exogenous nutrient requirements for germination are known for many spores, and in spores of about 20 fungi tested a clear relation seems to exist between a requirement for external nutrients and failure to germinate in soil, and between nutritional independence and ability to germinate in soil (Ko and Lockwood, unpublished). If lack of nutrients is the cause of fungistasis, the question remains to what extent the critical factor is active microbial competition for nutrients in the spore vicinity or the pre-existing absence of required nutrients in the soil at large. However this question is resolved, it is the soil microbes which cause the impoverished condition. Lockwood (1964) has recently reviewed the phenomenon of soil fungistasis.

*Soil mycolysis*

Also significant to the survival of fungi in soil is another property of soils which causes the destruction of fungi (Lloyd, 1965; Lockwood, 1960). Mycolysis, like fungistasis, is microbial in origin and relatively non-specific as regards the fungi affected, although dematiaceous types seem relatively more resistant to it. Also, soluble nutrients will temporarily annul soil mycolysis and permit fungi to flourish. Lytic action has so far been restored to sterilized soil only by actinomycetes, many of which can induce mycolysis, and by relatively few bacteria. The mechanism by which the lytic organisms induce mycolysis is still obscure. One possibility is that cell-wall decomposing enzymes from the lytic organisms are involved but no one has yet shown that such enzyme preparations can cause the lysis of living fungal mycelium at temperatures favourable for fungus growth, despite attempts to do this (Lloyd, 1965). Such enzymes can, however, cause partial lysis of dead fungal mycelium or cell wall preparations (Lloyd, 1965; Skujins and Potgieter, 1964).

Lysis of living mycelium can occur, however, in conditions which exclude extracellular enzymes. Fungal mycelium was lysed on the surface of membrane filters with pores 4·0 or 5·0 μ across, when filters were placed in contact with soil (Lloyd, 1965). This suggested that the lytic micro-organisms in soil may induce the fungi to digest their own substance. As further evidence that autolysis may account for mycolysis, lysis characteristic of that occurring in soil was induced, in the absence of soil or other microbes, by exposing fungal mycelium to a combination of starvation conditions and an antifungal antibiotic. When germinated spores of *Glomerella cingulata* and *Helminthosporium victoriae* were incubated on dialysis tubing through which water was constantly circulating, the application of 0·2 ml. of a 100 μg. per ml. solution of any of several antifungal antibiotics to the starved mycelium resulted in complete disappearance of mycelium within 1–2 days. Starvation alone or exposure to antibiotics alone resulted in little or no lysis. The applicability of this model to soil mycolysis is not yet established, but its essential requirements may be met in soil. Only low levels of available nutrients, particularly carbon, exist in soil, and lysis occurs only when available nutrients are exhausted (Lloyd, 1965). Though antibiotic production in the soil mass is generally considered unlikely, production on microsubstrates remains a possibility (Garrett, 1965). Some evidence that fungal mycelium may provide a nutrient substrate for antibiotic production is indicated by extraction of antibiotic activity from soil amended 2–3 days earlier with fungal mycelium (Lloyd, 1965). In this connection, Rehm (1954, 1959*a*) and Winter (1950*a*) have speculated that antibiotics are produced by actinomycetes growing on exudates from fungal mycelium, and that they may be important in killing the hyphae which then are utilized saprophytically. Garrett (1965), on the other hand, has recently expressed the view that autolysis from starvation is the primary cause of death and decomposition of fungi on glass slides in soil. He considers that the micro-organisms associated with the hyphae accelerate autolysis through competition for a limited supply of nutrients, but concedes that any remaining hyphal fragments may be directly assimilated. Regardless of whether the mechanism of lysis is heterolytic or autolytic or a combination of both, more pertinent to our discussion is the fact that microbial utilization of soluble or insoluble fungus substance seems required for lysis to occur.

*Chlamydospore formation*

Another consequence of microbial development in soil, which also bears on fungus survival, is the formation of chlamydospores. This type of resting spore development usually accompanies the onset of unfavourable conditions for growth and may occur concurrently with lysis of mycelium. Possibly the same stimuli which induce the destruction of mycelium and the inhibition of spore germination also induce the formation of chlamydospores in fungi capable of producing them. Chlamydospore formation in fungi has been attributed to inhibitory factors (Park, 1954; Ram, 1952), but starvation conditions are known to initiate their production (Park, 1954). It is tempting to speculate that competition for nutrients by bacteria and actinomycetes on or near fungi in soil is the key factor in the control of germination, growth, lysis and resting spore development of fungi in soil.

In summary, soluble and insoluble constituents of mycelium and even spores of many kinds of fungi may serve as nutrient substrates for bacteria and actinomycetes in soil, although we cannot yet be certain of the extent to which actual physical colonization of the living hyphae occurs. Little can be said concerning the significance of the fungal substrate since we have little knowledge of its specificity for bacteria and actinomycetes, and of the amount of fungal protoplasm in soil, or the species of bacteria or actinomycetes involved. Those organisms capable of inducing the lysis of fungus cell walls should be selectively favoured by the fungus substrate, but there is no evidence that the presence of a fungus is an obligatory requirement for any group of micro-organisms.

Bacterial and actinomycete development on or near fungi appears to exhaust the nutrients in the fungal environment, and may cause the destruction of the fungus and its utilization as food. Despite this, the microbial induction of starvation conditions seems to be of survival value for soil fungi by stimulating the production of chlamydospores, and by inhibiting germination of these or other spores in the absence of a potentially colonizable food base.

## *ACKNOWLEDGEMENT*

Appreciation is expressed to Miss Christiane Seidenschnur for assistance in translating the articles in German.

## REFERENCES

ALEXANDER, M. (1961). *Introduction to soil microbiology*. New York. Wiley.

BAMBERG, R. H. (1931). Bacteria antibiotic to *Ustilago zeae*. *Phytopathology*, **21**, 881.

BURGES, A. (1958). *Micro-organisms in the soil*. Hutchinson. London.

CARTER, H. P. & LOCKWOOD, J. L. (1957). Lysis of fungi by soil microorganisms and fungicides including antibiotics. *Phytopathology*, **47**, 169.

CHINN, S. H. F. (1953). A slide technique for the study of fungi and actinomycetes with special reference to *Helminthosporium sativum*. *Can. J. Bot.*, **31**, 718.

CHOLODNY, N. (1930). Über eine neue Methode zur Untersuchung der Bodenmikroflora. *Arch. Mikrobiol.*, **1**, 620.

CHOLODNY, N. G. (1934). A soil chamber as a method for the microscopic study of the soil microflora. *Arch. Mikrobiol.*, **5**, 148.

CLARK, F. E. (1965). The concept of competition in microbial ecology. In *Ecology of Soil-borne Plant Pathogens*. Ed. Baker, K. F. & Snyder, W. C. Berkeley. University of California Press.

CLARK, F. E. & MITCHELL, R. B. (1942). Antibiosis in the elimination of *Phymatotrichum omnivorum* sclerotia from soil. *J. Bact.*, **44**, 141.

COCHRANE, V. W. (1958). *Physiology of Fungi*. New York. Wiley.

CONN, H. J. (1922). A microscopic method for demonstrating fungi and actinomycetes in soil. *Soil Sci.*, **14**, 149.

CONN, H. J. (1932*a*). A microscopic study of certain changes in the microflora of soil. *Tech. Bull. N.Y. St. agric. Exp. Stn.*, **204**.

CONN., H. J. (1932*b*). The Cholodny technic for the microscopic study of the soil microflora. *Zentbl. Bakt. ParasitKde, Abt. II*, **87**, 233.

DEMETER, K. J. & MOSSEL, H. (1933). Über die Brauchbarkeit von Cholodnys mikroskopischer 'Aufwuchsplattenmethode' bei mikrobiologischen Boden-Untersuchungen. *Zentbl. Bakt. ParasitKde, Abt. II*, **88**, 384.

DOBBS, C. G. & HINSON, W. H. (1953). A widespread fungistasis in soils. *Nature, Lond.*, **172**, 197.

GARRETT, S. D. (1938). Soil conditions and the take-all disease of wheat. III. Decomposition of the resting mycelium of *Ophiobolus graminis* in infected wheat stubble buried in the soil. *Ann. appl. Biol.*, **25**, 742.

GARRETT, S. D. (1965). Towards biological control of soil-borne plant pathogens. In *Ecology of soil-borne plant pathogens*. Ed. Baker, K. F. and Snyder, W. C. Berkeley. University of California Press.

GLATHE, H. (1955). Die direkt mikroskopische Untersuchung des Bodens. *Z. PflErnähr. Düng. Bodenk.*, **69**, 172.

GRIFFIN, G. J. (1962). Production of a fungistatic effect by soil microflora in autoclaved soil. *Phytopathology*, **52**, 90.

HECK, A. F. (1929). A study of the nature of the nitrogenous compounds in fungus tissue and their decomposition in the soil. *Soil Sci.*, **27**, 1.

JENSEN, H. L. (1931). The fungus flora of the soil. *Soil Sci.*, **31**, 123.

JENSEN, H. L. (1934). Contributions to the microbiology of Australian soils. II. A comparison of the Rossi-Cholodny method and the plate method for studying the soil microflora. *Proc. Linn. Soc. N.S.W.*, **59**, 200.

JOHNSON, D. A. (1931). The antibiosis of certain bacteria to smuts and some other fungi. *Phytopathology*, **21**, 843.

KHUDYAKOV, J. P. & RAZNITZYNA, E. A. (1939). The use of mycolytic bacteria for the inoculation of seed during vernalization. *Izv. Akad. Nauk SSSR, Ser. Biol.*, **1**, 117. (Abstr., *Rev. appl. Mycol.*, **18**, 659 (1939).)

KING, C. J., HOPE, C. & EATON, E. O. (1934). Some microbiological activities affected in manurial control of cotton root rot. *J. agric. Res.*, **49**, 1093.

KRASILNIKOV, N. A. (1958). *Soil microorganisms and higher plants. Acad. Sci., U.S.S.R.* Translation by Y. Halperin. Israel Program for Translations, Washington. U.S. Dept. Commerce. 1961.

KRASILNIKOV, N. A. & RAZNITZYNA, E. A. (1946). A bacterial method of controlling damping-off of Scot's pine seedlings caused by *Fusarium*. *Agrobiologiya*, **5–6**, 109. (Abstr., *Rev. appl. Mycol.*, **28**, 259 (1949).)

KUBIËNA, W. L. (1938). *Micropedology*. Ames. Collegiate Press.

KUBIËNA, W. L. & RENN, C. E. (1934–5). Micropedological studies of the influence of different organic compounds upon the microflora of the soil. *Zentbl. Bakt. ParasitKde, Abt. II*, **91**, 267.

LEVINE, M. N., BAMBERG, R. H. & ATKINSON, R. E. (1936). Microorganisms antibiotic or pathogenic to cereal rusts. *Phytopathology*, **26**, 99.

LINGAPPA, B. T. & LOCKWOOD, J. L. (1961). The nature of the widespread soil fungistasis. *J. gen. Microbiol.*, **26**, 473.

LINGAPPA, B. T. & LOCKWOOD, J. L. (1964). Activation of soil microflora by fungus spores in relation to soil fungistasis. *J. gen. Microbiol.*, **35**, 215.

LLOYD, A. B. (1965). *Lysis of fungal mycelium by soil.* Ph.D. thesis. Michigan. Michigan State Univ.

LOCKWOOD, J. L. (1959). *Streptomyces* spp. as a cause of natural fungitoxicity in soils. *Phytopathology*, **49**, 327.

LOCKWOOD, J. L. (1960). Lysis of mycelium of plant-pathogenic fungi by natural soil. *Phytopathology*, **50**, 787.

LOCKWOOD, J. L. (1964). Soil Fungistasis. *A. Rev. Phytopath.*, **2**, 341.

LOCKWOOD, J. L. & LINGAPPA, B. T. (1963). Fungitoxicity of sterilized soil inoculated with soil microflora. *Phytopathology*, **53**, 917.

MESSIAEN, C. M. (1962). Formes de résistance des *Fusarium* dans le sol. *Rapp. Activ. Stn. Pathol. Veg., Montfavet*, 1.

MESSIAEN, C. M. & BEYRIES, A. (1963). Les *Fusarium* dans le sol: causes de la lyse mycélienne. *Rapp. Activ. Stn. Pathol. Veg., Montfavet*, 2.

MITCHELL, R. (1963). Addition of fungal cell-wall components to soil for biological disease control. *Phytopathology*, **53**, 1068.

MITCHELL, R. & ALEXANDER, M. (1962). Microbiological processes associated with the use of chitin for biological control. *Proc. Soil Sci. Soc. Am.*, **26**, 556.

MITCHELL, R. & ALEXANDER, M. (1963). Lysis of soil fungi by bacteria. *Can. J. Microbiol.*, **9**, 169.

MITCHELL, R. B., HOOTON, D. R. & CLARK, F. E. (1941). Soil bacteriological studies on the control of the *Phymatotrichum* root rot of cotton. *J. agric. Res.*, **63**, 535.

MOLLENHOFF, H. H., SMITH, F. B. & BROWN, P. E. (1936). The Rossi-Cholodny technic as an aid in the study of the decomposition of lignin. *Proc. Iowa Acad. Sci.*, **43**, 117.

MORTON, A. G. & BROADBENT, D. (1955). The formation of extracellular nitrogen compounds by fungi. *J. gen. Microbiol.*, **12**, 248.

NAUMOVA, A. N. (1939). The influence of seed bacterization on the infection of summer wheat seedlings by parasitic fungi and on the yield of the crop. *Microbiologiya*, **8**, 198. (Abstr., *Rev. appl. Mycol.*, **20**, 534 (1941).)

NIKITINA, E. T. (1958). Mycolytic bacteria and the possibility of their use for the control of fusariosis wilt of potatoes. *Trudy Inst. Mikrobiol. Virus., Alma-Ata*, **2**, 24. (Abstr., *Rev. appl. Mycol.*, **38**, 29 (1959).)

NOVOGRUDSKI, D. M. (1936). The use of microorganisms in the control of fungal diseases of cultivated plants. *Izv. Akad. Nauk. SSSR., Ser. Biol.*, **1**, 277. (Abstr., *Rev. appl. Mycol.*, **16**, 204 (1937).)

Novogrudski, D. M. (1948). The colonization of soil bacteria on fungal hyphae. *Microbiologiya*, **17**, 28. (Abstr., *Soils Fertil.*, **12**, 348 (1949).)

Novogrudski, D. M. & Mitrofanova, N. S. (1957). New methods of detecting *Azotobacter* in soil. *Microbiologiya*, **26**, 578.

Oginsky, E. L. & Umbreit, W. W. (1959). *An introduction to bacterial physiology.* 2nd Edn. San Francisco. Freeman.

Park, D. (1954). Chlamydospores and survival in soil fungi. *Nature, Lond.*, **173**, 454.

Park, D. (1955). Experimental studies on the ecology of fungi in soil. *Trans. Br. mycol. Soc.*, **38**, 130.

Park, D. (1956). Effect of substrate on a microbial antagonism, with reference to soil conditions. *Trans. Br. mycol. Soc.*, **39**, 239.

Park, D. (1963). The ecology of soil-borne fungal disease. *A. Rev. Phytopath.*, **1**, 241.

Payen, J. (1962). Recherches sur le comportement des Champignons dans le sols. I. Expérience préliminaires. *Bull. Éc. nat. sup. agron., Nancy*, **4**, 53.

Pon, D. S., Townsend, C. E., Wessman, G. E., Schmidt, C. G. & Kingsolver, C. H. (1954). A *Xanthomonas* parasitic on uredia of cereal rusts. *Phytopathology*, **44**, 707.

Ram, C. S. Venkat (1952). Soil bacteria and chlamydospore formation in *Fusarium solani. Nature, Lond.*, **170**, 889.

Rehm, H. (1954). Untersuchungen über das Verhalten von Pilzen und Streptomyceten in Mischkultur. *Zentbl. Bakt. ParasitKde., Abt. II*, **107**, 418.

Rehm, H. (1956). Über die Beziehungen zwischen *Aspergillus niger* und Streptomyceten der *Streptomyces albus*-Gruppe. *Zentbl. Bakt. Parasit Kde., Abt. II*, **109**, 413.

Rehm, H. (1958). Untersuchungen über des Verhalten von *Aspergillus niger* und einem *Streptomyces albus*-Stamm in Mischkultur. I. Mitteilung: Die Wechselbeziehungen imkünstlichen Substrat. *Zentbl. Bakt. Parasit Kde., Abt. II*, **111**, 260.

Rehm, H. (1959*a*). Untersuchungen über des Verhalten von *Aspergillus niger* und einem *Streptomyces albus*-Stamm in Mischkultur. II. Mitteilung: Die Wechselbeziehungen im Erdboden. *Zentbl. Bakt. ParasitKde., Abt. II*, **112**, 235.

Rehm, H. (1959*b*). Untersuchungen über des Verhalten von *Aspergillus niger* und einem *Streptomyces albus*-Stamm in Mischkultur. III. Mitteilung: Die Wechselbeziehungen im naturlichen Standort. *Zentbl. Bakt. ParasitKde., Abt. II*, **112**, 382.

Rehm, H. (1959*c*). Untersuchungen über das Verhalten von *Aspergillus niger* und einem *Streptomyces albus*-Stamm in Mischkultur. IV. Mitteilung: Über die Häufigkeit parasitischer Streptomyceten und über die Anti-biotikabildung von *Streptomyces albus* im Boden. *Zentbl. Bakt. ParasitKde., Abt. II*, **112**, 388.

Russell, E. W. (1961). *Soil conditions and plant growth.* 9th Edn. London. Longmans, Green & Co.

Sequeira, L. (1962). Influence of organic amendments on survival of *Fusarium oxysporum* f. *cubense* in the soil. *Phytopathology*, **52**, 976.

Skinner, F. A. (1956*a*). Inhibition of the growth of fungi by *Streptomyces* spp. in relation to nutrient conditions. *J. gen. Microbiol.*, **14**, 381.

Skinner, F. A. (1956*b*). The effect of adding clays to mixed cultures of *Streptomyces albidoflavus* and *Fusarium culmorum. J. gen. Microbiol.*, **14**, 393.

Skujins, J. J. & Potgieter, H. J. (1964). Lysis and chemistry of the walls of fungal hyphae. *Bact. Proc.*, **31**.

Starkey, R. L. (1938). Some influences of the development of higher plants upon the microorganisms of the soil. VI. Microscopic examination of the rhizosphere. *Soil Sci.*, **45**, 207.

STEVENSON, I. L. (1956). Antibiotic activity of actinomycetes in soil as demonstrated by direct observation techniques. *J. gen. Microbiol.*, **15**, 372.

STOVER, R. H. (1958). Studies on *Fusarium* wilt of bananas. III. Influence of soil fungitoxins on behavior of *F. oxysporum* f. *cubense* in soil extracts and diffusates. *Can. J. Bot.*, **36**, 439.

SUBRAMANIAN, C. V. (1946). Some factors affecting the growth and survival of *Fusarium vasinfectum* Atk., the cotton wilt pathogen in the soil, with special reference to microbiological antagonism. *J. Indian bot. Soc.*, **25**, 89.

SUBRAMANIAN, C. V. (1950). Soil conditions and wilt disease in plants with special reference to *Fusarium vasinfectum* on cotton. *Proc. Indian Acad. Sci., Sec. B.*, **31**, 67.

THORNTON, R. H. (1953). Feature of growth of actinomyces in soil. *Research Correspondence*, **6**, 38.

TIMONIN, M. I. (1940). The interaction of higher plants and soil microorganisms. II. Study of the microbial population of the rhizosphere in relation to resistance of plants to soil-borne diseases. *Can. J. Res., C*, **28**, 444.

TRIBE, H. T. (1957). Ecology of microorganisms in soils as observed during their development upon buried cellulose film. *Microbial. Ecology*, 7th Symposium Soc. Gen. Microbiol. Ed. Williams, R. E. O. & Spicer, C. C., Cambridge University Press.

WAID, J. S. (1960). Disscusion. In *The Ecology of Soil Fungi*. Ed. Parkinson, D. & Waid, J. S., Liverpool. Liverpool University Press.

WAID, J. S. & WOODMAN, M. J. (1957). A method of estimating hyphal activity in soil. *Pédologie, Gand., No. spec.*, **7**, 155.

WAKSMAN, S. A., UMBREIT, W. W. & CORDON, T. C. (1939). Thermophilic actinomycetes and fungi in soils and in composts. *Soil Sci.*, **47**, 37.

WALLHÄUSER, K. H. (1951). Untersuchungen über das antagonistische Verhalten von Mikroorganismen am natürlichen Standort. *Arch. Mikrobiol.*, **16**, 237.

WARCUP, J. H. (1957). Studies on the occurrence and activity of fungi in a wheatfield soil. *Trans. Br. mycol. Soc.*, **40**, 237.

WINTER, A. G. (1950*a*). Untersuchungen über die Beziehungen zwischen *Ophiobolus graminis* und anderen Organismen mit Hilfe der Aufwuchsplattenmethode. *Arch. Mikrobiol.*, **14**, 240.

WINTER, A. G. (1950*b*). Weitere Beobachtungen über das Zusammenleben von *Ophiobolus graminis* und anderen Bodenmikroben mit Hilfe der Aufwuchsplatten. *Arch. Mikrobiol.*, **14**, 588.

ZIEMIECKA, J. (1934–5). The use of a modified Rossi-Cholodny technique for studying the organisms that decompose certain organic compounds in soil. *Zentbl. Bakt. ParasitKde., Abt. II*, **91**, 379.

# THE ANIMAL HABITAT OF SOIL BACTERIA

A. MACFADYEN

*Dept. of Zoology, University College of Swansea and Molslaboratoriet, Femmøller, Denmark*

## *INTRODUCTION: THE DIRECT STUDY OF ANIMAL-BACTERIA RELATIONSHIPS*

We, as biologists, have become accustomed to thinking of soil as an immensely complicated ecosystem. The invariable conclusion from biological studies is that soil is a heterogeneous system consisting of a large variety of biological habitats at varying successional stages. The application of sectioning techniques (Haarløv and Weis-Fogh, 1953; Alexander and Jackson, 1954; Hepple and Burges, 1956) indicates the spatial heterogeneity of solid, liquid and gas phases. Microbiological studies (Webster, 1956, 1957) have revealed fungal successions associated with rotting of the leaves of *Dactylis glomerata* indicating the extent of complexity which can arise through succession.

The lead given by Burges (1960) who drew attention to this outlook and by pioneers such as Kubiëna (1938, 1953) who first attempted to examine soil organisms *in situ* have lead to a variety of soil sectioning studies and to devices such as Tribe's baited slides (Tribe, 1960, 1961; Warcup, 1960), in an attempt to understand what really constitutes the habitat of a soil organism and how different kinds of organisms are spatially related to one another. A related approach is that of the Russian workers (Gabe, 1961; Aristovskaya and Parinkina, 1961; Foster, 1964) who have placed minute capillaries with optically flat surfaces in the soil. These are coated inside with various substrates including humic and fulvic acids and have become invaded by a range of micro-organisms whose existence, at least in the form described, had not been previously detected. They thrive in these very fine capillaries in a way which does not occur with dilution plates, Cholodny slides, etc.

A few animal biologists have also tried to penetrate the structural heterogeneity of the soil. The direct approach with the soil microscope has been limited because animals are mobile, but Haarløv and Weis-Fogh (1953) and Haarløv (1960) have used fairly thick sections of soil which was quickly frozen and then fixed in formalin vapour. These have provided new information about the feeding habits and life histories of soil arthropods as well as the relations between their distribution and that of soil air spaces.

## *THE FUNCTIONAL STUDY OF SOIL PROCESSES*

Whilst some attempt is being made to study soil organisms at an appropriate scale, other workers have been impressed with the need to quantify the processes of litter breakdown, chemical change and nutrient liberation which are going on in the soil. Some of these studies have been mainly concerned with rates of disappearance of litter usually placed on the soil surface in net bags or marked in such a way that the processes of breakdown can be followed quantitatively (Gilbert and Bocock, 1960; Bocock *et al.*, 1960; Cadwalladr, 1965; Crossley and Hoaglund, 1962; Witkamp, and Olson, 1963; Edwards and Heath, 1963). Another approach has been to assess the total respiratory activity involved in litter breakdown as measured by chemical analysis or calorimetry of the litter and by gas exchange due to successive groups of organisms. In this way the chemical pathways of decomposition can be followed and the relative roles of different groups traced (Bornebusch, 1930; Cragg, 1961; Macfadyen, 1963*a*, *b*; Nielsen, 1949, 1961; Phillipson, 1963). Comparable studies concerning the nitrogen cycle have been initiated (Satchell, 1963; Needham, 1957). A whole series of respiration studies by microbiologists has been reported (Birch and Friend, 1956; Bunt and Rovira, 1955*a*, *b*; Chase and Gray, 1953; Gaarder, 1957; Parkinson and Coups, 1963; Rovira, 1953; Witkamp, 1963). This work has given us a general insight into orders of magnitude to be expected and factors which influence the respiration rate, such as temperature, humidity, position in the profile and soil type. However, most measurements have been made with samples removed from the field and therefore subject to disturbance and often processed by air drying, grinding and other drastic measures.

It has been claimed (Parkinson and Coups, 1963), that the effect of sample removal is relatively trivial and that respiration rates soon revert to a steady level but there seems, in principle, much to be said for methods which can operate on undisturbed soil in the field. The idea of placing a container over a known area of soil and absorbing the carbon dioxide produced has long been considered and results reported by Wallis and Wilde (1957) confirmed suspicions that factors such as leakage, disturbance of the soil, respiration by higher plants and increased ventilation might produce excessively high readings. However, the idea of sinking an open-ended cylinder in the soil some time before measurements begin and only sealing the upper end for the duration of the measurements has been exploited by Witkamp (1963 and personal communication) using a microdiffusion technique based on methods devized by Conway (1950) and Köpf (1952). An ingenious electrolytic titration method was used by the latter to determine $CO_2$ concentration in sub-samples of the confined air. I have used an apparatus similar to Witkamp's on soil under *Pteridium aquilinum* and have been struck by two features of the results. Firstly that there is a surprising degree of uniformity between adjacent samples and secondly, that when soil respiration figures are compared with primary plant production measurements there is a rather close correspondence between the two (Table 1).

TABLE 1

*Approximate comparisons of primary production and soil respiration in units of k cal./m.²/annum*

| Vegetation: region and type | Net Primary Production | Soil Respiration |
|---|---|---|
| Temperate: range | 900–6,400[1] | — |
| Rough grazing | 3,300[1] | — |
| *Pteridium* | 4,050[1] | 4,500[2] |
| Managed grassland | 4,200[3] | 4,500[4] |
| Arable | — | 3,200[5] (2,900–11,000)[4] |
| Woodland | 1,100–6,400[1] | 6,900–10,600[4] |
| Equatorial forest (Congo) | 30,000[6] | 13,000–16,100[7] |

*Notes:* Primary production is converted to equivalent $CO_2$ content on the basis: 5 k Cal./annum = 0·5 g. carbon/annum = 0·1 ml. $CO_2$/hr.

Daily soil respiration rates taken in summer at about 18°–20° have been roughly corrected to annual values by multiplying by $\frac{365}{2}$ (Nielsen, 1961).

The sources of the above figures are:
[1] Pearsall and Gorham (1956).
[2] Macfadyen unpublished.
[3] Macfadyen (1964).
[4] Russell (1950).
[5] Köpf (1952).
[6] Bray and Gorham (1964).
[7] Maldague and Hilger (1963).

A major criticism of this type of approach is that it ignores the microstructure of the soil by treating it as a uniform medium and frequently demands the application of highly unnatural treatments to the soil. Obviously we need a marriage between the purely descriptive approach which allows for the microscopic heterogeneity of soil on the one hand and the functional approach on the other, thus locating on a scale which is appropriate to soil structure the main centres of functional activity and measuring what is going on there. If I were able to report progress in this direction my topic of the animal habitat of soil bacteria would be a relatively easy one, but since at the present time almost no progress has been made, I must content myself with pointing out a few promising approaches which may eventually lead to an understanding of the quantitative interrelations between the two groups.

## *THE INVERTEBRATE FAUNA OF SOIL*

The biologist who attempts a census of small animals in the soil of a meadow or a deciduous wood is faced with a task so great that no one person has yet succeeded in covering all groups. A composite summary of such work from a variety of different studies, which will serve as a rough basis for discussion, is presented in Table 2. There are some hundreds of species of arthropods, represented by about one-third of a million individuals per square metre of soil. Nematodes occur in tens of millions per square metre and belong to 20 or so species.

TABLE 2

*Table of numbers, biomass and respiration of main invertebrate groups in temperate grassland soil. Main sources are detailed in Macfadyen (1963*a*), supplemented by Phillipson (1963) and Duffey (1962). Note that since figures apply to normal populations in those places where the groups are found the total respiration of nearly 1400 K Cal. is two or three times too high*

| | Number of species | Number of individuals per m.$^2$ | Biomass g./m.$^2$ | Respiration K Cal./m.$^2$/annum |
|---|---|---|---|---|
| Protozoa | 30 | $5 \times 10^8$ | 38 | 113 |
| Nematoda | 20 | $1 \times 10^7$ | 12 | 355 |
| Lumbricidae | 510 | $1 \times 10^3$ | 120 | 180 |
| Enchytraeidae | <10 | $1 \times 10^5$ | 12 | 160 |
| Mollusca | 5 | $5 \times 10^1$ | 10 | 62 |
| Myriapoda | 5 | $5 \times 10^2$ | 12 | 96 |
| Isopoda | 3 | $5 \times 10^2$ | 5 | 38 |
| Opiliones | 5 | $1 \times 10^2$ | 0·7 | 55 |
| Acari- | | | | |
| Mesostigmata | 25 | $5 \times 10^3$ | 1·0 | 64 |
| Prostigmata | 25 | $1 \times 10^5$ | 2·0 | 30 |
| Oribatei | 25 | $2 \times 10^5$ | 2·0 | 30 |
| Araneae | 90 | $6 \times 10^2$ | 6·0 | 34 |
| Coleoptera | 100? | $1 \times 10^2$ | 1·0 | 8 |
| Diptera | 100? | $2 \times 10^2$ | 1·0 | 6 |
| Collembola | 25 | $5 \times 10^4$ | 5·0 | 153 |

Tables of this kind, varying in completeness and accuracy, can be found in the works of Kevan (1962), Kühnelt (1961), Cragg (1961), Macfadyen (1963a), Franz (1943), Nielsen (1949, 1961) and Bornebusch (1930).

There are two features of such studies to which I want to refer: firstly, the comparative estimates of metabolic activity and secondly, the very great variations in the numbers of animals per sample unit. When the sampling areas are between 10 cm$^2$. and 100 cm$^2$., it is invariably found that the variance exceeds the mean, implying a patchy (infradispersed or aggregated) distribution of the individuals within a species (Berthet, in the press).

It is apparent from a comparison of the animal respiration figures given in Table 2 with the total soil metabolism figures given in Table 1 that animal metabolism represents only some 10 per cent of the total (Macfadyen, 1961, 1963*a*). It follows that the remainder of the oxidation of organic matter must be due to micro-organisms. The low metabolic activity of the fauna might also be predicted from the failure of the pattern of total respiration to correspond with that of animal distribution; it is a common experience when sampling soil animals to find some samples with low counts of all species and others in which many species are abundant whilst soil respiration values remain very uniform.

Of course, the detection of pattern and of non-random distribution is highly dependent on the size of sample used (Pielou, 1957) and if it were possible to measure $CO_2$ output from small enough soil particles a patchiness might well be detected in this respect too. Also it must not be forgotten that animals are highly mobile and because, once sampled, an area is destroyed, we do not know how rapidly their distribution patterns change in time. A very limited amount of work has, however, been done on the mobility of individual soil animals and if the findings of Berthet (1964), using radioisotopes, are typical it seems likely that even the sluggish Oribatid mites normally move several centimetres in 24 hrs. and occasionally some tens of centimetres.

## *INTERACTION OF MICROBES WITH SOIL INVERTEBRATES*

It would appear to follow from consideration of field sampling data that animal metabolism is low compared with total soil metabolism. On a centimetre scale animal dispersion is not reflected in a corresponding patchiness of soil respiration because the microbes (presumably mainly fungi in acid soils and bacteria in neutral and alkaline soils) dictate the gross pattern of biological activity in the soil.

A rather different impression is gained from the admittedly scanty and purely qualitative evidence on the direct influences of animals and microbes on one another. In many cases such observations have been confined to fungi (Burges, 1965) but it seems likely that similar relationships with actinomycetes and bacteria will be detected.

Firstly there are well-developed bacterial floras in the guts of most soil invertebrates; for recent work see Healey (1965) on Collembola, Bocock (1963) on the millipede *Glomeris marginata* and Parle (1963*a*, *b*) on earthworms. The very considerable changes in the chemistry of food substances which occur during passage through these animals' guts (Gere, 1956, 1957; Bocock, 1963; van der Drift and Witkamp, 1959), indicate that conditions here are suitable for very high rates of chemical change. Further, animals such as the millipedes and earthworms consume and pass out an enormous amount of plant litter during the course of the year. Bocock has reported that up to 10 per cent of the total woodland litter may be consumed by a single species, *Glomeris*; Nielsen (personal communication) has reported higher figures for animals inhabiting limestone grassland. 'Moder' soils have been recognized by Kubiëna (1953) which consist almost entirely of faeces. Certainly in such cases the bacterial flora of invertebrate guts must play a most important role as a result of a symbiosis in which the animal provides not only suitable chemical and physical conditions but also a constant supply of well-titurated and moistened food.

Secondly, as has been recognized since the time of Darwin (1881), and pointed out by Russell (1950), soil animals, particularly those which are large and strong enough to make their own passages through the soil, produce a constant mixing of material from different layers of the soil and create channels which increase aeration and drainage of the soil. The effect of accidentally killing the larger species through excessive use of arsenic sprays has recently been reported by Raw (1962) who found that an anaerobic mor soil had been produced from a brown earth through such a treatment.

Thirdly, consequences of great importance to the development of microbial activity follow from the fact that animals are mobile. Witkamp (1960) has introduced small mites and collembola in glass tubes containing sterilized litter and shown how their movement through the medium can be followed by a trail of germinating spores. Most of these animals are armed with spines, bristles and sometimes scales and it needs little imagination to understand how spores can be spread, especially in the light of estimates of the mobility of Oribatid mites, normally thought of as being the most sluggish of soil animals (Berthet, 1964). Mobility must enhance enormously the chances of inoculating microhabitats which are suitable for microbial development with both active forms, previously prevented from growth by shortage of substrate or by antibiotic substances, and also with spores whose germination depends on changes in environmental conditions.

Fourthly, we have the intriguing demonstration by Lingappa and Lockwood (1964) of a micro-succession in which the addition of fungus spores or their exudates to soil promoted bacterial growth and a several-fold increase in total soil respiration, apparently due to liberation of nutrients into the soil by the fungi. The growth of the bacteria was accompanied by liberation of a fungistatic substance and the decline of fungal spore germination. In the present context it is interesting to note that if such phenomena are at all general the presence of animals and their faeces are likely to stimulate bacterial growth in this, and perhaps other indirect ways.

Finally, of course, the animals themselves produce waste substances which are complementary to the needs of microbes. In the literature of soil microbiology it has been repeatedly emphasized that microbial decay is contingent on the supply of inorganic nutrients, particularly nitrates and phosphates. These are produced in abundance by animals in excreta and are also found in their corpses when they die. Both these sources of nutrients may be centres for the development of microbial colonies.

In short bacteria are characterized by the possession of an unparalleled repertoire of biochemical transformations. This repertoire is rarely exhibited to the full because the bacteria are not sufficiently mobile. Soil animals on the other hand are more uniform from a biochemical point of view but possess the one great asset of being able to move through the soil, carrying microbes with them on their bodies and inside their guts. Although there must be many variations on the same theme one can appreciate how bringing together the properties of the two groups results in a symbiosis between them and a great enhancement of the biological importance of both.

## *SOME SUGGESTIONS FOR AN EXPERIMENTAL APPROACH*

I have shown (Macfadyen, 1964) that far more of the energy which terrestrial plants incorporate in the products of photosynthesis is liberated through organisms in the soil and litter than through herbivore food chains. How can we proceed if we are to gain an understanding of such a system which is remarkable both for the variety of species involved and the magnitude of its role in the total energy flow of terrestrial communities?

The content and flow of energy through different organisms remain the most generally applicable criteria by which we can select the most important pathways at the expense of the more trivial, but as the above considerations on the roles of soil animals demonstrate, the effectiveness of different organisms depends to a great extent on their biological idiosyncracies. The one animal characteristic of mobility, for instance, results in their disproportionate biological importance. Thus a relatively unimportant group, metabolically speaking, determines the level of respiratory activity of the microflora and therefore of the soil as a whole. We shall obviously have to try out a wide range of approaches to the general theme of detecting the catalytic effect of particular organisms on the system as a whole. One approach is through a much more detailed knowledge of life histories of soil organisms. There are at present whole groups, especially amongst the insect larvae and the mites, whose feeding habits are quite unknown. A combination of laboratory culture methods with soil sectioning and various kinds of field observation—including even the glass-lined underground observation chamber recently installed at East Malling—is indicated here. At present many protozoan and nematode species have been shown to feed on bacteria and some mites among the Tydaeidae, Scutacaridae and Oribatei are thought to do so, but none of these, as far as I am aware, have actually been cultured on bacteria, nor do we know anything about the specificity of their feeding habits.

A second approach is through the use of various kinds of baited traps such as the slides used by Tribe and others for stimulating growth of micro-organisms on particular substrates. This is a technically difficult and rather unrewarding method and should, perhaps, be supplemented by field experiments in which particular microbes are stimulated by the artificial addition of known substrates to the soil. Nevertheless, this method has provided badly needed direct evidence of feeding relations.

A third approach to the problem is the modification of field sites so as to select particular elements of the biota, using techniques which sterilize or repel certain organisms. These techniques include the use of chemical sterilizers and repellants, heat, cold and $\gamma$-radiation. All these treatments have undesirable features but almost nothing has yet been done to investigate their effects in different combinations and to trace the results of elimination and perhaps re-infestation of different groups of organisms. We have found that $\gamma$-irradiation is followed by a surprisingly rapid return of soil arthropods over a period of a few weeks and re-establishment of a microbial flora of a kind.

A fourth approach involves the use of artificial media such as air dried, ground soil which has been re-wetted and either allowed to develop its own flora from spores or else inoculated with known microbes after sterilization. Such materials are characterized by clearly defined respiration regimes. Presumably the history of nutrient exploitation would also prove predictable. What would happen if, when the microflora has spored and become senescent, various members of the fauna were introduced? Obviously this approach, based on highly artificial substrates and ignoring natural soil structure, would demand very careful interpretation, but it offers the attractive attribute of repeatability and should throw light on information gained from more natural conditions.

Finally we must try to extend quantitative methods to a truly microscopical level: chemical methods and tracer techniques of fantastic sensitivity are now available and it is surely not impossible to apply them, in order, for instance, to study the exploitation of the nutrient reserves in the dead body or the faeces of a small soil arthropod, perhaps using the optically flat capillaries that were mentioned earlier.

The soil biologist is today faced with an embarrassingly rich variety of technical methods and a multitude of intriguing questions. I have tried to select some of both which are relevant to investigations of the relations between invertebrates and microbes because I believe this to be one of the key problems which faces us at present and one which could enormously enhance our understanding of the relevance of both groups of organisms to soil processes.

## *REFERENCES*


ALEXANDER, F. E. S. & JACKSON, R. M. (1954). Examination of soil microorganisms in their natural environment. *Nature, Lond.*, **174**, 750.

ARISTOVSKAYA, T. V. & PARINKINA, V. V. (1961). New methods for studying soil microorganism associations. *Pochvovedeniye*, 12.

BERTHET, R. L. (1964). Field study of the mobility of Oribatei (Acari) using radioactive tagging. *J. Anim. Ecol.*, **33**, 443.

BIRCH, H. F. & FRIEND, M. T. (1956). Humus decomposition in E. African soils. *Nature, Lond.*, **178**, 500.

BOCOCK, K. L. (1963). The digestion and assimilation of food by *Glomeris*. In *Soil Organisms*. Ed. Doeksen, J. & van der Drift, J. Amsterdam. North Holland Publ. Co.

BOCOCK, K. L. *et al.* (1960). Changes in leaf litter. I. Losses in dry weight of oak and ash leaf litter. *J. Soil Sci.*, **11**, 1.

BORNEBUSCH, C. H. (1930). *The Fauna of Forest Soil.* Copenhagen.

BRAY, J. R. & GORHAM, E. (1964). Litter production in forests of the world. *Adv. ecol. Res.*, **2**, 101.

BUNT, J. S. & ROVIRA, A. D. (1955*a*). Microbiological studies of some sub-antarctic soils. *J. Soil. Sci.*, **6**, 119.

BUNT, J. S. & ROVIRA, A. D. (1955*b*). The effect of temperature and soil treatment on soil metabolism. *J. Soil Sci.*, **6**, 129.

BURGES, A. (1960). Time and size as factors in ecology. *J. Anim. Ecol.*, **29**, 1.

BURGES, A. (1965). Biochemical processes in the decomposition of organic matter. In *Experimental pedology*. Ed. Crawford, D. V. & Hallsworth, E. G. London. Butterworth.

CADWALLADR, D. A. (1965). Thesis. Swansea. University College of Swansea.

CHASE, F. E. & GRAY, P. H. H. (1953). Use of the Warburg respirometer to study microbial activity in soils. *Nature, Lond.*, **171**, 481.

CONWAY, E. J. (1950). *Microdiffusion and volumetric error*. Lockwood, London.

CRAGG, J. B. (1961). Some aspects of the ecology of moorland animals. *J. Ecol.*, **49**, 477.

CROSSLEY, D. A. & HOAGLUND, M. P. (1962). A litter-bag method for the study of microarthropods inhabiting leaf litter. *Ecology*, **43**, 571.

DARWIN, C. (1881). *Earthworms and vegetable mould*. London. Murray.

DRIFT, J. VAN DER (1959). Field studies on the surface fauna of forests. *Meded. Inst. toegep. biol. Onderz. Nat.*, **41**, 79.

DRIFT, J. VAN DER & WITKAMP, M. (1959). The significance of the breakdown of oak litter by *Enoicyla pusilla* Burm., *Archs. Néerl. Zool.*, **13**, 486.

DUFFEY, E. (1962). A population study of spiders in limestone grassland. *J. Anim. Ecol.*, **31**, 571.

EDWARDS, C. A. & HEATH, G. W. (1963). The role of soil animals in breakdown of leaf material. In *Soil Organisms*. Ed. Doeksen, J. & van der Drift, J. Amsterdam. North Holland Publ. Co.

FOSTER, J. W. (1964). General biology in the Soviet Union. *Bioscience*, **14**, 15.

FRANZ, H. (1943). Die Landtierwelt der miltleren Hohen Tauern. *Deutschr. Akad. Wiss., Wien, Math-nat Kl.*, **107**.

GAARDER, T. (1957). Studies in soil respiration in Western Norway, the Bergen District. *Univ. Bergen Arb.*, **3**.

GABE, D. R. (1961). Capillary method for studying microbe distribution in soils. *Pochvovedeniye*, No. 1, 70.

GERE, G. (1956). Investigations concerning the energy turn-over of the *Hyphantria cunea* Drury caterpillars. *Opusc. Zool. Bpest.*, **1**, 29.

GERE, G. (1957). Productive biologic groupings of organisms and their role in ecological communities. *Annls Univ. Scient. bpest. Rolando Eötvös Sect. Biol.*, **1**, 61.

GILBERT, O. & BOCOCK, K. L. (1960). Changes in leaf litter. II. Changes in the nitrogen content of oak and ash leaf litter. *Soil Sci.*, **11**, 10.

HAARLØV, N. (1960). Microarthropods from Danish Soils: Ecology, Phrenology. *Oikos*, suppl. **3**.

HAARLØV, N. & WEISS-FOGH, T. (1953). A microscopical technique for studying the undisturbed texture of soils. *Oikos*, **4**, 44.

HEALEY, I. N. (1965). Thesis. Swansea. University College of Swansea.

HEPPLE, S. & BURGES, A. (1956). Sectioning of soil. *Nature, Lond.*, **177**, 1186.

KEVAN, D. K. MC. E. (1962). *Soil Animals*. London. Witherby.

KÖPF, H. (1952). Laufeude Messung der Bodenatmung in Freiland. *Landw. Forsch.*, **4**, 186.

KUBIËNA, W. L. (1938). *Micropedology*. Iowa. Ames.

KUBIËNA, W. L. (1953). *The Soils of Europe*. London. Murby.

KÜHNELT, W. (1961). *Soil biology*. Transl. N. Walker. London. Faber.

LINGAPPA, B. T. & LOCKWOOD, J. L. (1964). Activation of soil microflora by fungus spores in relation to soil fungistasis. *J. gen. Microbiol.*, **35**, 215.

MACFADYEN, A. (1961). Metabolism of soil invertebrates in relation to soil fertility. *Ann. appl. Biol.*, **49**, 216.

MACFADYEN, A. (1963*a*). *Animal Ecology: aims and methods*, 2nd Edn. London. Pitman.

MACFADYEN, A. (1963*b*). Heterotrophic productivity in the detritus food chain in soil. *Proc. 16th. int. Congr. Zool.*, **4**, 318.

MACFADYEN, A. (1964). Energy flow in ecosystems and its exploitation by grazing. In *Symposium on Grazing*. Ed. Crisp, D. J. British Edological Society. Oxford. Blackwell.

MALDAGUE, M. E. & HILGER, F. (1963). Observations faunistiques et microbiologiques dans quelques biotopes forestiers equitoriaux. In *Soil Organisms*. Ed. Doeksen, J. & van der. Drift, J. Amsterdam. North Holland Publ. Co.

NEEDHAM, A. E. (1957). Components of nitrogen excreta in earthworms. *J. exp. Biol.*, **34**, 425.

NIELSEN, C. O. (1949). Studies on the soil microfauna. II. The soil-inhabiting nematodes. *Natura Jutl.*, **2**, 1.

NIELSEN, C. O. (1961) Respiratory metabolism of some populations of enchytraeid worms and free-living nematodes. *Oikos*, **12**, 17.

PARKINSON, D. & COUPS, E. (1963). Microbial activity in a podzol. In *Soil Organisms*. Ed. Doeksen, J. & van der. Drift, J. Amsterdam. North Holland Publ. Co.

PARLE, J. N. (1963*a*). Microorganisms in the intestines of earthworms. *J. gen. Microbiol.*, **31**, 1.

PARLE, J. N. (1963*b*). A microbial study of earthworm casts. *J. gen. Microbiol.*, **31**, 13.

PEARSALL, W. H. & GORHAM, E. (1956). Production Ecology 1: Standing crops of natural vegetation. *Oikos*, **7**, 193.

PHILLIPSON, J. (1963). The use of respiratory data in estimating annual respiratory metabolism, with particular reference to *Leiobunum rotundum* (Latr.) Phalangida. *Oikos*, **14**, 212.

PIELOV, E. C. (1957). The effect of quadrat size on the estimation of the parameters of Neyman's and Thomas's distributions. *J. Ecol.*, **45**, 31.

RAW, F. (1962). Studies of earthworm populations in Orchards. I. Leaf burial in apple orchards. *Ann. appl. Biol.*, **50**, 389.

ROVIRA, A. D. (1953). Use of the Warburg apparatus in soil metabolism studies. *Nature, Lond.*, **172**, 29.

RUSSELL, E. J. (1950). *Soil conditions and plant growth*. 8th Edn. London. Longmans.

SATCHELL, J. E. (1963). Nitrogen turnover by a woodland population of Lumbricus terrestris. In *Soil Organisms*. Ed. Doeksen, J. & van der Drift, J. Amsterdam. North Amsterdam Publ. Co.

TRIBE, H. T. (1960). Aspects of decomposition of cellulose in Canadian soils. *Can. J. Microbiol.*, **6**, 309.

TRIBE, H. T. (1961). Microbiology of cellulose decomposition in soil. *Soil Sci.*, **92**, 61.

WALLIS, G. W. & WILDE, S. A. (1957). A rapid method for the determination of carbon dioxide evolved from forest soils. *Ecology*, **38**, 359.

WARCUP, J. H. (1960). Methods for isolation and estimation of activity of fungi in soil. In *The Ecology of Soil Fungi*. Ed. Parkinson, D. & Waid, J. S. Liverpool. Liverpool University Press.

WEBSTER, J. (1956). Succession of fungi on decaying cocksfoot culms. I. *J. Ecol.*, **44**, 517.

WEBSTER, J. (1957). Succession of fungi on decaying cocksfoot culms. II. *J. Ecol.*, **45**, 1.

WITKAMP, M. (1960). Seasonal fluctuations of the fungus flora in mull and mor of an oak forest. *Meded. Inst. toegep. biol. Onderz. Nat.*, **46**.

WITKAMP, M. (1963). Microbial populations of leaf litter. *Ecology*, **44**, 370.

WITKAMP, M. & OLSON, J. (1963). Breakdown of confined and non-confined oak litter. *Oikos*, **14**, 138.

# THE AGRICULTURAL ENVIRONMENT OF SOIL BACTERIA

E. W. RUSSELL

*Department of Soil Science, University of Reading*

## *INTRODUCTION*

This paper will be primarily concerned with such problems as the effects of altering the soil environment on the activity of the soil bacteria, and the converse problems of the effects of the activities of the soil bacteria on the soil environment. There will inevitably be some overlap with other papers in this Symposium, as the agricultural environment must cover a very wide range of specific conditions.

## *HOW DO THE SOIL BACTERIA GET ACCESS TO THEIR FOOD SUPPLY?*

A group of problems that has received comparatively little attention is that of how the soil bacteria obtain access to their food supply if it is insoluble. A direct examination of the soil shows that the bacteria are present as isolated individuals or in small colonies, often rather concentrated together, with relatively large volumes of soil apparently unoccupied, so that in no sense can the bacteria be considered to be uniformly distributed throughout the body of the soil when judged on the scale of bacterial dimensions.

The two principal ways they obtain access to their food are presumably either by the food being brought into their neighbourhood, or by them moving through the water films to their food. It is difficult to know how to determine how far and how fast a flagellate bacterium, for example, will move to its food supply, or if non-flagellates, how they move over the surface of soil particles. Nor, as far as I know, has it been determined at what distance from the bacterial surface its own exo-enzymes are effective.

Food can be brought into the immediate neighbourhood of a bacterium by two means. Plant roots and fungal hyphae are continually growing through the soil, and so come into contact with increasing numbers of resident bacteria in the soil. On their senescence or death these bacteria can either attack them directly, or feed on their autolytic products, or on those of other micro-organisms initiating the decomposition of these roots. Again the soil fauna by moving through the soil make their own waste products accessible to groups of bacteria which were far distant from the plant products the animal fed on. To some extent also the movement of animals through the soil may move bacteria through the soil by the displacement of soil particles caused by their movements. In soils containing earthworms, the worms must play a considerable role in bringing soil bacteria into contact with plant debris during the process of maceration in their gut.

The relative importance of these two processes for bringing the soil bacteria into close contact with their food supply is not known, nor is it known what proportion of the energy supply of the bacterial population is directly derived from the hydrolysis of insoluble organic compounds.

## *THE EFFECT OF THE FOOD SUPPLY ON THE BACTERIAL POPULATION*

Winogradsky's separation of the soil micro-organisms into zymogenous and autochthonous is reasonably valid for the soil bacteria, and indeed it is probable that most of the autochthonous population consists of coccoid bacteria or similar organisms. Regular additions of a source of decomposable organic matter, such as farmyard manure, appears to increase both the zymogenous and the autochthonous population, although this separation is difficult to make in practice.

An example of this effect is given by the comparison of the microflora on the unmanured plot on Broadbalk Field at Rothamsted with the adjacent plot which has received 14 tons per acre of farmyard manure in most years since 1843. Table 1 shows that manure has doubled the humus content of the soil, and almost doubled the total cell count; however, the number of protozoa has increased five-fold, which could indicate that the autochthonous flora is more active, and hence more rapidly consumed by the protozoa in the farmyard manure plots than in the unmanured.

A soil appears to be able to contain only a certain definite concentration of any particular species of bacteria in it, under conditions of unlimited food supply. This result is based on the results of perfusion experiments in which a soluble compound, such as an ammonium salt (Lees and Quastel, 1946) or an amino acid (Greenwood and Lees, 1960) for example, is perfused through the soil and is oxidized to another soluble compound. For any given soil there is a maximum rate of

TABLE 1

*Effect of annual dressings of farmyard manure on the microbial population. Broadbalk, Rothamsted*

Counts: mean of six determinations made at monthly intervals from 20.1.48 to 23.6.48. Numbers of organisms expressed in millions per gram of soil.

| | Unmanured | Complete fertilizer | Farmyard manure |
|---|---|---|---|
| Number of bacteria | | | |
| total cell count | 1,600 | 1,600 | 2,900 |
| plate count | 50 | 47 | 67 |
| Number of protozoa | | | |
| active | 0·01 | 0·04 | 0·052 |
| Per cent organic carbon (1944) | | | |
| 0–9 in. | 1·09 | 1·20 | 2·59 |

oxidation, and this can be interpreted as showing that there are only a certain number of sites on the surfaces of soil particles on which these organisms can be held, and once these sites have all been occupied, the biochemical reaction they bring about will proceed at its maximum rate. There is also other evidence that soils can absorb a definite number of bacteria per gram of soil, but it is not known what determines the number of spots on which bacteria can be held, and whether all bacteria compete for the same spots. This is a problem in great need of further investigation.

## *CHARACTERISTIC BIOCHEMICAL REACTIONS BROUGHT ABOUT BY THE SOIL BACTERIA*

It is probably not yet possible to distinguish between the various biochemical changes brought about by the zymogenous population when readily decomposable plant residues are added to the soil. A very wide range of organisms can decompose polysaccharides, celluloses, proteins and other typical plant constituents. Lignins appear to be the only common plant constituent that is resistant to attack by most groups of micro-organisms and it is possible that only certain members of the Basidiomycetes can oxidize them.

There are, however, a number of very important biochemical reactions that can only be brought about by certain species of soil bacteria. These include the oxidation of a number of inorganic substances, which are brought about by autotrophic bacteria, and the degradation of rare or man-made organic compounds, such as many pesticides. Bacteria are also the dominant organisms which are active under conditions of poor aeration.

The principal autotrophic oxidations taking place in a soil are the oxidation of ammonia to nitrite, of nitrite to nitrate, of sulphides and thiosulphates to sulphates, of methane and hydrogen to carbon dioxide and water, and probably of manganous and ferrous ions to manganese dioxide and ferric hydroxide. With the possible exception of the last two, the other oxidations are probably confined to bacteria. The most studied of these oxidations is that of ammonia to nitrite by *Nitrosomonas*, and of nitrite to nitrate by *Nitrobacter*. There may be conditions under grasslands where the soil contains an inhibitor of *Nitrosomonas*, when ammonium ions accumulate in the soil (Theron,1951; Greenland,1958; Boughey *et al.*, 1964). Unfortunately, although various claims and inconclusive evidence have been put forward for this inhibition, it has not received the critical study necessary for its validity to be established. There is, however, much stronger experimental evidence for the sensitivity of *Nitrobacter* to free ammonia, and conditions can arise in alkali soils when the ammonia concentration can rise sufficiently high for the activity of *Nitrobacter* to be depressed so nitrites accumulate in the soil at concentrations sufficiently high to damage crops growing on the soil. There is, in fact, considerable evidence that *Nitrobacter* is more sensitive to adverse conditions than *Nitrosomonas*, such as low and high temperatures and drought, and under these conditions nitrites may accumulate slowly (Justice and Smith, 1962).

Bacteria seem to be the principal agents in oxidizing certain aromatic compounds such as toluene, phenol and cresol, also of some paraffins. It is possible that the former group also contain some aromatics either present as such in plant tissue, or produced from plant tissue by other members of the microflora. In a sense bacteria can be considered scavengers of microbial toxins produced during general microbial activity. Bacteria also appear to be the organisms responsible for the first stage in the breakdown of many of the pesticides which find their way into the soil under intensive farming conditions.

Bacteria are the principal organisms active when the aeration of the soil becomes poor for any reason. Under conditions of a low oxygen supply but an ample supply of decomposable organic matter, they will bring about a wide variety of reductions involving the production of methane, hydrogen and sometimes butyric acid, the reduction of nitrates and nitrites to nitrous oxide or nitrogen gas, the reduction of sulphates to sulphides and of ferric iron and manganic manganese to ferrous and manganous ions. Hydrogen sulphide is very toxic to plant roots, and so probably is butyric acid, and the former is probably a very common cause of the loss of vigour of crops growing on a soil that becomes waterlogged. However, if the soil is also well supplied with ferric compounds, the oxidation-reduction potential of sulphate to sulphide and ferric to ferrous are near enough the same for the insoluble ferrous sulphide to be formed. These reactions are of fundamental importance in rice soils, for the rice roots grow in waterlogged soils but are easily damaged by hydrogen sulphide and perhaps by butyric acid.

It is possible that reducing conditions occur very commonly in soils, but confined to isolated volumes distributed throughout the soil. Thus, any crumbs or clods containing no pores wide enough to be emptied by drainage will be waterlogged when the soil is wet but well drained; and if it contains pockets of decomposable organic matter, or active roots, reducing conditions will soon be set up within the clod. Similarly it is possible that an actively growing grass ley may induce pockets of poor aeration around their roots, both because of a high oxygen demand by their roots and also because the roots excrete readily oxidizable soluble compounds into the soil. If these pockets contain any nitrates, these will be reduced to gaseous nitrogen compounds (Woldendorp, 1962). It certainly seems to be a fact of experiment that a part of any nitrate fertilizer given to actively growing grass disappears, but it is not easy to prove if the loss comes direct from the soil, or if denitrification takes place within the plant itself. Denitrification also appears to be of considerable importance in soils high in nitrogen-rich organic matter, or high in organic matter to which ammonium or nitrate fertilizers are being added, particularly if the soil is neutral or calcareous (Bremner and Shaw, 1958).

There is a further biochemical reaction that appears to be brought about predominantly by bacteria and that is the conversion of atmospheric nitrogen into amino acid nitrogen. There are in soils several groups of bacteria which will fix atmospheric nitrogen when grown on suitable culture media in the laboratory, and it is commonly assumed that they will do the same in the soil. Judging from laboratory experience, the conditions necessary for good fixation are an abundant supply of decomposable organic matter low in nitrogen and a medium low in available nitrogen compounds; and it is probable that it is only under these conditions that this non-symbiotic nitrogen fixation takes place. Further it appears to take place easiest under conditions of rather poor aeration and all the proven nitrogen fixers will either tolerate poor aeration or else require it.

There has been a great deal of loose thinking about the role of these organisms in the nitrogen economy of the soil, and it is probably best to consider that this non-symbiotic nitrogen fixing is of no importance in agricultural soils. In the first place the numbers of these organisms in the soil, in so far as they can be counted, are very low. The organisms which can tolerate good aeration, such as *Azotobacter* and *Beijerinckia*, often only occur in numbers of the order of hundreds per gram of soil, and those less tolerant of good aeration, such as *Clostridium*, in tens or hundreds of thousands; so it is difficult to believe the former group can be of any practical significance. Unfortunately no adequate quantitative examination of the nitrogen fixing organisms present in soils have been made in soils where nitrogen fixation has been proved to be active, as, for example, in run-down arable land allowed to revert to natural vegetation under conditions where legumes are not present but in which the nitrogen content of the soil organic matter is increasing. At Rothamsted, on a piece of wet land in poor tilth, the rate of increase of organic nitrogen in the soil was 60 lb. per acre per year for the first 20 years after it was abandoned, and it has been assumed that this was due to non-symbiotic fixation because of the absence of legumes. Moore (1963), working at Ibadan, W. Nigeria, found a very high rate of nitrogen fixation under actively growing millet (*Eleusine coracana*) of the order of 100–130 lb. per acre of nitrogen in a 4 month period. This was in a soil containing no *Azotobacter* or *Beijerinckia*, but which did contain *Clostridium*.

Bacteria of the genus *Rhizobium* are the principal micro-organisms involved in symbiotic nitrogen fixation in agricultural soils, because this is invariably brought about by suitable species of legumes. However, under natural conditions there are some non-leguminous plants having root-nodules which fix nitrogen, but for which the provenance of the micro-organism involved has not been determined.

## *SOIL HUMUS AS A SOURCE OF FOOD FOR THE SOIL BACTERIA*

Humus is relatively resistant to microbial decomposition, and the usual explanation is that it has a constitution which the soil organisms have difficulty in breaking up. But there is some evidence which is concordant with the hypothesis that humus itself is fairly readily decomposable by the soil organisms but that it only becomes resistant when it is absorbed on some mineral surfaces. There are two lines of evidence for this. In the first place the humus content of soils under comparable systems of farming tends to be higher the higher the clay content of the soil, or perhaps the higher the readily extractable aluminium in the soil (Williams, Scott and McDonald, 1958), implying that humus can only accumulate, that it is only resistant to decomposition, if it is absorbed on clay surfaces possibly through aluminium linkages. There is another line of evidence which is concordant with this. If a soil is dried and then wetted, there will be a rapid flush of microbial activity, dying down after about ten days to a fairly low steady level. If the soil is now re-dried and then re-wetted, this same flush of decomposition will again be observed (Birch, 1958, 1959, 1960).

The amount of carbon dioxide produced in each flush is dependent on the intensity with which the soil was dried, and the length of time it was kept dry before being re-wetted, but it is of the order of 1 per cent of the organic carbon present in the soil. H. F. Birch, working with a soil derived from trachyte which had been under pasture for a number of years, took a soil through about 50 of these drying and wetting cycles and found the same behaviour persisted throughout these cycles, and the amount of $CO_2$ and nitrate produced in each flush remained a constant proportion of the organic carbon and nitrogen present in the soil. Birch also found that after each wetting a certain proportion of the organic matter in the soil dispersed in the soil water, and this amount was proportional to the amount of organic matter oxidized. It is therefore possible that the soil microbial population can decompose humus relatively easily if it is dispersed in the soil solution and it is only the humus held on the clay surface that is resistant to attack.

Unfortunately no fully satisfactory explanation can be given of this effect. It can also be brought about—at least to some extent—by treating the soil with a chemical such as formalin which partially sterilizes the soil. The organisms responsible for the flush appear to be rod-shaped bacteria, belonging to the zymogenous population, for the number of small cocci is not much affected (Griffiths, 1960).

## *BACTERIA AS PRODUCERS OF HUMUS*

It is possible that the soil bacteria are the principal agents producing humus in soils. This theory was put forward a number of years ago by Kononova, and has been put into a more specific form by Swaby and Ladd (1962). The great difficulty in formulating any theory of humus formation which can be experimentally verified lies in our very inadequate knowledge of the composition of humus. It is, however, possible that it consists of a mixture of bacterial cell wall constituents, such as polyuronides containing some amino-sugars and the polymerization product of amino acids with, perhaps, polyphenols. Swaby and Ladd suggested that the site of this latter polymerization was within the bacterial cell, and it was the autolytic products produced from the bacterial cytoplasm on the death of the cell which polymerized before the cell wall was hydrolysed. If the cells were absorbed on the clay surface, these polymerization products could be immediately absorbed on the same spot as the bacterium itself. It is possible that even if this process is operative, it is not the only one as there is also evidence that some fungi can produce humus-like substances when growing on suitable media.

## *MUTUAL INTERACTIONS BETWEEN SOIL BACTERIA AND PLANT ROOTS*

Plant roots growing in a soil are not merely passive absorbers of water and nutrients, nor do the soil organisms simply convert the organic substances they absorb into cell material and carbon dioxide. Both roots and micro-organisms are excreting a very wide range of organic compounds into the soil solution. Very little is yet known about what these substances are, for until the advent of gas and liquid chromatography there was really no means of separating and identifying them, and unfortunately no serious application of gas-liquid chromatography to this problem has yet been made. But it is known that the roots of different plants excrete different substances in the soil (Rovira, 1962), some of which are active against the roots of other species, and that different micro-organisms excrete different substances, some of which again are phyto-active.

The environment of the plant root is therefore the site of microbial activity, particularly somewhat behind the growing tip of actively growing roots as well as on senescent roots or on sloughed-off root hairs. This population, which is concentrated around the root, is the rhizosphere population and contains fungi as well as bacteria. An interesting problem that is not easy to solve is the source of the bacteria forming the rhizosphere population in the soil. Some fungi, once they are in contact with a root, will grow along its surface, but there is no evidence that most of the rhizosphere bacteria move over the root surface as fast as the roots grow, so most of the bacteria on the root may be derived from bacteria existing in the soil very close to the growing or swelling root. The rhizosphere bacterial population differs in several important respects from the main body of the bacterial population in that it is probably closer to the zymogenous group, being able to grow fairly fast if supplied with simple nutrients, such as simple carbon compounds, amino acids and growth factors.

It has proved extremely difficult to demonstrate what specific effects this population has on the functioning of the root or the nutrition of the plant. There are examples where this population appears to interfere with the uptake of manganese by the plant, possibly because the population is oxidizing the available manganous ion and converting it into the relatively insoluble manganese dioxide. It is also possible that this population takes up some of the nitrate formed in the soil and converts it into insoluble, presumably humic compounds. It certainly appears that growing crops suppress nitrification in the soil (Russell, 1950; Goring and Clark, 1949), but the experimental evidence cannot distinguish between a suppression of nitrification and a conversion of nitrates back into humic nitrogen, although Bartholomew and Clark (1950) and Hiltbold, Bartholomew and Werkman (1951) using $N^{15}$ showed this population immobilized nitrogen from soluble sources.

There has been considerable controversy on whether *Azotobacter* is a rhizosphere bacterium or not. Early evidence indicated it is sometimes concentrated in the rhizosphere, although this is not always found, and it was assumed that it would use high-carbon low-nitrogen soluble organic compounds excreted by the roots, fix nitrogen and excrete a proportion of this as soluble products into the soil solution for the crop to take up. It was further assumed that if a seed was inoculated with *Azotobacter* before it was sown, this would increase the number of *Azotobacter* in the rhizosphere, as it is normally a fairly rare soil organism, and so the plant would grow better due to this extra nitrogen. This operation has been widely used in Russia (Cooper, 1959), and although the published experiments do not look very convincing, winter wheat appears to have its yield increased by about 10 per cent on about 70 per cent of the area on which it is sown. This practice has recently received more critical attention elsewhere, and the general conclusion from this work broadly confirms the Russian claims. The cause of the improvement of yield is not known, but is unlikely to be due to an increase of nitrogen supply to the crop. An observation of Brown, Burlingham and Jackson (1964) at Rothamsted, however, may give a clue, for they found the wheat responded better to the inoculation when grown on soil infected with the take-all fungus *Ophiobolus graminis*.

Some soil bacteria excrete compounds such as 2-ketogluconic acid which will form chelation compounds with calcium and other metals and will remove calcium from insoluble compounds such as phosphates and other metals from silicates (Duff, Webley and Scott, 1963; Webley, Henderson and Taylor, 1963). Some species which solubilize phosphates have been added to the seed of crops before sowing, in the hope that they would thrive in the rhizosphere and increase the phosphate supply to the crop. But the field evidence for the value of this practice is very poor, and there are few if any examples of this practice definitely increasing the supply to the crop.

## *SOME ADDITIONAL EFFECTS OF SOIL CONDITIONS ON THE BACTERIA*

### *Crop rotations*

There is little evidence that normal arable crops have any important differential effects on the soil bacteria, though they have a very marked effect on the fungal flora of the soil and rhizosphere.

### *Effect of acidity and of liming acid soils*

The amount of critical work on the effects of increasing acidity of the soil or of liming an acid soil on the biochemical changes brought about in the soil by the bacteria has not been studied in great detail, largely because of the technical difficulty of separating out the effects of the bacteria from those of other members of the soil microbial population. Certain specific processes, such as the oxidation of ammonium to nitrate is retarded at low pH, but as with agricultural crops, pH is not the controlling factor, so there is no particular pH applicable to all soils at which the rate of nitrification has been reduced to say one-half or one-tenth of the rate for the soil if it were in the range pH 6–7 for example. The general impression from the literature is that not until the soil pH is below 5 is one likely to find large effects on the bacterial flora.

### *Mulches*

Surface mulches in general agricultural practice are composed of mature plant tissue low in nitrogen, as for example sugar cane trash, mature long grass and straw, so they have three effects. Mulches reduce the rate of drying out of the soil surface and the rate of temperature change there. Thus in winter a mulched soil is likely to be warmer than one that is unmulched, but in spring will warm up more slowly. In dry weather a mulched soil is likely to be moister than an unmulched one but it will take longer to dry out after wet weather. Mulches increase the amount of root tissue and the general biological activity in the surface soil compared with unmulched soil, and this is very noticeable in periods of warm dry weather. Finally mulches of natural mature vegetation will decompose in a zone between the bottom of the mulch and the top of the soil, and since the mulch is low in nitrogen, this will induce a very low level of available nitrogen in the surface soil and will therefore encourage non-symbiotic nitrogen fixation to take place in this zone.

### *Waterlogging of the soil*

This induces anaerobic conditions in the soil in which certain members of the bacterial population become the dominant active organisms. The effects of waterlogging have already been discussed.

### *Drying the soil*

The effect of drying the soil on the activity of the soil population probably follows its effect on plant growth. As the moisture content of the soil drops from below field capacity the activity of the population tends to fall, but it is not yet possible to say at what soil suction the activity is appreciably affected. When the soil water is at 15 atm. suction, microbial activity has certainly been affected, but different groups have been affected to different degrees (Dommergues, 1962). As the suction, rises above 15 atm., activity is dropping fairly rapidly, but it is very difficult to make reliable studies in these dry soils as in practice one can never dry out a soil absolutely uniformly—there will always be pockets of moister soil. Hence, if there appears to be microbial activity at a fairly low level in a dry soil, it is not permissible to assume it is occurring in the body of the soil; it could all be taking place in these isolated pockets.

### *Partial sterilization*

Soils are partially sterilized, either with steam or with chemicals, to kill many of the pathogens of the crop to be grown; and partial sterilization when properly carried out gives a greatly increased subsequent crop. But this process has many other effects on the activity of the micro-organisms besides killing the pathogens, some of which are not yet understood.

Partial sterilization will give a flush of ammonium production which will not nitrify for a considerable period of time, probably due to the presence of some toxin in the soil. It also causes a rapid rise in the soluble organic matter and the rate of $CO_2$ evolution. Partially sterilized soil may also be an unfavourable environment for many fungal species for many months after treatment (Szladits, 1952).

## *REFERENCES*


BARTHOLOMEW, W. V. & CLARK, F. E. (1950). Nitrogen transformations in soil in relation to the rhizosphere microflora. *4th int. Congr. Soil Sci.* (*Amsterdam*), **2**, 112.

BIRCH, H. F. (1958). The effect of soil drying on humus decomposition and nitrogen availability. *Pl. Soil*, **10**, 9.

BIRCH, H. F. (1959). Further observations on humus decomposition and nitrification. *Pl. Soil*, **11**, 262.

BIRCH, H. F. (1960). Nitrification in soils after different periods of dryness. *Pl. Soil*, **12**, 81.

BOUGHEY, A. S., MUNRO, P. E., MEIKLEJOHN, J., STRANG, R. M. & SWIFT, M. J. (1964). Antibiotic reactions between African savanna species. *Nature, Lond.*, **203**, 1302.

BREMNER, J. M. & SHAW, K. (1958). Denitrification in soil. II. Factors affecting denitrification. *J. agric. Sci.*, **51**, 40.

BROWN, M. E., BURLINGHAM, S. K. & JACKSON, R. M. (1964). Studies on *Azotobacter* species in soil. III. Effects of artificial inoculation on crop yields. *Pl. Soil*, **20**, 194.

COOPER, R. (1959). Bacterial fertilizers in the Soviet Union. *Soils Fertil., Harpenden*, **22**, 327.

DOMMERGUES, Y. (1962). Contribution à l'étude de la dynamique microbienne des sol en zone semi-aride et en zone tropicale sèche. *Annls Agron.*, **13**, 391.

DUFF, R. B., WEBLEY, D. M. & SCOTT, R. O. (1963). Solubilization of minerals and related materials by 2-ketogluconic acid-producing bacteria. *Soil Sci.*, **95**, 105.

GORING, C. A. I. & CLARK, F. E. (1949). Influence of crop growth on mineralization of nitrogen in the soil. *Proc. Soil Sci. Soc. Am.*, **13**, 261.

GREENLAND, D. J. (1958). Nitrate fluctuations in tropical soils. *J. agric. Sci.*, **50**, 82.

GREENWOOD, D. J. & LEES, H. (1960). Studies on the decomposition of amino acids in soils. III. The process of amino acid aerobic decompositions and some properties of amino acid-oxidizing organisms. *Pl. Soil*, **12**, 175.

GRIFFITHS, E. (1960). Microbiological changes in freshly moistened soil. *E. Afr. Agric. For. Res. Org., A. Rept.*, 25.

HILTBOLD, A. E., BARTHOLOMEW, W. V. & WERKMAN, C. H. (1951). The use of tracer techniques in the simultaneous measurement of mineralization and immobilization of nitrogen in soil. *Proc. Soil Sci. Soc. Am.*, **15**, 166.

JUSTICE, J. K. & SMITH, R. L. (1962). Nitrification of ammonium sulphate in a calcareous soil as influenced by combinations of moisture, temperature and levels of added nitrogen. *Proc. Soil Sci. Soc. Am.*, **26**, 246.

LEES, H. & QUASTEL, J. H. (1946). Biochemistry of nitrification in soil. II. The site of soil nitrification. *Biochem. J.*, **40**, 815.

MOORE, A. W. (1963). Nitrogen fixation in a latosolic soil under grass. *Pl. Soil*, **19**, 127.

ROVIRA, A. D. (1962). Plant-root exudates in relation to the rhizosphere microflora. *Soils Fertil., Harpenden*, **25**, 167.

RUSSELL, E. W. (1950). *Soil conditions and plant growth, 8th ed.* Longmans, London.

SWABY, R. J. & LADD, J. N. (1962). Chemical nature, microbial resistance and origin of soil humus. *Proc. int. Soc. Soil Sci. Comm. IV & V (New Zealand)*, 197.

SZLADITS, I. (1952). Interactions of soil and antiseptics. *Soils Fertil., Harpenden*, **15**, 299.

THERON, J. J. (1951). The influence of plants on the mineralization of nitrogen and the maintenance of organic matter in the soil. *J. agric. Sci.*, **41**, 289.

WEBLEY, D. M., HENDERSON, M. E. K. & TAYLOR, I. F. (1963). The microbiology of rocks and weathered stones. *J. Soil Sci.*, **14**, 102.

WILLIAMS, E. G., SCOTT, N. M. & MCDONALD, M. J. (1958). Soil properties and phosphate sorption. *J. Sci. Fd Agric.*, **9**, 551.

WOLDENDORP, J. W. (1962). The quantitative influence of the rhizosphere on denitrification. *Pl. Soil*, **17**, 267.

# *DISCUSSION*

## THE ENVIRONMENT OF SOIL BACTERIA

*Chairman: N. A. Burges, University of Liverpool*

*Prof. N. A. Burges.* Listening to the speakers this morning, it seems to me that they have stressed many of the points which are vital in any discussion of ecology. Much of microbiology has been involved with organisms in pure culture and with the activity of detached enzyme systems under laboratory conditions. Therefore, I think it is particularly valuable that the true essence of ecology, what the organism is doing in its natural environment, was stressed by all the speakers. Furthermore, as Professor McLaren pointed out, we must not think only of the bulk medium in which organisms are growing; we must think in terms of the pH, the activity of the water and the redox potential at the *surface* of the substrate.

The availability of the substrate is a matter that is very far removed from the simple picture which biochemists so often give us when they are considering enzyme reactions. At a meeting a little while ago I offended one of my biochemical colleagues by saying that the ordinary concept of enzymology had very little interest to living organisms, other than biochemists. It represents hardly anything of that which takes place in the real world of living organisms. I feel even more strongly convinced of that, having listened to Professor McLaren and others. The difficulty is getting substrate and enzyme together. If we had needed to be reminded of the complexity of such systems, I think Dr. Bacon's comments on the vast range of substances available should have humbled us a bit, particularly when he made the point that even if we list these compounds, we still have virtually no quantitative data on how much of each of these compounds are present.

The availability of substrate came up again in Dr. Macfadyen's paper, especially the very vital function that animals play in presenting new surfaces for exploitation. Whether the animal is a mite chewing up fungal hyphae and plant tissue, or a man turning over the soil, it is all part of the same picture.

In conclusion, I wish to stress again, as did Professor Russell, the important difference between what occurs in the natural environment and in the laboratory. We can prepare beautifully complicated diagrams of the nitrogen cycle. We can prove that various organisms carry out reactions involved in this cycle. However, when we consider the multiplicity of natural environments, we know that perhaps only a portion of the possible pathways are in use. We have virtually no evidence concerning the quantitative role of the different species in any of these possible conversions.

*Prof. A. D. McLaren.* Professor Russell has raised one or two questions on which we have some experimental information. It concerns the accessibility of macromolecular substrates to the micro-organisms and how far a micro-organism can rely on the availability of substrate as far as its nutrition is concerned. One can take the clay mineral, montmorillonite, which has a layer lattice structure, with a series of about 10 Å (determined by X-ray crystallography) and add to it protein. The layer then expands to the order of 50 Å, the diameter of the protein molecule being 40 Å. In other words, this is an additive process; the layer expands and admits a protein molecule. Now one can add two species of *Pseudomonas*, one of which is adsorbed on the clay particles, and one which is not. Both organisms secrete exo-enzymes which are themselves proteinaceous. The exo-enzymes diffuse in between the clay sheets and hydrolyse the substrate. Peptides and amino acids diffuse back out and the micro-organisms grow very well. It makes no difference whether the bacterium is adsorbed on the clay particles or not. X-ray crystallographic data show that the layer then collapses and the original spacing is restored. The organisms multiply and ammonia is released. However, there is no evidence that proteins or humic materials appear within the crystal lattice of montmorillonite in natural soil. Apparently, in nature, any adsorption of these materials occurs only on the outside of the montmorillonite or kaolin package. There is nothing limiting about this; in fact the adsorption and concentration of the substrate on the mineral may augment and increase the rate of disappearance of material. Conversely, if the protein is complexed with silicic acid gel or lignin, there is a diminution in the rate of enzymic attack. Nevertheless, the organisms and their exo-enzymes are able to break down such materials in a matter of hours under laboratory conditions. What happens in the soil remains to be determined, but there seem to be no good explanations for the resistance of organic matter in soil. Any experiments we have done with models show that, whatever explanation is offered, it always breaks down when applied to soil.

*Dr. D. J. Greenwood.* Professor McLaren, there is one point which I don't understand. When you are dealing with layers in the region of 40 Å in the clay particles, the viscosity of the water must be much increased and the diffusion of substrates through decreased (up to 30-fold according to P. F. Low). What I do not follow is that if there is an increase in viscosity, how is it that you get these rapid rates of decomposition of added substrates?

*Prof. A. D. McLaren.* Fortunately I have given some thought to this question. There are very few enzyme reactions in nature which are diffusion limited, as far as the rate of combination of enzyme and substrate is concerned. Even a 50-fold increase in viscosity would have very little bearing on the rate of reaction. The invertase reaction is a case in point. When using 70 per cent sucrose, the viscosity is increased by a factor of 50. Yet it turns out that this is not the rate-limiting factor at all. Perhaps only in the case of catalase, fumarase and related enzymes is diffusion a limtiing process. The rate of breakdown is normally controlled by the activation energy requirements for the breakdown of the enzyme-substrate complex once it appears in the clay lattice, not by any limiting of diffusion in and out of clay particles.

*Dr. H. L. Jensen.* Professor McLaren, if I understood your graph concerning the pH optimum for nitrification in a mineral medium and in a soil suspension, I did not get the impression that there was a real difference between the two optima, rather that in the presence of soil you got a narrow peak, whilst in the mineral medium you got quite a broad optimum zone.

*Prof. A. D. McLaren.* That is correct. What I should have said was 'The pH of half relative maximum activity'.

*Dr. M. Alexander.* I would like to ask two questions. Firstly, how do you explain the occurrence of nitrification in soils at a lower pH than is a minimum for the organisms in pure culture? Secondly, what do you think will be the major physical and chemical determinants that govern the composition of the bacterial population in the different natural ecosystems, e.g. freshwater, marine and terrestrial ecosystems?

*Prof. A. D. McLaren.* Our study on nitrification in soil, comparing it with nitrification in solutions containing a single species, shows that the pH is often shifted to higher levels for that species. I think the fact that nitrification does occur in some soils of a low pH, means that the particular species involved is one adapted to a lower pH. We have described two types of nitrifiers which differ by 0·5 of a pH unit in their optimum pH, even in soil conditions. It is quite likely that there are other strains in soil, which have not yet been isolated, which have lower pH optima.

The charge phenomena as an explanation would require a shift in pH in the other direction than that which you have suggested.

With regard to your second question, I think I will pass the ball to my colleague.

*Dr. J. S. D. Bacon.* My attitude to this question is an empirical one. Let us take the viewpoint of a bacterium in the soil. When I first listened to people telling me that cellulose was a very resistant material, that is chemically, inferring that it was also a very resistant material biologically speaking, my reaction was that if I were a bacterium in the soil, the first thing I would do would be to try to eat the cellulose, since there was plenty of it there. Presumably organisms adapt themselves, perhaps very specifically, so that they can find only a very limited source of food at any one point in the soil. You may therefore expect to find a highly specialized bacterial population arising during the later stages of organic matter decomposition whose nature is dependant upon the *origin* of the organic matter.

*Prof. E. W. Russell.* In further answer to Dr. Alexander, may I quote D'Arcy Thompson on the virtue of being the right size. You have got to be awfully small to want to live in the soil and the smaller you are, the happier you will be. In the ocean, you can be as big as you like; you have got lots of space. Steric hindrance probably influences the distribution of micro-organisms in certain groups in the soil.

Humus. I think the real position is this. Unless a substance can be *made* resistant to decomposition by being adsorbed, you won't find it in the soil. There are no proteins in the soil worth mentioning. You only find adsorbed things that cannot be decomposed when they are adsorbed; that is why they are there.

Possibly the more you push aluminium into these organic compounds, the less do organisms like consuming them. Thus, inositol phosphates push in aluminium ions and reduce their decomposability quite a lot. Again, if humus accumulates in the soil, there is often a lot of aluminium there. I am not saying that aluminium is the sole cause; I am saying that the things you find accumulating in the soil are the things that become difficult to decompose when they are adsorbed.

*Dr. H. L. Jensen.* Your remarks about the accumulation of humus may be true for field soils, particularly arable soils, for it is a general rule that you get higher humus accumulation in clay soils than in sand soils; but surely there are occasions when you get plenty of humus without there being any clay present. Think, for instance, of low moor peat where a lot of humus accumulates and there is a great deal of aluminium present. Whilst this is true under natural conditions where you have poor aeration, when low moor peat soil is placed under aerobic laboratory conditions, you get much $CO_2$ released, indicating decomposition.

*Dr. H. M. Hurst.* There are one or two things that I would like to say about humic acid. We have a new degradation process for breaking down humic acid into small identifiable monomer units. This has led us to the following conclusions. Firstly, we do not consider that humic acid has any nitrogen in it. Secondly, we do not feel that humic acid has anything to do with black fungal pigments. Our degradation process shows that these fungal pigments, although very similar to humic acid, are in fact quite different from them in respect of the phenolic units of which humic acids are composed. We can break down humic acids by this chemical process and obtain a 30 per cent yield of identifiable phenolic units. In the absence of any evidence to the contrary, we are quite sure that humic acid is essentially a poly-phenolic unit and nothing else. We have never detected any carbohydrates or amino nitrogen compounds associated with humic acid.

Our studies also show that humic acid is not a constant chemical entity. There are many different kinds of humic acid; humic acids on one site may be quite distinct from humic acids only a few metres away. Further, humic acids in the upper horizon of a well developed podzol are quite distinct from the humic acids of the lower horizon, e.g. the $B_1$ horizon.

There are two main types of poly-phenolic unit in humic acid. One of these is derived from lignin and the other is a flavonoid contribution. These units are quite stable and are found in tertiary and quaternary humic acid preparations.

Therefore, we should not consider humic acid to be a constant environmental influence; it is a highly variable organic complex, and a very complex organic complex at that.

*Dr. H. Potgieter.* Dr. Hurst, it is well known that quite a lot of fungi, bacteria and streptomycetes can form melanins which may also be extracted with alkali from the soil. How are you able to distinguish between a melanin and a humic acid?

*Dr. H. M. Hurst.* I have never decomposed a melanin, only other black fungal pigments. These give small yields of phenolic monomers which are quite distinct from the phenolic monomers that you find in humic acids. I won't say that they never contribute, but we have no evidence that they do. Melanin contains nitrogen. Humic acids are exceedingly low in nitrogen.

*Dr. H. Potgieter.* It has been shown that some melanins, especially those from fungi, contain no nitrogen at all.

*Dr. H. M. Hurst.* I would not consider them to be melanins. Surely melanins have to be formed via dihydroxyphenylalanine?

*Dr. M. Alexander.* Before we bury humic acids back in the ground, I would like to point out that a common feature of resistant molecules in soil is the presence of a polyaromatic structure. We have this in humic acids; we have it in synthetic melanins; we have it in authentic lignin, which is clearly a very resistant component; we have it also in fungal structures which are quite resistant to degradation, e.g. sclerotia and the hyphae of some fungi. I would maintain that it is the polyaromatic material which is extremely important. The persistence of organic compounds in nature is due either to their association with polyaromatic molecules or because they are polyaromatic themselves. These compounds may or may not be associated with clay, which undoubtedly increases their resistance. I don't know about the aluminium relationships. We have no data on this.

*Dr. E. Grossbard.* I would like to add something concerning the persistence of freshly decomposed organic material. We have studied the decomposition of radioactive, labelled grass material, similar to that used by Jenkinson, which Dr. Bacon referred to. Using autoradiographic techniques, we followed the decomposition of small fragments of grass leaves on the surface of the soil. Like Jenkinson, we obtained very rapid breakdown in the first few months, followed by slower decomposition. As decomposition proceeded, the tissue between the veins disappeared.

The veins (lignin) persisted for up to a year. Furthermore, the sclerotia of fungi attacking the leaves became labelled. These structures persisted for a very long time; so did the faecal pellets of mites which contained radioactive plant remains. Why do these pellets persist? Is it because a pellet, by definition, is an accumulation of that part of the plant residue which is most difficult to digest, or are there cementing substances which protect the pellet from microbial attack?

*Dr. A. Macfadyen.* I don't know.

*Prof. N. A. Burges.* This is quite a well marked feature of pellets in soil. They retain their structure for such a long time and yet they are nothing more than chewed-up pieces of plant debris. This contrasts markedly with the excreta of enchytraeid worms which spread out to form what looks like one of the early stages of humus formation.

*Prof. E. W. Russell.* I have often wondered if the length of life of these pellets is governed by the fact that it takes some time for the specialized basidiomycetes to get to the pellets and decompose the lignin in them.

*Dr. E. Grossbard.* Yes, but animals walk about voiding the pellets. This should bring them into close contact with the fungi.

*Dr. J. E. Satchell.* I don't know why pellets persist, but I feel that it is not for any of the reasons that have been offered. In most pellets, rather less than 5 per cent of the dry weight of the material has been digested. This means that we must look for an explanation other than that particularly resistant residues are left.

*Dr. J. S. D. Bacon.* In this connection, the mobility of soil micro-organisms seems to be a problem. Surely, unless some agency can transfer them from place to place, they will just sit around doing nothing. Perhaps the reason that organic matter persists in soil is not that it is intractable, but that the decomposers cannot reach the material.

*Prof. H. Veldkamp.* The mobility of micro-organisms is interesting from other points of view also. Anaerobic spirochaetes are very numerous in freshwater and marine muds. They are able to move through fine capillaries and being only about 0·3 μ in diameter, are even able to move through the capillaries in soft agar. If you make agar shake cultures, the colonies of most bacteria become localized. However, spirochaetes move through the capillaries and gather round colonies of other bacteria. I don't know why. Perhaps it is due to the occurrence of optimal redox potential conditions around these colonies.

Similarly, when you make wet mounts of the micro-aerophilic spirilla, they often congregate some distance from the edge of the cover glass. Both these cases are examples of movement directed to optimum conditions.

*Dr. L. Quesnel.* It would seem to me that bacteria, flagellated ones at any rate, are quite remarkably mobile. If you take a piece of thin delivery tubing, punch out a colony of *Pseudomonas viscosa* growing on agar and then top up the delivery tube with water, the bacteria swim up the tube. *Pseudomonas viscosa* will swim about 5 to 6 cm. in 8 hrs. In terms of the soil, 8 or 9 hrs. is a very short time indeed. Given a food supply to provide the energy for the swimming action and a water film to swim in, I should think that motile bacteria would permeate the soil in a surprisingly short time. I doubt if mobility will limit colonization of soil particles.

*Prof. N. A. Burges.* There may be differences between the behaviour of such a culture in a tube and in the soil.

*Dr. C. G. Dobbs.* I would like to comment on Dr. Lockwood's paper. I think that there is more evidence than he gave credit for, for the existence of inhibitory effects due to a labile substance produced by micro-organisms in the soil. Some of this evidence is based on somewhat variable results, due to the lability of the inhibitor. Dr. Lockwood and his colleagues have themselves produced sterile agar discs which are inhibitory to fungus spores, after removal from contact with the soil. We have found that sterilized marine sand allows 95 per cent germination of a test fungus. If you re-infect this sand with soil or more sand, you get inhibition of fungal spores. You can detect this inhibition in a sterile disc incubated over the sand on top of a cellophane separator. Tested afterwards it inhibits completely, unless you heat the disc to a temperature of 60°–70°. The particular sand that we have used also has a residual inhibition after sterilization, which is not susceptible to temperature. Thus there are two types of inhibition:

(a) microbial inhibition, possibly due to Gram-negative bacteria, and
(b) residual inhibition due, in this case, to iron.

This is not incompatible with the fact that the fungus spores may have a low nutrient status. Fungus spores which have their own nutrient supply, sufficient for germination in distilled water, will not be affected by the inhibitor. Presumably, any fungus must have nutrients for germination. These may be reduced to the level where the spore won't germinate in water, possibly as a result of prolonged respiration or washing in water.

*Dr. J. L. Lockwood.* May I offer another possible interpretation of inhibition in the agar disc. The common way to demonstrate fungistasis is to place an agar disc on the soil, separated from it by sterile cellophane to keep the agar sterile. When one removes this disc, you can put spores onto the disc or else remove the disc and put it in a Petri dish containing spores. Inhibition of fungal spore germination will occur. The usual interpretation is that fungistatic substances are moving into the disc. It seems equally possible that nutrients in the agar may be moving out into the soil since microbes may act as a sink for nutrients. We have obtained good fungistasis simply by placing sterile water agar discs on the surface of dialysis tubing and allowing water to run through the system overnight. The sterile agar discs are then inhibitory to the germination of spores, almost to the same degree as those from soil. Moreover, if these are autoclaved, they will then allow more germination. Possibly the heat treatment makes nutrients remaining in the agar more available. I suggest that fungistasis can be explained on the basis of nutrient relations.

*Dr. F. E. Clark.* Dr. Lockwood, you referred to the extensive microparasitism within fungal hyphae, caused by other fungi and actinomycetes. However, throughout your discussion you talked about bacteria on the surface of hyphae. I am convinced that I have seen bacteria within fungal hyphae. Have you observed internal parasitism by bacteria and is it documented in the literature?

*Dr. J. L. Lockwood.* I have not worked on this problem myself; nor have I found reports of this sort of thing in the literature.

*Dr. F. E. Clark.* Surely there is no *a priori* reason why bacteria should not parasitize internally?

*Dr. J. L. Lockwood.* How would they get in?

*Dr. F. E. Clark.* How do actinomycetes get in? How do other fungi get in? It would be much easier for a bacterium to get in than it would for another fungus. It would be simply a matter of lysis and penetration. They get into man and other animals; they get into plants. I am convinced they are inside.

*Dr. J. L. Lockwood.* I don't want to argue about this because I just don't know. I was thinking that filamentous organisms might have means of mechanically penetrating into tissue. Bacteria would have to dissolve away something.

# METHODS FOR THE ISOLATION AND ESTIMATION OF ACTIVITY OF SOIL BACTERIA

# METHODS FOR THE ISOLATION AND ESTIMATION OF ACTIVITY OF SOIL BACTERIA

L. E. CASIDA, Jr.

*The Pennsylvania State University, U.S.A.*

## *INTRODUCTION*

The soil may be considered as a refuse heap for the world's debris. As such, it contains myriads of micro-organisms able to degrade or chemically change all manner of organic and inorganic materials. These organisms may act singly, decomposing *in toto* organic compounds to $CO_2$, $H_2O$, cell substance and by-products, or a succession of different organisms may be required to carry out this process. Man has been interested in this process, other than out of mere curiosity, because of its relationship to soil fertility, the numbers and types of micro-organisms present in a given soil often reflecting the fertility of that soil (Waksman, 1922*a*, *b*, *c*, 1927; Taylor and Lochhead, 1937; Taylor, 1938). Additional impetus for the examination of the soil microflora stemmed from a desire to know whether certain oxidative and reductive soil processes were of a biological nature, and, if so, what micro-organisms or groups of micro-organisms were responsible for effecting these chemical reactions. It was hoped that this knowledge could then be utilized by man to direct these reactions to his benefit in the growing of his crops and in the containing of plant disease.

Recent years have seen the development of a much wider interest in determining what micro-organisms constitute the soil microflora. The search for new industrial fermentation processes requires that many micro-organisms of different types be screened for their ability to produce in good yield products of commercial interest. Such screening programmes are particularly evident in the search for micro-organisms producing new and useful antibiotics. Industrial screening programmes have quickly exhausted libraries of known stock cultures, and, in fact, these cultures have usually yielded little of value in the way of economic cultures. Inevitably, this search for micro-organisms has been directed to the soil because only in the soil (and comparable marine sediments) can one hope to find enough different micro-organisms with a wide enough range of potential synthetic capabilities to perform specific syntheses in pure culture.

The microbial physiologist studying metabolic mechanisms also requires micro-organisms with specific enzymatic abilities, and these organisms often are secured from the soil. The late Professor A. J. Kluyver summed up the situation most eloquently in his statement to his students, 'All the organisms you will ever need can be obtained from the heel of your shoe.' (J. C. Hoogerheide, personal communication).

Man, in his continual struggle against insects and weeds, has prepared many new organic pesticides by chemical synthesis and has applied these compounds directly or indirectly to the soil. Questions have been raised as to the relative longevity, toxicity, and decomposability of these compounds and their degradation products in soil, and the effects of these compounds on the microbial equilibrium conditions and natural processes of the soil (Jensen, 1962; Katznelson, 1962). To secure answers to these questions, the microbiologist must evaluate the microbial status of the soil in the presence and absence of these compounds. He must attempt to isolate soil micro-organisms representative of those degrading these compounds in soil so that he can determine the relative sensitivity of the pesticides to microbial attach and at the same time establish their chemical pathways of degradation.

New areas of microbiological exploration have recently gained popularity. These areas require techniques for examination of microbiological activities and for isolation of micro-organisms. Also, they often require that knowledge of an eco-system such as that of soil be available as a reference standard. Such new areas of exploration are typified by studies of samples of frozen soil or ice from arctic and antarctic regions (Flint and Stout, 1960; Brockman and Boyd, 1963) and by studies of marine waters and muds (ZoBell, 1946; Wood, 1958; Gray, 1963). In the latter instance, one would like to know if there is a separate and distinct marine microflora or merely an accumulation of terrestrial forms which have been washed into and become adapted to the sea.

Man's ventures into space may soon lead to the availability of samples from various moons and planets. This possibility poses many problems to the microbiologist, in addition to that of obtaining and returning uncontaminated samples to earth. Principally, man would like to know whether any form of life, even if it be only a primitive micro-organism, exists under these extra-terrestrial conditions. One would assume that the microbiologist familiar with soil examination and isolation techniques would have the most suitable experience for evaluating these extra-terrestrial dusts. But is this true? Are the techniques of the soil microbiologist for examination of microbial activities in soil and for the isolation of soil micro-organisms good enough to be employed successfully in the study of extra-terrestrial dusts? This question, to some extent, must be answered in the negative. The techniques available to the soil microbiologist are poor if one considers the possibility that to date only a relatively small portion of the soil microbial population has been examined. Thus, the microbial population of extra-terrestrial dusts would need to be similar to that with which man is already familiar before he could hope for any great success in their study.

What, then, are the problems which confront the microbiologist in studying the activities of soil micro-organisms and their isolation from soil to a state of pure laboratory culture? Historically, the microbiologist has isolated mainly those micro-organisms which carried out soil processes with which he was familiar: the organisms responsible for nitrogen fixation, nitrification, denitrification, nitrate reduction, oxidation and reduction of sulphur, iron and manganese compounds, organic matter decomposition, known pathogens of various types, and so forth. He has counted, isolated and classified those organisms which showed up regularly and in quantity when he plated soil for total numbers of various micro-organisms. It was realized that all organisms in soil did not grow on the conventional plating media, but the colonies which did appear were considered to provide a representative picture of the soil microflora (Stevenson, 1958; Jensen, 1962). However, several investigators (Conn, 1918; Waksman, 1927; Thornton and Gray, 1934; Jones and Mollison, 1948; Russell, 1950; Skinner, Jones and Mollison, 1952; Seifert, 1958), utilizing microscopic techniques for observing and counting the soil microflora, realized that a discrepancy existed between total counts as determined by the plate and microscopic procedures. In general, their results indicated that only 1–10 per cent of the soil microflora grew on the best of plating media.

This anomaly was explained by the assumption that the nutrients in plating media were not adequate or that at any one time a large part of the soil microflora was dead but still stainable by conventional dyes (Russell, 1950; Skinner *et al.*, 1952; Topping, 1958). The advent of vital staining of soil micro-organisms with acridine orange combined with ultraviolet fluorescence microscopy (Strugger, 1948) raised questions as to the validity of the latter assumption (Strugger, 1948; Seifert, 1958; Macaulay Institute Report, 1959). Thus, microscopic counts of soil organisms by this technique revealed a similar disparity between plate and microscopic counts. Also, in using microscopic techniques, it was realized that a large part of the soil microflora consisted of small coccoid rods (Conn, 1918; Winogradsky, 1925*b*; Waksman, 1927; Jones and Mollison, 1948; Strugger, 1948; Russell, 1950; Casida, 1962*a*), a morphology not necessarily shared by the flora observed on soil dilution plates.

Additional possible explanations for the relatively greater microscopic soil counts and for the difficulties encountered in isolation of some soil micro-organisms may be summarized as follows. Autotrophic populations in soil, in addition to those with which we are familiar, may oxidize or reduce inorganic compounds of nitrogen, sulphur, iron, phosphorus, manganese, copper etc. Cellulose, lignin and humic materials may support a large, highly oxygen-sensitive, anaerobic population which to isolate would require techniques of anaerobic isolation and cultivation similar to those described for the rumen microflora (Hungate, 1950; Bryant, 1959; Hungate, 1960; Kistner, 1960; Kistner and Gouws, 1964).

The soil may contain large populations of parasitic bacteria such as *Bdellovibrio* species (Stolp and Starr, 1963) which are parasitic on other bacteria or possibly on other representatives of the microflora and which require the presence of an acceptable host for their demonstration. Actinomycete and bacterial spores in soil may germinate only with difficulty in the absence of heat shocking or other activation procedures. Much of the soil bacterial population may exist as the coccoid elements of L form growth (Laidlaw and Elford, 1936; Russell, 1950; Krasilnikov, 1958; Jagnow, 1961), being stabilized in this form in soil by soil antibiotics or other inhibitors and requiring reversion to the parent bacterial form before growth could ensue in laboratory media.

Many soil bacteria grow as microcolonies within the larger pores of soil aggregates and are embedded in the clay humic complex of soil (Waksman, 1927; Lees and Quastel, 1946; Jones and Mollison, 1948; Krasilnikov, 1958; Tyagny-Ryadno, 1962). These features make difficult the elution of cells from soil particles and the distribution of the bacteria as single particles, so that obtaining separate colonies on a plate may not necessarily reflect a colony's origin from a single cell although only one species may be present. The soil atmosphere contains a higher level of $CO_2$ and concentrations of other gases varying from that of the atmosphere of the laboratory (Alexander, 1961). Thus, laboratory growth of soil organisms may require increased but not toxic levels of $CO_2$ (Micev, 1958) or perhaps a narrow partial pressure range.

Symbiotic or commensal associations are known or may be postulated to occur in soil. Examples are local oxygen removal (Alexander, 1961) or catalase provision by the aerobe for the anaerobe (McClung, 1956; Burton and Morita, 1964), production of unusual growth factors by one organism for another (Lochhead and Burton, 1953), removal of toxic metabolic products of one organism by another (Alexander, 1961), formation by one organism of gaseous nutrients and growth stimulants for another (Krasilnikov, 1958; Lu and Bollen, 1958; Lu, Gilmour, Zagallo and Bollen, 1958; Chandra and Bollen, 1960; Vančura, 1961; Monteulle and Cheminais, 1964), and partial degradation of complex nutrients by one organism to produce unique nutrients for another.

The competition for soil nutrients existing under most soil conditions tends to keep much of the population as spores or in a state of suspended animation with a relatively lowered metabolic rate and an extended generation time for vegetative cells (Gooding and McCalla, 1945). The latter cells may require a period of metabolic adjustment and revitalization before growth will ensue on laboratory media. Production of antibiotics, inorganic and organic acids and other inhibitors of growth by rapidly growing flora on plating media may prevent growth of the more sensitive and less competitive segments of the microflora. Conventional plating media such as soil extract agar for total soil counts prevent spreaders and production of inhibitors by providing only low levels of various nutrients. However, these media do not provide the nutritive requirements of the more fastidious soil microflora but provide too high a nutritive level for most autotrophic forms. Incorporation of inhibitors into plating media to allow the isolation of specific segments of the microflora, while effective, does prevent growth of a varying proportion of the desired flora. Lastly, colonies appearing on a plate or in a broth dilution tube may be difficult to further purify, as for example the nitrifiers with their heterotrophic scavengers (Imshenetsky, 1946; Meiklejohn, 1950; Gunderson, 1955).

Experimental errors occur during pipetting and dilution of soil samples (Wieringa, 1958; Jensen, 1962). Cells become adsorbed to the glass walls of these vessels and also settle from suspension with the soil particles. In addition, the fluids used in dilution of soil may cause death of cells from improperly adjusted conditions of oxygen tension, pH and ionic strength.

Regardless of the above described difficulties in isolating and evaluating soil micro-organisms, there has been an accumulation of good procedures for the microbiologist to use in studying conventional soil forms. Some of these will be considered in the following discussion and others may be found in the printed collections of techniques by Fred and

Waksman (1928), Meiklejohn (1950), Pochon (1954), Allen (1957), Thornton and Meiklejohn (1957), Wieringa (1958), Johnson, Curl, Bond and Fribourg (1959), Durbin (1961) and Pramer and Schmidt (1964). Also, Johnson *et al.* (1959) present a detailed discussion of data analysis, experimental design and statistical procedures.

## *MICROSCOPIC TECHNIQUES*

The simplest technique for observing the microbial flora of soil is the buried microscope slide (Rossi and Riccardo, 1927; Cholodny, 1930). A plain slide or one coated with nutrients is buried in soil with or without nutrient amendments and left for several hours to a few days so that soil micro-organisms may become attached to the glass. To evaluate this microflora, the slides are removed from the soil, cleaned of gritty materials and stained with conventional or fluorescent dyes (Lehner, Nowak and Seibold, 1958; Lehner and Nowak, 1959). Much information about the general status of the microbial ecology of soil is gained with this technique, but one must remember that it is a picture generalized by the time period of burial. Also, staining by conventional dyes requires experience in distinguishing the microbial cells from much of the morphologically similar soil debris. This problem is not as critical when acridine orange vital staining is used combined with ultraviolet fluorescence microscopy. Thus, this procedure should allow more extensive use of the buried slide technique than has been made to date.

Minderman (1956) described a technique for preparation of microtome sections of unaltered soil so as to observe the microbial flora at a given moment of time. Sand was removed with hydrogen fluoride, and a quadruple staining procedure was employed. Alexander and Jackson (1954) stained soil with cotton blue before vacuum impregnation with a polyester resin and preparation of sections.

Quantitative microscopic estimations of numbers of soil bacteria have usually involved placing a known amount of soil over a defined small area of a microscope slide with a binder such as agar, gelatin or immersion oil added to hold the soil to the slide (Conn, 1918; Winogradsky, 1925*b*; Thornton and Gray, 1934; Jones and Mollison, 1948; Strugger, 1948). Staining has been with conventional or fluorescent dyes. Because uneven spreading of the soil on the slide may cause variations in the counts from fields observed, Thornton and Gray (1934) utilized indigotin as an internal standard so that bacterial counts could be related to the known numbers of the standard particles. To the author's knowledge, similar use of internal standards has not been reported for ultraviolet fluorescence microscopy of soil micro-organisms.

As previously mentioned, except for vital staining with acridine orange, there is difficulty encountered in differentiating the living from the dead cell. Darken (1961, 1962) recently reported the use of 'fluorescent brighteners', such as the disodium salt of 4,4′-bis (4-anilino-6-bis-(2-hydroxyethyl) amino-s-triazin-2-ylamino) -2-′-stil-bene-disulfonic acid, as vital stains for ultraviolet fluorescence microscopy. Possibilities for the use of these compounds in observing and counting soil bacteria *in situ* have not been reported, and limited studies in the author's laboratory have not shown promise.

Microscopic counts of soil bacteria usually do not distinguish coccoid bacteria from actinomycete spores (Conn, 1948; Russell, 1950). However, the stain of Tchan (1947) and the slide culture-stain procedure of Jones and Mollison (1948) do allow a limited differentiation.

Recently, two interesting variations have been reported for the use of fluorescence microscopy in evaluating soil micro-organisms. Zvyagintsev (1962*a*, *b*) employed a microscope with reflected ultraviolet light to observe bacteria on the surfaces of soil particles and root hairs. Schmidt and Bankole (1962) introduced *Aspergillus flavus* into sterilized soil containing buried slides and followed its development by immunofluorescence with fluorescein conjugated antibody. This technique should find use in locating, observing and following bacteria in soil if non-specific fluorescence can be contained.

The capillary method for observation of soil micro-organisms has been studied by Perfiliev and Gabe (Foster, 1964). This technique is based on the fact that growth of soil bacteria occurs mainly in the capillary water between soil particles. Tiny glass capillary tubes with flat parallel sides are buried in the soil to duplicate the normal capillary conditions within soil, then the capillaries are removed and observed microscopically. It is claimed that not only is the soil microflora observed in this way, but also that one observes the sequences in floral changes which occur with time. Aristovskaya and Parinkina (1961, 1962) and Parinkina (1963) in their pedoscope procedure have also utilized capillary tubes to observe the soil microflora.

As reported by Foster (1964), the electron microscope studies of soil microflora by Nikitin would appear most interesting. Several new types of soil micro-organisms, ranging from virus particles to bacteria, were observed in these studies. These organisms did not grow to any extent on normal laboratory media, although some of them produced limited colonial growth on a mixture of one part soil and three parts agar.

## *DIRECT ISOLATION OF INDIVIDUAL MICROBIAL CELLS FROM SOIL*

Mention has been made of the high soil bacterial counts obtained by microscopy as compared with plating methods. Considering the magnitude of these microscopic counts, one should theoretically be able to isolate some of the 'extra' micro-organisms if one could microscopically observe an individual cell in soil, then pick up that cell and transfer it to laboratory media. A technique of this type should allow a general determination of whether bacteria in soil possess cellular morphological characteristics similar to those evident in the laboratory.

Two techniques of this type have been described. Casida (1962*a*) spread soil, which had been stained by acridine orange (Strugger, 1948), in a thin film on a slide previously coated with an agar medium. The inoculated slide was observed directly by ultraviolet microscopy or was preincubated for 4 hours in a humidified chamber before observation. Microbial cells of interest were removed by micromanipulation and released into a suitable medium for growth. Because of the limited working distance for the manipulation tool, objectives of relatively low magnification were required ·A × 32 objective with long working distance has since been found useful. Also, a manipulation tool of metal, to cast a visible shadow in ultraviolet light, or a glass tool lit by fibre optics (Casida, 1962*b*), was necessary so that the position of the tool might be observed. The preincubation period before micromanipulation was utilized to allow cells to reach a late lag phase in their growth cycle with consequent increase in cell size. Obviously, those cells growing quickly under these conditions were isolated with greater frequency. Use of higher magnification objectives with long working distance and elimination of the preincubation step should reduce this problem.

Perfiliev and Gabe (Foster, 1964) adapted their capillary tube method to selectively pick a single bacterial cell from soil. This was accomplished by microscopically observing the capillary for an area frequented only by the desired micro-organism. A special device was used to cut out this area of the capillary so that it could be introduced into the growth medium.

Direct isolation of a specific group of bacteria from soil is exemplified by the study of Sacks and Alderton (1961) who utilized a two-phase aqueous polymer system to extract bacterial spores. Webley and Duff (1962) isolated soil micro-organisms attacking specific substances by introducing into soil the substrate incorporated in a kaolinite pellet, incubating, then recovering the pellet and plating it.

## *ENRICHMENT CULTURE*

Enrichment culture is a technique for selectively increasing the numbers of a desired micro-organism by manipulating the growth conditions such that it grows at a faster rate than the unwanted microflora. This is accomplished by withholding or adding a specific nutrient or growth factor, adding a toxic material, or in general altering physical or chemical factors to the advantage of the desired micro-organism. Enrichment is continued in successive cultures so that the influence of the soil becomes diluted and the manipulative practice has time to be expressed. Enrichment culture is employed in the study of metabolic rates of a specific micro-organism or group of organisms without their removal from soil, as for instance in the study of soil nitrification rates by adding ammonium sulphate to selectively stimulate growth of the nitrifiers.

Studies of the latter type often utilize percolation devices in which oxygenated nutrient solution is cycled (Audus, 1946; Lees, 1949; Temple, 1951; Bryner, Beck, Davis and Wilson, 1954; Greenwood and Lees, 1959) or not cycled (Macura and Málek, 1958) through an undisturbed column of soil. Samples for analyses of the percolation fluid are removed periodically with ease. Percolation devices can also be used for enrichment culture for isolations of desired bacteria because of the excellent aeration characteristics of this growth vessel. Microaerophilic and anaerobic organisms can be selectively increased in numbers by utilizing inert gases instead of air to cycle the nutrients in the apparatus.

Enrichment culture usually does not provide estimates of the abundance of an organism in soil, although it does allow one to isolate organisms normally present in low numbers or which because of slow growth rate or lack of competitive ability only rarely, if at all, produce colonies on soil dilution plates. Enrichment culture also is of value when one wishes to obtain a bacterium to do a specific job, such as a bacterium to degrade a new pesticide. In the latter instance, one usually wishes to determine whether soil micro-organisms exist which can attack a given chemical molecule and, if so, the pathway of chemical degradation. However, enrichment culture does not provide much idea of the range of micro-organisms in soil which can attack an added chemical. Thus, a major problem of enrichment culture is that for a given set of conditions this technique provides the same organism or a narrow spectrum of organisms. It provides those organisms which adapt quickly to the particular situation and at the same time grow rapidly and with good competitive ability. To solve this problem, R. E. Hungate (personal communication) has suggested that enrichment culture be carried out, not on soil itself, but on dilutions made from the soil.

## *SOIL SAMPLING*

The choice of techniques for securing and handling a soil sample depends to some extent on the type of biological information which one wishes to obtain from the sample. Bacterial counts in soil vary from season to season and from day to day, even hour to hour (Taylor, 1936), depending on moisture and other factors. Counts also vary with depth (Alexander, 1961) and with the presence or absence of roots (Clark, 1940; Katznelson, Lochhead and Timonin, 1948; Starkey, 1958). One can use a sterile or nonsterile spade, soil auger or other device to obtain replicate samples (Johnson *et al.*, 1959). If the depth from which a sample is taken is of importance, then some provision should be made to prevent contamination of the sample from the desired depth with soil or organisms from greater or lesser depths (Gilmore, 1959). If depth is not of importance, then one can remove the top $\frac{1}{4}$ in. to 1 in. and sample the soil to a depth of approximately 6 in. (Waksman, 1922*a*; Johnson *et al.*, 1959).

The time lapse between securing the soil sample and evaluating it in the laboratory is of importance because of rapid changes which may occur in the flora (Jensen, 1962). The sample as taken in the field is placed in polyethylene bags and the top of the bag sealed (Stotzky, Goos and Timonin, 1962). As a precaution against pinpoint punctures this bag may be sealed inside a second polyethylene bag containing a few drops of water (Casida, Klein and Santoro, 1964). Polyethylene allows relatively free passage of air but not of moisture.

The sample should be immediately sieved, mixed and plated or otherwise evaluated and not stored. Air drying of the soil is not recommended because small to marked changes in solubility occur for inorganic and organic soil components, and certain segments of the microbial population, such as some of the Gram-negative population, may die at a rapid rate with this treatment (Stevenson, 1956; Jensen, 1962; Casida *et al.*, 1964). Also, if one remoistens the soil before evaluation, a 'burst' of microbial activity may occur (Stevenson, 1956). If limited drying is necessary to allow sieving and handling, the soil may be placed in a parchment bag and suspended in an air stream. This step quickly removes moisture in a manner similar to that used for concentrating enzyme preparations.

Selection of sieve pore size depends somewhat on the type and physical state of the soil; Jensen (1962) recommends a 2 mm. sieve. The sieve pore size should be large enough to pass the smaller soil aggregates which contain large microbial populations.

If the soil sample is to be stored in moist conditions for a period of time, particularly if it is to be used as a reference sample, it should be held in the double polyethylene bags or in tightly capped polyethylene bottles. The lid of the latter container is loosened periodically to insure the maintenance of a normal atmosphere. The samples should be stored at room temperature (Casida *et al.*, 1964) and not under refrigeration (Jensen, 1962). It has been the author's experience that microbial counts may change markedly with the latter storage conditions.

## *SOIL DISPERSAL AND DILUENTS*

Bacteria exist in soil as single cells, in groups of a few cells or as micro-colonies. They occur on the surfaces or within the pores of aggregates and often are embedded in a clay-humic gel (Waksman; 1927; Lees and Quastel, 1946; Jones and Mollison, 1948; Krasilnikov, 1958; Tyagny-Ryadno, 1962). It is necessary to elute and disperse the organisms from these areas so that individual colonies will originate only from a single cell and so that cells will not be lost by sedimentation with the larger soil particles in the dilutions. This has been accomplished by various techniques such as manual shaking of dilutions, use of a dipper for transferring aliquots (Menzies, 1957), applying a high shear force as with a Waring blender (Gamble, Edminster and Orcutt, 1952; Casida, 1965), sonic vibration (Stevenson, 1958), mechanical vibration (Thornton, 1923; Whittles, 1923), trituration in a mortar (Pochon, 1954) and deflocculating agents (Orcutt, 1940; Gamble *et al.*, 1952; Homrighausen and Rohmer, 1959; Jensen, 1962; Zvyagintsev, 1962*a*). Combinations of these also may be used both on the initial dilution and on all dilutions of a series. As Stevenson (1958) points out, these techniques are more or less effective, but each procedure tends to be selective for the elution, dispersal and survival of specific segments of the soil bacterial population. Thus, each technique is in a sense representative of the total population but requires that the exact technique be reproduced each time it is used.

Sterile tap water is often used as a diluent for soil, and physiological saline also may be used. If the desired organism(s) survives only poorly in these diluents, one may use a growth medium, although foaming of the latter may present problems during dispersal of the organisms (Casida, 1965).

With some rhizosphere soil samples it is difficult to determine the actual amount of soil which has been diluted. However, the dry weight of soil washed from plant roots may be calculated by the formula of Herr, Weaver and Horst (1961).

## *PLATING TECHNIQUES*

The most widely used approach for counting, isolating and evaluating soil bacteria is through dispersal and dilution of a soil sample followed by plating on agar media. This technique allows growth of representatives of both the zymogenous and autochthonous microflora (Winogradsky, 1924; Conn and Darrow, 1935), but does not necessarily reflect the biological state of the organisms as they exist in soil. This fact should be considered in comparing the results of plate counts with other methods of evaluating activities of the soil microflora.

Early workers used gelatin for plating soil and encountered its inherent problems of destruction by proteolytic micro-organisms and its requirement for incubation at relatively low temperatures. Conn (1948) continued the use of this medium for soil bacteria, because, in his opinion, the pigment production and colony characteristics on this medium outweighed its faults.

Today, a widely accepted medium for total counts of soil bacteria (and actinomycetes) is soil extract agar (Pochon, 1954; Allen, 1957; James, 1958, 1959; Jensen, 1962; Casida *et al.*, 1964). This medium is made from a heated aqueous extract of soil, phosphate and agar, although small amounts of sugar and other nutrients are added by some workers. A broad range of heat-stable soil nutrients is provided in small amounts without the presence of enough carbon for perceptible antibiotic or organic acid production or for growth of spreaders. Growth occurs slowly in this medium, requiring two weeks of incubation, and care should be taken that drying of the medium does not stop microbial growth. Because of the relatively small colony size on soil extract agar and the presence of actinomycete colonies, one should mark the backs of the plates with parallel lines and count colonies with a low power stereo microscope (Casida *et al.*, 1964). By this procedure, one observes the pinpoint colonies and can to some extent distinguish the bacterial and actinomycete colonies.

Soil extract agar is also employed when one is interested in securing a random, non-biased cross section of the bacterial microflora of soil for studies of nutritional types or other groups of organisms. Lochhead and Chase (1943) subcultured every colony appearing on a plate or section of a plate of soil extract agar for testing on media of various nutritional levels so that they could study amino-acid requiring and other groups of soil bacteria.

We have observed that total counts of soil bacteria on soil extract agar and other plating media are increased if larger plates, such as a glass pie plate, and a deeper layer of agar are used. These plates allow greater separation of the organism through the medium or on its surface (depending on the technique used), thus decreasing the effects of antagonisms and spreading colony growth. This phenomenon would appear to be analagous to that described by Meiklejohn (1957) in which plate count estimates of soil organisms increased with increasing dilution of the soil.

With either large plates or with Petri dishes, one may mix the soil dilutions with the molten, tempered agar, or 0·1 to 0·5 ml. portions of appropriate dilutions may be spread across the surface of the solid agar with a sterile glass rod (Wieringa, 1958; Casida *et al.*, 1964). Although micro-organisms may become attached to the spreading rod, the latter procedure does have the advantage that every colony is formed on the surface of the medium where colony morphology of all organisms and sporulation of actinomycetes and fungi, if present, are easily observed.

Inhibitors are often incorporated into plating media when it is desired to count or isolate specific micro-organisms or groups of micro-organisms. Usually, a more nutritious medium than soil extract agar is utilized, and the inhibitors may include antibiotics, dyes and other selectively toxic compounds. Phenethyl alcohol is an inhibitor of potential interest for the counting and isolation of aerobic, Gram-positive bacteria or estimation of anaerobic Gram-positive and Gram-negative bacteria without growth of facultative aerobes (Dowell, Hill and Altemeir, 1964). It must be realized that with incorporation of inhibitors in the medium one will obtain representatives of the desired organism(s) but not necessarily all strains or species of this organism(s) capable of growing on the same medium without inhibitors.

Alternatively, a nutritive source may be selected to allow growth of only the desired organism(s), as with the use of gaseous nitrogen as a nitrogen source for *Azotobacter*, or the use of mannitol to grow *Az. chroococcum* and *Az. agilis* but not *Az. indicus* (Breed, Murray and Smith, 1957; Brown, Burlingham and Jackson, 1962).

Autotrophs, and particularly the nitrifiers (Winogradsky, 1891), have, over the years, been plated largely on silica gel media. These media are difficult to prepare, and have had various modifications

(Sterges, 1942*a*, *b*; Meiklejohn, 1950; Taylor, 1950; Funk and Krulwich, 1964). Alternative media utilize purified agar (Beijerinck, 1896; Engel and Alexander, 1958) or gypsum blocks (Omeliansky, 1899; Makrinov, 1910). Winogradsky (1925*a*) also proposed the use of silica gel for the study of other soil organisms such as *Azotobacter* species. Charpentier (1960) and Riviere (1961) employed modifications of this medium for the enumeration and isolation of cellulolytic soil organisms.

Winogradsky's initial attempts to isolate the nitrifying bacteria employed a 'negative plating' technique (Meiklejohn, 1950). This technique was based on the assumption that even though the nitrifiers did not form recognizable colonies on the gelatin medium which he was using, they must have been present on the plates and should produce growth if transferred from areas of medium between the visible colonies of other organisms to more suitable media. It is possible that this technique may yet hold promise for isolation of soil microorganisms, although not necessarily nitrifiers, by selection of areas of soil extract agar plates between visible colonies for transfer to highly nutritious or other specialized media. The author has observed that areas between colonies on soil extract agar soil dilution plates if stained by Dienes' L form stain and observed microscopically show microcolony growth similar to that pictured by Dienes and Weinberger (1951) for immature L form colonies.

The anaerobic and microaerophilic microflora of soil have been largely overlooked except for the clostridia which are relatively easy to isolate and cultivate (Emard and Vaughn, 1952; McClung, 1956; Skinner, 1960; Emtsev, 1962; Forget and Fredette, 1962; Sinclair and Stokes, 1964). Nonsporulating anaerobes of high oxygen sensitivity do not grow when the anaerobic plating techniques usually applied to soil samples are used. To properly evaluate these anaerobes, it might be advantageous to apply the techniques employed in the study of rumen anaerobes and discussed by Hungate (1950), Bryant (1959), Hungate (1960), Kistner (1960) and Kistner and Gouws (1964). Some of the microaerophilic and anaerobic bacteria also may not appear on dilution plates because of an increased requirement for carbon dioxide. Atmospheres containing 95 per cent $N_2$ and 5 per cent $CO_2$ are useful for culturing these organisms. If pyrogallic acid plus alkali is used to remove oxygen, the alkali should be $Na_2CO_3$ so that reasonable levels of $CO_2$ can be maintained in the atmosphere (Casida, 1965).

Psychrophilic bacteria are discussed by Ingraham (1958) and Ingraham and Stokes (1959). Upadhyay and Stokes (1962) describe the isolation of anaerobic psychrophilic bacteria from soil. Studies of thermophilic soil bacteria by Lajudie (1957) indicate that these bacteria may comprise as much as 1 per cent of the total soil bacterial flora.

Conventional plating of soil dilutions misses a recently described group of soil bacteria, viz. bacteria such as *Bdellovibrio* species parasitic on other bacteria (Stolp and Starr, 1963). To demonstrate these organisms, soil dilutions are passed through a 0·45 $\mu$ millipore filter, and the filtrates plated with a sensitive indicator bacterium in a manner analagous to that for obtaining and estimating numbers of bacteriophage. In both instances plaques are formed, but with *Bdellovibrio* species, the plaques require a longer period to form and once formed continue to increase in size.

Isolation and maintenance of *Bdellovibrio*-like bacteria from soil requires the use of a sensitive bacterial indicator strain and media which allow development of the parasite while slightly restricting the growth of the host bacteria. A limited study of the specificity range of *Bdellovibrio* for its host bacteria was presented by Stolp and Starr (1963). Thus, determinations of total numbers of these bacteria in soil and development of general techniques for their isolation require that species of indicator host bacteria be found which are parasitized by most of the variants of *Bdellovibrio*. Securing such indicator strains from soil may require special techniques since observations in the author's laboratory indicate the possibility that on many soil dilution plates the bacteria sensitive to these parasites may be devoured before they are able to form recognizable colonies.

## *EXTINCTION DILUTION TECHNIQUES*

The numbers of an organism which is present infrequently in soil can be estimated by the extinction dilution method if the organism possesses a unique and detectable metabolic reaction. Aliquots from a series of soil dilutions are inoculated into tubes of broth medium, usually at 5 or 10 tubes per soil dilution, and the tubes are incubated. The initial presence in a tube of 1 or more of the desired organisms is indicated by the occurrence after incubation of its unique metabolic reaction. It is assumed that tubes at the dilution endpoint for occurrence of the reaction represent inoculation with only 1 cell of the desired organism, and the numbers of tubes with and without growth of the desired organism around this endpoint are evaluated by comparison with most probable number tables to estimate the original numbers of this organism in soil. This procedure has found use in estimating numbers of nitrifying bacteria in soil by checking growth tubes initially containing ammonium or nitrite ion for the respective products of nitrification (Walker, Thorne and Brown, 1937; Coppier and Pochon, 1953; Thornton and Meiklejohn, 1957).

The extinction dilution method, with or without inhibitors in the medium, also finds use in estimating total numbers of soil bacteria or in isolation of bacteria present in high numbers in soil. The technique may be used in place of plating when one wishes to utilize media more nutritious than soil extract agar without problems of antibiosis or spreader growth. This procedure is especially adaptable to nutritionally fastidious soil organisms and particularly for those also showing poor competitive abilities with the rest of the soil population (James and Sutherland, 1940; Russell, 1950; Casida, 1965). Five or ten tubes per dilution are used, and the numbers of positive tubes per dilution at or near the growth endpoint are compared with most probable numbers tables to estimate total numbers of bacteria.

If one wishes to use this procedure to isolate soil bacteria, then a greater number of tubes, e.g. 50, are prepared for soil dilutions at or beyond the growth-dilution endpoint (Casida, 1965). Media showing growth must be streaked for purification because one cannot be certain that growth in an endpoint tube has actually resulted from the presence of a single cell.

This procedure also finds use in isolating soil micro-organisms which require a prolonged period to adapt to laboratory media or which must undergo some change, e.g. reversion from an L form, before growth can be expressed (Casida, 1965). Water does not evaporate from the medium and contamination is avoided if screw-cap tubes are used with the caps screwed tight. At intervals during incubation, the tubes, whether or not showing visible growth, are streaked on suitable agar media, or blind transfers of tubes lacking growth are made to fresh similar liquid media for incubation and later streaking (Sabin, 1941). This technique, with the inclusion of tiny agar slants beneath the liquid surface, was used by Casida (1965) to isolate bacteria which are present in high numbers in soil but which do not grow with conventional plating or dilution frequency procedures.

## *SYMBIOTIC GROWTH AND OTHER ASSOCIATIONS*

For proper evaluation, one should consider both or all components of a soil microbial association. However, most laboratory procedures for counting and isolating soil bacteria do not include this consideration. A few of the known associations and procedures of potential use in their study are listed. One organism may be removing and/or metabolizing the toxic metabolic products of another. In laboratory culture, the function of the latter organism is supplied to some extent by utilization of large Petri plates or other procedures for increasing diffusion from the colonies.

Provision by aerobic bacteria of anaerobic conditions for other more oxygen sensitive bacteria probably is of widespread occurrence in soil. It is possible that in some instances this association is due to the aerobic organism merely providing the anaerobic or microaerophilic organism with catalase or peroxidase to prevent the build-up of toxic levels of peroxides (McClung, 1956; Burton and Morita, 1964). These conditions are met in the laboratory by providing anaerobic cultural conditions and, possibly, by the additional incorporation of catalase into the growth medium (McClung, 1956; Mateles and Zuber, 1963; Burton and Morita, 1964; Ledford and Kosikowski, 1964). However, in establishing cultural conditions, one should also consider the possibility that one bacterium might provide another with a specific and narrow oxidation-reduction potential range which is required by the latter for growth.

Nutritional associations of soil micro-organisms are well known. In their simplest form these associations consist of one organism partially degrading a complex molecule to simpler compounds which are then available as nutrients for other micro-organisms. However, more subtle examples also have been documented. Lochhead and Burton (1953, 1956) described the 'terregens' factor produced by *Arthrobacter terregens* and required for growth by *Arthrobacter pascens*, which is also present in soil extract and certain laboratory nutrients. Lochhead and Chase (1943) and Lochhead and Burton (1957) isolated amino acid and vitamin requiring bacteria from the rhizosphere which depend on other rhizosphere bacteria for the synthesis of these growth factors. The nitrifying bacteria utilize ammonia resulting from microbial deamination of proteinaceous compounds and from nitrate reduction. In laboratory attempts to purify cultures of nitrifying bacteria, concurrent growth of heterotrophs utilizing organic compounds synthesized by the autotroph has been observed (Meiklejohn, 1950). It is possible also that in soil the heterotroph reverses the process by lowering the level of organic compounds in the vicinity of the growth of the autotroph and concurrently provides the reduced inorganic compounds required for autotrophic oxidations.

Obviously, many of these nutritional associations are circumvented by the usual laboratory media, particularly by those containing soil extract. However, one should consider the possibility of providing at least low levels of heat labile or as yet unrecognized growth factors. Sources of these may be found in non-heated (filter sterilized) soil extract or rumen fluid, yeast or other microbial autolyzates, plant extracts or filtrates of partially or fully grown laboratory cultures. Gaseous nutrients are beneficial in certain instances (Krasilnikov, 1958) and these may be provided by including actively metabolizing soil in a closed container with the cultures under study.

## *RE-INTRODUCTION OF BACTERIA INTO SOIL*

The obvious corollary to isolation of bacteria from soil is the re-introduction into soil of these same bacteria. This is of interest in studying the competitive abilities of organisms with the object of controlling plant pathogens by introduction of antagonists into soil. Also, it allows determination of the morphology of an organism in soil as contrasted to growth on laboratory media, and satisfying the rationale of Koch's postulates to show that a given isolate actually accomplishes in soil reactions attributed to it in the laboratory (Conn, 1917; Jensen, 1962). But how is one to determine that the introduced organism has survived in soil even though it may have been isolated from this environment? This is difficult to answer because most bacteria cannot with certainty be identified microscopically, and there is no guarantee that the bacterium will retain its cellular morphological characteristics when introduced into soil (Krasilnikov, 1958). One can, however, introduce a large population of bacteria and then re-isolate the organism on the assumption that one can recognize its colony morphology, pigmentation, immunofluorescence (Wagner and Unger, 1963) or other characteristics.

Two techniques which have been applied in limited instances to fungi may find use for bacteria. As mentioned previously, Schmidt and Bankole (1962) labelled *Aspergillus flavus* antiserum with fluorescein so as to use ultraviolet fluorescence microscopy to follow the spread of or identity of this organism in sterile soil. However, non-specific absorption and autofluorescence are likely to hamper the use of this technique with bacteria. Grossbard (1958) labelled a fungus with caesium-137 and cobalt-60 before introduction into soil. After incubation, the soil was placed in proximity to X-ray film to locate the position of the fungus. The short life span of the bacterial cell and rapid death of a considerable portion of the population on introduction into soil may rule out application of this technique to bacteria since the radioactivity likely to occur would be picked up by other soil micro-organisms within a relatively short time. However, this diffusion of radioactivity presents little difficulty in studies concerning the incorporation of bacterial cellular material into humus as shown in studies by Mayaudon and Simonart (1963) and Simonart (1964) utilizing $^{14}C$-labelled cells.

## *SOIL RESPIRATION AND ENZYMATIC ACTIVITY*

Soil respiration has been measured by trapping evolved carbon dioxide in alkali (Fred and Waksman, 1928; Gray and Wallace, 1957; Soulides and Allison, 1961), or by using the Warburg apparatus or similar instruments (Rovira, 1953; Katznelson and Stevenson, 1956; Katznelson and Rouatt, 1957; Gilmour, Damsky and Bollen, 1958; Stotzky, 1960) to measure either soil oxygen uptake or carbon dioxide evolution. For larger soil samples, Wieringa (1958) devised a soil respirometer in which oxygen was supplied by electrolysis of water, and the hydrogen evolved measured manometrically.

Soil respiration has also been measured by adding tetrazolium dyes, particularly, 2, 3, 5-triphenyltetrazolium chloride, to soil followed by anaerobic incubation. The dye serves as the electron acceptor of respiration and in the process is reduced to the coloured, water insoluble formazan. The latter is extracted from the soil with methanol or a similar solvent and the colour density determined colorimetrically (Lenhard, 1956; Stevenson, 1959; Casida *et al.*, 1964).

Specific activities of microbial and other enzymes in soil have been determined by adding the respective substrate, incubating and evaluating residual substrate or product formed. Techniques are available for catalase, peroxidase, invertase, amylase, tyrosinase, phosphatase, urease, phenolase, asparaginase, protease and $\beta$-glucosidase (Krasilnikov, 1958; Hofmann, 1963). In addition, reaction rates of oxidative enzymes have been measured in soil percolation or similar vessels (Audus, 1946; Lees, 1949; Temple, 1951; Bryner *et al.*, 1954; Greenwood and Lees, 1959).

These techniques all possess a similar fault in that they measure soil enzymatic activities in addition to those of microbial origin. Respiration and other enzymatic activities are general characteristics of the flora and fauna (both macro- and micro-) of the soil. Hence, the sum of these activities is measured in the above determinations. Addition of toluene to soil to kill micro-organisms and higher forms of life liberates enzymes by autolysis (Hofmann and Niggemann, 1953; Drobnik, 1961), and the toluene itself serves as a nutrient for certain bacteria causing a 'bloom' of growth and a consequent increase in soil enzyme activity.

Dead cells in soil apparently retain some enzymatic activity as shown by studies in which soil has been subjected to gamma radiation (McLaren, Luse and Skujins, 1962; Peterson, 1962). In addition, it has been proposed that a backlog of active, 'free' enzymes occurs in soil (Hofmann, 1963*a*), although these enzymes have not been recovered from soil (Hofmann, 1963*b*). Thus, by various techniques one can measure respiratory and other enzymatic activities occurring in soil, but must consider that the information gained is an overall evaluation of soil biological activities and not necessarily limited to living microorganisms.

## *REFERENCES*

ALEXANDER, M. (1961). *Introduction to soil microbiology*. New York. Wiley.

ALEXANDER, F. E. S. & JACKSON, R. M. (1954). Examination of soil micro-organisms in their natural environment. *Nature, Lond.*, **174**, 750.

ALLEN, O. N. (1957). *Experiments in soil bacteriology*, 3rd Edn. Minneapolis. Burgess Publishing Co.

ARISTOVSKAYA, T. V. & PARINKINA, O. M. (1961). Methods for the study of soil microbial communities. *Pochvovedenie*, No. 1, 20.

ARISTOVSKAYA, T. V. & PARINKINA, O. M. (1962). Study of microbial populations of soils of the Leningrad region. *Microbiologiya*, **31**, 385.

AUDUS, L. J. (1946). A new soil perfusion apparatus. *Nature, Lond.*, **158**, 419.

BEIJERINCK, W. M. (1896). Kulturversuche mit Amöben auf festem Substrate. *Zentbl. Bakt. ParasitKde., Abt. I*, **19**, 257.

BREED, R. S., MURRAY, E. G. D. & SMITH, N. R. (1957). *Bergey's manual of determinative bacteriology*, 7th Edn. Baltimore. Williams & Wilkins Co.

BROCKMAN, E. R. & BOYD, W. L. (1963). Myxobacteria from soils of the Alaskan and Canadian Arctic. *J. Bact.*, **86**, 605.

BROWN, M. E., BURLINGHAM, S. K. & JACKSON, R. M. (1962). Studies on *Azotobacter* species in soil. 1. Comparison of media and techniques for counting *Azotobacter* in soil. *Pl. Soil*, **17**, 309.

BRYANT, M. P. (1959). Bacterial species of the rumen. *Bact. Rev.*, **23**, 125.

BRYNER, L. C., BECK, J. V., DAVIS, D. B. & WILSON, D. G. (1954). Microorganisms in leaching sulfide minerals. *Ind. Engng Chem. Analyt. Edn*, **46**, 2587.

BURTON, S. D. & MORITA, R. Y. (1964). Effect of catalase and cultural conditions on growth of *Beggiatoa*. *J. Bact.*, **88**, 1755.

CASIDA, L. E. Jr. (1962*a*). On the isolation and growth of individual microbial cells from soil. *Can. J. Microbiol.*, **8**, 115.

CASIDA, L. E. Jr. (1962*b*). Illumination of micromanipulator tools in ultraviolet fluorescence microscopy. *J. Bact.*, **84**, 1343.

CASIDA, L. E. Jr. (1965). An abundant microorganism in soil. *Appl. Microbiol.*, **13**, 327.

CASIDA, L. E. Jr., KLEIN, D. A. & SANTORO, T. (1964). Soil dehydrogenase activity. *Soil Sci.*, **98**, 371.

CHANDRA, P. & BOLLEN, W. B. (1960). Effects of potassium gibberellate (Gibrel) on nitrification and sulfur oxidation in different Oregon soils. *Appl. Microbiol.*, **8**, 31.

Charpentier, M. (1960). The distribution of cellulolytic organisms in soil. I. Techniques. *Annls Inst. Pasteur, Paris*, **99**, 153.

Cholodny, N. (1930). Über eine neue Methode zur Untersuchung des Bodenmikroflora. *Arch. Mikrobiol.*, **1**, 620.

Clark, F. E. (1940). Notes on types of bacteria associated with plant roots. *Trans. Kans. Acad. Sci.*, **43**, 75.

Conn, H. J. (1917). The proof of microbial agency in the chemical transformation of soil. *Science, N.Y.*, **46**, 252.

Conn, H. J. (1918). The microscopic study of bacteria and fungi in soil. *N.Y. State Agr. Expt. Sta. Tech. Bull.*, **64**.

Conn, H. J. (1948). The most abundant groups of bacteria in soil. *Bact. Rev.*, **12**, 257.

Conn, H. J. & Darrow, M.A. (1935). Characteristics of certain bacteria belonging to the autochthonous microflora of soil. *Soil Sci.*, **39**, 95.

Coppier, O. & Pochon, J. (1953). Investigations on nitrification in relation to the microflora. *Trans. int. Soc. Soil Sci., Comm. II & IV 1952, Dublin*, **2**, 52.

Darken, M. A. (1961). Application of fluorescent brighteners in biological techniques. *Science, N.Y.*, **133**, 1704.

Darken, M. A. (1962). Absorption and transport of fluorescent brighteners by microorganisms. *Appl. Microbiol.*, **10**, 387.

Dienes, L. & Weinberger, H. J. (1951). The L forms of bacteria. *Bact. Rev.*, **15**, 245.

Dowell, V. R. Jr., Hill, E. O. & Altemeir, W. A. (1964). Use of phenethyl alcohol in media for isolation of anaerobic bacteria. *J. Bact.*, **88**, 1811.

Drobnik, J. (1961). On the role of toluene in the measurement of the activity of soil enzymes. *Pl. Soil*, **14**, 94.

Durbin, R. D. (1961). Techniques for the observation and isolation of soil microorganisms. *Bot. Rev.*, **27**, 522.

Emard, L. O. & Vaughn, R. H. (1952). Selectivity of sorbic acid media for the catalase negative lactic acid bacteria and clostridia. *J. Bact.*, **63**, 487.

Emtsev, V. T. (1962). Quantitative determination of anaerobic nitrogen-fixing butyric-acid bacteria of the genus *Clostridium* in soil. *Microbiologiya*, **31**, 288.

Engel, M. S. & Alexander, M. (1958). Growth and autotrophic metabolism of *Nitrosomonas europaea*. *J. Bact.*, **76**, 217.

Flint, E. A. & Stout, J. D. (1960). Microbiology of some soils from Antarctica. *Nature, Lond.*, **188**, 767.

Forget, A. & Fredette, V. (1962). Sodium azide selective medium for the primary isolation of anaerobic bacteria. *J. Bact.*, **83**, 1217.

Foster, J. W. (1964). General biology in the Soviet Union. *Bioscience*, **14**, 15.

Fred, E. B. & Waksman, S. A. (1928). *Laboratory manual of general microbiology.* New York. McGraw Hill.

Funk, H. B. & Krulwich, T. A. (1964). Preparation of clear silica gels that can be streaked. *J. Bact.*, **88**, 1200.

Gamble, S. J. R., Edminster, T. W. & Orcutt, F. S. (1952). Influence of double-cut plow mulch tillage on number and activity of microorganisms. *Proc. Soil Sci. Soc. Am.*, **16**, 267.

Gilmore, A. E. (1959). A soil sampling tube for soil microbiology. *Soil Sci.*, **87**, 95.

Gilmour, C. M., Damsky, L. & Bollen, W. G. (1958). Manometric gas analysis as an index of microbial oxidations and reductions in soil. *Can. J. Microbiol.*, **4**, 287.

GOODING, T. H. & MCCALLA, T. M. (1945). Loss of carbon dioxide and ammonia from crop residues during decomposition. *Proc. Soil Sci. Soc. Am.*, **10**, 185.

GRAY, T. R. G. (1963). Media for the enumeration and isolation of heterotrophic salt-marsh bacteria. *J. gen. Microbiol.*, **31**, 483.

GRAY, P. H. H. & WALLACE, R. H. (1957). Correlation between bacterial numbers and carbon dioxide in a field soil. *Can. J. Microbiol.*, **3**, 191.

GREENWOOD, D. J. & LEES, H. An electrolytic rocking percolator. *Pl. Soil*, **11**, 87.

GROSSBARD, E. (1958). Autoradiography of fungi through a layer of soil and in agar culture. *Nature, Lond.*, **182**, 854.

GUNDERSON, K. (1955). Observations on mixed cultures of *Nitrosomonas* and heterotrophic soil bacteria. *Pl. Soil*, **7**, 26.

HERR, L. J., WEAVER, C. R. & HORST, R. K. (1961). A soil dilution procedure applicable to rhizosphere microorganism assays. *Can. J. Microbiol.*, **7**, 277.

HOFMANN, E. (1963*a*). The origin and importance of enzymes in soil. *Recent Prog. Microbiol.*, **8**, 216.

HOFMANN, E. (1963*b*). Synthetic effects of soil enzymes. *Recent Prog. Microbiol.*, **8**, 230.

HOFMANN, E. & NIGGEMANN, J. (1953). Über das Enzymsystem unserer Kulturboden. *Biochem. Z.*, **324**, 308.

HOMRIGHAUSEN, E. & ROHMER, W. (1959). Investigations on various techniques of dispersion as pre-treatment for microbial counts in soil by fluorescence microscopy. *Landw. Forsch.*, **12**, 253.

HUNGATE, R. E. (1950). The anaerobic mesophilic cellulolytic bacteria. *Bact. Rev.*, **14**, 1.

HUNGATE, R. E. (1960). Symposium: selected topics in microbial ecology. I. Microbial ecology of the rumen. *Bact. Rev.*, **24**, 353.

IMSHENETSKY, A. A. (1946). Symbiosis between myxobacteria and nitrifying bacteria. *Nature, Lond.*, **157**, 877.

INGRAHAM, J. L. (1958). Growth of psychrophilic bacteria. *J. Bact.*, **76**, 75.

INGRAHAM, J. L. & STOKES, J. L. (1959). Psychrophilic bacteria. *Bact. Rev.*, **23**, 97.

JAGNOW, G. (1961). Numbers and types of bacteria from the rhizosphere of pasture plants: possible occurrence of L-forms. *Nature, Lond.*, **191**, 1220.

JAMES, N. (1958). Soil extract in soil microbiology. *Can. J. Microbiol.*, **4**, 363.

JAMES, N. (1959). Plate counts of bacteria and fungi in a saline soil. *Can. J. Microbiol.*, **5**, 431.

JAMES, N. & SUTHERLAND, M. L. (1940). Effects of numbers of colonies per plate on the estimate of the bacterial population in soil. *Can. J. Res. C*, **18**, 347.

JENSEN, V. (1962). Studies on the microflora of Danish beech forest soils. I. The dilution plate count technique for the enumeration of bacteria and fungi in soil. *Zentbl. Bakt. ParasitKde., Abt. II*, **116**, 13.

JENSEN, H. L. (1963). The influence of herbicidic chemicals on soil metabolism and the zymogenic soil microflora. *Recent Prog. Microbiol.*, **8**, 249.

JOHNSON, L. F., CURL, E. A., BOND, J. H. & FRIBOURG, H. A. (1959). *Methods for studying soil microflora–plant disease relationships*. Minneapolis. Burgess Publishing Co.

JONES, P. C. T. & MOLLISON, J. E. (1948). A technique for the quantitative estimation of soil micro-organisms. *J. gen. Microbiol.*, **2**, 54.

KATZNELSON, H. (1963). Effect of chemical and biological control measures on soil micro-organisms. *Recent Prog. Microbiol.*, **8**, 247.

KATZNELSON, H., LOCHHEAD, A. G. & TIMONIN, M. I. (1948). Soil microorganisms and the rhizosphere. *Bot. Rev.*, **14**, 543.

KATZNELSON, H. & ROUATT, J. W. (1957). Manometric studies with rhizosphere and non-rhizosphere soil. *Can. J. Microbiol.*, **3**, 673.

KATZNELSON, H. & STEVENSON, I. L. (1956). Observations on the metabolic activity of the soil microflora. *Can. J. Microbiol.*, **2**, 611.

KISTNER, A. (1960). An improved method for viable counts of bacteria of the bovine rumen which ferment carbohydrates. *J. gen. Microbiol.*, **23**, 565.

KISTNER, A. & GOUWS, L. (1964). Cellulolytic cocci occurring in the rumen of sheep conditioned to lucerne hay. *J. gen. Microbiol.*, **34**, 447.

KRASILNIKOV, N. A. (1958). *Soil microorganisms and higher plants*. Acad. Sci., USSR. Translation by Y. Halperin (1961). Israel program for scientific translations. Washington. U.S.Dept.Commerce.

LAIDLAW, P. P. & ELFORD, W. J. (1936). A new group of filterable organisms. *Proc. R. Soc. B*, **120**, 292.

LAJUDIE, J. (1957). Quantitative techniques for the study of thermophilic soil bacteria. *Pédologie, Gand, No. spéc.*, **7**, 112.

LEDFORD, R. A. & KOSIKOWSKI, F. V. (1964). Anaerobiosis produced by glucose oxidase to control growth of test bacteria in antibiotic assays. *J. Dairy Sci.*, **47**, 758.

LEES, H. (1949). The soil percolation technique. *Soil and Sci.*, **1**, 221.

LEES, H. & QUASTEL, J. H. (1946). Biochemistry of nitrification in soil. 2. The site of soil nitrification. *Biochem. J.*, **40**, 815.

LEHNER, A. & NOWAK, W. (1959). New results of the direct determination of soil bacteria by a combined growth and fluorochromation technique. *Zentbl. Bakt. ParasitKde., Abt. II*, **113**, 32.

LEHNER, A., NOWAK, W. & SEIBOLD, L. (1958). An improved combination-technique for the fluorochromation of soil using acridine orange. *Landw. Forsch.*, **11**, 121.

LENHARD, G. (1956). Die Dehydrogenaseaktivitat des Bodens als Mass für Mikroorganisementatigkeit in Boden. *Z. PflErnähr. Düng. Bodenk.*, **73**, 1.

LOCHHEAD, A. G. & BURTON, M. O. (1953). An essential growth factor produced by microbial synthesis. *Can. J. Bot.*, **31**, 7.

LOCHHEAD, A. G. & BURTON, M. O. (1956). Incidence in soil of bacteria requiring vitamin $B_{12}$ and the terregens factor. *Soil Sci.*, **82**, 237.

LOCHHEAD, A. G. & BURTON, M. O. (1957). Qualitative studies of soil microorganisms. XIV. Specific vitamin requirements of the predominant bacterial flora. *Can. J. Microbiol.*, **3**, 35.

LOCHHEAD, A. G. & CHASE, F. E. (1943). Qualitative studies of soil microorganisms. V. Nutritional requirements of the predominant bacterial flora. *Soil Sci.*, **55**, 185.

LU, K. C. & BOLLEN, W. B. (1958). Effect of Gibrel, a potassium salt of gibberellic acid, on microbial activities in soil. *Pl. Soil*, **9**, 318.

LU, K. C., GILMOUR, C. M., ZAGALLO, A. C. & BOLLEN, W. B. (1958). Effects of gibberellic acid on soil microorganisms. *Nature, Lond.*, **181**, 189.

MACAULAY INSTITUTE FOR SOIL RESEARCH (1959). *Rep. Macaulay Inst. Soil Res.*, 1958–1959, 37.

MACURA, J. & MÁLEK, I. (1958). Continuous-flow method for the study of microbiological processes in soil samples. *Nature, Lond.*, **182**, 1796.

MAKRINOV, J. (1910). Magnesia-Gipsplatten und Magnesia-Platten mit organischer Substanz als sehr geeignetes festes Substrat für die Kultur der Nitrifikationsorganismen. *Zentbl. Bakt. ParasitKde., Abt. II*, **24**, 415.

MATELES, R. I. & ZUBER, B. L. (1963). Effect of exogenous catalase on the aerobic growth of clostridia. *Antonie van Leeuwenhoek*, **29**, 249.

MAYAUDON, J. & SIMONART, P. (1963). Humification of soil microorganisms labelled with $C^{14}$. *Annls Inst. Pasteur, Paris*, **105**, 257.

McCLUNG, L. S. (1956). The anaerobic bacteria with special reference to the genus *Clostridium*. *A. Rev. Microbiol.*, **10**, 173.

McLAREN, A. D., LUSE, R. A. & SKUJINS, J. J. (1962). Sterilization of soil by irradiation and some further observations on soil enzyme activity. *Proc. Soil Sci. Soc. Am.*, **26**, 371.

MEIKLEJOHN, J. (1950). The isolation of *Nitrosomonas europaea* in pure culture. *J. gen. Microbiol.*, **4**, 185.

MEIKLEJOHN, J. (1950). Numbers of bacteria and actinomycetes in a Kenya soil. *J. Soil Sci.*, **8**, 240.

MENZIES, J. D. (1957). A dipper technique for serial dilutions of soil for microbial analysis. *Proc. Soil Sci. Soc. Am.*, **21**, 660.

MICEV, N. (1958). The role and significance of $CO_2$ as an ecological factor in the culture and propagation of the soil microflora. *Zemlj. Biljka*, **7**, 241.

MINDERMAN, G. (1956). The preparation of microtome sections of unaltered soil for the study of soil organisms *in situ*. *Pl. Soil*, **8**, 42.

MONTUELLE, B. & CHEMINAIS, L. (1964). Synthesis of substances of the gibberellin group by bacteria. *C. r. Seanc. Soc. Biol.*, **258**, 6016.

NORMAN, A. G. (1951). Role of soil microorganisms in nutrient availability. In *Mineral nutrition of plants*. Ed. Truog, E. Madison. University of Wisconsin Press.

OMELIANSKY, W. L. (1899). Magnesia-Gipsplatten als neues estes Substrat für die Kultur des Nitrifikationsorganismen. *Zentbl. Bakt. ParasitKde., Abt. II*, **5**, 652.

ORCUTT, F. S. (1940). Methods for more accurately comparing plate counts of bacteria. *J. Bact.*, **39**, 100.

PARINKINA, O. M. (1963). Determination of the time for which pedoscopes must be exposed in soil in order to reveal the microbial population. *Microbiologiya*, **32**, 99.

PETERSON, G. H. (1962). Respiration of soil sterilized by ionizing radiations. *Soil Sci.*, **94**, 71.

POCHON, J. (1954). *Manuel technique d'analyse microbiologique du sol*. Paris. Masson et Cie.

PRAMER, D. & SCHMIDT, E. L. (1964). *Experimental soil microbiology*. Minneapolis. Burgess Publishing Co.

RIVIERE, J. (1961). Isolation and purification of aerobic cellulose-decomposing bacteria in soil. *Annls Inst. Pasteur, Paris*, **101**, 253.

ROSSI, G. & RICCARDO, S. (1927). L'esame microscopico e bacteriologico diretto del terreno agrario. *Nuovi Annali Minist. Agric.*, **7**, 457.

ROVIRA, A. (1953). Use of the Warburg apparatus in soil metabolism studies. *Nature, Lond.*, **172**, 29.

RUSSELL, E. W. (1950). *Soil conditions and plant growth*, 8th Edn. New York. Longmans, Green and Co.

SABIN, A. B. (1941). The filterable microorganisms of the pleuropneumonia group. *Bact. Rev.*, **5**, 1.

SACKS, L. E. & ALDERTON, G. (1961). Behavior of bacterial spores in aqueous polymer two-phase systems. *J. Bact.*, **82**, 331.

SCHMIDT, E. L. & BANKOLE, R. O. (1962). Detection of *Aspergillus flavus* in soil by immunofluorescent staining. *Science, N.Y.*, **136**, 776.

SEIFERT, Y. (1958). The use of fluorescence microscopy in soil microbiology. *Pochvovedenie*, No. 2, 50.

SIMONART, P. (1964). Microorganisms and humus. *Annls Inst. Pasteur, Paris*, Suppl. No. **3**, 7.

SINCLAIR, N. A. & STOKES, J. L. (1964). Isolation of obligately anaerobic psychrophilic bacteria. *J. Bact.*, **87**, 562.

SKINNER, F. A. (1960). The isolation of anaerobic cellulose-decomposing bacteria from soil. *J. gen. Microbiol.*, **22**, 539.

SKINNER, F. A., JONES, P. C. T. & MOLLISON, J. E. (1952). A comparison of a direct- and a plate-counting technique for the quantitative estimation of soil micro-organisms. *J. gen. Microbiol.*, **6**, 261.

SOULIDES, D. A. & ALLISON, F. E. (1961). Effect of drying and freezing soils on carbon dioxide production, available mineral nutrients, aggregation, and bacterial population. *Soil Sci.*, **91**, 291.

STARKEY, R. L. (1958). Interrelations between microorganisms and plant roots in the rhizosphere. *Bact. Rev.*, **22**, 154.

STERGES, A. J. (1942*a*). Simplified method for the preparation of silica gels. *J. Bact.*, **44**, 138.

STERGES, A. J. (1942*b*). Adaptability of silica gel as a culture medium. *J. Bact.*, **43**, 317.

STEVENSON, I. L. (1956). Some observations on the microbial activity in remoistened air-dried soils. *Pl. Soil*, **8**, 170.

STEVENSON, I. L. (1958). The effect of sonic vibration on the bacterial plate count of soil. *Pl. Soil*, **10**, 1.

STEVENSON, I. L. (1959). Dehydrogenase activity in soils. *Can. J. Microbiol.*, **5**, 229.

STOLP, H. & STARR, M. P. (1963). *Bdellovibrio bacteriovorus* gen. et sp. n., a predatory, ectoparasitic, and bacteriolytic microorganism. *Antonie van Leeuwenhoek*, **29**, 217.

STOTZKY, G. (1960). A simple method for the determination of the respiratory quotient of soils. *Can. J. Microbiol.*, **6**, 439.

STOTZKY, G., GOOS, R. D. & TIMONIN, M. I. (1962). Microbial changes occurring in soil as a result of storage. *Pl. Soil*, **16**, 1.

STRUGGER, S. (1948). Fluorescence microscope examination of bacteria in soil. *Can. J. Res.*, *C*, **26**, 188.

TAYLOR, C. B. (1936). Short period fluctuations in the numbers of bacterial cells in soil. *Proc. R. Soc. B.*, **119**, 269.

TAYLOR, C. B. (1938). Further studies of *Bacterium globiforme* and the incidence of this type of organism in Canadian soils. *Soil Sci.*, **46**, 307.

TAYLOR, C. B. (1950). An improved method for the preparation of silica gel media for microbiological purposes. *J. gen. Microbiol.*, **4**, 235.

TAYLOR, C. B. & LOCHHEAD, A. G. (1937). A study of *Bacterium globiforme* Conn in soils differing in fertility. *Can. J. Res. C*, **15**, 340.

TCHAN, Y. (1947). As reported in Pochon, J., and Tchan, Y. (1948). *Précis de microbiologie du sol*. Paris. Masson et Cie.

TEMPLE, K. L. (1951). A modified design of the Lees soil percolation apparatus. *Soil Sci.*, **71**, 209.

THORNTON, H. G. (1923). On the vibration method of obtaining a suspension of the bacteria in a soil sample, developed by C. L. Whittles. *J. agric. Sci.*, **13**, 352.

THORNTON, H. G. & GRAY, P. H. H. (1934). The numbers of bacterial cells in field soils, as estimated by the ratio method. *Proc. R. Soc. B*, **115**, 522.

THORNTON, H. G. & MEIKLEJOHN, J. (1957). Soil microbiology. *A. Rev. Microbiol.*, **11**, 123.

TOPPING, L. E. (1958). The predominant microorganisms in soils. II. The relative abundance of the different types of organisms obtained by plating, and the relation of the plate to total counts. *Zentbl. Bakt. ParasitKde.*, *Abt. II*, **98**, 193.

TYAGNY-RYADNO, M. G. (1962). Microflora of soil aggregates, and plant nutrition. *Izv. Akad. Nauk Ser. Biol.*, **2**, 242.

UPADHYAY, J. & STOKES, J. L. (1962). Anaerobic growth of psychrophilic bacteria. *J. Bact.*, **83**, 270.

VANČURA, V. (1961). Detection of gibberellic acid in *Azotobacter* cultures. *Nature, Lond.*, **192**, 88.

WAGNER, M. & UNGER, H. (1963). Staining of bacterial colonies with fluorescent antibodies. A method of macroscopic observation and quantitative evaluation of immune fluorescence. *Zentbl. Bakt. ParasitKde., Abt. I*, **189**, 482.

WAKSMAN, S. A. (1922*a*). Microbiological analysis of soil as an index of soil fertility: I. The mathematical interpretation of numbers of microorganisms in the soil. *Soil Sci.*, **14**, 81.

WAKSMAN, S. A. (1922*b*). Microbiological analysis of soil as an index of soil fertility: II. Methods of the study of numbers of microorganisms in the soil. *Soil Sci.*, **22**, 283.

WAKSMAN, S. A. (1922*c*). Microbiological analysis of soil as an index of soil fertility: III. Influence of fertilization upon numbers of microorganisms in the soil. *Soil Sci.*, **14**, 321.

WAKSMAN, S. A. (1927). *Principles of soil microbiology*. Baltimore. Williams and Wilkins Co.

WALKER, R. H., THORNE, D. W. & BROWN, P. E. (1937). The numbers of ammonia-oxidizing organisms in soils as influenced by soil management practices. *J. Am. Soc. Agron.*, **29**, 854.

WEBLEY, D. M. & DUFF, R. B. (1962). A technique for investigating localized microbial development in soils. *Nature, Lond.*, **194**, 364.

WHITTLES, C. L. (1923). The determination of the number of bacteria in soil. *J. agric. Sci.*, **13**, 18.

WIERINGA, K. T. (1958). The problems of standardization of methods in use in microbiological soil research. *Neth. J. agric. Sci.*, **6**, 61.

WINOGRADSKY, S. (1891). Recherches sur les organismes de la nitrification. *Annls Inst. Pasteur, Paris*, **5**, 92.

WINOGRADSKY, S. (1924). Sur la microflore autochtone de la terre arable. *C. r. hebd. Acad. Sci. Seanc., Paris*, **178**, 1236.

WINOGRADSKY, S. (1925*a*). Sur une methode pour apprecier le pouvoir fixateur de l'azote dans les terres. *C. r. hebd. Acad. Sci. Seanc., Paris*, **180**, 711.

WINOGRADSKY, S. (1925*b*). Etudes sur la microbiologie du sol. I. Sur la méthode. *Annls Inst. Pasteur, Paris*, **39**, 299.

WOOD, E. J. F. (1958). The significance of marine microbiology. *Bact. Rev.*, **22**, 1.

ZOBELL, C. E. (1946). *Marine microbiology*. Waltham. Chronica Botanica Co.

ZVYAGINTSEV, D. G. (1962*a*). The question of the adsorption of microorganisms by soil particles. *Pochvovedenie*, No. 2, 19.

ZVYAGINTSEV, D. G. (1962*b*). Study of rhizosphere microflora by means of fluorescence microscopy in reflected light. *Microbiologiya*, **31**, 111.

# ENRICHMENT TECHNIQUES AND THE ELECTIVE CULTIVATION OF BACTERIA

J. POCHON and P. TARDIEUX

*Institut Pasteur, Paris*

## *INTRODUCTION*

When considering the ecology of soil micro-organisms, it is unrealistic to try to separate bacteria from other living organisms, particularly algae, fungi and, above all, animals. The soil is an interconnected biological system. It is equally unrealistic to determine the number, activity and metabolic characters of soil bacteria in laboratory cultures, away from their natural environment; both the physical and chemical conditions in the soil are important. Indeed, artefacts arising from distortions of the natural environment have been the basis of much criticism of soil bacteriology and the feeling that the only valid and objective tests are the analyses of chemical changes associated with bacterial metabolism. This is an extreme viewpoint; nevertheless, it is essential to define the problems and to state clearly what one expects from qualitative and quantitative studies of the activities of soil bacteria.

Classical bacteriological methods are based upon the isolation of pure cultures and on the analysis of the behaviour of these cultures in the laboratory. Such methods have been widely adopted by soil micro-biologists and have led to important discoveries. They remain the only way of revealing the potentialities of all the species present in the soil; but they reveal only the potentialities. It is clear that all soil organisms, especially the bacteria, when competing with one another, do not realize their potentialities equally; the activity of a particular organism at any one time is determined by a balance between the physiological requirements of the organism and the environmental conditions; many bacteria that are dormant in the soil become active when examined in the laboratory.

In contrast with the classical techniques, ecological methods which view the soil as a whole have been used, following the work of Wino-gradsky. The large and varied microbial population allowed the soil to be treated as a living organism. The co-ordination of the population led to a concept of 'organization', comparable with that applied to higher organisms. Thus the idea of *functional groups* changed the problem from one at the cellular or species level to one concerning 'organs'. Not only did this present new possibilities for analysis, but it required the development of a new methodology.

Essentially, the purpose of this methodology is to determine functional groups. These are defined as 'populations of bacteria, possibly consisting of systematically unrelated forms, which have a common physiological (biochemical or metabolic) property, enabling them to act together'. Thus we are dealing with population bacteriology, not species bacteriology.

The methods used must not only detect particular functional groups, but must also determine the approximate numbers of bacteria in each group, in a given soil, at any given moment, and ultimately give an idea of the activity of each group. Activity depends not only on the number of bacteria within a group, but also on the level of their metabolism and their growth rate. Furthermore, the methods must provide a common basis for the assessment of all functional groups. This is essential if comparisons between different groups in the same habitat are to be made.

Investigations based upon such principles usually involve the use of enrichment techniques and elective media, i.e. media containing chemicals which allow the development of bacteria with a definite physiological property. An example of such a medium is one with no combined nitrogen. This medium will support only the growth of bacteria which can fix atmospheric nitrogen and hence utilize the other materials in the medium. Again, a medium where the sole source of carbon is cellulose or starch can be used to demonstrate cellulolytic or amylolytic groups of micro-organisms.

It is clear that if one were to inoculate such media with the whole soil microflora, there would be an enrichment in each of them, the elective cultivation of a definite functional group. The purpose of this paper is to describe how such a method, devised at the *Institut Pasteur*, can be used quantitatively, enabling one to estimate the activity of most groups.

Enrichment techniques are, of course, mainly useful for the first step in the isolation and subsequent examination, in pure culture, of the many bacteria in soil. Many micro-organisms that carry out important activities in the soil are not present in very large numbers, e.g. nitrogen fixing bacteria, nitrifiers and the bacteria that contribute to the breakdown of some complex organic substances. In such cases, one can try to increase the numbers of the particular bacteria in the soil before inoculating synthetic media with an appropriate dilution of a soil suspension. Usually, enrichment is achieved by the use of special media, devised to stimulate the growth of a single species, a small number of species or a functional group.

## *TECHNIQUES OF ENRICHMENT IN THE SOIL ITSELF*

Every change in the environmental conditions (transport of soil to the laboratory and incubation under controlled conditions of aeration, temperature and humidity) causes a change in the biological equilibrium, rapid and marked in some instances, so that some species and groups are preferentially stimulated and others preferentially suppressed. During the enrichment process, the action of these factors is combined with the introduction of a more-or-less specific substrate into the soil.

### *Functional groups in the nitrogen cycle*

*Free-living nitrogen fixing bacteria.* Preferential stimulation of free-living, aerobic or anaerobic, nitrogen fixing bacteria is easily achieved in the soil itself by using Winogradsky's soil block method, incorporating a suitable carbon source in the soil. Glucose, sucrose, mannitol and sodium pyruvate give the best results. When the soil is water-saturated, species of *Clostridium* usually develop, causing expansion of the sample and the production of a characteristic butyric odour.

The appearance of rows of *Azotobacter* colonies on the smooth soil surface is not only dependent on the presence of these bacteria in the sample. If the specimen is deficient in calcium or phosphate, either one or both must be added to allow enrichment; thus the test may be used to demonstrate available phosphate deficiency. Conversely, it has also been observed that an excess of phosphate will restrict the development of *Azotobacter* in some soils. Early development of *Clostridium*, and the consequent production of acid, may also interfere with the enrichment of *Azotobacter*.

*Proteolytic and ammonifying bacteria.* The breakdown of proteins in the soil and the production of ammonia which accompanies it, are the work of a widespread and varied microflora. For each soil, however, and for each type of nitrogenous substance, there is only a relatively restricted range of species that is active *in situ* in the process of mineralization. The addition of natural plant or animal proteins to soil does not stimulate all the proteolytic species *in vitro*, but only those most fitted to compete for the substrate in the particular environment. For this reason, techniques of enrichment in the soil have been developed which allow a more certain identification of the active species.

Thus, the incorporation of pieces of fresh, sterile guinea-pig liver or kidney into soil in a Petri dish or Borrel flask initiates a succession of zymogenous bacteria (Pochon and Chalvignac, 1952). Gram-positive, sporeforming bacteria appear at first, sporulating after a few days and then giving way to non-sporeforming, Gram-negative rods, particularly species of *Pseudomonas* and *Achromobacter*. Anaerobic forms are comparatively unimportant at this stage, unless the soil is water-saturated or at a temperature above 30°. At the same time, tests show that bacteria attacking the breakdown products of complex proteins, e.g. polypeptides and amino acids, and not the proteins themselves are also enriched. Both groups of organisms participate in nitrogen mineralization, and produce ammonia, but they act at different stages in the breakdown chain.

The addition of natural, highly nitrogenous substances, such as vegetable meal, dried blood, casein hydrolysate and urea, have also been used for the study of factors controlling ammonification and for enrichment of ammonifiers (Löhnis and Green, 1914; Pochon and Tchan, 1947). Percolation techniques may also be used for the same purposes in the study of soluble proteins, peptones, polypeptides and amino acids in solution (Voets, Vorger and Coolsaet, 1955; Greenwood and Lees, 1956, 1960).

*Nitrifying bacteria*. The autotrophic nitrifying bacteria are slow growing forms which never form large populations in the soil; they cannot be detected, isolated or studied without considerable enrichment. Consequently, many of the ideas about nitrification and the physiology of nitrifying bacteria have been acquired by using techniques for enriching the soil. The perfusion method used by Lees (1949), and other similar techniques, result in the saturation of the soil with *Nitrosomonas* and *Nitrobacter*. The behaviour of these bacteria in the soil columns is probably a more accurate reflection of the activity of these organisms in the soil than that obtained from pure culture studies.

By incubating soil with ammonium sulphate, potassium sulphate and calcium superphosphate at a suitable pH and humidity, Ishizawa and Matsuguchi (1962) increased the numbers of nitrifying bacteria 50 to 100 fold. The soil block technique has also been used by incorporating an ammonium salt in the soil and coating the surface with calcium carbonate (Lundberg, 1962). The development of nitrifying bacteria causes the dissolution of the calcium carbonate and haloes appear around the colonies as on Winogradsky plates.

*Functional groups in the carbon cycle*

All heterotrophic bacteria use their carbon sources as sources of energy and so the enrichment of organisms involved in the carbon cycle is very simple. The ideas associated with concept of a zymogenous flora are applicable. In the presence of a carbon source, introduced into the soil, the organisms capable of utilizing it multiply actively, their development only being limited by competition with other organisms from the same energy source.

Cellulolytic organisms can be demonstrated by simply burying strips of paper or by attaching squares of paper or cellophane to cover glasses (Went, 1959; Tribe, 1960, 1961), or by measuring the tensile strength of cellulosic substrates (Richard, 1945; Gray and Martin, 1947; Orenski, 1962). Pochon and Tchan (1947) used filter paper impregnated with an Eh colour indicator to determine the relative importance of aerobic and anaerobic cellulose decomposers in a soil column. Generally, enrichment of aerobic cellulolytic bacteria by the soil block method is enhanced by the addition of a small quantity of mineral nitrogen to the soil.

In all of these techniques, the development of fungi interferes with the growth of the bacteria. Further, the multiplication of true cellulolytic organisms is followed rapidly by the growth of many forms, incapable of using cellulose, but thriving on its breakdown products. Nevertheless, the isolation and characterization of aerobic, cellulolytic organisms are made easier by the close attachment of these bacteria to their substrate and their association with coloured patches.

Other functional groups in the carbon cycle can be enriched in similar ways by replacing cellulose with another substrate. The breakdown of hemicellulose is brought about by a zymogenous microflora more varied but less specialized than that attacking cellulose (Pochon and Augier, 1954). Similarly, starch hydrolysis is brought about mainly by aerobic and facultative anaerobic bacteria in normal temperate soils; the strict anaerobes are much more limited in their importance (Prévot and Pochon, 1951). Chitin breakdown, as observed on buried chitin strips by a modification of Tribe's cellophane technique, is brought about simultaneously by fungi and Gram-negative, motile bacteria (Gray and Bell, 1962).

## *ELECTIVE CULTIVATION*

There is no such thing as a perfect elective medium, allowing the growth of only one species of bacterium or group of bacteria from soil. Bacteria with a unique metabolism such as the autotrophic nitrifiers, cannot be separated completely from contaminating heterotrophs, even after a series of transfers in media entirely devoid of organic material. The initially elective medium becomes less elective as it is modified by the products of bacterial metabolism. Thus elective cultivation rarely provides pure cultures, merely enriched populations. Pure cultures may be isolated later, but this is not essential; enriched cultures themselves can provide valuable information, including estimates of the size of the populations taking part in each biochemical transformation. Thus, elective media can be used for qualitative purposes (characterization of active species) and quantitative purposes (enumeration of the principal groups and their activity).

Most quantitative methods depend upon the preparation of soil suspensions, their serial dilution and subsequent inoculation into elective media. As fine a suspension as possible is made of a known weight of soil in a known volume of water and a decimal series of dilutions prepared. The main difficulties which have to be overcome are the heterogeneity of the soil, the adherence of the bacterial cells to soil particles and the cohesion of cells in colonies. The following techniques have been put forward for dispersing bacteria: (*a*) grinding in a mortar (wet or dry) (Pochon, 1955); (*b*) placing the sample in a diluent on a shaker at an optimal level and for an optimal time (Hirte, 1962); (*c*) the controlled use of ultrasonic waves (Stevenson, 1958); (*d*) the use of chemical deflocculants, e.g. sodium pyrophosphate (Hirte, 1962). The best disruption of soil aggregates and dispersal of bacterial cells is probably achieved by careful use of ultrasound, or by chemical deflocculants. Nevertheless, the results are not always perfect and vary with the type of soil (clay-humus colloid content).

The diluted suspensions can be inoculated into liquid or solid media. In the former instance, the colonies that develop are counted; at the same time, it is possible to isolate them and study factors affecting their metabolism. When liquid media are used, 3, 4 or 5 replicate cultures are prepared from each dilution and the most probable number of organisms in each group determined by using statistical tables. The test performed must eliminate any possibility of interference from organisms in other groups. If the medium is strongly elective, it is necessary only to record the last dilution in which growth occurs. Sometimes, the development of micro-organisms leads to the appearance of a macroscopic feature, characteristic of a particular functional group. In other cases, it results in a readily detectable evolution of gas or a change in pH. Lastly, in many cases, it is an alteration in the specific substrate which discloses the limiting dilution, e.g. a metabolic product appears or the original substrate disappears.

If the substrate is altered in this way, it is possible to compare different samples, not only for the number of bacteria present, but also for the intensity of their activity. The speed with which a substrate vanishes is a function both of the number of bacteria able to use it and the degree of their metabolic activity. Resting forms, such as spores and cysts, must germinate before they can multiply, thus introducing a lag phase. On the other hand, bacteria that have a very active metabolism will show an immediately rapid growth rate and quickly exhaust the substrate. Thus, if one plots a graph of time against the mean limiting dilution corresponding to the total disappearance of the substrate, the initial slope of the curve produced may be regarded as an index of the actual activity. Daily readings, followed by regular readings at greater intervals of time, should be taken to obtain all the information that this technique makes it possible to determine.

*Functional groups in the nitrogen cycle*

*Free-living, nitrogen fixing bacteria.* Media for the cultivation of nitrogen fixing bacteria are made elective by omitting combined forms of nitrogen from them and including a readily utilizable carbon source. Impurities in agar make it desirable to use silica gel to solidify the media. Mannitol has long been a favourite carbon source for elective cultivation and enumeration of *Azotobacter*. However, Brown, Jackson and Burlingham (1962) have shown that it usually gives lower counts than glucose and sucrose. Further, by using sucrose it is possible to count *Azotobacter* and *Beijerinckia* in tropical soils in a single operation (Dobereiner and Ruschel, 1964; Meiklejohn, 1965). It is easy to distinguish between colonies of *Azotobacter* and *Beijerinckia*. They have a different macroscopic appearance and they develop at different rates, i.e. 2 to 3 days for the former and 2 to 3 weeks for the latter. On the other hand, Hilger (1962) counted the 2 genera separately by adjusting the pH of media for *Beijerinckia* to 5·5 and for *Azotobacter* to 7·0. Furthermore, *Beijerinckia* would grow in a calcium-free medium; the requirement for calcium by *Azotobacter* is well known. The importance of the concentration of phosphate and the different trace elements, especially molybdenum in the absence of combined nitrogen, must also be considered. The same media, when incubated in the absence of oxygen, may be used to isolate anaerobic nitrogen fixers. Hilger has recommended that the pH be adjusted to 6·0 for *Clostridium*.

The liquid elective media are similar to the solid media. For *Azoto-*

*bacter*, the limiting dilution for growth is indicated by the development of a characteristic film (Tchan, 1952; Augier, 1956). This technique cannot be used for counting *Beijerinckia*. To count clostridia, the medium is dispensed into narrow tubes to a depth sufficient to maintain relatively anaerobic conditions. A Durham tube enables one to detect the evolution of gas which marks the development of *Clostridium* at the limiting dilution.

*Symbiotic nitrogen fixing bacteria.* The demonstration and enumeration of symbiotic nitrogen fixing bacteria is not achieved, strictly speaking, by elective culture. Instead, the capacity of bacteria to infect the appropriate species of legume and form nodules is used (Vincent and Waters, 1954; Brockwell, 1963).

*Proteolytic and ammonifying bacteria.* Proteolytic bacteria include a large number of functional groups, each adapted to the breakdown of protein molecules of varying origin and complexity. Clearly, it is not possible to study each of them in isolation. The estimation of their activity is somewhat arbitrary, depending upon the choice of nitrogenous substance to incorporate in the medium, a substance that must also act as a source of carbon.

Gelatin is often used because it is easy to detect its liquefaction by bacterial colonies. One can use the extinction dilution method, either by dispersing the gelatin in the medium (Lajudie and Chalvignac, 1950) or by introducing it in cube form or as pieces of photographic film (Remacle and Coyette, 1964). A graph of activity can be plotted, expressing the limiting dilution as a function of time.

To study ammonifying bacteria, single amino acids, e.g. tyrosine and asparagine are often used (de Barjac and Pochon, 1953; Chalvignac, 1962) or a mixture of amino acids (casein hydrolysate). The last dilution in which ammonia is formed or in which amino acids are decomposed is recorded. However, these substrates are metabolized by so many bacteria that they cannot really be regarded as elective media.

*Nitrifying bacteria.* By contrast, the unique physiology of the autotrophic nitrifying bacteria enables one to prepare media that are theoretically extremely elective; organic carbon is excluded from the medium and the sole energy source and nitrogen source is either an ammonium salt or a nitrite.

The oldest method (Winogradsky, 1933) consists of the inoculation of soil crumbs onto the surface of a silica gel medium containing the appropriate salts and coated with a thick paste of calcium carbonate or kaolin. If nitrifiers develop, haloes indicating the solution of the calcium carbonate will appear around the colonies.

Isolation by transfer through a series of liquid cultures (ammonium sulphate, calcium carbonate and no organic carbon—Meiklejohn, 1950), does not give pure cultures, even after four months, but it does give a considerable enrichment of *Nitrosomonas* when the following conditions are observed: (*a*) regular renewal of the ammonium salt and the calcium carbonate; (*b*) absence of pyrophosphate; (*c*) presence of trace elements. Recently, various authors have claimed to have obtained pure cultures by a dilution procedure in liquid media, in hanging drops (Ulianova, 1960), going as far as dilutions of the order of $10^{-10}$ (Lewis and Pramer, 1958), with a medium containing chelating agents.

For the isolation of *Nitrobacter*, Gould and Lees (1960) recommended successive transfer through media containing antibiotics (matromycin and terramycin), to obtain an enrichment, followed by purification on normal media.

Quantitative measurements of nitrifiers are rather easier and are made by inoculating soil dilutions in liquid elective media and noting the last dilution in which nitrites or nitrates appear. Their slow growth rate makes any attempt to plot graphs of their activity unrewarding. One must also allow for the presence of denitrifying bacteria which are invariably associated with nitrifying organisms in the soil and which may reduce the nitrates and nitrites produced. Nitrites and nitrates are detected using various analytical solutions, e.g. Griess-Ilosvay's reagent, Tromsdorf's reagent, a sulphur diphenylamine reagent (Coppier and de Barjac, 1952) or by spectrophotometry (Skujins, 1964).

*Denitrifying bacteria*. The incorporation of nitrate in a medium as a sole source of nitrogen does not necessarily make it elective for denitrifying bacteria which reduce nitrates to gaseous nitrogen, but does make it suitable for organisms that can reduce it in some way. The last dilution in such media in which nitrates disappear enables one to calculate the most probable number of nitrate reducing bacteria (de Barjac, 1952), but does not tell one in what form the reduced nitrogen appears. A variation of this technique has been proposed by Treccani (1961), who determined the total nitrogen in the culture at the end of the experiment and calculated the amount lost in gaseous form. Whatever the cause, the activity of nitrate reducers estimated in this way is only the potential activity, the real level being determined by the physical condition of the soil, particularly in relation to oxygen diffusion.

### *Functional groups in the carbon cycle*

*Cellulolytic bacteria*. Winogradsky's old technique (Winogradsky, 1929) of placing soil crumbs on plates of silica gel containing a salt solution with a mineral nitrogen source and covered with a sheet of filter paper, is still useful for the enrichment of aerobic, cellulolytic bacteria. Several variants of this method have been proposed, e.g. the substitution of washed agar for silica gel and the inoculation of agar covered with filter paper with a dilution of a soil suspension (Charpentier, 1960). The isolation of pure strains is very difficult. Often one is left with impure colonies on the filter paper or on precipitated cellulose agar. Dickermann and Starr (1951) have recommended using finely powdered cellulose obtained from the pellicle of *Acetobacter xylinum*. The subsequent procedure adopted depends on the organisms required, e.g. *Sporocytophaga*, *Cellvibrio*, *Cellulomonas* or *Corynebacterium*.

*Sporocytophaga* spp. will grow on agar media containing a low concentration of filter-sterilized glucose (Sijpenstein and Fåhraeus, 1949). To facilitate the purification procedures, gentle warming of the organisms has been suggested (Speyer, 1953; Drozdowicz, 1961) or the addition of antibiotics, e.g. kanamycin (Rivière, 1961) and penicillin or streptomycin (Speyer, 1953). Holding (1960) has observed that species of *Cytophaga* are prevalent in soil, amongst the Gram-negative, starch hydrolysing rods, and will grow on a soluble starch-potassium nitrate agar, made more selective by the addition of crystal violet.

The motility of *Cellvibrio* enables one to enrich them on strips of paper, together with antibiotics such as penicillin or aureomycin (Chalvignac, 1952). Colonies can be obtained on precipitated cellulose agar (Voets and van Hove, 1953, 1954) or on starch agar (Alarie and Gray, 1947).

Anaerobic cellulose decomposing bacteria can also be isolated on precipitated cellulose agar. It is essential to prepare a film of the medium on the inside wall of test tubes, in the presence of bicarbonate buffer and under an atmosphere of carbon dioxide. The medium must be inoculated while the agar is still molten at 40°, before preparing the film (Hungate, 1950). The technique is useful for thermophilic organisms (McBee, 1948, 1950). Sometimes, reducing agents are added, e.g. cysteine or ascorbic acid. When liquid media are inoculated with soil dilution, counts are made by detecting the production of gas from powdered cellulose.

*Starch hydrolysing bacteria.* Elective media containing starch as a sole source of carbon enable one to make enrichments and counts of starch hydrolysing bacteria. Alarie and Gray (1947) counted colonies on plates which were surrounded by clear haloes when the media were treated with iodine. Chalvignac (1953) distinguished between those which had produced acid, detected with phenol red, and those which only hydrolysed the starch, as determined with iodine. Readings are difficult to make; the halo is often invisible, since breakdown occurs only in the underlying agar.

The disappearance of starch in liquid media may also be detected with iodine; by recording the last dilution in which this occurs, the numbers of bacteria and a graph of their activity may be obtained (de Barjac and Chalvignac, 1954).

*Other groups.* Elective media, embodying the same principles, can be used for bacteria attacking most natural carbohydrates, especially hemicelluloses and pectins. Pectins form gels in the presence of calcium ions and one can make a plate count of the numbers of colonies which liquefy these gels after inoculation with soil dilutions (Wieringa, 1947) or determine the last dilution which will liquefy the gels in the tubes (Kaiser and Chalvignac, 1960). Using this latter method, graphs of activity can be plotted; their shape varies markedly, according to whether the dominant pectinolytic organisms are eubacteria, actinomycetes or fungi.

*Functional groups in the sulphur cycle*

*Sulphur oxidizing bacteria.* Autotrophs such as *Thiobacillus*, which obtain their energy from the oxidation of sulphur, may be grown in media containing no organic carbon. Sulphur is incorporated as elementary sulphur, in a reduced state, e.g. as a sulphide, or in a partially oxidized state, e.g. as a thiosulphate or polythionate. Media can be made elective for different species by exploiting their different degrees of acid tolerance. Normally, liquid media are used which may be incubated on a shaker (Starkey, Jones and Frederick, 1956). All these techniques are suspect when used for counting sulphur oxidizing bacteria.

*Sulphate reducing bacteria.* Many different synthetic media have been used to enrich *Desulphovibrio* spp. An organic hydrogen donor is added in addition to sulphate, and a ferrous salt is used as an indicator, ferrous sulphide being formed as the bacteria grow. Anaerobic conditions may be maintained in liquid media by simply introducing a piece of metallic iron (Abd-el-Malek and Rizk, 1960).

## *CONCLUSIONS*

The microbial population of soil is so varied and changeable that it would defy analysis, were it not for the fact that its diversity enables one to use elective culture to make systematic analyses of the organisms which constitute it. Before these analyses can be interpreted correctly, however, a great deal more needs to be learned about the character of life in the soil.

In the absence of exogenous food supplies, e.g. in a soil left fallow for several years, the total microflora diminishes and then reaches a stable equilibrium; the residual population, called the autochthonous population by Winogradsky, lives on reserve materials within the soil, e.g. humus. These organisms are a permanent feature of the soil and are comparatively insensitive to environmental changes. They are mainly slow growing. It is difficult to detect them because they are unable to survive and grow on artificial media.

One other feature of life in the soil disturbs the balance that one should find in an ecological analysis. Although the idea of an autochthonous microflora and functional groups is useful for the interpretation of observed facts, nevertheless it is incorrect to think of the whole population as consisting of perfectly distinct groups. Many organisms have less strict requirements and can participate in the endogenous activity of a soil in equilibrium (autochthonous state) and yet multiply vigorously in elective media (zymogenous state). Further, many organisms participate concurrently in numerous biochemical processes and can therefore be placed in several functional groups.

Finally, during the breakdown of organic matter, some bacteria make use of the catabolic products of other bacteria growing on a particular substrate. Thus, an initially elective medium will allow bacteria to grow which cannot attack the test substrate, but which were introduced during the inoculation of the total microflora.

The concepts of the whole microflora and of the autochthonous bacteria and functional groups on the one hand, and of elective media on the other, must be carefully interpreted in the light of our knowledge of life in the soil itself. The results must always be related to the whole ecological system being examined.

## *REFERENCES*

ABD-EL-MALEK, Y. & RIZK, S. G. (1958). Counting of sulphate-reducing bacteria in mixed bacterial populations. *Nature, Lond.*, **182**, 538.

ALARIE, A. M. & GRAY, P. H. H. (1947). Aerobic bacteria that decompose cellulose isolated from Quebec soils. *Canad. J. Res. C*, **25**, 228.

AUGIER, J. (1956). A propos de la numération des *Azotobacter* en milieu liquide. *Annls Inst. Pasteur, Paris*, **91**, 759.

BARJAC, H. DE (1952). La puissance dénitrifiante du sol. Mise au point d'une technique d'evaluation. *Annls Inst. Pasteur, Paris*, **83**, 207.

BARJAC, H. DE & CHALVIGNAC, M. A. (1954). Nouvel essai sur la détermination du pouvoir amylolytique. *Annls Inst. Pasteur, Paris*, **87**, 84.

BARJAC, H. DE & POCHON, J. (1953). Titrage du pouvoir ammonifiant de la microflore du sol. *Annls Inst. Pasteur, Paris*, **85**, 82.

BROCKWELL, J. (1963). Accuracy of a plant-infection technique for counting population of *Rhizobium trifolii. Appl. Microbiol.*, **11**, 377.

BROWN, M. E., BURLINGHAM, S. K. & JACKSON, R. M. (1962). Comparison of media and techniques for counting *Azotobacter* in soil. *Pl. Soil*, **17**, 309.

CHALVIGNAC, M. A. (1952). Recherches sur les techniques d'isolement des *Cellvibrio. Annls Inst. Pasteur, Paris*, **83**, 417.

CHALVIGNAC, M. A. (1953). Mesure des pouvoirs amylolytique et protéolytique des terres en aérobiose. *Annls Inst. Pasteur, Paris*, **84**, 816.

CHALVIGNAC, M. A. (1962). Sur quelques caractères morpho-physiologiques des bactéries de la rhizosphère du lin. *Annls Inst. Pasteur, Paris*, **102**, 763.

CHARPENTIER, M. (1960). Répartition des bactéries cellulolytiques dans le sol. Les techniques. *Annls Inst. Pasteur, Paris*, **99**, 153.

COPPIER, O. & BARJAC, H. DE (1952). De la richesse d'un sol en micro-organismes nitrificateurs. *Annls Inst. Pasteur, Paris*, **83**, 118.

DICKERMANN, J. M. & STARR, T. J. (1951). A medium for the isolation of pure cultures of cellulolytic bacteria. *J. Bact.*, **62**, 133.

DOBEREINER, J. & RUSCHEL, A. P. (1964). Methods for the study of *Beijerinckia. Soil Biology, NS*, **1**, 3.

DROZDOWICZ, A. (1961). Investigation on cellulose decomposition by myxobacteria from the genus *Sporocytophaga. Acta microbiol. pol.*, **10**, 255.

GOULD, G. W. & LEES, H. (1960). The isolation and culture of the nitrifying organisms. 1. *Nitrobacter. Can. J. Microbiol.*, **6**, 299.

GRAY, T. R. G. & BELL, T. F. (1962). The decomposition of chitin in an acid soil. In *Soil Organisms*. Ed. Doeksen, J. & van der Drift, J. Amsterdam. North Holland Publishing Co.

GRAY, W. & MARTIN, G. W. (1947). Improvements on soil burial testing method. *Mycologia*, **39**, 358.

GREENWOOD, D. J. & LEES, H. (1956). Studies on the decomposition of amino acids in soil. I. A preliminary survey of techniques. *Pl. Soil*, **7**, 253.

GREENWOOD, D. J. & LEES, H. (1960). Studies on the decomposition of amino acids in soil. II. The anaerobic metabolism. *Pl. Soil*, **12**, 69.

GREENWOOD, D. J. & LEES, H. (1960). Studies on the decomposition of amino acids in soil. III. The process of amino acid aerobic decomposition and some properties of amino acid-oxidizing organisms. *Pl. Soil*, **12**, 175.

HILGER, F. (1962). Contribution à l'étude des bactéries libres fixatrices d'azote élémentaire dans les sols tropicaux. Thesis. Gembloux. Institut Agronomique.

HIRTE, W. (1962). Einige Untersuchungen zur Methodik der mikrobiologischen Bodenprobenverarbeitung. *Zentbl. Bakt. ParasitKde., Abt. II*, **115**, 394.

HOLDING, A. J. (1960). The properties and classification of the predominant Gram-negative bacteria occurring in soil. *J. appl. Bact.*, **23**, 515.

HUNGATE, R. E. (1950). The anaerobic mesophilic cellulolytic bacteria. *Bact. Rev.*, **14**, 1.

ISHIZAWA, S. & MATSUGUCHI, T. (1962). Studies on the nitrification in soil. I. *Soil Pl. Fd. Tokyo*, **8**, 239.

KAISER, P. & CHALVIGNAC, A. (1960). Une méthode nouvelle pour la mesure quantitative de l'activite pectinolytique aérobie des terres. *Annls Inst. Pasteur, Paris*, **99**, 462.

LAJUDIE, J. & CHALVIGNAC, M. A. (1956). Appréciation de l'activité proteolytique de la microflore du sol. *Annls Inst. Pasteur, Paris*, **90**, 359.

LEES, H. (1947). A simple automatic percolator. *J. agric. Sci.*, **37**, 27.

LEWIS, R. F. & PRAMER, D. (1958). Isolation of *Nitrosomonas* in pure culture. *J. Bact.*, **76**, 524.

LÖHNIS, F. & GREEN, H. H. (1914). Methods in Soil Bacteriology. V. Ammonification in soil and solution. *Zentbl. Bakt. ParasitKde., Abt. II*, **37**, 534.

LUNDBERG, G. A. (1962). Emploi des plaques de terre moulée pour la culture des nitrificateurs. *Annls Inst. Pasteur, Paris*, **102**, 215.

MCBEE, R. H. (1948). The culture and physiology of a thermophilic cellulose fermenting bacterium. *J. Bact.*, **56**, 653.

MCBEE, R. H. (1950). The anaerobic thermophilic cellulolytic bacteria. *Bact. Rev.*, **14**, 51.

MEIKLEJOHN, J. (1950). The isolation of *Nitrosomonas europea* in pure culture. *J. gen. Microbiol.*, **4**, 185.

MEIKLEJOHN, J. (1965). Counting *Beijerinckia* in soils. *Soil Biology, NS*, **3**, 10.

ORENSKI, S. W. (1959). A simple quantitative method for measuring the rate of cellulose decomposition in soils. *Commun. Rom. Acad. Sci.*, **9**, 579.

POCHON, J. (1955). Techniques de préparation des suspensions-dilutions de terre pour analyse microbiologique. *Annls Inst. Pasteur, Paris*, **89**, 464.

POCHON, J. & AUGIER, J. (1954). Premieres recherches sur l'attaque des hemicelluloses dans le sol. *5th Int. Congr. Soil Sci., Leopoldville*, **4**, 43.

POCHON, J. & CHALVIGNAC, M. A. (1952). Recherches sur la protéolyse bactérienne au sein du sol. *Annls Inst. Pasteur, Paris*, **82**, 690.

POCHON, J. & TCHAN, Y. T. (1947). Recherches sur les phénomènes biologiques d'ammonification dans le sol. *Annls Inst. Pasteur, Paris*, **73**, 696.

POCHON, J. & TCHAN, Y. T. (1947). Recherche sur l'activité relative des microorganismes cellulolytiques aérobies et anaérobies dans le sol. *Annls Inst. Pasteur, Paris*, **73**, 29.

PRÉVOT, A. R. & POCHON, J. (1951). Etude de l'amylolyse bactérienne dans le sol par la méthode de la colonne de terre amidonnée. *Annls Inst. Pasteur, Paris*, **80**, 672.

REMACLE, J. & COYETTE, J. (1964). Application de la methode de Le Minor et Piéchaud à la mise en évidence de l'activité protéolytique des sols. *Soil Biology, NS*, **2**, 54.

RICHARD, F. (1945). In *Mitt. schweiz. Anst. forstl. Verswes.*, **24**, 3.

RIVIÈRE, J. (1961). Isolement et purification des bactéries cellulolytiques aérobies du sol. *Annls Inst. Pasteur, Paris*, **101**, 253.

SIJPENSTEIN, A. K. & FÅHRAEUS, G. (1949). Adaptation of *Sporocytophaga myxococcoides* to sugars. *J. gen. Microbiol.*, **3**, 224.

SKUJINS, J. J. (1964). Spectrophotometric determination of nitrate with 4-methyl umbelliferone. *Analyt. Chem.*, **36**, 240.

SPEYER, E. (1953). Untersuchungen an *Sporocytophaga myxococcoides*. *Arch. Mikrobiol.*, **18**, 245.

STARKEY, R. L., JONES, G. E. & FREDERICK, L. R. (1956). Effects of medium agitation and wetting agents on oxidation of sulphur by *Thiobacillus thiooxidans*. *J. gen. Microbiol.*, **15**, 329.

STEVENSON, I. L. (1958). The effect of sonic vibration on the bacterial plate count of soil. *Pl. Soil*, **10**, 1.

TCHAN, Y. T. (1952). A note on the estimation of *Azotobacter* in soil. *Proc. Linn. Soc. N.S.W.*, **77**, 89.

TRECCANI, V. (1961). Ricerche sul potere denitrificante del terreno e proposta di un metodo quantitativo di valutazione. *Annali Microbiol.*, **11**, 15.

TRIBE, H. T. (1957). Ecology of microorganisms in soil as observed during their development upon buried cellulose films. *7th Symp. Soc. gen. Microbiol.* Ed. Williams, R. E. O. & Spicer, C. C. Cambridge. Cambridge University Press.

TRIBE, H. T. (1960). Aspects of decomposition of cellulose in Canadian soils. Observations with the microscope. *Can. J. Microbiol.*, **6**, 309.

ULIANOVA, O. M. (1960). Isolation of pure culture of *Nitrosomonas* from various natural substrates and their characteristics. *Mikrobiologiya*, **29**, 813.

VINCENT, J. M. & WATERS, L. M. (1954). The root-nodule bacteria as factors in clover establishment in the red basaltic soils of the Lismore district, N.S.W. II. Survival and success of inocula in laboratory trials. *Aust. J. agric. Res.*, **5**, 61.

VOETS, J. P., VORGER, R. DE & COOLSAET, A. (1955). Étude biochimique de bactéries ammonifiantes. I. Isolement et pouvoir ammonifiant. *Revue Ferment. Ind. Aliment.*, **10**, 7.

VOETS, J. P. & VAN HOVE, J. K. (1953). Purification and cellulolytic activity of *Cellvibrio*. *Nature, Lond.*, **171**, 1073.

VOETS, J. P. & VAN HOVE, J. K. (1954). Recherches sur la fermentation de la cellulose par les *Cellvibrio*. *Revue Ferment. Ind. Aliment*, **9**, 64.

WENT, J. C. (1959). Cellophane as a medium to study the cellulose decomposition in forest soil. *Acta bot. neerl.*, **8**, 490.

WIERINGA, K. T. (1947). A method for isolating and counting pectolytic microbes. *4th Int. Congr. Microbiol.*, Copenhagen.

WINOGRADSKY, S. N. (1929). Sur la dégradation de la cellulose dans le sol. *Annls Inst. Pasteur, Paris*, **43**, 549.

WINOGRADSKY, S. N. (1935). The method in soil microbiology as illustrated by studies on *Azotobacter* and the nitrifying organisms. *Soil Sci.*, **40**, 59.

# MEASUREMENT OF MICROBIAL METABOLISM IN SOIL

D. J. GREENWOOD

*National Vegetable Research Station, Wellesbourne, Warwick, U.K.*

## *INTRODUCTION*

An aim of soil microbiologists is to devise methods of predicting from laboratory measurements the amounts of any given microbial product such as nitrate that will be formed in a field soil when it is subjected to given weather conditions. This aim is at present partially fulfilled; thus in qualitative terms it is frequently possible to forecast whether a soil will lose or gain nitrate and whether much or little ammonia and nitrate will be made available for plant growth during the growing season (Eagle, 1961). Quantitative predictions have been made of the effects of drying (Birch, 1960) and of water-logging, and the effects of crumb size on the amount of ammonia and nitrate released from soils in the laboratory (Greenwood, 1963). The next stage would therefore appear to be to review existing information to find the most promising way of making quantitative predictions of microbial activities in field soils.

The decomposition of organic matter usually determines the amounts of ammonia, nitrate etc., that are produced in the soil. Thus the first purpose of this paper is to develop more unified hypotheses for the rates of soil organic matter decomposition and the types of products. The second purpose is to apply these hypotheses to evaluate existing laboratory methods for measuring microbial activities and to suggest how these laboratory measurements may be related to the activities in field soils.

## *PRODUCTS OF MICROBIAL METABOLISM*

The wide variety of micro-organisms that inhabit soils and the diversity of compounds that have been produced by micro-organisms suggest that it may be a formidable task to make predictions about microbial activities in soil. However, Kluyver (1953) has argued that microbial metabolism does conform to a definite pattern which may be stated in simplified form as follows.

In micro-organisms the chemical conversions of food serve a twofold purpose; partly they are used for building up the cell constituents (anabolic processes) and partly they are used for providing the necessary energy (catabolic processes). Both anabolic and catabolic processes can be reduced to chains of elementary reactions belonging to a very restricted number of types and these are similar in all organisms. As for anabolism, there is a remarkable degree of uniformity in the anabolic end products, independent of the primary food components and of the type of organism. Catabolic processes are characterized by the excretion of the final products from the cell; the products may differ and include such diverse compounds as carbon dioxide, nitrogen, alcohol and acetic acid. Nevertheless all these catabolic products result from the transfer of hydrogen from one molecule to another and differ only in the specific nature of the molecules. It appears therefore that it is the catabolic processes which primarily determine differences between the products of microbial metabolism.

All micro-organisms whether in pure culture or in soil are continually subjected to environmental changes and many micro-organisms minimize the adverse effects by adjusting the relative activities of their enzymes. Dean and Hinshelwood (1959) concluded that the adjustments in all micro-organisms take place in such a way as to maintain growth at the highest possible rate. A good illustration of the theorem is given by *Bacterium lactis aerogenes* which, after being grown under anaerobic conditions using a glucose metabolite as H-acceptor, was transferred to aerobic conditions where it immediately used oxygen exclusively as H-acceptor. A larger proportion of the glucose absorbed by the micro-organisms would be converted into cell material if oxygen and not the glucose metabolite was the H-acceptor: cell synthesis would thus be faster, so that it follows from Dean and Hinshelwood's theorem that oxygen would always be used in preference to the glucose metabolite as H-acceptor. The products of aerobic microbial metabolism would thus tend to be carbon dioxide, water, and cell material, and since the cell material has similar composition in different organisms (Kluyver, 1953), the products would tend to be similar irrespective of microbial species. The widespread adjustments that take place in micro-organisms in response to changes in environment, therefore, tend to induce micro-organisms under similar environmental conditions to produce similar products.

The implication from these notions is that despite variations in microbial populations, the combined microbial activities in different soils, when maintained under the same defined aeration conditions might be expected to decompose added materials in similar ways. This appears to be borne out by the limited experimental evidence with soils.

Irrespective of soil type, single amino acids or sugars, decomposed on addition to soils in the following way. Under aerobic conditions they disappeared within 5 days, by which time about half of their carbon was converted into carbon dioxide and the remainder into cell material (Lees and Porteous, 1950; Greenwood and Lees, 1960*b*; Schmidt, Putnam and Paul, 1960). The cell material had a C/N ratio of between 3 and 6 (Winsor and Pollard, 1956; Barrow, 1960; Greenwood and Lees, 1956) and had enzymic activities characterized not by the soil type but by the substrate (Greenwood and Lees, 1960*b*). Under anaerobic conditions volatile fatty acids were produced in large quantities, but little cell material was synthesized (e.g. Greenwood and Lees, 1960*a*; Takijima, Sakuma and Chiba, 1961). Likewise the products of metabolism of inorganic compounds were primarily dependent on whether the conditions were aerobic or anaerobic; under aerobic conditions compounds such as nitrate, sulphate and ferric iron accumulated whereas under anaerobic conditions these ions were reduced to nitrogen gas, sulphide and ferrous iron. So far no two soils appear to have been found which, when maintained under the same defined conditions, decomposed added materials in different ways. Thus there is some evidence for believing that the aeration conditions and the substrate, rather than the initial microbial population in soil, will mainly determine the metabolic products. This is the conception behind many measurements of microbial activities in soil and is the basis of much of the subsequent argument.

## *HYPOTHESIS 1. THE RELATIVE RATES OF AEROBIC AND ANAEROBIC PROCESSES IN SOIL*

It is important to be able to assess the conditions necessary for the occurrence of anaerobic metabolism in soils, or better still, to be able to predict the relative extents of anaerobic and aerobic metabolism. A model that may be useful for this purpose can be developed on the following premises

1. That aerobic respiration and other aerobic metabolic processes are not impeded by lowering of the oxygen concentrations at the microbial surfaces unless the concentration falls to almost zero and that anaerobic processes do not occur unless the oxygen concentration is equally low.

2. That the micro-organisms are uniformly distributed and that any oxygen which they require travels by diffusion through the gas and liquid phases.

Soil can be considered to consist of a pile of aggregates; the characteristics of each aggregate being that when it holds sufficient water to permit active microbial metabolism it contains little gas-filled pore space. The oxygen requirements of micro-organisms may be limited by inadequate oxygen diffusion through the aqueous phase from the outside of aggregates towards their centres or by inadequate diffusion through the gas space between the aggregates. If the aggregates are spherical and have a radius $R_1$, a volume $V_2$, a diffusion coefficient $D_s$, an oxygen-free volume at their centre of $V_1$, and the rate of oxygen uptake per unit volume is M when it is not limited by lack of oxygen, then, if aggregates are surrounded by an oxygen concentration $C_1$, solution of the diffusion equation (Greenwood and Berry, 1962) gives

$$6D_sC_1 = MR_1^2(1 + 2V_1/V_2 - 3(V_1/V_2)^{2/3}) \qquad (1)$$

This equation thus defines the volume of the sphere where anaerobic processes occur.

If the aggregates were so small that the oxygen concentration at their centres was roughly the same as at their surfaces, then the only way anaerobic zones could result would be by inadequate diffusion in the gas phase. This can be visualized by considering a glass tube containing most soil crumbs, sealed at its base, but exposed to an oxygen concentration $C_1$ at its surface. The depth $x$ from the surface, where the oxygen concentration is zero, can be written in terms of $D_c$, the diffusion coefficient of oxygen through the column and $M_c$, the respiration rate per unit volume of column, when it is not limited by lack of oxygen: i.e. at all depths less than $x$. The equation which is obtained in a similar way to equation (1) is:

$$x = \sqrt{\frac{2D_cC_1}{M_c}} \qquad (2)$$

The diffusion coefficient terms $D_c + D_s$ can be calculated approximately from the water-filled or gas-filled pore space by means of formulae such as those of Penman (1940), and of Currie (1961).

In evaluating the evidence for the first premise, it is important to bear in mind that, because of technical difficulties it is not possible to measure the oxygen concentrations at the microbial surfaces. All actively metabolizing micro-organisms are covered with at least a thin layer of water, and since oxygen only diffuses slowly through water, there will be enormous variations of oxygen concentrations in any actively respiring soil system. In particular the mean oxygen concentration in the soil water, or the oxygen concentration in the gas phase above the soil, which are the two most frequently measured concentrations, will always be much greater than the oxygen concentration at the microbial surfaces. The difference will be greater if the water layer is thick than if it is thin. Therefore, only the experiments where attempts have been made to minimize this thickness are relevant to a discussion of the effect of oxygen concentration on microbial activities. These experiments were carried out with vigorously stirred suspensions of soil or with partially dried soils.

In soil or sewage, it was found that aerobic respiration had a $K_m$ value (the oxygen concentration required to reduce the rate to half that in the presence of excess oxygen), of 2–5 $\mu$M (Greenwood, 1961) and 3 $\mu$M (D.S.I.R., 1963), and nitrification had $K_m$ values of 2–5 $\mu$M (Greenwood, 1962) and 10 $\mu$M (D.S.I.R., 1963). Denitrification only took place, to a very small extent, in soil, unless the oxygen concentration was less than 6 $\mu$M (Wijler and Delwiche, 1954; Greenwood, 1962). Similar low oxygen concentrations were necessary to induce anaerobic organic matter decomposition in soil (Greenwood, 1961). Pure cultures of organisms also responded to changes in oxygen concentration in a similar way. Aerobic respiration rates of 9 species of bacteria had $K_m$ values of between 1 and 0·01 $\mu$M oxygen (Longmuir, 1954), and *Pseudomonas* species did not denitrify unless the oxygen concentration was less than 5 $\mu$M (Skerman, Lack, and Mills, 1951; Skerman and MacRae, 1957*a*, *b*, 1961). Nevertheless a different response to oxygen was found with *Achromobacter liquefaciens*; it was found to reduce nitrite, even when the oxygen concentration was 250 $\mu$M (Skerman, Carey and MacRae, 1958). With this exception, therefore, the evidence supports the validity of the first premise, namely, that in soil, aerobic processes are not inhibited and anaerobic ones not induced unless the oxygen concentration is reduced to a very low value.

The foregoing evidence indicates that both aerobic and anaerobic processes may be used to test the validity of the equations. By measurements of the effect of oxygen partial pressure on the rates of respiration of spherical aggregates (Greenwood and Berry, 1962; Greenwood and Goodman, 1964*a*) and of the rates of nitrification and denitrification in natural sieved soil aggregates (Greenwood, 1962) evidence has been obtained in support of equation 1. More direct evidence was provided by determinations of the oxygen concentration at different depths from the surface of moulded, water-saturated spherical aggregates by means of an electrode. The values agreed approximately with those calculated from diffusion theory and from measurements of $D_s$ and M (Greenwood and Goodman, 1964*b*). Some evidence in support of the validity of equation 2 has been obtained by determining the extents to which the respiration rates of columns of very small crumbs containing different amounts of inter-crumb water were impeded by inadequate oxygen. These rates were found to be similar (Greenwood and Goodman, 1965) to those calculated from equation 2 using a value for $D_c$ obtained from pore space measurements. Nevertheless this evidence is somewhat unsatisfactory because the columns of crumbs did not have uniform gas-filled pore spaces.

It appears that the equations define the approximate extents of aerobic and anaerobic zones in soil and thus the relative rates of the aerobic and anaerobic processes.

## *HYPOTHESIS 2. THE RATE OF ORGANIC MATTER DECOMPOSITION*

The organic nitrogenous materials that constitute the soil organic matter must first undergo enzymic hydrolysis into simpler compounds before they can be absorbed and metabolized by micro-organisms. These hydrolytic products include amino acids and sugars both of which, as has already been mentioned, decomposed rapidly on aerobic incubation with soils. Similarly mixtures of amino acids decomposed on anaerobic incubation. Neither amino acids nor sugars have been found in appreciable quantities in water extracts of soil (e.g. Bremner, 1950; Payne, Rouatt and Katznelson, 1956; Nagar, 1962); the greater quantities of amino acids that have been found in ammonium acetate or barium hydroxide extracts (Paul and Schmidt, 1960), could be explained by these extractants rupturing the microbial cell walls and thus releasing intracellular, free amino acids (Fry, 1955). This evidence against the accumulation of free amino acids and sugars in soils suggests it is the initial enzymic hydrolysis of organic materials that is the main step limiting their breakdown.

The organic matter in many soils is initially mixed with the inorganic constituents and plays an essential role in stabilizing soil aggregates. Emerson (1959) proposes, on the basis of physical measurements, that quartz, clay and organic matter are arranged in soil aggregates as shown in Fig. 1. The clay particles segregate together into domains which are cemented to the quartz particles by organic matter. The pore spaces may be inhabited by bacteria, and if the bacteria are to move freely and reach the organic matter, then the pores must be filled with water. The sizes of the pore spaces can be obtained from measurements of the water retained by the soil after it has been water-saturated and then subjected so various tensions. Such measurements on 18 soils, having various textural types, were made by Salter and Williams (1965). In all except one soil, more than half the water was retained, at a tension of 0·3 atmospheres, and this most of the pores have a diameter less than 5 μ. During the summer, the top 15 cm. of Wellesbourne soils seldom contained water at a tension of less than 0·3 atmospheres so that most of the water-filled pores would have diameters of less that 5 μ (Salter and Williams, 1964).

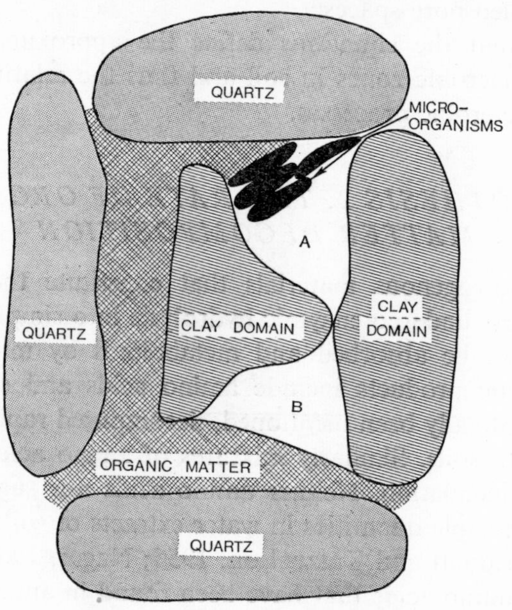


Fig 1. Model of soil aggregate.

The decomposition of the soil organic matter will, as previously argued, be limited by the rate of enzymic hydrolysis. In undisturbed soil, decomposition may be very slow because (1), much of the organic matter is protected by clay domains and quartz particles, (2), all enzymes that have been separated from cells are absorbed strongly by clays and colloids (McLaren, 1963; Briggs and Spedding, 1963), (3), movement of other enzymes will be slight; they are on surfaces of bacteria, which are of the same order of size (e.g. bacilli are c. 1 μ in dia. and 5–10 μ long) as many pores, and thus will be unable to move freely. However, any rearrangement of the components of soil crumbs would lead to greater contact between enzymes and organic matter and thus to a faster rate of decomposition. It would also lead to a weakening of the bonds between clay domains and quartz particles and in consequence a decrease in soil stability.

As an example of the implications of this model, consider the cross-section of the aggregate given in Fig. 1. It contains two water-filled pores A and B, but in only one of them are there organisms producing enzymes that will hydrolyse organic matter. None of the free enzymes could reach B because they would be absorbed by the clay and none of the micro-organisms could reach B because they are too large to pass through the connecting pore. If, however, the soil were dried and rewetted the resulting contraction and swelling would cause the clay domains and quartz particles to be displaced relative to one another. This would cause organic matter hitherto protected by clay or quartz to be exposed, enzymes absorbed in soil colloids to be pressed on to fresh substrate, microbial surfaces hitherto in contact with other microbial surfaces to be pressed on to the organic matter and might even permit organisms to move from A to B. In every case, there would be greater breakdown. In addition, the process would cause the rupture of numerous quartz clay domain bonds, and lead to a decrease in stability. Likewise, any other microbial process which alters structural stability would induce an increased rate of decomposition.

### *Evidence for hypothesis*

A test of this hypothesis would be provided by applying a treatment to cause an internal displacement of particles within aggregates and then measuring the decomposition of the organic matter and the structural stability of the aggregates. Since the decomposition is limited by the rate of enzymic hydrolysis and the products are rapidly oxidized in soil maintained under aerobic conditions, decomposition can be conveniently measured as aerobic respiration. A necessary condition is that the treatments would have to be so mild that few micro-organisms were killed; if many were killed, any enhanced respiration would be accounted for by the dead cells acting as readily decomposable substrate. Four treatments were imposed: (1) partial air drying of moist crumbs followed by remoistening, (2) freezing of moist crumbs followed by thawing, (3) moulding of moist crumbs into spheres and chopping these into 2–4 mm. crumbs, (4) shaking the crumbs with water. The data in Tables 1, 2 and 3 show that all treatments enhanced respiration and decreased structural stability. The only treatment which reduced the respiration rate of a soil, previously percolated with leucine solution, and subsequently shaken with fresh substrate, was drying to a water content of less

TABLE 1

*Effect of moulding, and freezing and thawing on the respiration rates and stability of soil crumbs*

| Treatment | Respiration rates (μl./g./min.) | | | | Stability % |
|---|---|---|---|---|---|
| | Soil percolated with water | | Soil percolated with DL-leucine solution | | |
| | 0–300 mins. after treatment | 3000–4000 mins. after treatment | Suspension in water | Suspension in leucine solution | |
| None | 0·11 | 0·07 | 0·90 | 1·70 | 33 |
| Moulded | 0·46 | 0·07 | 1·30 | 2·00 | 46 |
| Frozen and thawed | 0·19 | 0·09 | 1·30 | 2·30 | 82 |
| Standard error of the difference between means (degrees of freedom) | ±0·022(12) | ±0·008(12) | ±0·05(9) | ±0·1(9) | ±2·0(20) |

Air dry soil crumbs (10 g. of 2–4 mm.) were percolated under aerobic conditions either with 100 ml. of water or with 100 ml. of DL-leucine solution (1 mg./ml.). Some of the crumbs were not further treated (Treatment—None), some were moulded into spheres which were chopped into 2–4 mm. crumbs (Treatment—Moulded), and some were frozen for 1 hr. at −20° and then thawed (Treatment—Frozen and thawed). They were then immediately used for respiration and stability measurements. Soil (1 g.) that had been water-percolated was transferred to Warburg flasks and respiration rates measured whilst the flasks were stationary. Soil that had been percolated with leucine solution was suspended in 3 ml. of water or 3 ml. of leucine solution (1 mg./ml.), and respiration rates were measured for 240 mins. with the flasks vibrating. Stability was measured as the percentage of soil passing through a 1 mm. mesh after the crumbs had been shaken with water. Soil was a clay loam containing 2·6 per cent carbon.

than half that at saturation. This provides evidence that none of the other treatments killed the organisms, so that the enhanced rate of metabolism could not be explained by rapid decomposition of dead cells. It appeared, therefore, that the treatments rearranged the components of the soil aggregates and, in accord with the hypothesis, increased the rate of organic matter decomposition without killing the organisms.

Most of the results of other workers with other soils are in agreement with these findings. It has been thoroughly established that *complete* air drying greatly enhances the rate of metabolism when the soil is

TABLE 2

*Effect of partial drying on the respiration rates and stability of soil crumbs*

| Moisture content % dry weight | Water suction (atm.) | Respiration rates ± s.e. of the difference between means (degrees of freedom) (μl./g. dry soil/min.) | | | Stability (%) ± s.e. of the difference between means (degrees of freedom) |
|---|---|---|---|---|---|
| | | (Soil percolated with water for 150–180 days) | | (Soil percolated with DL-leucine solution for 3 days) | |
| | | 0–300 mins. after drying | 3000–4000 mins. after drying | | |
| > 45 (undried soil) | < 0·3 | 0·11 ±0·002(4) | 0·051 ±0·005(4) | 1·9 ±0·08(2) | 22 ±0·4(6) |
| 20–45 | < 12 | 0·15 ±0·014(4) | 0·069 ±0·021(4) | 2·2 ±0·09(13) | 25 ±1·4(11) |
| 9–20 | > 12 | 0·34 ±0·083(4) | 0·076 ±0·019(4) | 1·3 ±0·09(2) | 28 ±1·7(7) |

Air dry soil crumbs were percolated under aerobic conditions either with 100 ml. of water or with 100 ml. DL-leucine solution (1 mg./ml.). The soils were set out to dry, samples being taken at intervals and immediately used for respiration and stability measurements. Samples (1 g.) that had been water-percolated were transferred to Warburg flasks, water was added until the crumbs appeared to have the same moisture content as the undried soil, and respiration rates were measured whilst the flasks were stationary. Samples (1 g.) that had been percolated with leucine solution, were suspended in 3 ml. leucine solution and respiration rates were measured for 240 mins. with the flasks vibrating. Stability was measured as the percentage of soil passing through a 1 mm. mesh after crumbs had been shaken with water. Water suction was that necessary to bring the water content to that of partially air dried soil. Measurements were combined into groups according to water content and s.e. of the difference between means calculated from within group comparisons. Soil was a clay loam containing 2·6% carbon.

remoistened and incubated (Birch, 1958), affects structural stability (Sillanpää and Webber, 1961) and kills organisms (Stephenson, 1956). The effects of *partial* air drying have been little studied, but Wood (1965) showed that it induced the release of ammonia on remoistening and incubating the soil. Partial drying of the soil had no effect on the activities of amino acid oxidizing organisms (Greenwood and Lees, 1960) nitrifying organisms (Quastel and Schofield, 1951) and sulphur oxidizing organisms (Gleen and Quastel, 1953). Griffin (1963) deduced from osmotic considerations that micro-organisms in soil would not be killed unless the water content was lowered far below that of the per-

TABLE 3

*Effect of shaking with water on the respiration rates of soil crumbs*

| Period of incubation prior to respiration measurements (hours) | Respiration rate (μl./g. dry soil/min.) | | Standard error of the difference between means (degrees of freedom) |
|---|---|---|---|
| | Stationary soil crumbs | Shaken cell suspensions | |
| 0·5 | 0·41 | 0·45 | 0·012(6) |
| 72·0 | 0·21 | 0·35 | 0·008(6) |

Air dried soil crumbs (2–4 mm.) were successively water-saturated, drained, incubated under aerobic conditions for the indicated period, and transferred in 1 g. (dry weight) samples to Warburg flasks. No other addition was made to half the flasks and respiration rates were measured with the flasks stationary. To the other half of the flasks, 3 ml. of water was added and respiration rates were measured with the flasks vibrating. Soil was a clay loam containing 2·6% carbon.

manent wilting point. There are a few examples where air drying enhanced the respiration rate on subsequent incubation without killing many bacteria (Soulides and Allison, 1961).

Rovira and Greacen (1957) found that tillage enhanced the oxygen consumption of soil and reduced its structural stability. It was argued that tillage caused organic matter, which was in small pores and protected by inorganic particles, to be more accessible to microbial attack. Evidence that few micro-organisms were killed in the process was provided by Skinner, Jones and Mollison (1952) who found that plate counts of bacteria obtained after grinding soil with water were the same as those obtained after shaking soil with water.

Freezing and thawing of soil has been shown by many workers to increase the amount of carbon dioxide, ammonia and nitrate released on subsequent incubation (Gasser, 1958; Soulides and Allison, 1961; Mack, 1962) and to reduce the stability of soil aggregates (Sillanpää and Webber, 1961). The treatment did not affect denitrifying activity, glucose oxidizing activity or the respiration rates of shaken soil suspensions (McGarity, 1962; Ross, 1964). The treatment reduced the numbers of micro-organisms in some soils but not in others (Mack, 1962; Soulides and Allison, 1961). However, the data of Soulides and Allison (1961) provide examples where carbon dioxide release was enhanced but the numbers of bacteria were unaffected by freezing and thawing.

Other evidence in support of the hypothesis for organic matter decomposition is provided by the finding that the respiration rates of soils previously treated with different salt solutions were dependent on the type of cation (Birch, 1959*a*, *b*). Since the type of cation is known to influence structural stability it might be expected to influence the amount of organic matter exposed to microbial attack. More supporting evidence is provided by the greater release of ammonia on anaerobic incubation of small aggregates compared with that of larger aggregates (Waring and Bremner, 1964), and by the difficulty of separating micro-organisms from soil (Stephenson, 1958), or from each other (Skinner *et al.*, 1952). There is therefore some evidence which suggests that the hypothesis may partly explain some of the observed processes affecting organic matter decomposition in soils.

## *THE USES OF THE HYPOTHESES TO EVALUATE METHODS OF MEASURING SOIL METABOLIC PROCESSES*

### *General implication of the hypotheses to the assessment of metabolic rates in field soil from laboratory measurements*

The hypotheses suggest many ways in which weather conditions influence metabolic activities in soil and, in consequence, the types of laboratory measurements that will be necessary to evaluate the extents of metabolism in field soils. Many soils are continually subjected to rainfall, drainage, removal of water by evaporation from the soil surface, removal of water by plant transpiration and physical stresses due to freezing and thawing, root growth and to cultivation. The magnitude of each of these processes and the rate at which it occurs will affect the rearrangement of particles and thus the extent of organic matter decomposition. Many of them will also determine whether decomposition is aerobic or anaerobic, and thus the nature of the metabolic products. Ideally, therefore, to deduce the metabolic activities in the field from laboratory measurements on soil samples, the rates of decomposition should be measured on samples that are simultaneously subjected to identical rates of drying, drainage etc., with those in the field. This is seldom, if ever, possible because of the difficulty of exactly simulating field conditions in the laboratory; even removal of a sample from the field will change its aeration conditions and water stresses sufficiently to affect metabolism.

An alternative and perhaps more promising approach might be to study the effect of such factors as temperature, drying and wetting, water content and mechanical manipulation on organic matter decomposition. It may then be possible to find which factors are of most importance in determining decomposition in field soils and what measurements are likely to be of most use in predicting the extent of microbial activities in the field. With such an approach it appears necessary to study the effect on decomposition, of each factor independently of any other and in such a way that the results apply to a wide range of soils and conditions. For example, to study the effect of temperature on soil nitrification it is essential that no denitrification occurs. Temperature affects the respiration rate of soil, and in consequence, from equations 1 and 2, the volume of the oxygen-free zones of soil and the relative proportions of nitrifying and denitrifying activities. So, if denitrification did occur, unknown proportions of nitrifying and denitrifying activities would be studied; the results would be unrelatable to any other worker's results or to the effect on nitrification in any field soil. It is therefore essential to study aerobic processes uncomplicated by anaerobic processes. It may also be argued, by a similar type of reasoning, that it is essential to study the effects of mechanical manipulation, uncomplicated by the effects of drying, etc. The next question that demands discussion is, therefore, to what extent do existing laboratory methods satisfy these requirements.

*Aerobic incubation technique*

This is by far the most widely used method. Soil is air dried; the fraction passing through a 2 mm. sieve is placed in a container e.g. a beaker. Sufficient water is added to bring the soil to about 60 per cent field capacity, at which stage the gas-filled pore space is usually greater than 10 per cent. The soil is incubated at a standard temperature and at intervals any water lost by evaporation is compensated by the addition of the requisite quantity of distilled water. Metabolism is usually followed by measuring oxygen uptake, carbon dioxide, ammonia and nitrate production.

The frequent occurrence of denitrification in soil samples (e.g. Bremner and Shaw, 1958*a*), suggests that they often contain anaerobic zones. Thus measurements using such samples would not indicate the effects of aerobic metabolism but would indicate the net effects of a mixture of unknown proportions of aerobic and anaerobic metabolism, To examine the possibility, consider the use of the incubation method with a Wellesbourne soil that had been previously studied (Greenwood and Goodman, 1964*a*). After air drying and re-moistening the soil had a respiration rate, when it was not limited by a lack of oxygen, of about $1 \times 10^{-5}$ ml./ml./sec. Suppose low oxygen concentrations resulted entirely from inadequate diffusion in the gas space. Since, during incubation, only one surface of the soil sample is exposed to air, the maximum depth of the sample ($x$) if it is to contain no anaerobic zones will be given by solving equation 2. The equation's terms would have values of $C_1 = 0{\cdot}21$ (the oxygen concentration in air), $M = 1 \times 10^{-5}$ ml./ml./sec. (determined experimentally as described above) and $D_c = 1 \times 10^{-2}$ cm.$^2$/sec.$^{-1}$ (calculated from the diffusion coefficient of oxygen through air and a gas-filled pore space of 10 per cent from Penman's formula (Penman, 1940). Insertion of these values in equation 2 gives a value for the depth at which anaerobic zones occur ($x_1$) of 22 cm. If the gas-filled pore space was larger than 10 per cent, the value for $x$ would be even greater. Since the depth of soil samples used in incubation techniques is usually less than 20 cm. and the gas-filled pore space is usually larger than 10 per cent, it appears unlikely that anaerobic zones would occur in the soil samples used in this technique as a result of inadequate diffusion in the gas phase. However, anaerobic zones could occur by inadequate oxygen diffusion through the aqueous phase. The maximum radius that a spherical water-saturated volume of soil could have without containing an anaerobic zone at its centre is given by equation 1. The terms have values for the Wellesbourne soil of $M = 1 \times 10^{-5}$ ml./ml./sec. (as described above) $D_s = 10^{-5}$ cm.$^2$ sec.$^{-1}$ determined experimentally) (Greenwood and Goodman, 1964*a*) $C_1 = 5{\cdot}9 \times 10^{-3}$ ml./ml. (the oxygen concentration in air saturated water), and $V_1 = 0$ (there are no anaerobic zones). Insertion of these values in the equation gives a value for $R_1$ of about 0·2 cm. Thus, any zones in the incubated soil sample that are further than 0·2 cm. from a gas/water interface, would be anaerobic. Such anaerobic zones would be induced by an uneven distribution of water.

One reason why water in incubated samples of soil could be unevenly distributed is because it is added to dry soils. Youngs (1957, 1958*a*, *b*) has studied intensively the addition of water to columns consisting of small, dry particles. Immediately after water had been added to such columns, the depth to which it penetrated was completely saturated. After addition had ceased, a slow redistribution of water occurred in some columns, but not in others. When redistribution did occur, the bottom portion of the column sometimes became water-saturated, and the remainder unsaturated. These results fitted closely with those predicted from the theory of hydraulic conductivity.

Since many soil samples may have a particle size distribution similar to the particles in Youngs' experiments, the addition of water would produce water-saturated, and thus anaerobic zones. The problem can be overcome, however, by water-saturating the sample and then draining.

Another reason for the uneven distribution of water and thus the presence of anaerobic zones, is the use of a range of particle and aggregate sizes in the incubated soil sample. It is extremely difficult to prepare homogeneous columns of different sized particles; the small ones always tend to segregate into one region of the column, and the large ones into another region. Thus, my colleague, Mr. D. Goodman (unpublished data), found that most of the methods used for preparing uniform columns of horticultural sand gave partial segregation at least as bad as that shown in Table 4: in this column, most of the large

TABLE 4

*Distribution of particles in a column of horticultural sand*

| Radii defining position of sample | 0–0·5 cm. | 0·5–1 cm. |
|---|---|---|
| Depth of sample from sand surface | Percentage weight of sand particles retained on 0·42 mm. sieve | |
| 0–1 cm. | 30 | 39 |
| 1–2 cm. | 41 | 53 |

Horticultural sand consisting of particles, 90% of which were retained on sieves with diameters between 0·28 and 0·72 mm., was used to fill a column 2 cm. long and 1 cm. in diam. Samples having the indicated dimensions were removed from the column and were sieved.

particles were in the periphery of the column and most of the small ones in the centre. Almost certainly greater segregation would occur in the soil samples used for incubation because of a greater particle size distribution than that of Goodman's sand. The distribution of water in the samples would be affected because the force needed to drain a water-filled pore is inversely proportional to the radius of the pore. In consequence, if only a proportion of the pores between particles were filled with water, then many of the water-filled pores may be segregated in the regions of the small particles, and many of the unfilled pores may be segregated in the regions of the large particles. Thus, it is possible to have points in the column surrounded by more than 0·2 mm. of water which are thus anaerobic, even though the column has a high, mean gas-filled pore space. One way to eliminate this difficulty is to use only crumbs of uniform size as the soil sample.

Equation 1 shows that there is a greater likelihood of anaerobic metabolism when the soil's respiration rate is high than when it is low. Hence, if the respiration rate is greater than that of the Wellesbourne soil, anaerobic processes will occur in the centres of water-logged zones even if they have a radius less than 0·2 mm. It is therefore essential that the respiration rate be low.

The foregoing arguments might well explain why Broadbent and Stojanovic (1952) found that denitrification took place in columns of soil through which air was blown, whereas Bremner and Shaw (1958*b*) found that this did not occur. They may also explain other apparent contradictions in the literature.

The technique requires further modification if it is to be used for studying the effect on metabolism of such processes as air-drying, mechanical manipulation, and freezing and thawing on metabolism. It follows from the second hypothesis that the extent to which these treatments affect metabolism depends on the previous drying and handling of the soil. Thus the effect of mechanical manipulation on metabolism may be less on samples that have been freshly moistened after air-drying, than on samples that have been previously incubated in the moist state. The reason for this is that the initial rearrangement, caused by drying of the particles, may have exposed more than sufficient organic matter for attack by the existing microbial population. It appears from Tables 1 and 2, however, that the enhanced respiration, and thus metabolism, following drying and mechanical manipulation can be of short duration. The difficulty may be overcome therefore by incubating the soil under aerobic conditions before imposing any experimental treatment.

## *OTHER METHODS OF STUDYING SOIL METABOLISM*

Other incubation techniques are similar to the aerobic incubation technique in so far as they are based on the same principle of measuring the products of microbial metabolism after incubating soil. They are therefore subject to the same limitations; the products frequently result from undefined proportions of aerobic and anaerobic processes and are affected to unknown extents by previous drying and handling of the soil.

Anaerobic metabolism is sometimes studied in a water-logged soil under an atmosphere of air (Takijima *et al.*, 1961; Bremner and Shaw, 1958*a*). Although most of the soil is oxygen-free, the surface layer is not (equation 2). Volatile fatty acids formed by anaerobic metabolism can rapidly diffuse to the surface where they can be metabolized aerobically and lost (Greenwood, 1961); the amounts of volatile fatty acids measured after incubation would then be much less than those originally produced.

Aerobic metabolism is sometimes studied in stirred soil suspensions. For example, a suspension of soil is well aerated, then placed in a sealed container, vigorously stirred and the oxygen concentration continuously recorded. The rate of fall of oxygen concentration is equal to the respiration rate. More organic matter is exposed to enzymic attack in the suspension than in undisturbed soil so that decomposition is faster (Hypothesis 2). The method, however, is most valuable for studying the effect of oxygen concentration on microbial processes.

Forced air percolation techniques were originally devised to reduce the enormous variations in the nitrification rates during incubation of replicate samples of soil (Lees and Quastel, 1946). Air and water are continuously circulated through a column of soil crumbs (2–4 mm.). According to the first hypothesis, the aeration conditions are at a maximum, but if the respiration rates are high anaerobic metabolism can then occur (Wheeler, 1963). Percolation techniques have been modified in numerous ways which have been reviewed by Quastel (1963).

## *CONCLUSION*

It appears that the amount of organic matter exposed to enzymic attack, and the proportion of soil under aerobic and under anaerobic conditions are of major importance in determining the rates and products o microbial decomposition. Decomposition, as usually studied in the laboratory, results from unknown proportions of aerobic and anaerobic processes and is affected to unknown extents by the exposure of organic matter induced by the pre-treatment of the soil (e.g., by drying, mechanical manipulation, etc.). These limitations make it difficult to deduce from such measurements, what will be produced in the same soil subjected to slightly different environmental conditions. However, it does appear possible to modify existing methods to overcome the limitations and thus to permit each of the conditions influencing decomposition to be studied independently of one another. In this way it may be possible to relate the rate formation of metabolic products in laboratory samples to those produced in a field soil subjected to particular weather conditions.

## *REFERENCES*

Barrow, N. J. (1960). The effects of varying the nitrogen, sulphur, and phosphorus content of organic matter on its decomposition. *Aust. J. agric. Res.*, **11**, 317.

Birch, H. F. (1958). The effect of soil drying on humus decomposition and nitrogen availability. *Pl. Soil*, **10**, 9.

BIRCH, H. F. (1959*a*). Simultaneous decomposition processes in soils. *Nature, Lond.*, **183**, 1415.

BIRCH, H. F. (1959*b*). Further observations on humus decomposition and nitrification. *Pl. Soil*, **11**, 262.

BIRCH, H. F. (1960). Nitrification in soils after different periods of dryness. *Pl. Soil*, **12**, 81.

BREMNER, J. M. (1950). The amino acid composition of the protein material in soil. *Biochem. J.*, **47**, 538.

BREMNER, J. M. & SHAW, K. (1958*a*). Denitrification in soil. I. Methods of investigation. *J. agric. Sci., Camb.*, **51**, 22.

BREMNER, J. M. & SHAW, K. (1958*b*). Denitrification in soil. II. Factors affecting denitrification. *J. agric. Sci., Camb.*, **51**, 40.

BRIGGS, M. H. & SPEDDING, D. J. (1963). Soil enzymes. *Sci. Progr.*, **51**, 223.

BROADBENT, F. E. & STOJANOVIC, B. F. (1952). The effect of partial pressure of oxygen on some soil nitrogen transformations. *Proc. Soil Sci. Soc. Am.*, **16**, 359.

CURRIE, J. A. (1961). Gaseous diffusion in porous media. III. Wet granular materials. *Br. J. appl. Phys.*, **12**, 275.

DEAN, A. C. R. & HINSHELWOOD, SIR CYRIL (1959). Automatic adjustment mechanisms in bacterial cells. *Ciba Foundation Symposium on cell metabolism.*, 311.

D.S.I.R. (1963). Basic processes for the treatment of polluting liquids. *Water Pollution Research 1962*. London: H.M.S.O., 16.

EAGLE, D. J. (1961). Determination of the nitrogen status of soils in the West Midlands. *J. Sci. Fd Agric.*, **12**, 712.

EMERSON, W. W. (1959). The structure of soil crumbs. *J. Soil Sci.*, **10**, 235.

FRY, B. A. (1955). *The nitrogen metabolism of micro-organisms*. London. Methuen.

GASSER, J. K. R. (1958). Use of deep-freezing in the preservation and preparation of fresh soil samples. *Nature, Lond.*, **181**, 1334.

GLEEN, H. & QUASTEL, J. H. (1953). Sulfur metabolism in soil. *Appl. Microbiol.*, **1**, 70.

GREENWOOD, D. J. (1961). The effect of oxygen concentration on the decomposition of organic materials in soil. *Pl. Soil*, **14**, 360.

GREENWOOD, D. J. (1962). Nitrification and nitrate dissimilation in soil. II. Effect of oxygen concentration. *Pl. Soil*, **17**, 378.

GREENWOOD, D. J. (1963). Nitrogen transformation and the distribution of oxygen in soil. *Chemy Ind.*, 799.

GREENWOOD, D. J. & BERRY, G. (1962). Aerobic respiration in soil crumbs. *Nature, Lond.*, **195**, 161.

GREENWOOD, D. J. & GOODMAN, D. (1964*a*). Oxygen diffusion and aerobic respiration in soil spheres. *J. Sci. Fd Agric.*, **15**, 579.

GREENWOOD, D. J. & GOODMAN, D. (1964*b*). Distribution of oxygen in soil aggregates. *Rep. nat. Veg. Res. Sta. Wellesbourne for 1963*, **14**, 35.

GREENWOOD, D. J. & GOODMAN, D. (1965). Oxygen diffusion and aerobic respiration in columns of fine crumbs. *J. Sci. Fd Agric.*, **16**, 152.

GREENWOOD, D. J. & LEES, H. (1956). Studies on the decomposition of amino acids in soils. I. A preliminary survey of techniques. *Pl. Soil*, **7**, 253.

GREENWOOD, D. J. & LEES, H. (1960*a*). Studies on the decomposition of amino acids in soils. II. The anaerobic metabolism. *Pl. Soil*, **12**, 69.

GREENWOOD, D. J. & LEES, H. (1960*b*). Studies on the decomposition of amino acids in soils. III. The process of amino acid aerobic decomposition and some properties of amino acid-oxidizing organisms. *Pl. Soil*, **12**, 175.

GRIFFIN, D. M. (1963). Soil moisture and the ecology of soil fungi. *Biol. Rev.*, **38**, 141.

KLUYVER, A. J. (1953). The changing appraisal of the microbe. *Proc. R. Soc. B*, **141**, 147.

LEES, H. & PORTEOUS, J. W. (1950). The release of carbon dioxide from soils percolated with various organic materials. *Pl. Soil*, **2**, 231.

LEES, H. & QUASTEL, J. H. (1946). Biochemistry of nitrification in soil. I. Kinetics of, and the effects of poisons on, soil nitrification as studied by a soil perfusion technique. *Biochem. J.*, **40**, 803.

LONGMUIR, I. S. (1954). Respiration rate of bacteria as a function of oxygen concentration. *Biochem. J.*, **57**, 81.

MACK, A. R. (1962). Low-temperature research on nitrate release from soil. *Nature, Lond.*, **193**, 803.

MCGARITY, J. W. (1962). Effect of freezing of soil on denitrification. *Nature, Lond.*, **196**, 1342.

MCLAREN, A. D. (1963). Biochemistry and soil science. *Science, N.Y.*, **141**, 1141.

NAGAR, B. R. (1962). Free monosaccharides in soil organic matter. *Nature, Lond.*, **194**, 896.

PAUL, E. A. & SCHMIDT, E. L. (1960). Extraction of free amino acids from soil. *Proc. Soil Sci. Soc. Am.*, **24**, 195.

PAYNE, T. M. B., ROUATT, J. W. & KATZNELSON, H. (1956). Detection of free amino acids in soil. *Soil Sci.*, **82**, 521.

PENMAN, H. L. (1940). Gas and vapour movements in the soil. 1. The diffusion of vapour through porous solids. *J. agric. Sci., Camb.*, **30**, 437.

QUASTEL, J. H. (1963). Microbial activities of soil as they affect plant nutrition. *Plant Physiology*, 3, Ed. Steward, F. C. New York & London. Academic Press.

QUASTEL, J. H. & SCHOFIELD, P. G. (1951). Biochemistry of nitrification in soil. *Bact. Rev.*, **15**, 1.

ROSS, D. J. (1964). Effects of low temperature storage on the oxygen uptake of soil. *Nature, Lond.*, **204**, 503.

ROVIRA, A. D. & GREACEN, E. L. (1957). The effect of aggregate disruption on the activity of micro-organisms in the soil. *Aust. J. agric. Res.*, **8**, 659.

SALTER, P. J. & WILLIAMS, J. B. (1964). Studies on available water in soils. *Rep. nat. Veg. Res. Sta. Wellesbourne for 1963*, **14**, 51.

SALTER, P. J. & WILLIAMS, J. B. (1965). The influence of texture on the moisture characteristics of soils. II. Available water capacity and moisture release characteristics. *J. Soil Sci.*, **16**, 310.

SCHMIDT, E. L., PUTNAM, H. D. & PAUL, E. A. (1960). Behaviour of free amino acids in soil. *Proc. Soil Sci. Soc. Am.*, **24**, 107.

SILLANPÄÄ, M. & WEBBER, L. R. (1961). The effects of freezing-thawing and wetting-drying cycles on soil aggregation. *Can. J. Soil Sci.*, **41**, 182.

SKERMAN, V. B. D., CAREY, B. J. & MACRAE, D. C. (1958). The influence of oxygen concentration in the reduction of nitrite by washed suspensions of adapted cells of *Achromobacter liquefacians*. *Can. J. Microbiol.*, **4**, 243.

SKERMAN, V. B. D., LACK, J. & MILLS, H. (1951). Influence of oxygen concentration on the reduction of nitrate by a *Pseudomonas species* in the growing culture. *Aust. J. scient. Res. B*, **4**, 511.

SKERMAN, V. B. D. & MACRAE, I. C. (1957*a*). The influence of oxygen in the reduction of nitrate by adapted cells of *Pseudomonas denitrificans*. *Can. J. Microbiol.*, **3**, 215.

SKERMAN, V. B. D. & MACRAE, I. C. (1957*b*). The influence of oxygen availability on the degree of nitrate reduction by *Pseudomonas denitrificans*. *Can. J. Microbiol.*, **3**, 505.

SKERMAN, V. B. D. & MACRAE, I. C. (1961). The influence of oxygen on the formation of nitratase in *Pseudomonas denitrificans*. *Can. J. Microbiol.*, **7**, 169.

Skinner, F. A., Jones, P. C. T. & Mollison, J. E. (1952). A comparison of a direct- and plate-counting technique for the quantitative estimation of soil micro-organisms. *J. gen. Microbiol.*, **6**, 261.

Soulides, D. A. & Allison, F. E. (1961). Effect of drying and freezing soils on carbon dioxide production, available mineral nutrients, aggregation and bacterial population. *Soil Sci.*, **91**, 291.

Stevenson, I. L. (1956). Some observations on microbial activity in remoistened air dried soils. *Pl. Soil*, **8**, 170.

Stevenson, I. L. (1958). The effect of sonic vibration on the bacterial plate count of soil. *Pl. Soil*, **10**, 1.

Takijima, Y., Sakuma, H. & Chiba, M. (1961). Metabolism of organic acids in soils of paddy fields and their inhibitory effect on rice growth. 6. The accumulation of organic acids in the presence of sucrose and its relationship to growth inhibition of rice seedlings. *J. Sci. Soil, Tokyo*, **32**, 390.

Waring, S. A. & Bremner, J. M. (1964). Effect of soil mesh size on the estimation of mineralizable nitrogen in soils. *Nature, Lond.*, **202**, 1141.

Wheeler, B. E. J. (1963). The conversion of amino acids in soils. II. Denitrification in percolated soils. *Pl. Soil*, **19**, 219.

Wijler, J. & Delwiche, C. C. (1954). Investigations on the denitrifying process in soil. *Pl. Soil*, **5**, 155.

Winsor, G. W. & Pollard, A. G. (1956). Carbon-nitrogen relationships in soil. II. Quantitative relationships between nitrogen immobilized and carbon added to the soil. *J. Sci. Fd Agric.*, **7**, 142.

Wood, R. A. (1966). Analagous nitrogen mineralization effects produced by soils under grass leys and sugar cane. *8th Int. Congr. Soil Sci., Bucharest* (in the press).

Youngs, E. G. (1957). Moisture profiles during vertical infiltration. *Soil Sci.*, **84**, 283.

Youngs, E. G. (1958*a*). Redistribution of moisture in porous materials after infiltration. I. *Soil Sci.*, **86**, 117.

Youngs, E. G. (1958*b*). Redistribution of moisture in porous materials after infiltration. II. *Soil Sci.*, **86**, 202.

# THE PLATE COUNT TECHNIQUE

VAGN JENSEN

*Department of General Microbiology,*
*Royal Veterinary and Agricultural College, Copenhagen*

## *INTRODUCTION*

The plate count is a constituent part of most elementary courses in soil microbiology, and superficially it looks quite simple and easy. However, a closer examination of this technique tends to give an impression of uncertainty and unreliability. We do not know exactly what the resulting figures represent, except that they do not represent what was originally aimed at, the total microflora of the soil, and we know that the figures are complicated by large experimental errors.

It cannot be denied, therefore, that the value of these plate counts is dubious, and it has been questioned seriously whether it is even worth while to make this sort of experiment. The fact remains, however, that if we wish to study the soil microflora in general, we have no other suitable method at our disposal. In spite of strenuous attempts it has not yet been possible to find a technique which can replace the plate count.

Therefore, if we do not wish to completely abandon this kind of investigation, we cannot entirely reject the plate count; but it is obvious that when using a technique like this, the greatest care is needed and a thorough understanding of the many pitfalls and sources of error is essential to obtain the best possible results and avoid mistakes and misinterpretations.

It is not possible here to go into all the technical details, but some of the most important and fundamental aspects will be discussed.

## *STORAGE OF SOIL SAMPLES*

Storage of the samples is a problem which concerns not only plate counts, but all other quantitative, biological soil analyses as well. It is a problem which is still awaiting a satisfactory solution, because with the knowledge and techniques available to-day, it is simply impossible to store soil samples for more than a few hours, without both quantitative and qualitative changes occurring within the microflora. Several records can be found in the literature, which show that considerable changes may occur in a short time, no matter under what conditions storage takes place (see James and Sutherland, 1939; Golebiowska, 1957; Netzsch-Lehner and Nowak 1960; Robert, Pochon, Milkowska and Falcou, 1964; Grossbard and Hall, 1964).

If the purpose of the investigation is to obtain a picture of the microflora occurring in the soil at the moment of sampling, it is necessary to pour the plates within a few hours after sampling. This is a fact which has often been overlooked, or at least not kept in mind, with the unfortunate consequence that a considerable part of the data on the numbers of microbes in soil, which can be found in the literature, is of highly limited value.

The consequence of this situation is that the area which can be investigated is restricted to the vicinity of the laboratory, and it would therefore be very advantageous if a method could be found which would permit transport and storage of the samples for at least a few days without the microflora changing appreciably.

## *PREPARATION OF SOIL SUSPENSIONS*

The first step in the plate count method consists of the preparation of a soil suspension, usually in a concentration of 1:10, but, as the bacteria in soil usually grow as microcolonies in or on the organic debris, it is extremely difficult to bring the individual cells into suspension. A complete dispersion of all cells would require a very drastic treatment, which would inevitably cause damage to a large number of them.

The ideal soil suspension, therefore, is beyond our reach. Instead, we must aim at a suspension which contains the highest possible number of viable propagules per unit volume. Many different treatments have been used for this purpose, e.g. mere shaking by hand, mechanical shaking, mechanical or sonic vibration, and treatments in mortars, ball-mills or laboratory blenders. It is a common experience, however, that shaking alone is unsatisfactory, especially if the soil in question is rich in organic matter. According to our experience, the laboratory blender is the most expedient and most convenient device for this purpose (see also Paarlahti and Hanioja, 1962), and it has the great advantage that the treatment can be reproduced accurately, contrary to shaking by hand and treatment in a mortar.

It is possible to improve the degree of dispersion by adding dispersing agents to the suspension, e.g. sodium pyrophosphate. The addition of pyrophosphate has been reported to increase significantly the number of colonies on the plates (Augier and Lavergne, 1958). However, it seems to have a slightly toxic effect, and damage to the bacterial cells may outweigh the effect of the increased dispersion (Jensen, 1962).

It must be realized here that different types of soil may require different treatments, and, in order to illustrate this fact, a small experiment has been made using two forest soils, a mull and a mor soil. Suspensions of these soils were treated in a Waring blender for varying periods and then diluted and plated with soil extract agar (Table 1).

TABLE 1

*Average colony numbers obtained after varying periods of treatment in a Waring blender. Dilution 1:100 000, soil extract agar, incubation 12 days at 25°, 5 replicates*

| | Mixing time | | | | |
|---|---|---|---|---|---|
| | 15 sec. | 1 min. | 2 min. | 4 min. | 8 min. |
| Mull soil | 73·6 | 81·2 | 87·0 | 83·8 | 70·8 |
| Mor soil | 29·4 | 41·8 | 39·4 | 70·4 | 71·0 |

In the case of the mull soil the highest colony numbers were obtained after treatment for 2 mins. in the blender, and longer periods resulted in a clear reduction of the numbers of colonies. In the case of the mor soil, on the other hand, treatment for 4–8 mins. was necessary to obtain the maximum number of colonies.

The experiment gives a clear illustration of one of the pitfalls of the plate count. If mixing for 1–2 mins. had been chosen as standard treatment, a clearly significant difference would have been established between the 2 soils, whereas plating after 8 mins. treatment in the blender would have indicated practically equal numbers of microbes.

## *THE DILUTING MEDIUM*

The composition of the diluting medium is a matter of considerable importance, because the viability of the bacterial cells is influenced very markedly by the ionic environment, and because the degree of dispersion of the suspensions is strongly influenced by the ions, especially cations, in the medium.

Plain tap water is probably the most widely used diluent for plate counts of soil bacteria. However, the quality of the tap water varies from place to place, and it is not always entirely suitable for this purpose (Butterfield, 1932). It has been shown that a significant decrease in colony numbers will usually occur if the suspensions are left for more than a short time before pouring the plates, which indicates that tap water does not preserve satisfactorily the viability of the bacterial cells (Jensen, 1962, Paarlahti and Hanioja, 1962).

Salt solutions of known composition have the great advantage that they can be accurately reproduced, but some of the solutions, which have been used for plate counts, have a decidedly detrimental effect on soil bacteria. This is true for saline, phosphate buffers and, according to our experience, Ringer's solution.

In our laboratory we have for the most part used a salt solution, known as Winogradsky's standard salt solution, originally designed as a basal solution for different nutrient media for soil bacteria (Pochon, 1954). In this solution the viability of the micro-organisms is preserved unchanged for several hours, and higher counts are usually obtained with this solution than with tap water (Jensen, 1962). A few typical experimental results are recorded in Table 2.

TABLE 2

*Average colony numbers obtained by use of different diluting media and with varying interval between the preparation of the dilutions and the plating. Garden soil, dilution 1:100,000, soil extract agar, incubation 8 days at 25°, 2 replicates*

| Diluent | Interval between preparation of dilutions and plating, minutes | | | |
|---|---|---|---|---|
| | 15 | 30 | 60 | 120 |
| Tap water | 197·5 | 195·5 | 185·0 | 149·0 |
| Pyrophosphate, 0·1% | 216·5 | 246·5 | 226·5 | 217·5 |
| Ringer's solution | 148·5 | 151·0 | 165·0 | 146·5 |
| Winogradsky's solution | 275·5 | 306·5 | 302·0 | 307·0 |

According to Gossling (1958), sudden changes in the ionic environment may cause severe damage to bacterial cells. Such changes cannot be avoided entirely, when suspensions and dilutions are prepared, but they should be kept at a minimum.

The best way of obtaining minimum changes in the ionic environment is probably the use of soil extract both as a diluent and as a plating medium. This has been tried with good results by Gyllenberg and Eklund (1959) and by Paarlahti and Hanioja (1962). A few experiments have also been made at our laboratory with soil extract as a diluent, and the results indicate somewhat higher counts than with the aforementioned salt solution. More experiments are required, however, before a definite statement can be given.

Finally, another approach to this problem must be mentioned briefly, viz. the use of peptone solutions. It has been shown that low concentrations of peptone (0·1–0·05 per cent), can protect the bacteria effectively and preserve the viability for at least one hour (Straka and Stokes, 1957). Certain other organic substances have a similar effect, e.g. yeast extract. The amounts of these substances added to the plates in this way are probably so small that the increased numbers of colonies on the plates can hardly be explained as a nutritional effect (see also Paarlahti and Hanioja, 1962).

## *PREPARATION OF THE DILUTIONS*

The preparation of the dilutions is probably that part of the entire procedure which may give rise to the most severe errors. A comparison between plates prepared from different dilutions of the same soil will show that the numbers of colonies on the plates are never quite proportional to the degree of dilution used for the plating. When a suspension has been diluted in the ratio 1:10, it is very common to find that the number of colonies has decreased only in the ratio 1:5 or even less (Meiklejohn, 1957; Strunjak, 1959). This means that the final estimate of the microbial number is highly dependent upon the degree of dilution used, and that a comparison between such counts is possible only when the same dilution has been used throughout.

This phenomenon cannot be fully explained, but probably it is caused mainly by the adsorption of micro-organisms on the inner walls of the pipettes, by the increasing dispersion of the suspensions with increasing dilution and by mutual competition and other antagonistic phenomena on the plates.

The adsorption of cells in the pipettes has been studied by Lavergne and Augier (1955). It seems to differ for different types of soil and to be highest for calcareous soils. Because of this adsorption it is very important to use a clean, sterile pipette for each dilution, and thereby avoid erroneous transfer of cells. The loss of cells by adsorption can possibly be counteracted to some degree by sucking up the dilution in the pipette several times in order to saturate all points of adsorption (Wieringa,

1958). Furthermore the errors caused by adsorption can be kept at a minimum by the use of as large a pipette as possible.

Alteration of the degree of dispersion with increasing dilution can hardly be avoided, because the decreasing electrolyte concentration alone will give rise to increasing dispersion. Use of an artificial salt solution with a proportionally high concentration of divalent cations will help to retain the microstructure of the soil particles, but a certain degree of disintegration remains inevitable.

In addition to these more fundamental sources of error, there are errors connected directly with measuring the diluting media and the pipettings. These errors can be severe (Lorenz, 1962), but they can be kept at a minimum by using large quantities of media, large pipettes, and by making as few pipettings as possible.

The choice of a suitable dilution may give rise to considerable doubt because of the great influence that the degree of dilution has on the final results. The only rule which can be given for the choice is that the number of colonies on the plates must fall within certain limits, neither too few, nor too many.

In order to evade the difficulty, Lavergne (1954) worked out a graphic method and used a series of successive dilutions as a basis for calculation. The advantage obtained by this procedure, however, is doubtful, as the result is influenced not only by the microbial numbers, but also by the physico-chemical properties of the soil (Lavergne and Augier, 1955). Moreover the uncertainty will be very serious if the colony numbers do not fall on a straight line when plotted in a logarithmic system.

## *THE PLATING MEDIUM*

The choice of plating medium is a problem that has attracted much attention, and numerous papers containing comparisons between different plating media have been published. The criterion most widely used when judging the suitability of a medium for plate counts is the number of colonies appearing on the plates, but there are other properties which must also be considered. The medium must have a composition which can be reproduced with sufficient ease and accuracy, and which does not permit the development of large spreading colonies of bacteria or fungi. It must be clear, only slightly coloured and without precipitates, so that even very small colonies can be seen and recognized as colonies.

Different modifications of soil extract agar will, when properly prepared, fulfil these requirements better than most other media. The importance of soil extract for the enumeration and study of soil bacteria has been emphasized repeatedly by many soil biologists (Lochhead and Burton, 1956; Chalvignac, 1957). However, entirely synthetic media can also be used with satisfactory results. The medium given by Thornton (1922) is a very convenient medium for plate counts, although the number of colonies are usually somewhat lower than with soil extract agar. It must be kept in mind that, no matter what medium is used, only some of the soil bacteria will be able to develop and the results will represent only a certain section of the bacterial population.

The main objection to the use of soil extract agar has been the uncontrollable composition of this medium, but it is a general experience that the type of soil used for the preparation of the extract is of less importance than might be expected (Smith and Worden, 1925; James, 1959). It may seem probable that soil extract agar prepared from the type of soil under investigation would give the highest counts, but that is not the case (Egdell, Cuthbert, Scarlett, Thomas and Westmacott, 1960; Jensen, 1962). The use of a normal, fertile garden soil will usually give the best results.

Soil extract agar is most often used without any addition of extra nutrients, but in some cases, depending on the type of soil under investigation, a soil extract agar enriched with small amounts of glucose and yeast extract will give higher counts (Tables 3 and 4). For certain soil types the highest counts may be obtained with very rich media (Jensen, 1962; see Tables 5 and 6). It is obvious, therefore, that the choice of a plating medium must depend both on the type of soil under investigation and on the general purpose of the experiments.

As an aid in recognition and counting of the colonies, Unger (1958)

TABLE 3

*Summary of a series of experiments comprising 44 samples of mull soils and 44 samples of mor soils. Dilution 1:100,000, incubation 2 weeks at 25°. The figures indicate the average number of colonies obtained on the three different media*

| Plating medium | Forest mull soils | Forest mor soils |
|---|---|---|
| Soil extract agar | 188·0 | 94·0 |
| Thornton's agar | 137·6 | 76·0 |
| Tryptone glucose extract agar (Bacto) | 154·5 | 79·8 |

TABLE 4

*Average number of colonies obtained on plain soil extract agar without addition of extra nutrients and on soil extract agar enriched by addition of 1 g. glucose, 1 g. yeast extract and 1 g. peptone per litre. Dilution 1:100,000, incubation 3 weeks at 25°*

| Plating medium | Garden soil | Forest mull soil | Forest mor soils |
|---|---|---|---|
| Plain soil extract agar | 139·0 | 76·6 | 47·4 |
| Enriched soil extract agar | 106·0 | 88·5 | 57·4 |

recommends the addition of 2,3,5-triphenyl-tetrazolium salts to the plating medium. This addition will cause all bacterial colonies to assume a distinct red colour, making even very small colonies clearly visible and easily distinguishable from precipitates or soil particles. The

TABLE 5

*Average number of colonies obtained after varying periods of incubation at 25° and 30°. Soil extract agar, dilution 1:100,000*

| | | Incubation, days | | | | | |
|---|---|---|---|---|---|---|---|
| | | 2 | 4 | 6 | 8 | 12 | 20 |
| Garden soil | 25° | 172 | 283 | 361 | 401 | 465 | 519 |
| | 30° | 158 | 296 | 352 | 361 | 410 | 417 |
| Forest mull soil | 25° | 36 | 88 | 118 | 128 | 126 | 131 |
| | 30° | 21 | 41 | 47 | 53 | 57 | 59 |

TABLE 6

*Average number of colonies obtained after varying periods of incubation at 25° and 30°. Tryptone glucose extract agar (Bacto), dilution 1:100,000*

| | | Incubation, days | | | | | |
|---|---|---|---|---|---|---|---|
| | | 2 | 4 | 6 | 8 | 12 | 20 |
| Garden soil | 25° | 216 | 291 | 293 | 328 | 321 | 326 |
| | 30° | 259 | 334 | 310 | 290 | 303 | 254 |
| Forest mull soil | 25° | 74 | 130 | 149 | 146 | 141 | 136 |
| | 30° | 15 | 61 | 65 | 68 | 66 | 63 |

low concentration of the tetrazolium salts used in the medium (0·001 per cent) seems to be without significant toxic or growth-inhibiting effects.

## *PERIOD AND TEMPERATURE OF INCUBATION*

The period of incubation necessary to obtain the maximum number of colonies depends both on the temperature and the plating medium. With rich media the maximum numbers are reached within a comparatively short time. Waksman (1922) found very little increase in numbers by incubation for more than 7 days at 25° using egg-albumen agar. With the media generally used to-day, which are poorer in nutrients, a longer incubation period will usually be necassary. Lochhead and Burton (1956), found more colonies after 14 than after 9 days at 26° with soil extract agar as plating medium, and Skinner, Jones and Mollison (1952), found 2–3 times as many colonies after 5 weeks than after 2 weeks using a mineral medium with very low concentrations of glucose (0·001 per cent), and yeast extract (0·0005 per cent).

This aspect of the plate count, however, is also highly dependent on the type of soil under investigation, because the extremely slow-growing bacteria may form a dominant part of the population in some soil types, whereas they may be rare or absent in other soils. This is illustrated by the experiments recorded in Tables 5 and 6 (cf. Jensen, 1962, Figs. 4 to 6). In these experiments parallel plates with soil extract agar and tryptone glucose extract agar (Bacto), were incubated at 25° and 30°, and the colonies counted at intervals up to 20 days.

A garden soil and a forest mull soil were compared. In the case of the forest soil the maximum number of colonies was reached after 6 to 8 days on both media and at both temperatures, whereas in the case of the garden soil the colony number was still increasing on the soil extract agar after 20 days. Similar results were obtained in a considerable number of experiments, where the colonies were counted after incubation for 1, 2 and 3 weeks (Jensen, 1962).

Furthermore the experiments show that an increase in the temperature from 25° to 30° may result in a very marked decrease in the number of colonies. 25° is the temperature most often used for plate counts of soil bacteria, but if cooled incubators are available, a temperature of about 20°–22° will probably give still higher counts (Thornton, 1922).

## *THE PROBLEM OF STANDARDIZATION*

Is it possible to standardize the plate count technique to such a degree that identical or comparable results can be obtained by different investigators in different laboratories? This is a question which has been the subject of much discussion among soil microbiologists (Wieringa, 1958), but direct experimental evidence concerning this problem is sparse. The most important contribution is probably the work done by Egdell *et al.*(1960).

By collaboration between several laboratories it was demonstrated that plate counts on the same soil samples made in different laboratories under conditions standardized as strictly as possible still show significant differences. It was not possible to establish the causes of these differences exactly, but the plate count method involves many operations which are difficult to specify in detail. One of the most important sources of error was believed to be the variation in methods of preparation of the plating medium (soil extract agar).

The impossibility of obtaining a satisfactory standardization of the plate count is also indicated clearly, although more indirectly, by the numerous publications dealing with this technique. A study of these publications will show many examples of inexplicable divergences and disagreements between different investigators. In some laboratories the highest counts are obtained on one plating medium, and in other laboratories on a quite different medium. The same applies to the different solutions used as diluents, and this proves clearly that minor individual differences in the performance of the counts may have a strong influence on the results.

The consequence of this seems to be that direct comparison between plate counts should be restricted to results from the same series of experiments performed by the same person in the same laboratory using the same batch of medium, although a more indirect comparison may be possible by the use of 'control soils', which are plated and counted at the same time as the test soils, as proposed by Egdell *et al.* (1960).

The study also shows that methods described in the literature should not be adopted without thorough re-examination, because such methods may be found to be more or less unsuitable under laboratory conditions different from those under which they were elaborated.

## *ATTEMPT AT AN EVALUATION OF THE PLATE COUNT*

This picture of the plate count technique may seem rather discouraging. The main purpose of the presentation has been to demonstrate the limitations of this method, and to warn against uncritical use of the results. The main stress has been laid upon the demonstration of the uncertainty, the sources of error and the many other drawbacks of the plate count; all this does not mean that the method is useless.

It is a technique which demands the greatest care, but, properly performed, it can give valuable information, and it is practically indispensable for certain kinds of bacteriological soil investigation, e.g. for qualitative studies of the soil microflora as a whole. It has been shown beyond doubt that it is possible by means of plate counts to demonstrate differences between microbial numbers in different soils, and it is possible also to demonstrate the reaction of the microflora to different soil treatments, e.g. fertilizer treatment (Sauerlandt and Marzusch-Trappmann, 1962).

Plate counts are not completely fortuitous, but clearly related to the number of microbes in the soil. The exact nature of this relationship, however, is not so easily evaluated. Of course, the plate counts usually represent only the aerobic, heterotrophic, mesophilic species, but according to our knowledge this group of organisms should constitute by far the largest part of the bacterial population of soil. It is well known, however, that direct counts may give 100 times higher figures, or more, than the plate counts and this discrepancy has never been fully explained.

There seem to be at least two alternatives. One is that 99 per cent or more of the bacterial cells in the soil are alive, as indicated by fluorescence microscopy, perhaps metabolically active, but still non-viable, i.e. unable to multiply and form colonies on the plating media. The other alternative is that 99 per cent or more of the soil bacteria belong to extremely slow-growing species or to species with such complex growth requirements that they are unable to grow and form visible colonies on our plating media.

The value of the plate count method is highly dependent upon which of these alternatives is valid, or whether both of them are partly true. In the case of the first-mentioned alternative, the plate count will probably give a fair representation of the viable bacterial cells in the soil. In the case of the second alternative, the plate count represents only 1 per cent or less of the bacterial population, the remaining 99 per cent being entirely unknown to us and beyond the scope of our investigations with techniques available at the moment.

## *REFERENCES*

Augier, J. & Lavergne, D. (1958). Numération de la microflore totale et microstructure des sols. II. Conséquences pratiques. *Annls Inst. Pasteur, Paris*, **94**, 766.

BUTTERFIELD, C. T. (1932). The selection of a dilution water for bacteriological examinations. *J. Bact.*, **23**, 355.

CHALVIGNAC, M. A. (1957). Validité de l'extrait de terre pour la numération de la microflore totale. *Pédologie, Gand, No. spéc.*, **7**, 109.

EGDELL, J. W., CUTHBERT, W. A., SCARLETT, C. A., THOMAS, S. B. & WESTMACOTT, M. A. (1960). Some studies of the colony count technique for soil bacteria. *J. appl. Bact.*, **23**, 69.

GOLEBIOWSKA, J. (1957). L'influence du mode de prélèvement et de conservation des échantillons du sol sur son état microbiologique. *Pédologie, Gand, No. spéc.*, **7**, 98.

GOSSLING, B. S. (1958). The loss of viability of bacteria in suspension due to changing the ionic environment. *J. appl. Bact.*, **21**, 220.

GROSSBARD, E. & HALL, D. M. (1964). An investigation into possible changes in the microbial population of soils stored at −15° C. *Pl. Soil*, **21**, 317.

GYLLENBERG, H. G. & EKLUND, E. (1959). Selection of suitable diluents to avoid destruction of bacteria during the dilution of milk samples for plating. *15th Int. Dairy Congr.*, **3**, 1331.

JAMES, N. & SUTHERLAND, M. L. (1939). The accuracy of the plating method for estimating the numbers of soil bacteria, actinomycetes and fungi in the dilution plated. *Can. J. Res. C*, **17**, 72.

JAMES, N. (1959). Plate counts of bacteria and fungi in a saline soil. *Can. J. Microbiol.*, **5**, 431.

JENSEN, V. (1962). Studies on the microflora of Danish beech forest soils. I. The dilution plate count technique for the enumeration of bacteria and fungi in soil. *Zentbl. Bakt. ParasitKde., Abt. II*, **116**, 13.

LAVERGNE, D. (1954). Significations et interprétation de la numération sur plaques des germes telluriques. *Annls Inst. Pasteur, Paris*, **86**, 503.

LAVERGNE, D. & AUGIER, J. (1955). Numération de la microflore totale et microstructure des sols. *Annls Inst. Pasteur, Paris*, **89**, 447.

LOCHHEAD, A. G. & BURTON, M. O. (1956). Importance of soil extract for the enumeration and study of soil bacteria. *6th Int. Congr. Soil Sci. C*, 157.

LORENZ, R. J. (1962). Über die experimentellen Fehler bei der Volumenabmessung mit Pipetten. *Zentbl. Bakt. ParasitKde., Orig. I*, **187**, 406.

MEIKLEJOHN, J. (1957). Numbers of bacteria and actinomycetes in a Kenya soil. *J. Soil Sci.*, **8**, 240.

NETZSCH-LEHNER, A. & NOWAK, W. (1960). Verändert Bebrütung den Bakteriengehalt von Böden. *Z. PflErnähr. Düng. Bodenk.*, **90**, 146.

PAARLAHTI, K. & HANIOJA, P. (1962). Methodological studies on the colony counts of soil microbes. *Communs Inst. For. Fenniae*, **55**, No. 29, 1.

POCHON, J. (1954). *Manuel technique d'analyse microbiologique du sol.* Paris. Masson et Cie.

ROBERT, M., POCHON, J., MILKOWSKA, A. & FALCOU, J. (1964). Étude biologique de sols au cours de l'épreuve d'incubation. *Annls Inst. Pasteur* (supplement), 269.

SAUERLANDT, W. & MARZUSCH-TRAPPMANN, M. (1962). Einige Probleme der biologischen Untersuchung der Ackerböden. *Z. PflErnähr. Düng. Bodenk.*, **97**, 216.

SKINNER, F. A., JONES, P. C. T. & MOLLISON, J. E. (1952). A comparison of a direct- and a plate-counting technique for the quantitative estimation of soil micro-organisms. *J. gen. Microbiol.*, **6**, 261.

SMITH, N. R. & WORDEN, S. (1925). Plate counts of soil micro-organisms. *J. agric. Res.*, **31**, 501.

STRAKA, R. P. & STOKES, J. L. (1957). Rapid destruction of bacteria in commonly used diluents and its elimination. *Appl. Microbiol.*, **5**, 21.

STRUNJAK, R. (1959). Influence de la dilution employée sur les résultats de la numération des bactéries du sol par la technique sur plaques. *Annls Inst. Pasteur, Paris*, **97**, 259.

THORNTON, H. G. (1922). On the development of a standardized agar medium for counting soil bacteria, with especial regard to the repression of spreading colonies. *Ann. appl. Biol.*, **9**, 241.

UNGER, H. (1958). 2, 3, 5-Triphenyl-Tetrazoliumsalz als Hilfsmittel bei der Keimzählung nach dem Kochschen Gussplatten-Verfahren. *Arch. Mikrobiol.*, **32**, 20.

WAKSMAN, S. A. (1922). Microbiological analysis of soil as an index of soil fertility. II. Methods of the study of numbers of micro-organisms in the soil. *Soil Sci.*, **14**, 283.

WIERINGA, K. T. (1958). The problems of standardization of methods in use in microbiological soil research. *Neth. J. agric. Sci.*, **6**, 61.

# DIRECT OBSERVATION OF BACTERIA IN SOIL

T. R. G. GRAY, PAMELA BAXBY, I. R. HILL and M. GOODFELLOW

*Hartley Botanical Laboratories, The University, Liverpool*

## *INTRODUCTION*

There has always been a strong feeling amongst soil microbiologists that the results of cultural experiments with soil bacteria give an incomplete and biased picture of the soil microflora. It has been shown many times that cultural methods of counting soil bacteria are inaccurate, nearly always giving substantially lower counts than those obtained by using direct observational methods, e.g. Skinner, Jones and Mollison (1952). Furthermore, culture media are generally designed to encourage bacterial growth by incorporating large quantities of suitable nutrients. The relatively uniform physical and chemical environment of the bacterium in a culture vessel is entirely different from the complex and rigorous soil environment, where there is a heterogeneous mixture of solids, liquid and gaseous components. It is likely, therefore, that the organisms that do grow in these media will be of a different appearance from their starving relatives in the soil and that they will be able to carry out metabolic conversions that they had not the energy to do before isolation.

Such considerations have given rise to the idea that any form of cultural experimentation with soil bacteria will give misleading results and many microbiologists have been reluctant, therefore, to examine soil from an experimental viewpoint. A more realistic view has been adopted by other microbiologists who, whilst carrying out *in vitro* experiments, have supplemented their results by making direct observations of the soil microflora with various techniques of microscopy. The object of these techniques is to demonstrate the condition of soil bacteria *in vivo*, without distorting the activities or composition of the microflora. That this is not entirely possible will become evident. Unfortunately, these techniques are severely limited since it is rarely possible to identify the organisms that one sees, to know whether they are alive or to know what functions they have. However, four main purposes justify their use: (*a*) they reveal the spatial arrangement of bacteria in the soil; (*b*) they allow one to follow successions of bacteria colonizing a substrate; (*c*) they may permit one to count the number of bacterial cells present in soil; (*d*) they may show the form, morphological and colonial, in which the bacteria exist in the soil and reveal new microbial types. All of this information enables one to assess results from *in vitro* experiments more critically. Each method of observation has been evolved to fulfil one or more of these aims. The purpose of this paper is to show the value of this information in ecological investigations of soil bacteria.

## *SPATIAL ARRANGEMENT OF BACTERIA IN THE SOIL*

It has been stated from time to time that most of the bacteria that occur in soil are attached to soil particles and do not occur in large numbers in the soil solution (Waksman, 1952; Alexander, 1961). Part of the evidence for this belief has come from studies on the rates of metabolic conversions occurring in solution and in particulate systems (Lees and Quastel, 1946). Such conclusions have been supported by the results of direct observation of the soil. It has been estimated that only 0·1 per cent of the soil bacteria exist in a free state in the gravitational water (Novogrudsky, 1950). However, the attached bacteria may break away from the particles and swim into the gravitational water. Similarly, free living bacteria may become adsorbed onto the surface of soil particles. Winogradsky (1925) pointed out that many of the single bacterial cells observed on the surfaces of soil particles have probably been adsorbed in this way. More recently, Zvyagintsev (1962*a*) has suggested that some of these single bacteria have probably become dispersed during the preparation of samples and then been readsorbed. Nevertheless, he was able to observe natural movement of bacteria from colonies into the surrounding water. Zvyagintsev (1962*b*) also demonstrated that if one added bacterial suspensions to soil, the cells were either adsorbed onto particles, caused the aggregation of particles and bacteria or adsorbed very small soil particles onto their own surfaces.

It has also been suggested that certain types of particle are more densely colonized by bacteria than others. Burrichter (1953) claimed that, apart from humus, small mineral particles harboured the largest numbers. Thus particles with diameters of 20 to 25 $\mu$ were the most densely colonized. However, as particle size increases, it becomes pro-

TABLE 1

*The numbers of bacteria on mineral and organic particles in 1 g. of sand dune soil from the $A_1$ horizon*

| Soil sample | Organic matter content | Number of organic particles as a percentage of all particles | Numbers of bacteria | | | | | | |
|---|---|---|---|---|---|---|---|---|---|
| | | | Dilution plate count. 4 sub-samples | Fluorescence microscopy (acridine orange counts) | | | | | Ratio A:D |
| | | | | Mineral particles | | Organic particles | | Total Count | |
| | | | Number A | Number B | % | Number C | % | Number D | |
| 1 | 4·3 | 14·9 | $9{\cdot}8 \times 10^4$ | $3{\cdot}9 \times 10^5$ | 36 | $7{\cdot}0 \times 10^5$ | 64 | $1{\cdot}09 \times 10^6$ | 1:11·1 |
| 2 | 2·9 | 13·4 | $8{\cdot}3 \times 10^4$ | $4{\cdot}0 \times 10^5$ | 43 | $5{\cdot}3 \times 10^5$ | 57 | $9{\cdot}3 \times 10^5$ | 1:11·2 |

gressively more and more difficult to count the bacteria on them with any accuracy, using transmitted light because of the increasing opaqueness of the particles. Zvyagintsev (1962*b*), who used incident ultra-violet light to detect bacteria stained with acridine orange, found that large particles had more bacteria on them than was suspected, and were no less densely colonized than the smaller particles.

On the other hand, there are undoubtedly far more bacteria colonizing pieces of organic material than there are colonizing mineral particles. As one might suspect, root hairs and root surfaces are colonized by very large populations of bacteria (Zvyagintsev, 1962*a*, *b*; Trolldenier, 1965). Humus particles are also heavily colonized. Using an incident ultra-violet light source, we have been able to show that, although organic particles provide under 15 per cent of the available, colonizable surface in a sand dune soil (see p. 501), between 57 and 64 per cent of the bacteria in that soil are located on such particles (Table 1).

One further point emerges from a study of particle surfaces. If one makes a plate count of bacteria, or for that matter a direct count, one gets the impression that the soil is teeming with bacteria. Populations of $10^9$ bacteria per g. soil are not uncommon. On the other hand, when one examines particle surfaces, the bacteria appear to be spread out, with a large amount of space separating very small colonies. Alexander (1961) has estimated that, theoretically, a population of $10^8$ bacteria per g. soil would occupy only 0·01 per cent of the total soil volume. However, since most of the bacteria are adsorbed onto the surface of particles, it would seem more realistic to calculate the percentage of the surface area that they colonize. We have recently made such a calculation for bacteria attached to the surfaces of sand grains, in the soil referred to above.

About 2·0 g. sand were placed in a tube and 4 to 5 ml. phenol aniline blue (Maneval, 1936) added. After gently shaking the sand/dye mixture, the grains were allowed to settle and stand. After 30 mins., a number of grains were carefully transferred to a drop of water on a specially prepared slide. The slides were prepared by coating them with a layer of plain water agar. The depth of this agar exceeded the maximum diameter of the sand grains, so that when the grains were pressed into the agar with a cover glass, their upper surfaces were in approximately the same plane of focus and could be easily examined under a $\times 100$ oil immersion lens (Fig. 1). If slides without an agar layer were used, only a proportion of the grains could be brought into focus. The cover glasses were sealed to the slide with nail varnish to prevent evaporation of the water from the specimen during observation.

For each soil sample, eight slides were prepared and ten sand grains per slide scanned, using a $\times 100$ oil immersion lens. The number of cells and the lengths of the major and minor axes of the particles were recorded. Assuming that the grains were either oblate spheroids or

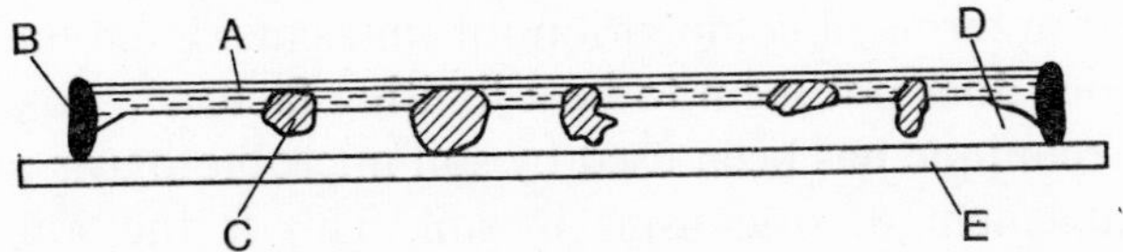


Fig. 1. Method for examining the occurrence of bacteria on sand grains. (A) cover slip; (B) varnish seal; (C) sand grain; (D) agar film; (E) microscope slide.

spheres, their surface areas were calculated. In this way it was possible to determine the number of cells per cm.² and the percentage of the available surface colonized. Further, knowing the average number of sand grains per g. soil, the total number of bacteria per g. soil could be calculated. The results of such calculations are given in Table 2. Assuming that the average soil bacterium measures $1{\cdot}0 \times 0{\cdot}8\ \mu$, the percentage of the surface area of sand grains colonized is about 0·02 per cent. However, if, as we have shown, about 60 per cent of the bacteria are on organic particles, which represent 15 per cent of the colonizable surface (Table 1), then the actual percentage of the *total* available surface area colonized is about 0·042 per cent.

TABLE 2

*Colonization of sand grains by bacteria in terms of the area covered, assuming that the average bacterium measures $1{\cdot}0 \times 0{\cdot}8\ \mu$*

| | Soil horizon | |
|---|---|---|
| | $A_1$ | C |
| Number of soil particles per g. sand | $5{\cdot}6 \times 10^4$ | $5{\cdot}6 \times 10^4$ |
| Surface area of sand grains per g. in cm.² | 72·24 | 72·45 |
| Number of bacteria per g. sand | $1{\cdot}85 \times 10^6$ | $2{\cdot}39 \times 10^6$ |
| Density of bacteria per cm.² | $2{\cdot}57 \times 10^4$ | $3{\cdot}30 \times 10^4$ |
| % area colonized | 0·02% | 0·026% |

Such calculations underline the fact that competition for space is not likely to occur in soil (Clark, 1965). However, it may be that the actual space available for colonization is not that calculated from the measurement of particle axes, but is limited to the areas in which nutrients are available; since some of the nutrients must exist in solution, such areas are presumably large and any limitations that do exist are probably better viewed in terms of competition for nutrients. Even on the humus particles, space does not seem to be a limiting factor.

Another technique has been used by soil microbiologists to study the spatial arrangement of organisms in soil. This is the soil sectioning technique (Alexander and Jackson, 1955; Hepple and Burges, 1956; Burges and Nicholas, 1961). Although this technique is helpful for studying the distribution of fungi in the soil, it would seem to have limited value for bacteriological work. The soil-resin sections are generally so thick that unstained bacteria cannot be seen. Furthermore, since most of the bacteria are attached to the surfaces of the particles and do not occur so commonly in the interstitial spaces, the chances of the section actually cutting through a particle at a point where bacteria are present is remote. A method, similar to the sectioning technique, that has been used is the observation of freshly cut soil surfaces stained with acridine orange and illuminated by reflected ultra-violet light (Krasilnikov and Zvyagintsev, 1958). Thin, stained soil sections have been prepared by Jones and Griffiths (1964) for investigating the distribution of bacteria inside soil aggregates. Whilst they were able to observe and map colonies of 6 or more cells, they could not readily distinguish smaller ones.

The relationship between bacteria and fungi in the soil may also be detected by various observational methods. The results of such investigations are reviewed by Lockwood elsewhere in this symposium (p. 44).

The electron microscope has also been used to demonstrate the arrangement of bacteria in the soil. So far, most of this work has been concerned with the relationships of roots with *Rhizobium* spp. Thus Sahlman and Fåhraeus (1963) have demonstrated the orifice of the infection thread in the root hair, and the bacteria within this thread, whilst Dart and Mercer (1964) have shown the presence of a membranous structure outside the root, within which the bacteria seem to develop. The nature of this structure is not clear, although Fåhraeus has suggested elsewhere in this symposium (p. 410) that it is the cuticle of the root. Electron microscopy has also been used to show that there are large populations of soil bacteria on the root surface which occur in a layer called the mucigel (Jenny and Grossenbacher, 1963). Other applications of the electron microscope are dealt with later.

## *COLONIZATION OF SUBSTRATES: BACTERIAL SUCCESSIONS*

Direct observational techniques can also be used to demonstrate changes in bacterial distribution which occur over a period of time. Most of the techniques used to demonstrate these microbial successions are based on the Rossi-Cholodny buried slide technique (Rossi, 1928; Cholodny, 1930). In this well-known method, slides are either pressed onto a freshly exposed soil surface, removed, stained and then observed, or are buried in the soil and recovered after different periods of time before staining and observation. By observing the micro-organisms colonizing these slides, changes in the bacterial flora over a period of time, possibly following amendment of the soil, can be detected. Pfennig (1958) has used this technique to follow the development of streptomycetes in soil. However, as Chesters and Thornton (1956) have pointed out, Rossi-Cholodny slides create an unnatural, continuous surface in the soil and allow the local accumulation of water and, one must presume, nutrients. These changes may be expected to alter the pattern of colonization. As a result, mycologists have tried to use buried nylon mesh (Waid and Woodman, 1957) which presents a discontinuous surface; this technique has not been widely used by bacteriologists, although Waid and Woodman did observe the lysis of fungal hyphae by bacteria. Instead, bacteriologists have developed a method of using special, optically flat, glass capillaries called pedoscopes (Perfiliev and Gabe, 1961; Aristovskaya and Parinkina, 1961). Fine capillaries, it is argued, more closely approximate to natural soil conditions; organisms colonizing the inside of such capillaries are surrounded by water films similar to those in the natural soil pores and events at air-water interfaces may be conveniently examined. The maintenance of a natural water regime is ensured by arranging the capillaries in the soil, in the direction of moisture flow (Gabe, 1961). The insides of the capillaries may be coated with nutrients. These may be readily available nutrients or humic acid extracts (Aristovskaya and Parinkina, 1961). The capillaries are filled with the nutrients in solution. The excess liquid is removed by placing the end of the capillary on absorbent cotton wool. Upon drying, the capillary walls become evenly coated with a nutrient film. If necessary the capillaries can be buried in this form, or partially filled with water. After burial, the capillaries are left for some time so that an equilibrium is reached. Parinkina (1963) has estimated that it takes from 1 to 2½ months to establish equilibrium. After the requisite period of burial, the capillaries are removed, and stained with erythrosin. It should be noted that because the organisms to be examined are inside the capillaries, there is a minimum of disturbance. Consequently, even the most delicate forms of soil micro-organisms, which might be destroyed or removed from the surface of a microscope slide, can be observed.

Using these pedoscopes, Aristovskaya (1962) showed that changes occur in the microflora of podzol soils during different seasons of the year. Generally, the populations of micro-organisms were relatively uniform in the spring and were characterized by germinating spores and the development of rod and spiral shaped bacteria, hyphomicrobia, caulobacters and many mobile bacterial colonies. Iron accumulating bacteria were conspicuous. In the summer, much sterile fungal mycelium was seen, together with chlamydospores and zygotes. Actinomycetes appeared and the bacteria were mostly small rods and cocci. Such changes were linked with the dryness of the soil. With the onset of rain in the autumn, a flush of algae occurred; fungi were present at all stages of development and actinomycetes sporulated profusely. Hyphomicrobia, caulobacters and iron accumulating bacteria also reappeared. Later in the autumn and in the winter, the fungi passed into a resting state and their mycelium was surrounded by slime. The actinomycetes decreased in number, whilst large numbers of small bacterial colonies were present. Bacilli were mostly in the form of spores.

If one accepts that the simulated environment provided by these capillaries is an accurate copy of the soil environment, then this technique could be most useful in much experimental work, not only for determining successions of organisms, but for the detection of different types of bacteria and evaluating their response to different treatments. The technique deserves much greater attention than it has hitherto received.

Another modification of the buried slide technique has been the burial of slides coated with specific nutrients. These nutrients have sometimes been incorporated in an agar film (Rybalkina and Kononenko, 1961). It has been claimed (Rybalkina, 1964) that these slides enable one to determine the active microflora, the latter being defined as 'that group of micro-organisms which develop in soil under certain specific conditions'; the active organisms are assumed to be in a vegetative state. However, it is difficult to see how one can extrapolate from the results of such experiments to determine forms that are active in undisturbed soil. Not only is a strange surface being thrust into the soil, but also nutrients are being presented to the organisms in a wholly unnatural way. A somewhat better form of this technique is the burial of strips of substrate, in pure or impure form, either free or attached to microscope slides or cover glasses. Such techniques have the virtue that the substrate presented to the organisms more closely resembles that which might occur in soil. So far the succession of organisms on cellulosic and chitinous substrates have been the most widely studied, though not always from a bacteriological standpoint. Kuźniar (1952) buried strips of linen cloth in soil and noted the different discolouration patterns caused by micro-organisms at different depths. Tribe (1957, 1960) attached transparent cellophane strips to cover glasses and observed their colonization after different periods of time. He observed that the early colonizers were mainly fungi and that bacteria only became prominent at a later stage. One of the advantages of Tribe's technique is that after observations have been made, colonized material can be transferred to agar plates and the micro-organisms grown and identified. Occasionally, this is unnecessary since fungi sporulate on the strips and can be identified *in situ*. The isolation of bacteria from the strips is difficult, especially when fungi are the dominant colonizers; the incorporation of antifungal antibiotics in the plating medium (Williams and Davies, 1965), coupled with the maceration of the substrate, helps to solve this problem. More recently, Gray and Bell (1963) and Okafor (1964) have made similar observations, using strips of chitin obtained from *Sepia* shells. Some new data will serve to illustrate the use of these techniques.

Chitin strips, freed of contaminating protein by alternate acid and alkali treatment, were attached to microscope slides and placed in 3 contrasting habitats: (*a*) a soil from a pine forest, established on dune sand (H, $A_1$ and C horizons, see p. 501); (*b*) mud from the intertidal zone on the coast of Sylt, West Germany; (*c*) water from the open sea near Heligoland. The colonization of these strips by the major groups of micro-organisms present in these habitats is recorded graphically in Fig. 2 (*a*, *b* and *c*) and Fig. 3 (*a* and *b*). It is evident that both the speed of decomposition and the types of organisms involved are different in the different environments and that a definite succession of forms occurs in the forest soils.

Decomposition was most rapid in sea water; it was impossible to recover the strips after only 12 days incubation at 20°. In the intertidal mud, strips were easily recovered until the 25th day, although at this time some of the strips had decomposed completely. In the drier forest soils, more or less complete decomposition took much longer. In the $A_1$ horizon, 84 days elapsed before the strips were impossible to recover. In the H horizon, only 80 per cent of the fields of view showed extensive

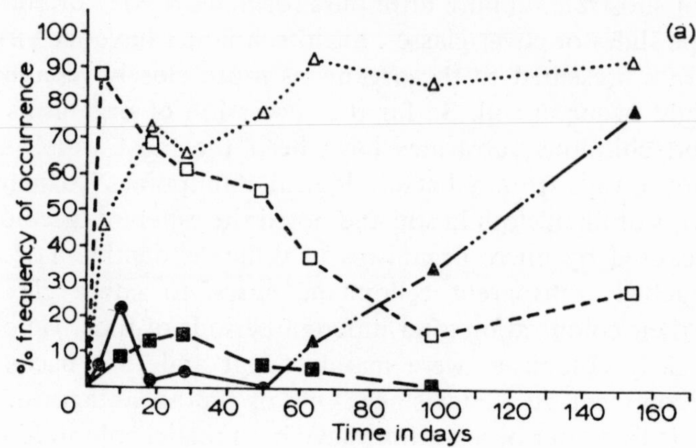

(a)
% frequency of occurrence
100
90
80
70
60
50
40
30
20
10
0
20
40
60
80
100
120
140
160
Time in days


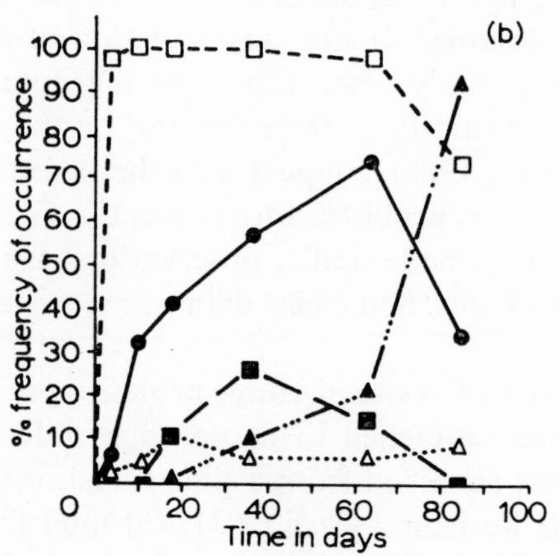

(b)
% frequency of occurrence
100
90
80
70
60
50
40
30
20
10
0
20
40
60
80
100
Time in days


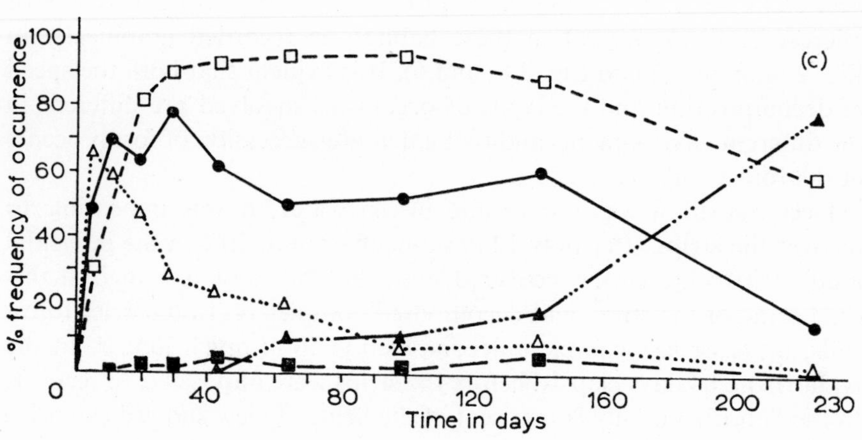

(c)
% frequency of occurrence
100
80
60
40
20
0
40
80
120
160
200
230
Time in days

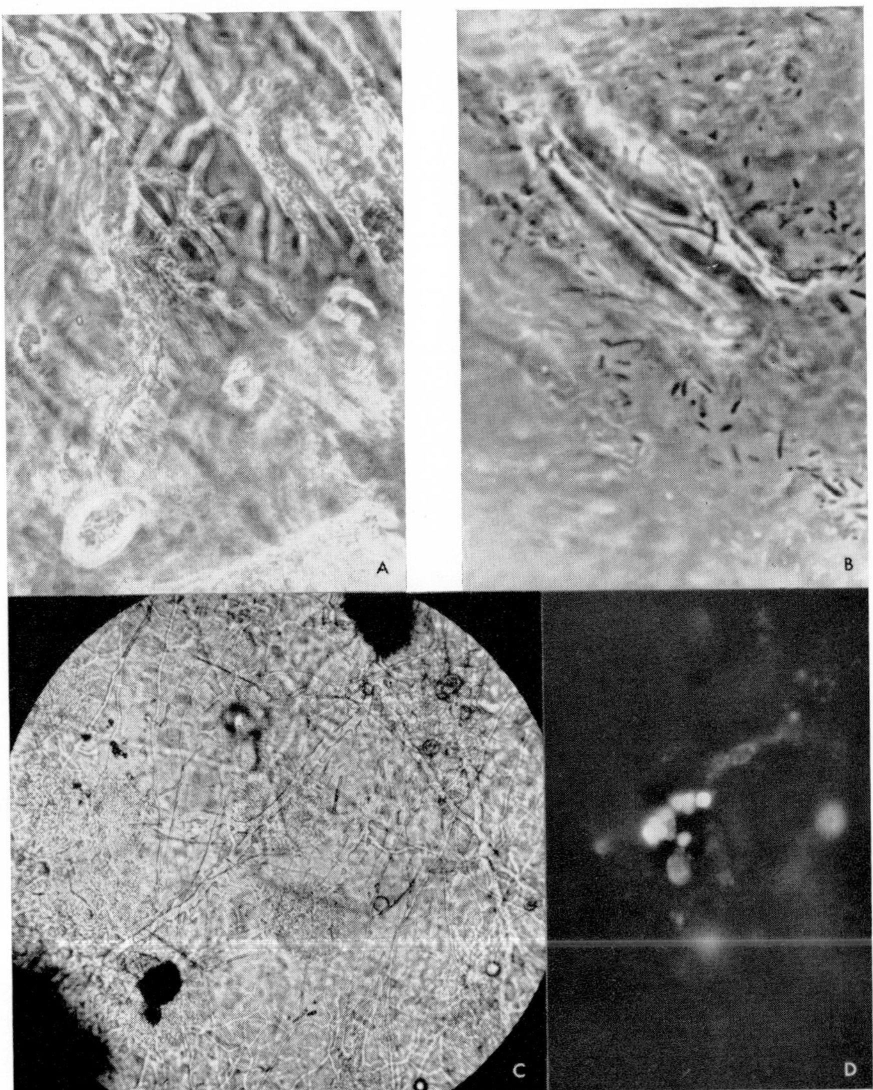


Plate 1. (A) and (B) Decomposing chitin strips in sea water showing colonization by bacteria and the fibrous nature of the chitin. (C) Micro-organisms colonizing a chitin strip after 19 days burial in $A_1$ horizon soil. (D) Cells of *Bacillus circulans* on a soil particle after staining with a specific fluorescent antiserum.

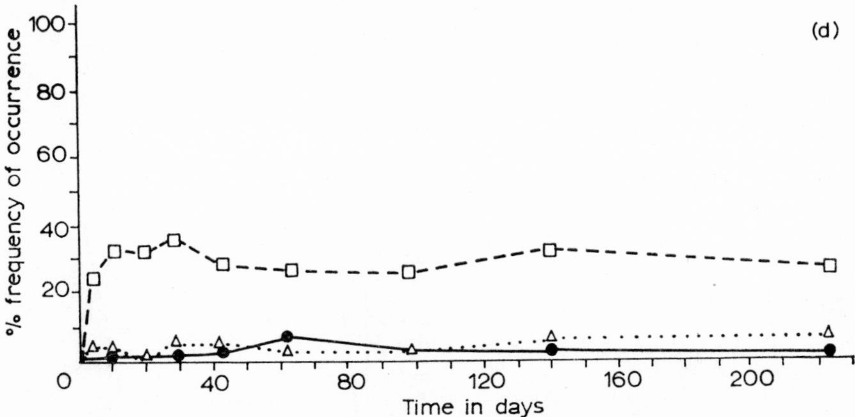


Fig. 2. Changes in the percentage frequency of occurrence of micro-organisms on chitin strips. (a) H horizon soil. (b) $A_1$ horizon soil. (c) C horizon soil. (d) Rossi-Cholodny control slide in C horizon soil. ●——● = bacteria; □- - - - -□ = fungi; △······△ = actinomycetes; ■— —■ = animals; ▲—····—▲ = decomposition.

decomposition after 154 days, whilst in the C horizon the same degree of decomposition had not been achieved until 224 days after burial. During the decomposition process, the apparently fibrous nature of the chitin became evident and bacteria could be seen colonizing the fibres (Plate 1, *a* and *b*).

The nature of the micro-organisms attacking the chitin also varied. In the marine environments, colonization was due entirely to bacteria, although occasional diatoms and protozoa were observed. The bacteria were mainly rod shaped, although spiral forms and long creeping filaments also occurred. Fungi were absent. In the forest soils, bacteria were predominant only in the very early stages of decomposition in the alkaline C horizon soil. Rod shaped organisms were the most common. At later stages of decomposition, fungi formed a fairly complete cover on the strips, although in the H horizon (pH 3·5), streptomycetes appeared on the strips during the later stages of decay. They were visible to the naked eye, sporulating profusely. Their occurrence under such acid conditions was not expected and attempts are being made to isolate and characterize these forms. The appearance of chitin strips after burial for 19 days in $A_1$ horizon soil is shown in Plate 1*c*. The organisms colonizing these strips have been isolated and their ability to attack chitin and the decomposition products of chitin tested. This data will be published elsewhere.

During experiments of this type, it is necessary to bury control slides which carry no attached substrate. Some estimate can then be made of

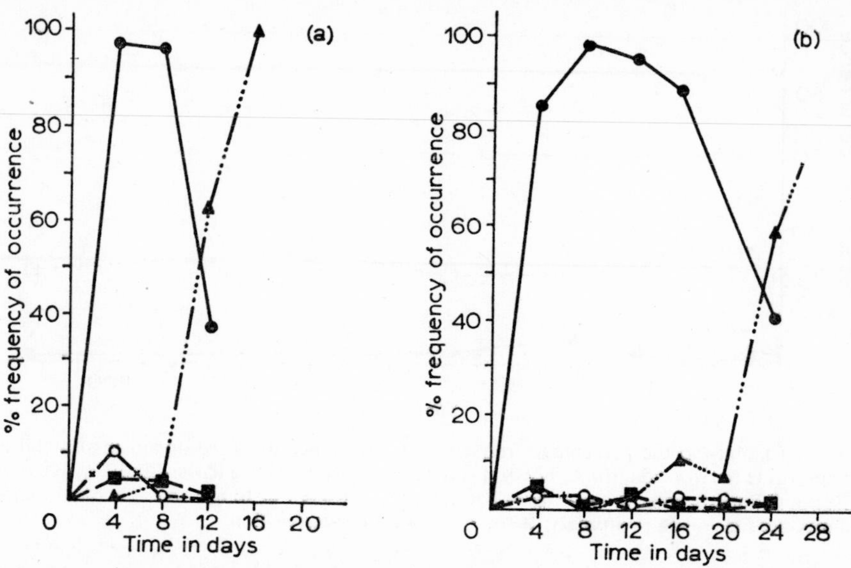


Fig. 3. Changes in the percentage frequency of occurrence of micro-organisms on chitin strips. (a) in sea water. (b) in intertidal mud. ●———● = bacteria; o— + —o = algae; ■— —■ = protozoa; ▲—· · · ·—▲ = decomposition.

TABLE 3

*A comparison of the colonization of chitin and glass slides in marine habitats*

| | Number of fields (100 $\mu^2$) examined | | | |
|---|---|---|---|---|
| | Chitin | | Glass | |
| | Total number | Number with more than 10 bacteria | Total number | Number with more than 10 bacteria |
| Marine mud | 15,000 | 13,024 | 15,000 | 249 |
| Sea water | 15,000 | 14,965 | 15,000 | 249 |

how much of the observed colonization is due to the presence of the substrate and how much merely to the presence of a fresh surface. Figure 2*d* shows the degree of colonization of Rossi-Cholodny slides buried in C horizon soil. Table 3 shows another way of demonstrating this. Random fields of view of about 100 $\mu^2$ were examined and the number of squares with more than 10 bacteria recorded. A clear difference was established between the degree of colonization of the chitin and glass surfaces immersed in sea water and buried in intertidal mud.

## *COUNTING BACTERIA IN SOIL*

Many techniques for counting the number of bacterial cells in soil have been devised. Some of them also enable one to estimate the length of fungal mycelium present in the same sample and are therefore doubly useful. Most of the techniques involve drastic treatment of the soil, so that organisms attached to the particles are freed and made easier to see; this means that such methods are useless for determining the arrangement of bacteria in soil, although they give a good idea of the shapes and sizes of soil bacteria.

The earliest techniques, e.g. Conn (1918), involved counting stained bacteria in a known volume of soil suspension, smeared over a measured cm.$^2$ of a microscope slide. The difficulty of obtaining a homogeneous distribution of the organisms means that such counts are inaccurate. A more refined technique, which partly overcomes this difficulty, involves the incorporation of a known number of easily recognizable objects into the soil, e.g. indigo particles, before the soil is smeared onto slides and stained (Thornton and Gray, 1934). The numbers of both bacteria and introduced particles are counted and since the number of introduced objects per g. of soil is known, the number of bacteria per g. of soil can be calculated by a ratio method. Such methods have not been widely used, probably because foreign particles in the soil preparation could obscure the bacteria.

More recently, improved direct methods of counting bacterial cells have been tried. The best known of these methods is that devised by Jones and Mollison (1948). Weighed samples of soil are ground with a known amount of water and then mixed with a measured volume of agar. A drop of the resultant homogeneous mixture is pipetted onto a haemocytometer slide and allowed to set under a cover glass. The soil agar film is then stained in phenol aniline blue, mounted on a microscope slide and the stained cells counted. The advantages and disadvantages of the method have been reported and analysed in papers by Skinner, Jones and Mollison (1952) and Thomas, Nicholas and Parkinson (1965).

One of the most serious disadvantages associated with this and other similar techniques is that it is not possible to determine whether the counted cells are dead or alive. Possibly the less intensely stained cells are dead, but a continuous gradation in staining intensity occurs, making it impossible to arrive at anything other than an arbitrary decision on vitality. As a result of this, other workers have favoured the use of fluorescent dyes such as acridine orange (Strugger, 1948; Augier and Pochon, 1957; Lehner and Nowak, 1957; Casida, 1962; Haber, 1963; Zvyagintsev, 1964). Acridine orange is not readily taken up by living cells and so only low concentrations of dye occur within the cell. When irradiated with ultra-volet light, such cells fluoresce a bright green colour. Dead cells, on the other hand, absorb large quantities of the dye and fluoresce an orange or reddish colour. However, intermediate colours do occur so that a clear distinction between living and dead cells is still not possible. Furthermore, it has been stated that some living cells, e.g. Gram-positive bacteria, do take up large quantities of the dye and stain an orange colour (Stöckli, 1959). Quite apart from these considerations, the colour of the stained bacteria depends upon the concentration of acridine orange in the staining solution. In a soil containing large quantities of humus, which may absorb the dye, local changes in dye concentration might occur, which in turn could change the colour of the stained organisms.

Despite these drawbacks, fluorescence microscopy is very useful. Generally, the stained cells stand out clearly against a black or faintly fluorescing background. Zvyagintsev (1963) has claimed that the contrast can be further increased by treatment of the preparations with sodium pyrophosphate, a substance previously used by Augier and Pochon (1957) to release bacteria from soil particles. Moreover, by using incident illumination, any cells attached to opaque particles can be seen (Krasilnikov and Zvyagintsev, 1958). Unfortunately, acridine orange cannot be used satisfactorily in conjunction with the Jones and Mollison technique because of the strong auto-fluorescence of agar. Consequently, the counting techniques that have used acridine orange have been similar to those proposed by Conn (1918) and Winogradsky (1925), and therefore suffer from the same difficulty of preparing homogeneous soil smears.

Attempts have also been made to count bacteria in the soil using the electron microscope (Volarovich and Tropin, 1963). Using a field of view of about 12 $\mu$ in diameter, and making 400 to 500 random counts, they estimated that the bacterial population in peat samples varied from $1{\cdot}4 \times 10^8$ to $4{\cdot}7 \times 10^8$ organisms per g. It is difficult to assess the reliability of such results as these since the size of the fields of view is small and the heterogeneity of the sample at this level presumably great.

A feature of all the techniques that have been mentioned is that they give much higher counts than the dilution plate method, when used on the same sample. Alexander (1961) has calculated that only 10 per cent of the cells counted by direct methods appear on dilution plates, although other authors have found the percentage to be even smaller, i.e. 0·1 to 1·0 per cent (Skinner, Jones and Mollison, 1952). These differences occur whatever medium is used for the plate count. Table 4 shows the results of counting bacteria in a dune soil on 3 different media, peptone yeast extract at pH 5·5, peptone yeast extract at pH 7·0 and soil extract agar at pH 7·0, and compares them with the results of a series of Jones and Mollison direct counts. In this particular case the

TABLE 4

*A comparison of counts of bacteria in a dune soil obtained by the dilution plate method and the Jones and Mollison method*

| Soil horizon | Numbers of bacteria in hundreds of millions per gram of dune soil | | | |
|---|---|---|---|---|
| | Peptone yeast-extract agar pH 5·5 | Peptone yeast-extract agar pH 7·0 | Soil extract agar pH 7·0 | Jones & Mollison method |
| | 1·5 | 1·4 | 1·4 | 6·0 |
| $A_1$ | 1·6 | 1·4 | 1·6 | 4·9 |
| | 2·7 | 2·6 | 2·3 | 5·4 |
| | 1·9 | 1·9 | 2·3 | 3·9 |
| C | 3·9 | 3·4 | 3·4 | 3·5 |
| | 1·0 | 1·0 | 1·0 | 3·8 |

discrepancy between the two sets of counts is not marked; nevertheless, only 25 to 30 per cent of the bacteria developed on agar plates on most occasions.

The main reasons for this discrepancy have been reviewed elsewhere (Casida, p. 99), but one of the contributory factors is undoubtedly the uneven dispersion of bacteria in the dilution fluid, caused by the firm attachment of bacteria to soil particles. Table 5 records the density of bacteria on the surface of sand grains before and after sand grains had

TABLE 5

*The numbers of bacteria per cm.² of sand grain surface before and after treatment in ¼ strength Ringer's solution*

| Slide No. | No. of cells/cm.² before dispersal | Slide No. | No. of cells/cm.² after dispersal |
|---|---|---|---|
| 1 | $6·1 \times 10^4$ | A | $1·6 \times 10^4$ |
| 2 | $2·6 \times 10^4$ | B | $1·8 \times 10^4$ |
| 3 | $6·8 \times 10^4$ | C | $1·5 \times 10^4$ |
| 4 | $4·9 \times 10^4$ | D | $0·9 \times 10^4$ |
| 5 | $6·1 \times 10^4$ | E | $0·7 \times 10^4$ |
| 6 | $4·0 \times 10^4$ | F | $0·7 \times 10^4$ |
| 7 | $4·4 \times 10^4$ | G | $0·8 \times 10^4$ |
| 8 | $1·6 \times 10^4$ | H | $1·4 \times 10^4$ |
| Total | $36·5 \times 10^4$ | Total | $9·4 \times 10^4$ |

been very vigorously agitated in ¼ strength Ringer's solution for ½ hr. with a magnetic stirring bar revolving at 2,800 ± 40 rpm. Approximately ¼ of the bacteria remained attached to the sand grains. Zvyagintsev (1964) has also shown that about ¼ of the bacteria remained attached to soil particles after treatment with sodium pyrophosphate. Direct observation thus offers a rapid method of checking the efficiency of dispersion methods.

One other feature of bacterial counting deserves more attention than it has received. Any count that is obtained gives the number of bacteria present in the soil at the time of counting. In ecological terminology, this would be called a *standing crop* measurement. Such measurements can be very misleading. Thus a population of $10^5$ cells which divides every 2 hrs. could be physiologically more important than a population of $10^7$ cells which divides every 2 days. A standing crop measurement would imply that the larger population was the more important. A more accurate picture of the situation might be obtained from an estimate of the bacterial productivity of the soil and the rate at which cells are dividing and dying. As yet no methods exist for determining the multiplication rate of bacteria in the soil directly. Possibly the application of fluorescent brighteners to the problem would be useful. Darken (1962) has shown that bacteria can be labelled with brighteners and that the progeny of these labelled cells still carry a visible amount of dye, even after several divisions. Direct observation of the multiplication of labelled cells added to soil might be a useful aid to the interpretation of bacterial counts.

## *THE FORM OF THE BACTERIUM IN THE SOIL*

Winogradsky (1925) was one of the first soil bacteriologists to systematically observe soil particles and record the types of bacterial colonies and cells found on them. By separating particles into different size groups by centrifugation, he was able to observe that the majority of bacteria in the soil were either large cocci or coccobacilli, some of which resembled *Azotobacter.* Rods, especially spore-forming types, spirillae and actinomycetes were rarely observed. The cells were usually grouped into colonies containing up to 100 cells and were often associated with humic material. The photographs accompanying Winogradsky's paper show the characteristic types of organism that were seen by him and which have since become familiar to many soil bacteriologists. Essentially similar observations have been made by Jones and Mollison (1948), and Casida (1962).

Often the colonies of soil bacteria are quite small. Jones and Mollison (1948) found that many of the colonies they examined consisted of from 2 to 6 cells. Zvyagintsev (1962*b*) has also recorded the common occurrence of colonies with up to 10 cells. Our own observations of 3,325 colonies and isolated cells on 420 sand particles from a forest soil, have shown that although some large colonies do occur, the average number of cells per colony is 4·3. The situation in the rhizosphere is quite different. Zvyagintsev (1962*a*) has shown that the colonies may contain several hundred cells, many of which are rod shaped. Similar results have recently been obtained by Trolldenier (1965), who inoculated the rhizosphere with pure cultures of bacteria. The occurrence of these rod shaped organisms in the rhizosphere and the presence of more coccoid cells in the soil agrees with the general findings from cultural studies. Thus Rouatt and Katznelson (1961) showed that, whilst *Pseudomonas* spp. were common in the rhizosphere, *Arthrobacter* spp. occurred more commonly in the soil. However, it is difficult to be certain that a bacterium that appears to be a coccus or a very short rod in the soil will have the same appearance in culture. The morphological variability of soil bacteria is well known, and can be convincingly demonstrated by use of immunofluorescence staining techniques. Thus, if soil is stained with a specific fluorescent antiserum to *Bacillus circulans* and then examined, a variety of different shaped cells can be observed. Plate 1*d* shows a number of rounded cells that were detected in this way. Immunofluorescence could be used to solve a number of problems, including the demonstration of the presence of certain bacterial types in the soil and microhabitats in which they grow. Schmidt and Bankole

(1963) have already demonstrated that this technique can be applied to fungi in the soil, whilst Unger and Wagner (1965) have shown that fluorescent antisera can be used to identify bacterial colonies on dilution plates.

There are a number of other techniques that can be used to demonstrate the difference between cells in the soil and cells in culture. Jones and Mollison (1948) showed that if bacteria were suspended in nutrient agar when making soil-agar films for counting, and then incubated for a short time, the colonies that developed could be stained and observed. The morphology of the cells could then be compared with that of cells on unincubated slides. Unfortunately, the results can be interpreted in two ways. Either coccoid forms might grow into rod shaped bacteria, or initially common coccoid bacteria might fail to grow and be superseded by otherwise rare rod shaped organisms. Stöckli (1959) suggested using another method that could distinguish between these two alternatives, namely staining the bacteria with acridine orange, and, after observing their morphology, transferring them to agar media with the aid of micromanipulators. Casida (1962) succeeded in isolating a number of 'coccoid-rod' cells in this way and demonstrated that they would grow into a variety of different microbial types. Perfiliev and Gabe (1961) have also described a number of instruments for the micromanipulation of bacterial cells and colonies growing in pedoscopes. Many new and curious organisms are found growing in these pedoscopes, so that it is essential that they be isolated directly in order that their relationship with previously isolated forms can be properly assessed.

A common feature of colonies of bacteria in the soil is that they are enclosed in a gelatinous matrix. This was noted by Winogradsky (1925) and has been repeatedly observed since then. The function of this 'capsule' is not known. It has been suggested that it helps to attach bacteria to soil particles, that it protects them against dessication or ingestion by soil protozoa, and that it might attract and store nutrients (Paton, 1960). These structures can normally only be seen around the bacteria *in situ*; cultures derived from them are rarely capsulate unless they are grown on media enriched with sugars or other carbohydrates. By examining soil bacteria with the electron microscope, however, Nikitin (1964) has shown that soil bacteria, grown on nutritionally poor media, possess fimbriae. He suggested that these were organs of attachment, but he was unable to demonstrate them on bacteria growing in the soil itself.

Electron microscopy has also resulted in the discovery of new and unusual microbial forms in the soil (Volarovich and Tropin, 1963; Nikitin, 1965). Previous experience has shown that it would be wise to treat such reports with caution. Kriss (1963) described a supposedly new class of micro-organisms in sea water, the Krassilnikoviae, based on observations with the light microscope. Sorokin (1963) has since shown that these organisms are actually the colloblast cells from various ctenophoran animals. The chance of making an error of interpretation with the electron microscope must be great. Many of the umbrella shaped, star shaped and twisted structures seen in electron micrographs of soil preparations may well turn out to be detached parts of much larger organisms.

## *CONCLUSIONS*

Methods of direct observation have resulted, and will continue to result, in the revelation of many interesting facets of the life of bacteria in the soil. Although they do not always give the final answers to various problems, they nearly always show that final answers have not already been found by use of other techniques. Perhaps this accounts for their unjustifiable neglect.

## *ACKNOWLEDGEMENTS*

We wish to thank the West German Government for a grant which enabled T.R.G.G. to visit the Biologische Anstalt, Helgoland, where some of the work described in this paper was done, and Dr. W. Gunkel for his help with this work. We also wish to thank the Agricultural Research Council for a grant, enabling us to investigate aspects of fluorescence microscopy. I.R.H., P.B. and M.G. are indebted to the Agricultural Research Council, the Science Research Council and the University of Liverpool for financial support, enabling them to participate in this work. The data on the numbers of bacteria on the surfaces of sand grains was computed by Mr. J. Forster.

## *REFERENCES*

ALEXANDER, M. (1961). *Introduction to soil microbiology*. New York. J. Wiley and Sons.

ALEXANDER, M. & JACKSON, R. M. (1955). Preparations of sections for study of soil micro-organisms. In *Soil Zoology*. Ed. Kevan, D. K. McE. London. Butterworth.

ARISTOVSKAYA, T. V. (1962). Principles of ecological analysis in soil microbiology. *Soviet Soil Sci.*, 4.

ARISTOVSKAYA, T. V. & PARINKINA, O. M. (1961). New methods of studying soil micro-organisms associations. *Soviet Soil Sci.*, 636.

ARISTOVSKAYA, T. V. & PARINKINA, O. M. (1962). Study of microbe patterns of soils of Leningrad Oblast. *Microbiology*, **31**, 313.

AUGIER, J. & POCHON, J. (1957). La numération des germes telluriques par la microscopie directe en lumiere blanche et en fluoresence. *Pédologie, Gand, No. spéc.*, **7**, 116.

BURGES, A. & NICHOLAS, D. P. (1961). Use of soil sections in studying amount of fungal hyphae in soil. *Soil Sci.*, **92**, 25.

BURRICHTER, E. (1953). Beiträge zur Beuerteilung von Böden auf Grund fluoreszenzmikroscopischen Untersuchung ihrer Mikroflora. *Z. PflErnähr. Düng. Bodenk.*, **63**, 154.

CASIDA, L. E. Jr. (1962). On the isolation and growth of individual microbial cells from soil. *Can. J. Microbiol.*, **8**, 115.

CHESTERS, C. G. C. & THORNTON, R. H. (1956). A comparison of techniques for isolating soil fungi. *Trans. Br. mycol. Soc.*, **39**, 301.

CHOLODNY, N. G. (1930). Über eine neue Methode zur Untersuchung der Bodenmikroflora. *Arch. Mikrobiol.*, **1**, 620.

CLARK, F. E. (1965). The concept of competition in microbial ecology. In *The ecology of soil-borne plant pathogens.* Ed. Baker, K. F. & Snyder, W. C. Berkeley, Los Angeles. University of California Press.

CONN, H. J. (1918). The microscopic study of bacteria and fungi in soil. *Tech. Bull. N.Y. St. agric. exp. Stn.*, **64**.

DARKEN, M. A. (1962). Absorption and transport of fluorescent brighteners by micro-organisms. *Appl. Microbiol.*, **10**, 387.

DART, P. J. & MERCER, F. V. (1964). The legume rhizosphere. *Arch. Mikrobiol.*, **47**, 344.

GABE, D. R. (1961). Capillary methods for studying microbe distribution in soil. *Soviet Soil Sci.*, 70.

GRAY, T. R. G. & BELL, T. F. (1963). The decomposition of chitin in an acid soil. In *Soil organisms.* Ed. Doeksen, J. & van der Drift, J. Amsterdam. North Holland Publishing Co.

HABER, W. (1963). Ein ökologischer Zugang zur Bodenmikrobiologie. In *Soil organisms.* Ed. Doeksen, J. & van der Drift, J. Amsterdam.

HEPPLE, S. & BURGES, A. (1956). Sectioning of soil. *Nature, Lond.*, **177**, 1186.

JENNY, H. & GROSSENBACHER, K. (1963). Root-soil boundary zones as seen by the electron microscope. *Proc. Soil Sci. Soc. Am.*, **27**, 273.

JONES, D. & GRIFFITHS, E. (1964). The use of soil sections for the study of soil micro-organisms. *Pl. Soil*, **20**, 232.

JONES, P. C. T. & MOLLISON, J. E. (1948). A technique for the quantitative estimation of soil micro-organisms. *J. gen. Microbiol.*, **2**, 54.

KRASILNIKOV, N. A. & ZVYAGINTSEV, D. G. (1958). The use of fluorescence microscopy in reflected light for the study of the soil microflora. *Dokl. Akad. Nauk. SSSR.*, **123**, 366.

KRISS, A. E. (1963). *Marine microbiology* (*Deep sea*). Edinburgh. Oliver & Boyd.

KUŹNIAR, K. (1952). Energia rozkładu Błonnika w glebach Białowieskiego parku narodowego. *Acta microbiol. pol.*, **1**, 257.

LEES, H. & QUASTEL, J. H. (1946). Biochemistry of nitrification in soil. 1. Kinetics of, and the effects of poisons on, soil nitrification, as studied by a soil perfusion technique. *Biochem. J.*, **40**, 803.

LEHNER, A. & NOWAK, W. (1957). Bakeriologische Bodenuntersuchung mit Hilfe von Acridinorange nach Strugger. *Zentbl. Bakt. ParasitKde., Abt. II.*, **110**, 349.

MANEVAL, W. E. (1936). Lactophenol preparations. *Stain Technol.*, **11**, 9.

NIKITIN, D. A. (1964). Use of the electron microscope in the study of soil suspensions and cultures of micro-organisms. *Soviet Soil Sci.*, 636.

NIKITIN, D. A. (1965). Electronmicroscopy of total soil microorganism preparations. In *Plant microbes relationships*. Ed. Macura, J. & Vančura, V. Prague. Czechoslovak Academy of Sciences.

NOVOGRUDSKY, D. M. (1950). Problems of the intra- and inter-species interrelationships of soil microorganisms. *Agrobiologiya*, **5**, 48.

OKAFOR, M. N. (1964). *Studies on the microbiology of decomposition in soil with particular reference to chitin*. Ph.D. Thesis. Cambridge. University of Cambridge.

PARINKINA, O. M. (1963). Determination of necessary times of exposure of pedoscopes in soil for demonstration of the microbial community. *Microbiology*, **32**, 84.

PATON, A. M. (1960). The role of *Pseudomonas* in plant disease. *J. appl. Bact.*, **23**, 526.

PERFILIEV, B. V. & GABE, D. R. (1961). *Capillary methods of studying micro-organisms*. Moscow-Leningrad. Academy of Sciences, USSR.

PFENNIG, N. (1958). Beobachtungen des Wachstumsverhaltens von Streptomyceten auf Rossi-Cholodny aufwuchsplatten in Boden. *Arch. Mikrobiol.*, **31**, 206.

ROSSI, G. M. (1928). Il terreno agrario nella teoria e nelle realta. *Italia agric.*, 4.

ROUATT, J. W. & KATZNELSON, M. (1961). A study of the bacteria on the root-surface and in the rhizosphere soil of crop plants. *J. appl. Bact.*, **24**, 164.

RYBALKINA, A. V. (1964). S. N. Vinogradskiy's views and methods in soil microbiology. *Soviet Soil Sci.*, 391.

RYBALKINA, A. V. & KONONENKO, Y. V. (1961). Microflora and nitrogen regime of some humus-peat soils. In *Mikroorganizmy i organich veshchestvo pochv*. Moscow. Academy of Sciences, USSR.

SAHLMAN, K. & FÅHRAEUS, G. (1963). An electron microscope study of root-hair infection by *Rhizobium*. *J. gen. Microbiol.*, **33**, 425.

SCHMIDT, E. L. & BANKOLE, R. O. (1963). The use of fluorescent antibody with the buried slide technique. In *Soil organisms*. Ed. Doeksen, J. & van der Drift, J. Amsterdam. North Holland Publishing Co.

SKINNER, F. E., JONES, P. C. T. & MOLLISON, J. E. (1952). A comparison of a direct- and a plate-counting technique for the quantitative estimation of soil micro-organisms. *J. gen. Microbiol.*, **6**, 261.

SOROKIN, Y. I. (1963). On the true nature of the new class of micro-organisms Krassilnikoviae (Kriss). *Microbiology*, **32**, 362.

STÖCKLI, A. (1959). Die fluoreszenzmikroskopie in der bakteriologischen Bodenuntersuchung. *Scweiz. landw. Mh.*, No. 4/5, 162.

STRUGGER, S. (1948). Fluorescence microscope examination of bacteria in soil. *Can. J. Res., C*, **26**, 188.

THOMAS, A., NICHOLAS, D. P. & PARKINSON, D. (1965). Modifications of the agar film technique for assaying lengths of mycelium in soil. *Nature, Lond.*, **205**, 105.

THORNTON, H. G. & GRAY, P. H. H. (1934). The numbers of bacterial cells in field soils as estimated by the ratio method. *Proc. R. Soc., B*, **115**, 522.

TRIBE, H. T. (1957). Ecology of micro-organisms in soils as observed during their development upon buried cellulose film. In *Microbial ecology*. Ed. Spicer, C. C. & Williams, R. E. O. *Symp. Soc. gen. Microbiol.*, **7**, 287.

TRIBE, H. T. (1960). Decomposition of buried cellulose film, with special reference to the ecology of certain soil fungi. In *The ecology of soil fungi*. Ed. Parkinson, D. & Waid, J. S. Liverpool. Liverpool University Press.

TROLLDENIER, G. (1965). Fluoreszenzmikroskopische Untersuchung von Mikroorganismenreinkulturen in der Rhizosphäre. *Zentbl. Bakt. ParasitKde., Abt. II*, **119**, 256.

UNGER, H. & WAGNER, M. (1965). Das Verhalten enteropathogener Serotypen von *Escherichia coli* in zwei verschiedenen Böden. Modellversuche mit Hilfe der makroskopischen Immunofluoreszenzmethode. *Zentbl. Bakt. ParasitKde., Abt. II*, **119**, 474.

VOLAROVICH, M. P. & TROPIN, V. P. (1963). An electron-microscopic investigation of peat microflora. *Microbiology*, **32**, 241.

WAID, J. S. & WOODMAN, M. J. (1957). A method of estimating hyphal activity in soil. *Pédologie, Gand, No. spéc.*, **7**, 155.

WAKSMAN, S. A. (1952). *Soil microbiology*. London. Chapman & Hall.

WILLIAMS, S. T. & DAVIES, F. L. (1965). Use of antibiotics for selective isolation and enumeration of actinomycetes in soil. *J. gen. Microbiol.*, **38**, 251.

WINOGRADSKY, M. S. (1925). Etudes sur la microbiologie du sol. 1. Sur la méthode. *Annls Inst. Pasteur, Paris*, **39**, 299.

ZVYAGINTSEV, D. G. (1962*a*). Rhizosphere microflora as studied by fluorescent microscopy in reflected light. *Microbiology*, **31**, 88.

ZVYAGINTSEV, D. G. (1962*b*). Adsorption of micro-organisms by soil particles. *Soviet Soil Sci.*, 140.

ZVYAGINTSEV, D. G. (1963). Use of quenchers in the investigation of soil micro-organisms by fluorescence microscopy. *Microbiology*, **32**, 622.

ZVYAGINTSEV, D. G. (1964). Study of shapes and size of micro-organisms with the fluorescence microscope. *Soviet Soil Sci.*, 307.

## *DISCUSSION*

## METHODS FOR ISOLATION AND ESTIMATION OF ACTIVITY OF SOIL BACTERIA

*Chairman: E. L. Schmidt, University of Minnesota*

*Prof. E. L. Schmidt.* One of the things that emerges from this group of papers is that measuring the activity of micro-organisms is a very complicated problem. The closer you come to a soil system, the more complicated it becomes. This is not a new idea, but it is an idea that is worth recalling. It is good for the soul, good for the data and good for the interpretation of that data.

The application of the methods that have been described has been directed towards two main ends. Almost all the work that has been done has been in connection with *one* of these ends, namely the comprehensive study of the ecology of soil bacteria, examining a large number of soils to get some idea of the overall distribution of bacteria and their activity, or to investigate a particular soil under a wide range of circumstances. In contrast, the second direction that has been followed has been the study of particular soil micro-organisms within the soil complex to get an idea of the performance of the individual within the total ecological system. If you can take an organism that is of interest for some particular reason, e.g. it fixes nitrogen, produces an antibiotic or vitamin or decomposes a pesticide, and then select and study that organism by the use of new techniques, one may get some idea of the ecological system as applied to that organism. Given enough of these studies, one may certainly make a contribution to the total background information that we have already.

*Prof. D. Parkinson.* Professor Schmidt, when you put forward the view that we should be indulging in more intensive autecological investigation, presumably you were contemplating a biochemical and physiological approach being applied to systematically well-documented situations. Doesn't this put the cart before the horse? Should we make autecological observations before the soul-destroying synecological work has been attempted? We must think of the soil as a very heterogeneous biological-physical-chemical system in which there are many groups of organisms. Surely, we cannot conceive of nitrification in isolation; we must think of it in relation to all the other soil processes, antagonisms, synergisms and so forth. Until we get an idea of the microbial mass in the soil and the types of organisms that are present, against which these other organisms must compete, we cannot really do any constructive autecological work.

*Prof. E. L. Schmidt.* My only suggestion was that as soon as methods are available to investigate individual organisms within the soil environment, these should be used to provide clues as to what is happening to other organisms.

*Prof. D. Pramer.* Firstly, I want to comment briefly on Dr. Casida's statement that silica gel is difficult to prepare. It isn't any more. It can be prepared from sodium silicate solution by passing it through an ion exchange column. The silicic acid can then be sterilized and stored until required. It is just as convenient as making agar.

Secondly, we have done some work with the fluorescent brightener that Darken described, also referred to by Dr. Casida. We have worked with fungal spores, not with bacteria. They were pretreated with brightener and this proved to be helpful in studying spore germination in the soil. One could readily detect the spores, germinated and ungerminated, in the soil by using a UV microscope.

Finally, I would like to point out that immunofluorescence can be used to identify organisms in natural soil as well as in sterile soil.

*Dr. G. W. Harmsen.* I would like to ask Dr. Jensen whether it is really necessary to try to get the highest number of bacteria, using the plate-count method. Isn't it more important to use those media and those methods for plate counts whereby you approach, as far as possible, the situation that exists in the soil under field conditions. In this respect, soil extract media must be considered an improvement upon the old-fashioned, so-called rich media, e.g. meat extract, yeast extract and glucose media. We are all aware that plate counts detect only a small percentage of the total microbial populations in soil, so that to try to increase this percentage by improving the method is scarcely worthwhile.

*Prof. E. Küster.* How significant is the nature of the soil from which the soil extract is prepared? Dr. Harmsen said it was important to simulate natural conditions as much as possible. Dr. Jensen stated earlier that garden soil extract supports the greatest number of bacteria, whereas forest soil extract does not. Some years ago we studied this and found different numbers of soil organisms on soil extract agar prepared from different soils. The greatest numbers appeared on soil extract prepared from the soil that was being examined.

*Dr. G. W. Harmsen.* I fully agree with this. We always try to prepare the soil extract from the soil that we are studying. This is not always possible, but we try to do it.

*Dr. V. Jensen.* Our experience is quite the opposite. We have tried to use forest soils to make extracts for counting bacteria in forest soils. We get much lower counts. We have obtained the best results by using fertile garden soils. It appears from the literature that this is the common experience. Of course it is not always the highest number of bacteria that we must try to obtain because we can only study a certain section of the soil population. That section is determined partly by the media we use. We must choose our media according to the purpose of our investigation.

*Dr. J. Went.* I am much in favour of soil extract agar if you are going to isolate bacteria from dilution plates. If you use a rich medium, spreading bacteria will develop and make it impossible to isolate other forms. Soil extract stops bacteria spreading.

*Mr. I. R. Hill.* In order to prevent the development of spreading bacteria on peptone yeast extract agar, we pour a sterile basal layer of tap-water agar into the Petri dish (Orcutt, 1940. *J. Bact.*, **39**, 100). This is evidently effective since the majority of spreaders originate from between the agar and the glass surface.

*Dr. G. Trolldenier.* Many people feel that soil extract is the best medium for plate counting. However, we know that microbes are attached to the solid soil particles. Considering this, we took a soil, mixed it with agar which contained a little peptone and yeast extract, sterilized this medium and poured it into dishes. We incubated membrane filters on this medium, through which we had filtered a volume of soil suspension. A much greater number of soil bacteria developed than on normal media, i.e. about twice as many.

This medium can be used, with modifications, for counting actinomycetes and soil algae. Five or six-fold increases in numbers occur.

*Prof. E. L. Schmidt.* Does the diversity of the organisms increase also?

*Dr. G. Trolldenier.* We found that Gram-positive cocci were stimulated.

*Dr. H. Potgieter.* Dr. Jensen, have you any information on the variations in the types of organisms developing on the different media and under different conditions of incubation? This is just as important as knowing the numbers that develop.

*Dr. V. Jensen.* We have found only small differences in the morphological types of bacteria on the different media.

*Dr. F. E. Chase.* A few years ago we made soil extracts, using different degrees of heat, i.e. without autoclaving, autoclaving for $\frac{1}{2}$ hr., 1 hr. and 2 hrs. We used these extracts to make up soil extract agar for the isolation of organisms in nutritional grouping studies. We found that the different extracts picked out different nutritional groups. Furthermore, on two occasions one of the extracts isolated almost pure plates of actinomycetes, and as you went along the series, there were less and less actinomycetes and more and more bacteria. This has shaken my confidence in soil extract. Not only is the soil you use important, but also the soil extraction procedure.

*Mr. M. Goodfellow.* This emphasizes the unnatural nature of soil extract media. Autoclaving soil extract must change its composition drastically. Consequently this medium loses one of its supposed merits.

*Dr. G. W. Harmsen.* Autoclaving is, in this respect, a very bad treatment. Expression of the soil solution without heating, followed by sterilization by filtration would be ideal. This is very difficult.

*Mr. I. R. Hill.* Dr. Jensen, do you have any ruling concerning the rejection of plates from your counts if they are contaminated with fungi? We have evidence that *Trichoderma viride*, and species of *Penicillium*, *Mortierella* and *Aspergillus* have considerable inhibitory effects on bacterial colonies in the underlying agar. Most workers using the plate count technique must observe fungi on their plates, yet rarely is this recorded and rarely is any ruling given. We reject all plates that are contaminated with fungi.

*Dr. V. Jensen.* We reject all plates which are *overgrown* by fungi, e.g. *Trichoderma.* In all other cases, we count both bacteria and fungi because we found that to distinguish between fungi and bacteria on soil extract agar was very difficult; many fungi form very small colonies which cannot be distinguished from bacterial colonies except by microscopic examination.

*Dr. E. Grossbard.* All of us are aware of the shortcomings and the agony of the plate-count technique, at least those of us who are using it. The results are either non-significant or difficult to interpret. What is our alternative? Should we still use the plate count method and yet look out for new measures of microbial activity? Do other biologists have difficulties with the plate count or are the difficulties confined to soil bacteriology? Perhaps soil bacteriologists are more honest and more self-conscious!

*Prof. D. Parkinson.* I hope that soil mycologists don't have too many difficulties with the plate count, for I hope that they don't really use the technique, except for counting spores.

*Mr. D. Baxby.* The dilution plate count can be used successfully both for titrating uniform suspensions of bacteria and viruses, and also for enumerating mixed populations in milk, soup, food, water and skin. Media such as milk extract and soup extract do not appear to have been devised.

I feel that the technique is adequate but that it is being applied to an inappropriate habitat, using inappropriate media. When a suspension of $5{\cdot}0 \times 10^9$ vaccinia particles per ml. is titrated, after eight 10-fold dilutions, $50 \pm 5$ infective centres per dish are obtained with a regularity which might astonish soil bacteriologists. I think it is also important to include some measure of significance with the results from plate counts.

*Dr. C. Dickinson.* Dr. Gray, if you make dilution plate counts of bacteria down the soil profile that you described, do you get a marked reduction in numbers? If this is the case, this contrasts with the results you obtained from direct counts, which showed a slight increase down the profile. I wonder, therefore, if the bacteria on the soil particles represent the autochthonous flora and those in the interstitial spaces the zymogenous flora. This latter idea is a loose one, but it would fit in with the possible availability of nutrients in such a soil, readily available in interstitial spaces in the soil water and continually available on the soil particle surfaces.

*Dr. T. R. G. Gray.* A short answer, I think, is no. We do not get a reduction in the numbers of bacteria on dilution plates as we go down the profile, at any rate at the depths we have so far sampled. I should explain that the upper mineral horizon, the $A_1$ horizon, is acidic and the environment changes very markedly when we pass into the alkaline C horizon (parent sand). Perhaps, although other factors may not be so favourable to bacterial development, the higher pH permits a large population to develop.

If the other arguments you put forward were based on the fact that the plate count decreased down the profile whilst the direct count increased, then we have no evidence to support them.

*Dr. J. S. Waid.* Dr. Gray, in what way does the appearance of microbial growth on chitin resemble the type of growth you get when you bury glass slides in the soil? Do you think that you are getting a similar sort of artefact effect? Also, can you tell us what proportion of these organisms can utilize chitin?

*Dr. T. R. G. Gray.* We have, at the same time as burying the strips of chitin, also buried glass slides. The colonization of these is substantially lower, and in some cases, hardly detectable at all. It is certainly true that not all the isolates from the chitin strips can decompose chitin. Many of them are presumably growing on the decomposition products of chitin.

*Prof. D. Pramer.* In your studies with chitin, did you ever identify *Fusarium* among the chitin decomposers?

*Dr. T. R. G. Gray.* Never, though we have isolated *Verticillium.*

*Dr. J. L. Lockwood.* Another question about chitin. Are these chitins pure, Dr. Gray?

*Dr. T. R. G. Gray.* We used the method of purification described by Tribe and Okafor. Perhaps Dr. Tribe would like to comment on this method.

*Dr. H. Tribe.* Untreated cuttlefish chitin, which we also used as a starting material, does contain quite a lot of protein. This has to be removed by hydrolysis. Okafor purified his material by hydrolysis with hot potassium hydroxide and hydrochloric acid treatments. He submitted some of his preparations for X-ray crystallographic analysis, which showed them to be reasonably pure.

*Dr. C. G. Dobbs.* One point which has been mentioned several times is that micro-organisms are known to be attached to soil particles. Do we know whether most of them are? I am thinking of Dr. Greenwood's diagram of a micro-organism lying on a soil particle with a layer of water over it. In an aerated soil, isn't there a surface tension layer of water over the particles? When we get growth on buried glass slides, either bacterial or fungal, it is usually in condensed water on the surface of the slides. Things like fungal spores may lie in the water, or may protrude through the meniscus. May not many of the bacteria float on the water film around the soil particles, not attaching themselves until they die or are subjected to various preparative methods?

*Dr. T. R. G. Gray.* There must be many bacteria floating in the soil solution. It would be most surprising if there were not. However, if one compares counts of organisms attached to the surface of grains with Jones and Mollison total counts, the figures are similar. Nevertheless, I agree that this point needs further examination.

In connection with this, I should like to enquire about the scale of Dr. Greenwood's diagram of bacteria in the soil (p. 144). The particles we have been looking at are very much bigger and the bacteria very much smaller. Would such differences in relative size affect any of the arguments that Dr. Greenwood has put forward?

*Dr. D. J. Greenwood.* This requires a good deal of thought. What I had in mind was that bacteria rest on the organic matter and are physically constrained by means of material resistant to decomposition. They are likely to be covered with water, and held in this way, since when you percolate soil with leucine you get a large number of micro-organisms produced which are very difficult to get off the soil particles. I don't exclude the possibility that there are some floating on the water; I think it is a matter of proportion. It seems to me to depend on the way in which you imagine the organisms get there. I favour the view that plant material arrives in the soil partially colonized and is mixed into a homogeneous mass by worms and other animals.

*Dr. T. R. G. Gray.* Isn't there some evidence from Lees and Quastel's percolation studies that nitrification occurs on the particle surface, not in the free solution?

*Dr. D. J. Greenwood.* Yes, there is a lot of evidence based on this sort of thing; there is evidence based on similar experiments concerning the addition of organic materials to soil; there is also evidence based on plate count data.

Furthermore, if you take soil crumbs and measure the oxygen concentration in them at a different distance, they fit the model I have put forward.

*Dr. M. Alexander.* Dr. Greenwood, I would like to ask you to try to differentiate between your occlusion mechanism which separates micro-organisms from their substrate, from a mechanism which is important in methodological procedures, namely adsorption or sorption of bacteria. Other ways in which organism and substrate may be separated are by the external sorption of substrates on particular material and by sorption of substrates in the lattice structure of clay minerals. We must consider all of these from the biochemical viewpoint in soil and also in attempting to devise culture media, since the organisms are going to be sorbed, the substrates are going to be sorbed and I'm afraid that soil extracts are not going to get much out of either of them.

*Mr. D. Baxby.* Has anyone any idea what governs the size of bacterial colonies in soil? Are they self-limiting or are they limited by lack of nutrients, space, etc.?

*Dr. L. Quesnel.* May I shed some light on that. If one makes direct observations of bacteria growing on a cellophane film, in a continuous culture system such as that used by Powell for studying the growth of bacteria, one finds that the bacteria settle, presumably under the influence of gravity, and after a while they grow and form a sheet covering the entire cellophane film. In other words, the micro-colony becomes a colony of the same size as the cellophane film. The same organism, growing on agar, will never achieve this monolayer or multilayer spread. There is a maximum size for the colony. No matter how much longer you incubate it, it does not grow much more. This may be connected with the ability of stiff agar to stop the swarming of *Proteus*. It may well be that when one incubates an agar plate, it loses moisture, thus increasing the viscosity of the medium. I am suggesting a similar effect here. Nevertheless, given water, I think that the bacteria will spread in all directions.

*Mr. M. O. Aluko.* My results are somewhat different. After inoculation of agar with *Rhizoctonia*, I discovered that growth stopped after some time. I transplanted some parts of the hyphae onto other plates that were prepared at the same time; growth recommenced. If we accept the explanation based on dessication and an increase in viscosity that Dr. Quesnel put forward, then there should be no growth at all on these plates. I feel that metabolic products must be involved.

# THE PHYSIOLOGY OF SOIL BACTERIA

# BACTERIAL PHYSIOLOGY

H. VELDKAMP

*Laboratorium voor Microbiologie, Groningen, The Netherlands*

## *INTRODUCTION*

*'Each organism takes part in a competition, the struggle for life, in which the functional values of different types are compared. The comparison is a functional one. Evolution has necessarily selected the fittest types.'*

A. Lwoff (1962).

During the first decades of this century the existence of a great many ecological niches in the microbial world was revealed by means of the enrichment culture technique. The extensive application of this technique, as developed by Winogradsky and Beijerinck, showed that bacteria are unequalled as far as diversity in metabolism is concerned (cf. Veldkamp, 1966).

It was the great merit of Beijerinck's successors, Kluyver and van Niel to have shown the unity of biochemical principles underlying the great diversity of metabolic types. Their studies on the comparative biochemistry of micro-organisms were a major contribution to the concept of 'life's unity' (Kluyver and van Niel, 1956).

The great metabolic diversity of bacteria, as well as their high metabolic rates and rapid rate of reproduction, made these organisms popular as tools for metabolic studies. These studies resulted in the vast amount of present knowledge on metabolic pathways and contributed to recent discoveries on co-ordination and regulation of metabolic processes.

In comparison with the tremendous progress made in the field of microbial biochemistry, the advances in microbial ecology have been relatively slow. Fortunately, in recent years the interest in the interrelations between microbes and their biotic and abiotic environment is increasing. The approach to the study of these relationships is gradually changing from descriptive to experimental and the results of this change are very promising, as is shown by recent reviews of Alexander (1964), and Silverman and Ehrlich (1964).

Depending on what kind of questions one would like to answer, there are a number of different approaches to experimentation with the intact micro-organism. Many microbial physiologists dislike complex natural environments, and soil in particular. They prefer pure culture studies under well-defined conditions. The other extreme is typified by those microbiologists who want to study metabolic activities of soil organisms in their natural environment. Finally there is the hybrid physiologist who preferably works with simple model systems, as for instance pure cultures, or mixed cultures of known composition, which are absorbed on clay minerals. It seems beyond doubt that only a combination of these different approaches will eventually result in an improvement of our understanding of the natural functions of soil micro-organisms and of the complex network of processes in which they take part.

The ever-changing conditions in soil result in continuous changes in the dynamic equilibrium which exists among soil microbes. If we could make a snapshot of microbial activities in a soil sample at a given moment, we should see that under the existing conditions the metabolic machinery of only a fraction of the mixed population is directed towards growth. That is to say, at any moment the prevailing physico-chemical conditions favour only some of the organisms; other microbes are 'dormant', awaiting a change of conditions that enables them to multiply.

The abilities of any microbe to survive under unfavourable environmental conditions on one hand, and on the other hand, to make most efficient use of available nutrients under conditions that favour growth, are of paramount importance in matters where to be or not to be is a question to be answered by the metabolic machinery of the organism. Since the physiology of special groups of bacteria will be dealt with in other lectures of this symposium, these subjects of a more general character were chosen as main topic for this introduction.

## *THE MAINTENANCE ENERGY CONCEPT*

Under natural conditions nutrients generally become available to the bacterial cell as a flow of low rate and low concentration. The growth rate of bacterial populations undoubtedly will often be limited by the rate with which one particular substrate is supplied. A similar situation exists in the chemostat, although it should be realized that open systems in nature are not homogeneous and show continuous changes with time. Even though conditions in the chemostat differ from natural open systems, it presents a valuable tool for the study of microbial behaviour at low growth rates. It provides a system which automatically adjusts itself to steady state conditions if flow rate, culture volume and inflowing substrate concentration are kept constant. As pointed out by Herbert (1958), 'the key to the mode of action of the chemostat, lies in the way in which the growth rate $\mu$ depends on the concentration of a limiting growth substrate in the culture medium'.

The steady state equations for concentration of bacteria (x) and substrate concentration (s), are the following (Herbert *et al.*, 1956):

$$x = Y(s_R - s) \tag{1}$$

$$s = K_s\left(\frac{D}{\mu_m - D}\right) \tag{2}$$

x = concentration of bacteria; Y is the yield constant (=dx/ds); $s_R$ is the concentration of inflowing growth-limiting substrate; s is the concentration of that substrate in the vessel; $K_s$ is a saturation constant; $\mu_m$ is the maximum specific growth rate; D is the specific dilution rate, or flow rate divided by volume. The values of the constants Y, $K_s$ and $\mu_m$ can be determined, and once these are known, the steady state values of x and s for each value of D can be predicted.

On comparing theoretical and experimental results, Herbert (1958), found that in most cases agreement was qualitative rather than quantitative. One of the more interesting quantitative deviations was that encountered at low dilution rates when growth was limited by the carbon and energy source.

As can be seen from Fig. 1, the bacterial concentration at specific dilution rates $<0{\cdot}2$ is much lower than that at higher dilution rates; equation (1) predicts, however, that this should not be so. According to Herbert (1958), this phenomenon can be explained by assuming that a constant endogenous metabolism causes loss of cell material which becomes proportionally important at low growth rates. Direct evidence for this suggestion was obtained by measuring cell respiration at different growth rates. A linear relation appeared to exist and extrapolation of the straight line to zero growth resulted in finite values of $Q_{O_2}$ and $Q_{CO_2}$.

Herbert's experiments are in accordance with the opinion that a bacterial cell requires a certain amount of energy per unit time that is independent of the rate of growth, which is known as maintenance energy (Lamanna and Mallette, 1959; Mallette, 1963). Marr *et al.* (1963), reasoned that if this were true, the relation between substrate consumption and bacterial growth could be given by the equation:

$$\frac{dx}{dt} + ax = Y\frac{ds}{dt} \tag{3}$$

The term ax represents the amount of substrate used for time dependent maintenance purposes. Marr *et al.* (1963), called the term a, which like the specific growth rate has the dimension of reciprocal time, the

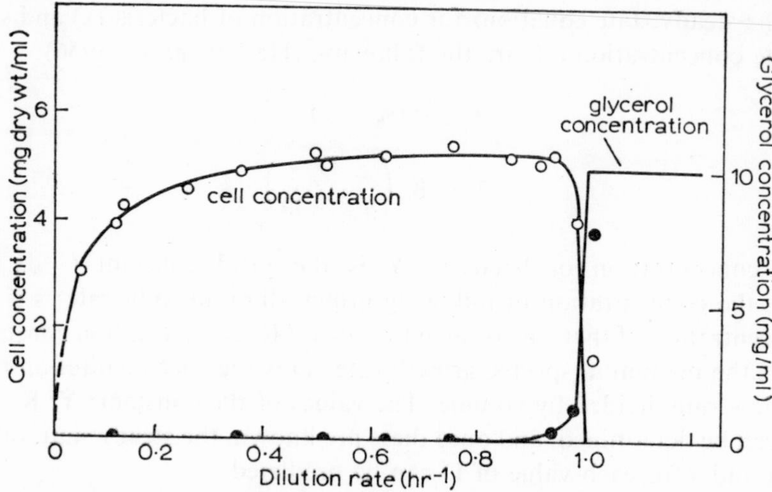


Fig. 1. Aerobic growth of *Aerobacter aerogenes* in continuous culture with glycerol as limiting substrate (Herbert, 1958).

specific maintenance rate. Herbert's equation (1) for the steady state value of the bacterial concentration x, was consequently modified as follows:

$$x = \frac{Ys}{1 + a/D} = \frac{x_{max}}{1 + a/D} \tag{4}$$

$x_{max}$ represents the concentration of bacteria obtained when a = O. Equation (4) may also be written as:

$$\frac{1}{x} = \frac{a}{x_{max}} \cdot \frac{1}{D} + \frac{1}{x_{max}} \tag{5}$$

Thus when the reciprocal of x is plotted against the reciprocal of D, a linear relation should be found with an ordinate intercept of $1/x_{max}$ and a slope of $a/x_{max}$.

Marr *et al.* (1963), grew *Escherichia coli* in a glucose-controlled chemostat and found that the culture behaved as predicted by the maintenance hypothesis; a value of 0·025 $hr^{-1}$ was found for the specific maintenance. A similar value was obtained by Schulze and Lipe (1964).

When cultures of *E. coli* are fed continuously with glucose at a rate equivalent to the specific maintenance, they remain viable (Marr *et al.*, 1963). Under natural conditions the bacterial cell often becomes deprived of exogenous sources of energy and appears to be able to survive prolonged periods of starvation. As a consequence of the requirement for maintenance energy, this means that in the 'dormant' cell processes must occur that provide this energy.

## *SYNTHESIS OF RESERVE MATERIAL*

Experimental evidence that maintenance energy required for specific purposes can be provided by hydrolysis of reserve polymers and subsequent oxidation of their sub-units is still scant. The available evidence does indicate, however, that the ability to form intracellular carbon and energy reserves certainly has survival value. A few remarks should therefore be made on environmental conditions that favour accumulation of this material. During unrestricted growth in media with excess nutrients little reserve material is formed. As soon as essential nutrients become exhausted, however, the cell may start to manufacture reserve polymers. The most commonly occurring ones are those of glucose and $\beta$-hydroxybutyric acid. Most bacteria store only one of these compounds. They are abundantly formed when the bacterial cell is provided with an excess of a source of carbon and energy and growth is limited by nitrogen deficiency. Most studies on accumulation of reserve material have been carried out under these conditions. One of the more elegant ones was that of Holme (1957) who grew *E. coli* in continuous culture under conditions of nitrogen limitation (Fig. 2). The steady state concentrations of bacteria at low growth rates appeared to be higher than predicted by equation (1), due to a considerable increase in the glycogen content of the cells. Similar experiments with glucose as limiting nutrient did not result in increased glycogen synthesis at low growth rates, indicating that it was not a low growth rate as such that caused glycogen accumulation (cf. Herbert, 1961).

Similar results were obtained in batch cultures with *Bacillus* species, which store poly-$\beta$-hydroxybutyric acid (Macrae and Wilkinson, 1958; Wilkinson, 1959). When *Bacillus megaterium* was grown in a medium containing 0·1 per cent glucose and 0·1 per cent $NH_4Cl$, the ratio of polymer to total nitrogen after 24 hr. growth was 0·3, whereas a value of 2·1 was obtained in a medium containing 0·5 per cent glucose and 0·05 per cent $NH_4Cl$.

Nitrogen limitation also results in an increased synthesis of poly-$\beta$-

hydroxybutyric acid in *Hydrogenomonas* when grown in a $H_2$—$O_2$—$CO_2$ atmosphere (Gottschalk, 1964). The polymer is also formed in *Rhodospirillum rubrum* at the expense of organic acids in the light, in absence of a nitrogen source (Doudoroff and Stanier, 1959). The effect of growth

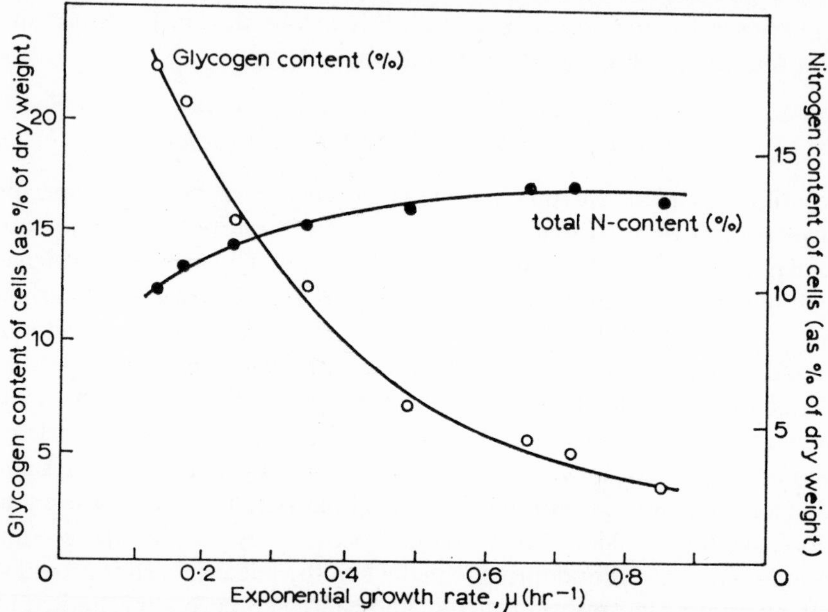


Fig. 2. Glycogen synthesis as a function of growth rate in *Escherichia coli* grown under conditions of nitrogen limitation. The organism was grown aerobically in continuous culture at a number of different growth rates in a lactate-$NH_3$-salts medium with $NH_3$ as growth-limiting nutrient. Data of Holme (1957), as plotted by Herbert (1961).

limiting factors other than nitrogen on the storage of poly-glucose or poly-$\beta$-hydroxybutyric acid has attracted relatively little attention. Holme and Palmstierna (1956) showed that phosphate starvation of *E. coli* in batch culture resulted in a relatively low glycogen synthesis; sulphate limitation too, affected glycogen synthesis unfavourably.

The energy storage compounds mentioned here are not the only substrates for endogenous metabolism. Dawes and Ribbons (1964), in an excellent review on endogenous metabolism, report experiments which show that protein, ribonucleic acid, and amino acids can also serve as substrates for endogenous respiration.

The question arises to what extent organic substrates, as for instance glucose, are mineralized in soil and to what extent glucose is assimilated in soils lacking combined nitrogen. These questions were recently studied by Macura, Szolnoki, Kunc, Vančura and Babicky (1965). They applied a continuous flow system to study microbiological processes in soil samples, which has the advantage that accumulation of metabolic products and exhaustion of substrates does not occur. A continuous flow of uniformly labelled glucose, either with or without added

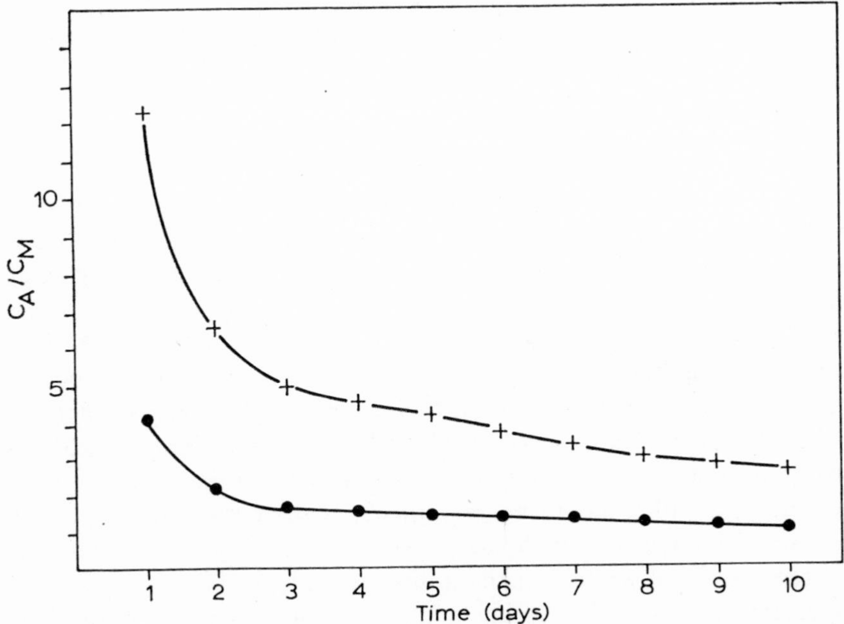


Fig. 3. Ratio of assimilated radioactive carbon (retained in soil) to carbon mineralized to $CO_2$. Continuous flow of solution of uniformly labelled glucose (0·9 mg./ml., w/v) through soil, with (●——●) and without (+——+) added $(NH_4)_2HPO_4$ (0·3 mg./ml., w/v). After Macura *et al.* (1965).

ammonium phosphate, was passed through soil samples. It appeared that glucose was mineralized to a much greater extent when applied together with ammonium phosphate. The ratio of glucose carbon assimilated by the microbial flora to carbon dioxide produced was much higher when no combined nitrogen was given together with glucose (Fig. 3). As might be expected, in the latter case a marked increase of the *Azotobacter* population was observed (Macura, 1964). This means that glucose carbon retained in these soils was at least partly used for protein synthesis by this organism. Since the efficiency of nitrogen fixation is rather low, however, it seems very likely that a large part of glucose in the soils lacking combined nitrogen was converted to reserve material by the mixed population. It would be worth while to carry out similar experiments with model systems of a more simple character.

Macura (1964, 1965), also showed that passage of a glucose solution through a soil sample results in a considerable increase of $CO_2$ production from native organic matter. Furthermore, a considerable increase in the number of sugars appearing in the effluent was observed, as compared to effluents of soils which were treated with water only. This clearly indicates that the addition of a single organic substrate to soil results in microbial activities which have a much greater effect than the breakdown of that particular substrate.

## *ENERGY CONSUMPTION BY NON-GROWING CELLS*

The term maintenance energy covers the total energy needed for processes which are not a function of the growth rate. Experimental evidence indicates that a considerable part of the required maintenance energy is used for protein turnover. It has been shown that this process does not occur in growing cultures of *E. coli* (cf. Mandelstam, 1960). In non-growing cells, however, protein degradation and resynthesis occurs at a rate of 0·05 $hr^{-1}$ (Mandelstam, 1958). This means that a considerable part of the specific maintenance is needed for the resynthesis of proteins during turnover. At first thought it seems surprising that only the non-growing cell, which has to be very thrifty with energy, shows protein turnover. Mandelstam (1958) has suggested, however, that hydrolysis and resynthesis of protein in the non-growing organism may have the important function of ensuring a flow of material through the free amino acid pool. This provides the cell with building units for the *de novo* synthesis of enzymes which may become necessary when nutrients become available to the starving cell. Wilkinson (1959) suggested that the energy needed for this purpose may be supplied by breakdown of reserve material. This suggestion is strongly supported by experiments of Gibbons (1964) with the homo-fermentative lactic acid bacterium *Streptococcus mitis*. Like all lactic acid bacteria, this organism can only use carbohydrates as a source of energy. Under suitable environmental conditions (excess of carbohydrate, absence of nitrogen), *S. mitis* synthesizes an intracellular polysaccharide of the glycogen-amylopectin type. A naturally occurring variant was isolated which lacked this ability.

By exposing glycogen-poor cells during different periods of time to a solution of 0·5 per cent glucose, cells with different polysaccharide content were obtained. These were subsequently incubated anaerobically in sugar-free broth in the presence of thiomethylgalactoside. This compound induces the synthesis of $\beta$-galactosidase, but is not metabolized. A similar experiment was carried out with the polysaccharide-negative variant strain. It appeared that increase of β-galactosidase activity of cells containing polysaccharide was proportional to the time they had been able to synthesize polysaccharide (Fig. 4). No increase in β-galactosidase activity was observed, however, in the glycogen-negative variant strain, irrespective of the time it had been incubated with glucose.

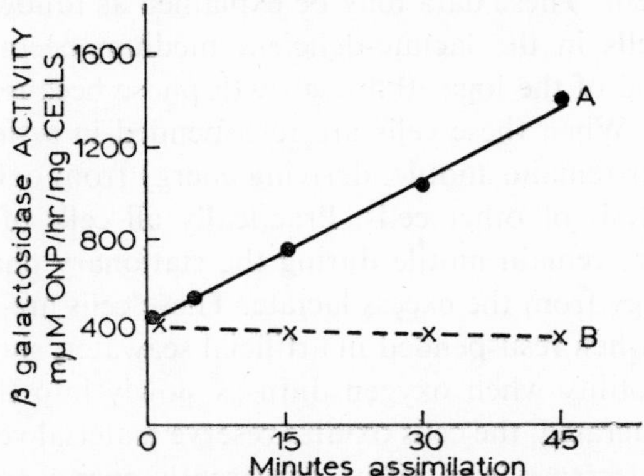


Fig. 4. Effect of time of glucose assimilation on the β-galactosidase activity of (A) *Streptococcus mitis* and (B) a polysaccharide-negative variant of *S. mitis*. After Gibbons (1964).

Gibbons (1964) thus clearly showed that energy required for the synthesis of inducible enzymes can be provided by intracellular reserve material. It seems very likely that this material serves similar purposes for protein turnover in non-growing bacteria. The same holds for energy needed by motile bacteria when moving in media lacking exogenous energy sources.

Experiments with marine *Spirillum* species (Veldkamp and Hartmans, 1965) showed that motility during the stationary growth phase depended on the C/N quotient of the growth medium. The spirilla were grown at 25° in shallow layers of a mineral salts medium containing either 0·2 per cent sodium lactate and 0·01 per cent $(NH_4)_2SO_4$, or 0·05 per cent sodium lactate and 0·2 per cent $(NH_4)_2SO_4$. When growth ceased, 95 per cent of the spirilla present in the nitrogen-deficient medium were motile, whereas a figure of 20 per cent was obtained with the lactate-deficient medium. Five hours after maximal growth was reached, the cells were harvested and resuspended to a density of $5 \times 10^7$ cells/ml. in shallow layers of artificial seawater lacking combined nitrogen. At regular intervals samples were taken throughout a period of 60 hours and the percentage of motile cells was estimated in a counting chamber. The cell suspension obtained from the lactate-deficient culture showed approximately 20 per cent motile cells throughout the entire period. During this time the percentage of motile cells in the suspension obtained from the nitrogen-deficient culture gradually decreased from 95 per cent to 40 per cent. In a similar experiment carried out with heavily aerated cell suspensions, motility of cells obtained from the lactate-deficient medium decreased from 17 to 7 per cent during 11 hours aeration; during this period motility of nitrogen-deficient cells decreased from 90 to 20 per cent. These data may be explained as follows. The greater part of the cells in the lactate-deficient medium become non-motile towards the end of the logarithmic growth phase because of lack of an energy source. When these cells are resuspended in artificial seawater, a small number remains motile, deriving energy from oxidation of products of autolysis of other cells. Practically all cells of the nitrogen-deficient culture remain motile during the stationary phase of growth, obtaining energy from the excess lactate. These cells are rich in reserve material and, when resuspended in artificial seawater, show only a slow decrease in motility when oxygen diffuses slowly into the suspension. When heavily aerated, the cells oxidize reserve material very rapidly and show a rapid decrease in motility. Apparently energy-generating catabolic processes and energy-consuming motility are uncoupled. Under natural conditions, a limited supply of oxygen and also a low temperature may favour the survival of starving cells since storage material is then oxidized only slowly.

Motile cells in the suspensions showed pronounced aerotaxis in wet mounts, especially those obtained from the nitrogen-deficient cultures. It seems beyond doubt that the presence of reserve material, enabling a starving cell to carry out directed movement, has definite survival value.

The rule 'no motility without ATP' (Weber, 1955; Newton and Kerridge, 1965) was nicely illustrated by experiments of Sherris, Preston and Shoesmith (1957) and Shoesmith and Sherris (1960) with *Pseudomonas*. The genus is strictly aerobic and the organisms used soon lost their motility in the absence of air, unless suspended in broth. The broth-activated anaerobic motility appeared to be due to arginine, and the duration of motility was proportional to the amount of arginine present. Energy (ATP) for bacterial movement appeared to be generated by the conversion of arginine to ornithine; no oxygen is required for this conversion, which explains anaerobic motility of these aerobic organisms.

## *ENERGY PRODUCTION AND CONSUMPTION IN THE GROWING CELL*

DeMoss, Bard and Gunsalus (1951), compared the molar growth yields (dry weight of cells/mole of energy source provided), of the homofermentative lactic acid bacteria *Streptococcus faecalis* and *Lactobacillus delbrückii* with that of the heterofermentative *Leuconostoc mesenteroides*. The organisms were grown anaerobically in a complex medium with glucose; very little glucose was assimilated, indicating that it was used almost exclusively as an energy source. Maximum growth of these organisms appeared to be a linear function of the initial glucose concentration; the molar growth yield of *Leuconostoc*, however, was considerably lower than that of the homofermentative lactic acid bacteria. DeMoss *et al.* concluded that *Leuconostoc* fermented glucose by a mechanism different from the Embden-Meyerhof scheme and providing less energy to the organism. Further work fully substantiated this suggestion (cf. Wood, 1961). It appeared that *Leuconostoc* dissimilated glucose via a hexose monophosphate pathway which yields only one mole of ATP per mole of glucose fermented. The homolactic fermentation shows the Embden-Meyerhof pathway which yields 2 moles of ATP for each mole of glucose dissimilated (cf. Wood, 1961). The observations of DeMoss *et al.* (1951), indicated a relationship between molar growth yield and amount of ATP produced. Bauchop and Elsden (1960), subsequently measured growth yields of *Streptococcus faecalis*, *Saccharomyces cerevisiae*, and *Zymomonas mobilis* (*Pseudomonas lindneri*); the ATP yields of fermentative processes of these organisms were known. They were grown under anaerobic conditions on complete media with the energy source as a limiting factor. It appeared that the yield of these organisms per mole of ATP produced ($Y^{ATP}$) was approximately constant and had a mean value of 10·5 g. (dry weight). In the experiments of Bauchop and Elsden the substrate was nearly exclusively used as energy source. This was not the case with *Aerobacter aerogenes* grown anaerobically by Hadjipetrou, Gerrits, Teulings and Stouthamer (1964) on a mineral medium with glucose as source of carbon and energy. Anaerobic dissimilation of glucose by this organism yields 3 moles of ATP per mole of glucose fermented. By determining the amount of glucose dissimilated and the dry weight of cells at the end of the fermentation, $Y^{ATP}$ could be calculated as 10·2.

Since $Y^{ATP}$ appears to be the same for so many organisms with different metabolic patterns, it seems justified to use this value for the calculation of the ATP yield of energy-producing processes from growth experiments. This has been done by Hadjipetrou *et al.* (1964) for aerobic growth of *A. aerogenes*. It was found that 72·7 g. of organisms was produced from 1 mole of glucose with a concomitant oxygen uptake of 1·14 mole. By dividing the yield per atom of oxygen consumed by $Y^{ATP}$

(as determined in the anaerobic experiment), the number of moles ATP formed per atom of oxygen consumed was found to be very close to three. Since nearly all ATP formed aerobically is derived from oxidative phosphorylation, these experiments indicate that three moles of ATP are produced per atom of oxygen consumed. A similar value has been obtained with mammalian mitochondria (Racker, 1961) which indicates that the efficiency of oxidative phosphorylation is the same in both cases.

Under certain environmental conditions uncoupling of energy generating and consuming processes may occur, which means that growth measurements as a means to calculate ATP production may not always be reliable. Senez (1962), has shown that the amount of lactate dissimilated by *Desulfovibrio desulfuricans* per g. of cells per hr. was the same in cultures growing with ammonium chloride or $N_2$ as nitrogen source. In the latter case, however, the growth rate and growth yield were about half that observed in cultures growing on combined nitrogen. The excess of energy was dissipated as heat. Similar observations were obtained with *Aerobacter aerogenes* when grown on different N-sources.

Uncoupling may also be a function of temperature (Senez, 1962). In *A. aerogenes*, growth rate and yield become zero at 42°, whereas respiratory activity reaches a maximum at that temperature. Thus, at 42° energy formation and consumption are completely uncoupled.

## *GROWTH RATES AND NATURAL SELECTION*

Two bacterial species may be able to live in the same ecological niche when grown separately. In mixed culture, however, even a small difference in growth rate results in predominance of one species. Ecologists have shown that the Volterra-Gause principle of one species per niche is frequently encountered in nature. A number of well-studied cases are known in which close examination of the behaviour of co-existing species revealed that their population sizes were not determined by exactly the same factors. By means of the enrichment culture technique, Winogradsky and Beijerinck made use of the above principle to select from mixed populations the organism best fitted to environments of known physico-chemical composition. Such an organism grows at a shorter generation time than all others and thus becomes the dominant form. Any deviation in bacterial metabolism that influences the growth rate unfavourably must be considered as a serious disadvantage for organisms which are exposed to competition. In nature such changes may soon lead to complete extinction. In the laboratory, however, when not exposed to selection pressure, variant strains with low growth rates have been repeatedly observed and cultivated for prolonged periods. A few examples will be given to illustrate the occurrence of metabolic derangements accompanied by low growth rates.

A well-known example of damage of the energy-generating system is that of respiratory deficient yeasts (Nagai, Yanagishima and Nagai, 1961). Such yeasts can only derive energy from a fermentation process and thus gain only two moles of ATP per mole of sugar consumed when grown aerobically. As a result their growth rate under these conditions is much lower than that of wild type strains, and the mutants therefore were characterized by French investigators as 'petite colonie'.

Marked derangements of another kind were encountered in metabolic processes of slow and rapid growing species of *Salmonella* by Stokes and Bayne (1961). Representatives of the slow growing *S. pullorum* form small colonies on a growth medium consisting of amino acids, whereas *S. typhimurium* and other species grow rapidly and form large colonies. A study of the amino acid metabolism of both types revealed that the rapid-growing strains oxidize more amino acids and most of these more rapidly than the slow-growing strains. The latter organisms were able to oxidize only alanine and serine rapidly, but these amino acids were oxidized to completion without assimilation. Thus the amino acids which were rapidly oxidized were not assimilated and those which could be assimilated were only slowly oxidized. Stokes and Bayne (1961) therefore suggested that the rate of oxidation and the extent of assimilation of amino acids controls the growth rate of salmonellae when grown on media with amino acids as source of carbon and energy.

*S. pullorum* also oxidizes lactate, pyruvate and acetate to completion and therefore would be unable to grow on these substrates. Uncoupling of substrate oxidation and biosynthesis in general must be disastrous to an organism which has to compete with bacteria for which such a substrate serves purposes of dissimilation as well as assimilation.

As was shown above, many bacteria synthesize about the same amounts of cell material per mole ATP available. The kinds of material synthesized by a bacterial species under different environmental conditions are markedly different, however (cf. Neidhardt, 1963). The synthesis of many enzymes appears to be under control of environmental conditions (cf. Pardee, 1962); the efficiency of the adjustment of the metabolic machinery to the extracellular environment is of great importance to organisms which are continuously exposed to competition. It might be expected for instance that maximal growth rates are not attained when an organism growing in a minimal medium wastes energy and amino acids for the synthesis of a useless protein. Such an organism may become rapidly outgrown by faster growing competitors which use their resources more efficiently. A case like this was reported by Novick (1961) who grew *E. coli* in a lactose-controlled chemostat. The original strain, which produced $\beta$-galactosidase only in the presence of lactose, was replaced after about 20 generations by a constitutive mutant that grew faster under the given conditions. Prolonged operation of the chemostat led to a succession of mutants containing higher and higher levels of $\beta$-galactosidase. After about 100 generations a 'super constitutive' organism was present which produced 25 per cent of its protein as $\beta$-galactosidase.

When such mutants were transferred to a synthetic medium with lactate or succinate as a source of carbon and energy, they continued to produce substantial amounts of $\beta$-galactosidase. The growth rate in such a medium, however, was relatively low and it seems very likely that this was due to the synthesis of the large amount of useless protein. On continued incubation in lactose-free medium the 'super constitutive' mutants were replaced by faster growing strains with low levels of $\beta$-galactosidase.

The experiments of Novick (1961) clearly show how during evolution on microscale in the chemostat there is a succession of populations of mutants, each of which grows faster than its predecessor. In nature, however, survival of a bacterial population is not only determined by the growth rates of its members under favourable conditions. The ability to survive starvation is equally important, and Harrison and Lawrence (1963) have shown that this ability is not necessarily correlated with a high growth rate during active proliferation. These authors studied the survival in phosphate buffer of *Aerobacter aerogenes*, harvested during the logarithmic and stationary phase of growth, respectively. The latter cells remained viable for a relatively long period, whereas the viability of log-phase cells decreased rapidly, though a small fraction remained viable. This fraction appeared to consist of two cell-types: the original wild type and a 'starvation-resistant' mutant. When the latter strain was isolated and again cultivated, harvested during the log-phase and starved, a relatively slow decline in viability was observed. A similar experiment carried out with a wild type isolate showed again a rapid decrease in viability. The growth rates (divisions/hr.), of mutant and wild type strain were 1·9 and 2·5, respectively. The mutant therefore formed only a small segment in the growing culture of the wild type strain, but became relatively numerous during the stationary growth-phase. The experiments of Harrison and Lawrence

(1963) indicate that increase of cell numbers during this phase was to a large extent due to re-growth of the mutant. These results show that evolutionary advantage is not always with the fast-growing components of a bacterial population.

## *ECONOMY OF BACTERIAL SYNTHESES*

The example of a 'super-constitutive' mutant producing very high levels of a particular enzyme, and growing slower than the wild type strain when the substrate for that enzyme is absent, indicates that it is a selective disadvantage when an organism produces cell material that is not strictly needed. When many bacteria produce large amounts of a material of unknown function there is a reason to speculate therefore on its possible survival value. Many soil bacteria produce copious amounts of extracellular polysaccharides, which clearly do not have the same function as internal polysaccharides since they are not used as substrates for endogenous metabolism. Wilkinson (1958) provided a number of suggestions as to the possible function of this material. He pointed out that pathogenic capsulated bacteria are more resistant to phagocytosis by leucocytes, and therefore more virulent, than non-encapsulated mutants. Extracellular polysaccharides may therefore confer a similar protection against protozoan attack on bacteria living in soil. Protozoa form an important factor in the regulation of bacterial numbers in soil and it would be worth while to study predation by protozoa of bacteria with respect to production of extracellular polysaccharides.

Many eubacteria are able to synthesize all or at least many of the amino acids needed for the synthesis of their proteins and use a large amount of carbon and energy for their production. Elaborate control mechanisms adjust the synthesis of amino acids and of the enzymes involved in their synthesis to the physiological needs. It is therefore not surprising that the amounts of amino acids released by the exponentially growing cell are very small as compared to those incorporated in cell material. Roberts, Abelson, Cowie, Bolton and Britten (1957) analysed extracellular products in cultures of *E. coli* growing exponentially in a minimal medium and found that glutamate was released in amounts up to 1 per cent of the total glutamate synthesized. This result was representative for the amino acids that were released. Similar results were obtained by Veldkamp, v.d. Berg and Zevenhuizen (1963) in a study of the release of amino acids by 300 *Arthrobacter* strains. Exceptions were found for alanine and glutamic acid. Ten per cent of all strains released very large amounts of alanine during the logarithmic phase of growth in a mineral salts-glucose medium. In extreme cases up to 50 per cent of total alanine synthesized was excreted. Glutamic acid was released in enormous amounts only by biotin-requiring *Arthrobacter* strains when the biotin concentration of the medium was sub-optimal for growth.

Though in general the amounts of amino acids excreted by bacteria are small as compared with total synthesis, they are certainly large enough to be of ecological importance, especially in a milieu like soil where they are not diluted to such an extent as in natural waters. A well-known example is the development of a secondary flora in enrichment cultures of *Azotobacter* due to the excretion of amino acids by this organism during exponential growth.

In contrast to amino acids, the vitamins excreted by bacteria often form a relatively high percentage of the total amount produced. Wilson and Pardee (1962) studied flavin synthesis in *Escherichia coli*, *Pseudomonas fluorescens* and *Bacillus subtilis*, and found that flavins were produced in great excess by these organisms. Excess production was observed in a wide variety of media and its extent ranged from 0·8–8 times the amount retained inside the cell. These experiments thus show that the synthesis of flavins is not as strictly controlled as that of amino acids. No evidence could be found for the occurrence of feed back inhibition, and the amounts of enzymes of the flavin biosynthetic pathway varied only by a factor of two under different environmental conditions. Wilson and Pardee (1962) list a number of examples of excess production of other vitamins and coenzymes and conclude that it might well be possible that as a general rule vitamins are overproduced to a much greater extent than amino acids, though the absolute rate at which the average amino acid is excreted is probably greater.

The amounts of carbon and energy utilized in coenzyme synthesis are negligible. Pardee and Beckwith (1963) suggested that it might be more economical therefore to produce vitamins and the enzymes involved in their synthesis at a steady and slightly greater rate than essential for growth, rather than creating control mechanisms which adjust synthesis exactly to the physiological needs. One would expect that only overproduction that greatly exceeds normal values may become the cause of a decrease in growth rate. In this connection it is of interest that a strain of *Arthrobacter globiformis* which released 40–50 times as much flavin as was retained in the cell showed a lower specific growth rate than a normal strain of the same species. The excessive riboflavin production was little influenced by the composition of the growth medium, and in all media tested the growth rate was comparatively low (Veldkamp *et al*, 1966).

The fact that the bacterial cell generally produces more vitamins than needed for its own metabolism and excretes the excess into its environment is of considerable ecological importance. This holds not only for the soil ecosystem in which local concentrations of released vitamins may be considerable, but even for natural waters. Many algae of the marine phytoplankton, for instance, require vitamin $B_{12}$ which is released by marine bacteria in concentrations high enough to allow algal growth (Provasoli, 1963).

The bacterial cell as a biological unit is wonderfully equipped to cope with the continuously changing environment; these changes are reflected in the chemical composition of the cell as a result of the activities of its regulatory mechanisms. Little is known, however, about the nature of the selective advantage of many adaptive responses (Neidhardt, 1963). Evolutionary aspects of processes occurring in the bacterial community in soil therefore deserve more attention from soil microbiologists.

## *REFERENCES*

ALEXANDER, M. (1964). Biochemical ecology of soil microorganisms. *A. Rev. Microbiol.*, **18**, 217.

BAUCHOP, T. & ELSDEN, S. R. (1960). The growth of micro-organisms in relation to their energy supply. *J. gen. Microbiol.*, **23**, 457.

DAWES, E. A. & RIBBONS, D. W. (1964). Some aspects of the endogenous metabolism of bacteria. *Bact. Rev.*, **28**, 126.

DEMOSS, R. D., BARD, R. C. & GUNSALUS, I. C. (1951). The mechanism of the heterolactic fermentation: a new route of ethanol formation. *J. Bact.*, **62**, 499.

DOUDOROFF, M. & STANIER, R. Y. (1959). Role of poly-β-hydroxybutyric acid in the assimilation of organic carbon by bacteria. *Nature, Lond.*, **183**, 1440.

GIBBONS, R. J. (1964). Metabolism of intracellular polysaccharide by *Streptococcus mitis* and its relation to inducible enzyme formation. *J. Bact.*, **87**, 1512.

GOTTSCHALK, G. (1964). Die Biosynthese der Poly-β-hydroxybuttersäure durch Knallgasbakterien. III. Synthese aus Kohlendioxyd. *Arch. Mikrobiol.*, **47**, 236.

HADJIPETROU, L. P., GERRITS, J. P., TEULINGS, F. A. G. & STOUTHAMER, A. H. (1964). Relation between energy production and growth of *Aerobacter aerogenes. J. gen. Microbiol.*, **36**, 139.

HARRISON, A. P. & LAWRENCE, F. R. (1963). Phenotypic, genotypic and chemical changes in starving populations of *Aerobacter aerogenes. J. Bact.*, **85**, 742.

HERBERT, D., ELSWORTH, R. & TELLING, R. C. (1956). The continuous culture of bacteria; a theoretical and experimental study. *J. gen. Microbiol.*, **14**, 601.

HERBERT, D. (1958). Some principles of continuous culture. In *Recent progress in microbiology*. Stockholm. Almquist & Wiksell.

HERBERT, D. (1961). The chemical composition of micro-organisms as a function of their environment. In *Microbial reaction to environment*. Ed. Meynell, G. G., Gooder, H. Symp. Soc. gen. Microbiol., **11**, 391.

HOLME, T. & PALMSTIERNA, H. (1956). Changes in glycogen and nitrogen-containing compounds in *Escherichia coli* B during growth in deficient media. II. Phosphorus and sulphur starvation. *Acta. chem. scand.*, **10**, 1553.

HOLME, T. (1957). Continuous culture studies on glycogen synthesis in *Escherichia coli* B. *Acta. chem. scand.*, **11**, 763.

KLUYVER, A. J. & VAN NIEL, C. B. (1956). *The microbe's contribution to biology.* Cambridge, Massachusetts. Harvard University Press.

LAMANNA, D. & MALLETTE, M. F. (1959). *Basic Bacteriology.* Baltimore. Williams & Wilkins Co.

LWOFF, A. (1962). *Biological order.* Cambridge, Massachusetts. M.I.T. Press.

MACRAE, R. M. & WILKINSON, J. F. (1958). Poly-β-hydroxybutyrate metabolism in washed suspensions of *Bacillus cereus* and *Bacillus megatherium. J. gen. Microbiol.*, **19**, 210.

MACURA, J. (1964). Application of the continuous flow method in soil microbiology. In *Continuous culture of microorganisms.* New York-London. Academic Press.

MACURA, J., SZOLNOKI, J., KUNC, F., VANČURA, V. & BABICKY, A. (1965). Decomposition of glucose continuously added to soil. *Folia Microbiol., Praha*, **10**, 44.

MALLETTE, M. F. (1963). Validity of the concept of energy of maintenance. *Ann. N. Y. Acad. Sci.*, **102**, 521.

MANDELSTAM, J. (1958). Turnover of protein in growing and non-growing populations of *Escherichia coli. Biochem. J.*, **69**, 110.

MANDELSTAM, J. (1960). The intracellular turnover of protein and nucleic acids and its role in biochemical differentiation. *Bact. Rev.*, **24**, 289.

MARR, A. G., NILSON, E. H. & CLARK, D. J. (1963). The maintenance requirement of *Escherichia coli. Ann. N. Y. Acad. Sci.*, **102** (3), 536.

NAGAI, S., YANAGISHIMA, N. & NAGAI, H. (1961). Advances in the study of respiration-deficient mutation in yeast and other microorganisms. *Bact. Rev.*, **25**., 404.

NEIDHARDT, F. C. (1963). Effects of environment on the composition of bacterial cells. *A. Rev. Microbiol.*, **17**, 61.

NEWTON, B. A. & KERRIDGE, D. (1965). Flagellar and ciliary movement in microorganisms. In *Function and structure of micro-organisms.* Ed. Pollock, M. R., and Richmond, M. H. Symp. Soc. gen. Microbiol., **15**, 220. Cambridge University Press.

NOVICK, A. (1961). Bacteria with high levels of specific enzymes. In *Growth in living systems.* Ed. Zarrow, M. X. New York. Basic Books Inc.

PARDEE, A. B. (1962). The synthesis of enzymes. In *The Bacteria*, vol. **3**. Ed. Gunsalus, I. C., & Stainier, R.Y. New York, London. Academic Press.

PARDEE, A. B. & BECKWITH, J. R. (1963). Control of constitutive enzyme synthesis. In *Informational macro-molecules.* Ed. Vogel, H. J., Bryson, V., & Lampen, J. O. New York, London. Academic Press.

PROVASOLI, L. (1963). Organic regulation of phytoplankton activity. In *The Sea*, vol. **2**. Ed. Hill, M. N. New York. London. Interscience Publishers.

RACKER, E. (1961). Mechanisms of synthesis of adenosine triphosphate. *Adv. Enzymol.*, **23**, 323.

ROBERTS, R. B., ABELSON, P. H., COWIE, D. B., BOLTON, E. T. & BRITTEN, E. T. (1957). *Studies of biosynthesis in* Escherichia coli. 2nd ed. Carneg. Inst. (Wash.) 607.

SCHULZE, K. L. & LIPE, R. S. (1964). Relationship between substrate concentration, growth rate, and respiration rate of *Escherichia coli* in continuous culture. *Arch. Mikrobiol.*, **48**, 1.

SENEZ, J. C. (1962). Some considerations on the energetics of bacterial growth. *Bact. Rev.*, **26**, 95.

SHERRIS, J. C., PRESTON, N. W. & SHOESMITH, J. G. (1957). The influence of oxygen and arginine on the motility of a strain of *Pseudomonas sp. J. gen. Microbiol.*, **16**, 86.

SHOESMITH, J. G. & SHERRIS, J. C. (1960). Studies on the mechanism of arginine-activated motility in a *Pseudomonas* strain. *J. gen. Microbiol.*, **22**, 10.

SILVERMAN, M. P. & EHRLICH, H. L. (1964). Microbial formation and degradation of minerals. *Adv. appl. Microbiol.*, **6**, 153.

STOKES, J. L. & BAYNE, H. G. (1961). Oxidative assimilation of amino acids by salmonellae in relation to growth rates. *J. Bact.* **81**, 118.

VELDKAMP, H. (1966). Enrichment cultures: history and prospects. In: Anreicherungskultur und Mutantenauslese. Symp. Deutsch. Gesellsch. Hyg. Mikr.; *Zentbl. Bakt ParasitKde.*, Abt. I, Suppl. Heft 1, 1.

VELDKAMP, H., VENEMA, P. A. A., HARDER, W. & KONINGS, W. N. (1966). Production of riboflavin by *Arthrobacter globiformis. J. appl. Bact.*, **29**, 107.

VELDKAMP, H., V.D. BERG, G. & ZEVENHUIZEN, L. P. T. M. (1963). Glutamic acid production by *Arthrobacter globiformis. Antonie van Leeuwenhoek*, **29**, 35.

VELDKAMP, H. & HARTMANS, K. (1965); unpublished data.

WEBER, H. H. (1955). *Adenosine triphosphate and motility of living systems.* The Harvey Lectures, ser. 49. New York. Academic Press.

WILKINSON, J. F. (1958). The extracellular polysaccharides of bacteria. *Bact. Rev.*, **22**, 46.

WILKINSON, J. F. (1959). The problem of energy-storage compounds in bacteria. *Expl. Cell Res. Suppl.*, **7**, 111.

WILSON, A. C. & PARDEE, A. B. (1962). Regulation of flavin synthesis by *Escherichia coli. J. gen. Microbiol.*, **28**, 283.

WOOD, W. A. (1961). Fermentation of carbohydrates and related compounds. In *The Bacteria*, vol. **2.** Ed, Gunsalus, I. C., & Stanier, R. Y. New York, London. Academic Press.

# SIGNIFICANT SYNTHESES BY HETEROTROPHIC SOIL BACTERIA [1]

DAVID PRAMER

*Department of Agricultural Microbiology, Rutgers—The State University, New Brunswick, New Jersey, U.S.A.*

## *INTRODUCTION*

When faced with a large canvas and limited time, the artist may work with a broad brush and apply a superficial coat that completely covers the area available for work. On the other hand, he may choose to ignore dimension and work with a fine brush in great detail covering only a portion of his canvas. The former approach has breadth but lacks depth. The latter approach sacrifices the whole for one or more of its parts, but it serves to focus the eye of the viewer on what the artist considers to be characteristic of his subject.

The symposium participant has much in common with the artist. Given a broad topic and limited time, he, too, must decide how his subject may best be treated. The synthetic activities of heterotrophic soil bacteria are too important to be treated superficially. In the last decade great progress has been made in understanding the mechanisms of the biosynthesis of proteins, nucleic acids, carbohydrates, and lipids, and current knowledge in these areas is much too broad to be covered here with the largest brush at my disposal. Recall, if you will, that a microbial cell, which occupies only $10^{-12}$ cm.$^3$ and has a dry weight of only $2{\cdot}5 \times 10^{-13}$ g., synthesizes thousands of different kinds of macromolecules organized in time and space (McQuillen, 1965) and, to perpetuate the species, is able to replicate the entire complex system in as little as 20 minutes. Thaysen (1956) calculated that the rate of synthesis of protein by micro-organisms is 100 times that of soybeans and 100,000 times greater than that of cattle. Biosyntheses are among the basic functions of life of all kinds. Growth entails synthesis of cellular constituents from small molecules and continued synthesis is necessary for maintenance as well as growth. Compounds synthesized for growth and

[1] Paper of the Journal Series, New Jersey Agricultural Experiment Station, Rutgers University, Department of Agricultural Microbiology, New Brunswick, New Jersey, U.S.A. This report was supported in part by National Science Foundation Grant GB-3252.

maintenance are very diverse, and so are the biogenetic routes that lead to their formation. This is not the place to plunge into the pool of biosyntheses that generate cell substance and become immersed in chemical particulars of so large a subject. Cells have a transient existence and, as part of the organic fraction of soil, their substance is eventually mineralized and cycled through nature.

I have no alternative here but to deal in detail with selected aspects of my assigned topic, and to hope that, in so doing, I will focus interest on areas of microbiology deserving of your attention. Possibilities for discussion are legion, making it difficult for me to be selective. Nevertheless, for the present purpose, a limited number of biosynthetic processes and products are designated as significant. They enable bacteria to survive and function as members of the large and varied microbial population of soil, and also influence soil fertility, crop production, and human health and welfare. You will note the frequent use here of species of one genus, *Streptomyces*, to illustrate diverse biosynthetic activities that are characteristic of bacteria of many types. This is intentional. *Streptomyces* are bacteria with fungal morphologies (Lechevalier, 1964). They are autochthonous, productive synthetically, and are highlighted because many *Streptomyces* and I have Rutgers University in common as a base of operations. Here, then, are gleanings from a voluminous literature that pertains to the synthetic activities of soil bacteria.

## *SOIL SCENT: 'GEOSMIN'*

When, in Paradise Lost (Book IV, line 639), John Milton wrote '. . . fragrant the fertile earth . . .' he was unknowingly referring to a characteristic shared by many *Streptomyces* spp. The earthy odour of these cultures is reminiscent of soil newly turned. It is a biosynthetic product that announces the arrival of spring, that inspires poets, and one that is responsible also for undesirable tastes and odours in drinking water and in fish taken from contaminated rivers (Thaysen, 1936; Issatchenko and Egorova, 1944). Various attempts have been made to isolate, identify, and control the odour, but volatile substances are difficult to manipulate by the usual laboratory methods and organoleptic assays lack the precision necessary for meaningful fractionation by conventional chemical procedures (Silvey and Roach, 1959). Romano and Safferman (1963), were able to concentrate the earthy odour of *Streptomyces* by distillation from culture media and adsorption on charcoal, but only 22 per cent of the material was recovered when the adsorbent was extracted continuously for 4 hr. with chloroform. These preliminary studies demonstrated the extreme intensity of the odour but the nature of the responsible agent remained to be established, and I am pleased to have this opportunity to describe recent progress towards this end.

Dr. Nancy Gerber (1965) of the Institute of Microbiology, Rutgers University, obtained odouriferous concentrates from *Streptomyces* by extracting broth or broth distillates with methylene chloride. The extracts were examined by gas chromatography using a 120 × 0·3 cm. silicone gum-rubber column (a non-polar material that separates compounds approximately in order of their volatility) and conditions such that naphthalene and anthracene had retention times of 1·7 and 10·6 min. respectively (detector 260°, injection port 300°, column 155°, programmed at 4°/min., bridge current 150 mV, carrier gas helium at 50 ml./min.). Detection of the earthy odour at the exit port of the instrument coincided with the appearance on the recorder of a peak with a retention time of 4 min. The sharpness and symmetry of the peak indicated that the fraction was homogeneous and that the odour was due to a specific compound which was designated *geosmin* (from the Greek *geodes*, meaning earth-like). Geosmin was produced by four species of *Streptomyces* and by *Streptosporangium*. In some cultures geosmin was masked. They lacked an earthy odour but gas chromatography resolved the mixtures and the compound was detected by retention time and scent. Broths had a maximum geosmin content of 1·0 mg./litre. Approximately nine litres of culture medium were distilled at atmospheric pressure, the first 1800 ml. of distillate were extracted twice with methylene chloride, and the dried methylene chloride solution concentrated to 1·0 ml. Successive portions (0·1 ml.) of this concentrate were injected into the gas chromatograph and the geosmin peaks collected and analysed. Geosmin is a clear, very pale yellow liquid with a boiling point of approximately 270°. It is optically active ($\alpha_D^{25} = -16{\cdot}5$), and demonstrates end absorption only in ultraviolet light. Geosmin is unstable in acid (concentrated HCl added dropwise to crude material in methylene chloride) forming a neutral, odourless product of higher volatility. It can be expected that continued study will reveal the identity of this intriguing compound.

## *EXTRACELLULAR ENZYMES*

Pollock (1963) divided bacterial enzymes into two groups: (*a*) those that are cell-bound; and (*b*) those that are extracellular and found free in the medium surrounding the cells. Group (*a*), the cell-bound enzymes, were subdivided into (i) truly intracellular and, (ii) surface-bound enzymes. Extracellular enzymes were defined as those that exist in the environment, 'having originated from the cell without any alteration to cell structure greater than the maximum compatible with the cells' normal processes of growth and reproduction'. Permit me to nominate extracellular enzymes as candidates for the distinction of being regarded as significant synthetic products of heterotrophic soil bacteria. Their qualifications for this position are summarized below.

Extracellular enzymes are the primary means of attack by soil organisms on resistant polymers present in animal and plant residues. In this process actinomycetes may play a more important role than do many other groups of bacteria, and one cannot help but be impressed by the frequent occurrence of *Streptomyces* spp. in compiled lists of microbial sources of extracellular enzymes (Pollock, 1962; Davies, 1963). Chitinase and keratinase will be cited here as examples of extracellular enzymes that act on high molecular weight, insoluble substrates, and initiate series of biochemical events that are of ecological and economic consequences.

Chitin is a mucopolysaccharide (straight chain 1,4 $\beta$ linked polymer of N-acetylglucosamine), that is widely distributed in nature and found in both the animal and plant kingdom. It occurs in the cell wall of fungi but the greater part of the chitin in soil probably originates from arthropods. Chitin is decomposed by *Pseudomonas* and *Bacillus* spp. (Veldkamp, 1955; Mitchell and Alexander, 1963) and chitinase was detected in 98 of 100 *Streptomyces* cultures examined (Jeuniaux, 1955). Chitin media have been recommended for the selective cultivation and isolation of actinomycetes from soil (Lingappa and Lockwood, 1962), and the chitinolytic activity of *Streptomyces griseus* has been investigated in some detail (Reynolds, 1954; Berger and Reynolds, 1958). Hydrolysis of chitin by the organism was due to an inducible complex that yielded as products, N-acetylglucosamine and the disaccharide, N,N-diacetylchitobiose. The system was resolved by electrophoresis on starch into two chitinases and a chitobiase. Although the chitinases differed in electrophoretic mobility and temperature stability, they demonstrated no difference in substrate specificity or enzymatic activity. The chitobiase hydrolysed the di- and trisaccharides of N-acetylglucosamine but not higher polymers. Chitinase remains to be crystallized and characterized chemically, and there is much to be accomplished before our understanding of the pathway of chitin degradation approaches completion. Nevertheless, chitinolytic enzymes and the organisms from which they are derived have recently been credited with a meaningful role in the system of checks and counterchecks that control the biological equilibrium in soil.

Veldkamp (1955) reported changes in the composition and size of the microbial population of soils supplemented with added chitin. These differed for each soil. However, it was observed that in every case a predominance of actinomycetes resulted, and that a large number of the *Streptomyces* in soils to which chitin was added were antagonistic to *Bacillus subtilis*. Study of the bacteriolytic properties of *Streptomyces* has revealed the production by these organisms of a number of different enzymes acting on various bacterial constituents, especially those located in the cell wall (Welsch, 1962).

The use of soil supplements to enhance selectively a desirable segment of the soil population has long interested microbiologists. This possibility assumes increased importance in studies of soil-borne plant pathogens, and it was for this reason considerable attention was given to the report of Mitchell and Alexander (1961) that the addition to soil of chitin markedly reduced the severity of root rot of bean (*Fusarium solani* f. *phaseoli*) and vascular wilt of radish (*Fusarium oxysporum* f. *conglutinans*). The small quantities of chitin needed (50-100 lbs./acre) for a statistically significant effect indicated a selective promotion of the development of fungal antagonists, and it was suggested that disease control was the result of the activities of mycolytic soil micro-organisms. Subsequent work to establish experimentally the mechanism of action of the chitin supplement emphasized the role of microbial extracellular enzymes lytic for *Fusarium* spp. A number of bacteria capable of lysing the pathogen were isolated from enriched soil, and, one of these, *Bacillus cereus*, was examined in detail (Mitchell and Alexander, 1963). It digested the hyphae of living and dead fungus tissue and hydrolysed chitin and laminarin (1,3 $\beta$ linked glucoside). However, no lysis was obtained when *Fusarium* mycelium was suspended in a solution of chitinase alone or in chitinase in combination with laminarinase, proteases, and cellulase. Although the biochemical basis of chitin induced biological control of soil-borne plant pathogens is not as yet clarified, the implication that extracellular enzymes influence the dynamics of the soil population is consistent with the thesis that they are ecologically significant.

Keratinase is an extracellular enzyme having economic significance as a depilatory agent that may meet the need of the leather industry for a rapid method of removing the hair from animal hides in preparation for tanning. The present use of lime-sulphide liquors has many disadvantages, not the least of which is an industrial waste disposal problem

(Cordon, Jones, Clarke, and Naghski, 1958). Numerous attempts have been made to utilize enzymes for unhairing animal hides (Green, 1952) but Noval and Nickerson (1958) appear to have been the first to apply enrichment culture techniques and isolate a keratin-utilizing micro-organism from soil. Keratin is a resistant, fibrous protein in horn, hide, hoof, hair and feathers. From soil that received wool and hoof meal, many isolations were made, but only one culture, later identified as *Streptomyces fradiae*, had appreciable keratinolytic activity.

The digestion of wool by pure cultures proceeded through an initial phase, in which the organism made limited growth but produced no visible change in the substrate, and a second phase, during which there was rapid proliferation of the organism and solubilization of 70–90 per cent of the wool. Growth was favoured by increasing the $Ca^{++}$ and/or $Mg^{++}$ concentration. Approximately two-thirds of the cystine of solubilized wool accumulated as sulphhydryl compounds and ammonium was the major nitrogenous decomposition product. Cell-free broth was capable of digesting wool and the enzyme was concentrated 16-fold by ammonium sulphate precipitation. It is my understanding that the keratinase of *Streptomyces fradiae* has been crystallized and is now available commercially. In a recent report (Cordon, Everett, Jones, Windus, and Naghski, 1961) that compared the elastase activity of 15 different marketed products it was stated of keratinase, 'there was no trace of elastin remaining throughout the entire cross section of the hide', and, 'this is the only time we have observed such complete removal of elastin'. Depilatory action and elastase activity are not necessarily correlated. Both are important to the tanning industry but the latter is useful also for tenderizing meat, and it has been suggested that administration of elastinase may be beneficial in cases of arteriosclerosis (Mandl, 1961). The economic significance of extracellular enzymes is evident from the fact that the market in 1965 for the United States only, was valued at sixty million dollars, with pharmaceuticals accounting for half of the total industry (Sizer, 1964).

The contribution of Academician Imshenetsky (p. 256) to these proceedings is concerned with cellulose decomposition and will, I am confident, recognize the involvement in this vital process of the extracellular enzyme, or enzyme complex, known as cellulase. Likewise, it will be noted from the discussion by Dr. Greenwood (p. 138) of metabolic measurements of bacterial activity, that extracellular proteins occupy a prominent position in studies of soil enzymes. Nevertheless, current interest in extracellular enzymes transcends ecological and economic problems; these compounds have contributed greatly to our understanding of protein synthesis and enzyme chemistry, and they continue to attract investigators (Pollock, 1962; Lampen, 1965), by offering for solution a number of provocative problems. It has been noted (Pollock and Richmond, 1962) that bacterial extracellular enzymes are relatively small proteins with few or no disulphide cross-linkages, and that Gram-positive organisms are the major source of extracellular bacterial enzymes. These assertions warrant further study and there is need for inquiry to determine the site of formation of extracellular enzymes. What is the mechanism by which intact cells liberate or secrete proteins into the surrounding medium? Need they pass through the cytoplasmic membrane in the process of liberation? Chitinase and keratinase are inducible and have as substrates and inducers large, insoluble molecules which are unlikely to permeate the cell. There is need for understanding of how and where compounds such as chitin and keratin act to transfer information that initiates and directs enzyme synthesis. Virtually nothing is known of the synthetic activities of extracellular enzymes, and it can be stated with certainty, that many important bacterial extracellular enzymes have not as yet been recognized and studied.

## *ANTIBIOTICS AND PROBIOTICS*

A major source of our professional strength is the infinite number and variety of micro-organisms in soil and their ability to catalyse innumerable reactions. Micro-organisms are a prime natural resource with a formidable potential. Jackson Foster (1964), wrote, 'to a degree matched only by engineering and agriculture, microbiology is essentially the application of scientific knowledge'. Seldom have the fundamentals of biology been applied with success to equal that enjoyed by those involved in the discovery and development of antibiotics. The impact of antibiotics on the treatment of infectious diseases and on the practice of human and veterinary medicine is well appreciated and, therefore, medical and public health features of the subject are excluded entirely from this discussion. A huge industry based on the domestication of microbial life for antibiotic production has developed, and the major contributors to this significant biosynthetic effort are *Streptomyces* spp. isolated from soil. Over the ten-year span 1951–61 the non-medical use of antibiotics increased steadily from 236,000 lbs. valued at 17 million dollars, to 1,800,000 lbs. valued at 45·4 million dollars. This figure of almost 2 million lbs. of antibiotics allocated in 1961 for other than medical use, was more than half of the total production for that year in the United States (3,311,000 lbs.). The antibiotics of major concern include the tetracyclines, streptomycin, penicillin and bacitracin. They have been applied in animal nutrition, plant disease control, food preservation, and as adjuncts in microbiological methods and research (Goldberg, 1964).

Antibiotics have tended to dominate and direct some phases of microbiological thinking and effort, and they have influenced fundamental aspects of biochemistry, organic chemistry and even engineering. A considerable quantity of relevant information has accumulated and there is ample speculation on the mechanisms of antibiotic syntheses and their relationships to metabolic processes of the involved microorganisms (Bu'Lock, 1961; Hockenhull, 1963). All evidence supports the thesis that the production of antibiotics does not differ in principle from other syntheses of similar molecular complexity. In general, antibiotics are what Bu'Lock (1961) describes as 'secondary metabolites'. There exist basic patterns of general metabolism that yield energy and support cell growth and reproduction. Superimposed on these basic patterns are special reactions, relatively minor modifications, responsible for the production of antibiotics and other secondary metabolites. Secondary metabolites are restricted in their distribution, they are almost but not quite species specific, and their role, if any, in general metabolism is obscure. The biosynthesis of antibiotics has been regarded by Hockenhull (1963), as the result of 'a series of inborn errors of metabolism' that can be exaggerated by mutagenic influences until the product of what was initially a minor metabolic route, represents a substantial portion of the cell's synthetic activity, and may account for as much as 20 per cent by weight of the nutrient supply. From these distortions of basic biosynthetic routes arise the fused rings, D-amino acid residues, and unusual sugars of various antibiotic molecules.

Further evidence that antibiotics are secondary rather than primary metabolites is derived from fermentation studies which reveal consistently that antibiotic synthesis is wholly or partly suppressed in growing cultures that are actively multiplying and is most rapid when cultures reach the stationary or resting stage. The view of Bu'Lock (1961) that cell proliferation and secondary biosyntheses, such as antibiotic production, are competing or incompatible, rather than parallel processes, appears meaningful and is supported by fermentation practice. Conditions for rapid development of *Streptomyces griseus* are not the same as those for streptomycin production. Little or no antibiotic is released by cultures during exponential growth (Hockenhull, 1963). Likewise, in the formation of actinomycin by *Streptomyces antibioticus*, antibiotic production commences when glucose, the source of energy and organic carbon for growth, is exhausted completely (Katz, Pienta, and Sivak, 1958). Similar phenomena have been observed during the production of tetracycline antibiotics. It is known generally that in the industrial fermentation for penicillin, it is only when nutrients become limiting, and growth slows down, that penicillin is produced.

I wish now to introduce into this discussion the word *probiotic*. It is not my creation but that of Lilly and Stillwell (1965) who used it to describe growth-promoting factors produced by micro-organisms. Antibiotics are substances of microbial origin that have the capacity to inhibit growth of micro-organisms or other living cells. For the present purpose, I will define probiotics as antithetic to antibiotics. Probiotics are substances of microbial origin that have the capacity to promote growth of micro-organisms or other living cells. The term is a convenient means for dealing collectively with amino acids, vitamins, auxins, gibberellins, and numerous other growth-factors of known and unknown composition. Both antibiotics and probiotics demonstrate selectivity. Each substance, within either category, has a characteristic spectrum of activity and is active at low levels.

The probiotic requirements of an organism are a measure of the failure of its biosynthetic capacity. However, many bacteria synthesize probiotics in excess of their needs and release the surplus into their environment. Certain of these organisms can be commercially valuable sources of probiotics. Microbial synthesis is the only source of vitamin $B_{12}$, whereas, of all the other water-soluble vitamins now marketed, only vitamin $B_2$ (riboflavin) is manufactured microbiologically to any significant extent. Riboflavin is produced by species of *Aerobacter*, *Azotobacter*, and *Pseudomonas*, but the only bacteria used commercially as sources of vitamin $B_2$ are species of the anaerobic solvent-producing genus *Clostridium*. The riboflavin yield is low (100 $\mu$g./ml. or less), but the dual function of the *Clostridium acetobutylicum* fermentation is attractive industrially (Goodwin, 1963). Vitamin $B_{12}$, the anti-pernicious anaemia factor, is produced by many bacteria, but it is species of the genus *Streptomyces* which produce industrially significant amounts (Perlman, 1959).

Fat-soluble vitamins are not produced industrially by fermentation methods but $\beta$-carotene, which is converted by animals to vitamin A, is the product of a microbiological process developed by Hasseltine (1961) to compete with the established chemical synthesis. Detailed descriptions of the biosyntheses of vitamins were prepared recently by Morris (1962) and Goodwin (1963). Kinoshita (1963) summarized amino acid synthesis. I am indebted to the authors and editors of the volume *Biochemistry of Industrial Micro-organisms* (Rainbow and Rose, 1963) for compiling a wealth of useful information that pertains to the production by micro-organisms of antibiotics and probiotics, including not only vitamins and amino acids, but also organic acids, polysaccharides, gibberellins, steroids and alkaloids. Their efforts obviate the need here for further coverage of biosynthesis and I wish, for my concluding remarks, to return to questions that relate to 'soil and the microbe'.

Antibiotics and probiotics are frequently invoked in explanation of interactions among micro-organisms and indicated to be the biochemical bases of interrelationships between micro-organisms and plant roots in soil. Implicit in the concept of a rhizosphere effect (Starkey, 1958) is the exchange of metabolic products by micro-organisms and plants. Bacteria develop in the rhizosphere because the plant provides them with food. Indeed, in addition to amino acids and sugars, root exudates contain organic acids, purines, pyrimidines, vitamins and various unidentified compounds having biological activity (Rovira, 1962). Micro-organisms in the vicinity of plant roots feed and multiply.

There is no doubt that exudates support an increase in population density, but the reasons for the selectivity of the rhizosphere habitat are, as yet, unknown. Roots release probiotics, but the abundance of bacteria that require these substances is circumstantial, and not unequivocal evidence that amino acids and other growth-promoting compounds exert a controlling influence on the composition of rhizosphere populations. There is also a lack of convincing evidence that synthetic products of rhizosphere organisms have important influences on plant growth and quality under natural conditions. Innumerable reports describe the production of antibiotics and probiotics by organisms that were isolated from the soil and rhizosphere and cultivated in the laboratory. There are also many reports that describe the absorption and translocation of complex organic compounds by higher plants (Pramer, 1959, 1961; Winter, 1961). Although it may appear reasonable to associate these two phenomena, there are few data to support the notion (Krasilnikov, 1962) that antibiotics and probiotics are produced in the rhizosphere, enter plants, and have important ecological consequences in natural soil.

Schmidt (1950) reviewed a considerable literature pertaining to the occurrence of plant growth substances in soil and the possible relationship of their occurrence to soil micro-organisms and higher plants. Various investigators detected vitamins and plant growth substances in soil organic matter, and when plant materials containing low levels of vitamins were introduced into soil, action by micro-organisms resulted initially in a marked increase and then a progressive decrease in vitamin concentration. The transformation was rapid. Little or no riboflavin or pantothenic acid were detected three days after addition of the vitamins to soil, and it was considered unlikely that higher plants benefit from growth substances present in soil or produced in connection with the transformation by micro-organisms of soil organic matter (Schmidt and Starkey, 1951).

McCalla and Haskins (1964) discussed some effects possibly caused by metabolic products of micro-organisms that are toxic to plants, and a great deal of effort has been expended in evaluating tests of the ecological significance of antibiotics. Brian (1957, 1960) published two very thought-provoking reviews of current knowledge concerning the production of antibiotics, with the conclusion that they do not accumulate in such quantity as to be detectable and exert a general biological effect throughout the soil. He was confident, however, of the production of antibiotics in microhabitats, such as seed coats and fragments of buried straw that are discontinuous in time and space. I am aware of only two reports that present evidence of antibiotic production in the rhizosphere: (1) approximately 10 $\mu$g. of fusaric acid were extracted from the rhizosphere soil of a 20-day-old tomato plant infected with *Fusarium lycopersici*, and the compound was identified by paper chromatography (Kalwanasundram, 1958); and (2) when inoculated into soil, a *Streptomyces* sp. reached the rhizosphere of corn plants and there caused inhibition, malformation and lysis of germ tubes of *Helminthosporium sativum*. The mycolytic effect was a specific bioassay, characteristic of an antibiotic derived from the actinomycete (Rangaswami and Vidyasekaran, 1963). Lingappa and Lockwood (1961) suggested that surfaces of individual spores serve as a source of nutrients which promote growth of micro-organisms in their immediate vicinity, and that this results in the production of antibiotics that prevent spore germination. This concept of a *sporosphere* does not differ greatly from that of the rhizosphere, and it provides additional circumstantial evidence for antibiotic production in localized environments.

Since antibiotics are a heterogeneous group of compounds, varying greatly in their chemical structure and reactivity, and soils are not homogeneous, but differ physically, chemically, and biologically within wide limits, no generalizations regarding the stability and biological effects of antibiotics in soil are possible. The fate of each antibiotic in any particular soil remains a unique situation that requires investigation. Although present knowledge indicates that some antibiotics in soil are unstable chemically, and many, if not all, are degraded microbiologically, it appears that several antibiotics can persist in some soils for sufficient time to have a biological effect (Pramer, 1958).

The subject of production in soil of antibiotics and probiotics has many ramifications. Possibly, man will learn to regulate root exudates and, thereby, to control the composition of rhizosphere populations with desirable results in terms of plant growth, protection and quality. It is logical to expect that biosynthetic products of micro-organisms in the root zone will have an effect on plants, but continued application of an analytical approach is required before it will be possible to substitute confidence for conjecture in naming antibiotics and probiotics as responsible for antagonistic and associative interrelationships of micro-organisms in soil. I conclude with a quatrain that summarizes all I have attempted to convey regarding the remarkable ability of soil bacteria to perform significant and superior syntheses.

Oh Lord, I fall upon my knees
And pray that all my syntheses
May no longer be inferior
To those conducted by bacteria.

(Anonymous, 1963)

## *REFERENCES*

ANONYMOUS. (1963). *European scientific notes. Office of Naval Research, London*, **17**, 21.

BERGER, L. R. & REYNOLDS, D. M. (1958). The chitinase systems of a strain of *Streptomyces griseus. Biochim. Biophys. Acta.*, **29**, 522.

BRIAN, P. W. (1957). The ecological significance of antibiotic production. In *Microbial Ecology*. Ed. Williams, R. E. O. & Spicer, C. C. *7th Symp. Soc. gen. Microbiol.* Cambridge. Cambridge University Press.

BRIAN, P. W. (1960). Antagoistic and competitive mechanisms limiting survival and activity of fungi in soil. In *The Ecology of Soil Fungi*. Ed. Parkinson, D. & Waid, J. S. Liverpool. Liverpool University Press.

BU'LOCK, J. D. (1961). Intermediary metabolism and antibiotic synthesis. *Adv. appl. Microbiol.*, **3**, 293.

CORDON, T. C., EVERETT, A. L., JONES, H., WINDUS, W., & NAGHSKI, J. (1961). Elasatase activity of some enzymes as related to their depilatory action. *J. Am. Leath. Chem. Ass.*, **56**, 68.

CORDON, T. C., JONES, H. W., CLARKE, I. D. & NAGHSKI, J. (1958). Microbial and other enzymes as depilatory agents. *Appl. Microbiol.*, **6**, 293.

DAVIES, R. (1963). Microbial extracellular enzymes, their uses and some factors affecting their formation. In *Biochemistry of Industrial Microorganisms*. Ed. Rainbow, C. & Rose, A. H. New York. Academic Press.

FOSTER, J. W. (1964). Microbes in diplomacy. *Grad. J.*, **6**, 322.

GOODWIN, T. W. (1963). Vitamins. In *Biochemistry of Industrial Microorganisms*. Ed. Rainbow, C., & Rose, A. H. New York. Academic Press.

GERBER, N. N. (1965). Personal communication.

GOLDBERG, H. S. (1964). Nonmedical uses of antibiotics. *Adv. appl. Microbiol.*, **6**, 91.

GREEN, G. H. (1952). Unhairing by means of enzymes. *J. Soc. Leath. Trades Chem.*, **36**, 127.

HASSELTINE, C. W. (1961). *Tech. Bull. U.S. Dep. Agric.*, **1245**. U.S. Government Printing Office, Washington, D.C.

HOCKENHULL, D. J. D. (1963). Antibiotics. In *Biochemistry of Industrial Microorganisms*. Ed. Rainbow, C. & Rose, A. H. New York. Academic Press.

ISSATCHENKO, B. & EGOROVA, A. A. (1944). Actinomycetes in reservoirs as one cause responsible for the earthy smell of their waters. *Mikrobiologiya*, **13**, 216.

JEUNIAUX, C. (1955). Production d'exochitinase par des *Streptomyces*. *C. r. Soc. Biol., Paris*, **149**, 1307.

KALWANASUNDARAM, R. (1958). Production of fusaric acid by *Fusarium lycopersici* in the rhizosphere of tomato plants. *Phytopath. Z.*, **32**, 25.

KATZ, E., PIENTA, P. & SIVAK, A. (1958). The role of nutrition in the synthesis of actinomycin. *Appl. Microbiol.*, **6**, 236.

KINOSHITA, S. (1963). Amino acids. In *Biochemistry of Industrial Microorganisms*. Ed. Rainbow, C. & Rose, A. H. New York. Academic Press.

KRASSILNIKOV, N. A. (1962). The role of microorganisms in plant life. *Proc. 8th Int. Congr. Microbiol., Montreal*, 283.

LAMPEN, J. O. (1965). Secretion of enzymes by microorganisms. In *Function and Structure in Microorganisms*. Ed. Pollock, M. R. & Richmond, M. H. Cambridge. Cambridge University Press, 115.

LECHEVALIER, H. A. (1964). The Actinomycetes. In *Principles and Applications in Aquatic Microbiology*. Ed. Heukelekian, H. & Dondero, N. C. New York. John Wiley and Sons, 230.

LILLY, D. M. & STILLWELL, R. H. (1965). Probiotics: growth-promoting factors produced by microorganisms. *Science, N.Y.*, **147**, 747.

LINGAPPA, B. T. & LOCKWOOD, J. L. (1961). The nature of the widespread fungistasis. *J. gen. Microbiol.*, **26**, 473.

LINGAPPA, Y. & LOCKWOOD, J. L. (1962). Chitin media for selective isolation and culture of actinomycetes. *Phytopathology*, **52**, 317.

MCCALLA, T. M. & HASKINS, F. A. (1964). Phytotoxic substances from soil microorganisms and crop residues. *Bact. Rev.*, **28**, 181.

MANDL, I. (1961). Collagenases and elastases. *Adv. Enzymol.*, **23**, 163.

MCQUILLEN, K. (1965). The physical organization of nucleic acid and protein synthesis. In *Function and Structure in Microorganisms*. Ed. Pollock, M. R. & Richmond, M. H. *15th Symp. Soc. gen. Microbiol.* Cambridge. Cambridge University Press.

MITCHELL, R. & ALEXANDER, M. (1961). Chitin and the biological control of *Fusarium* diseases. *Pl. Dis. Reptr.*, **45**, 487.

MITCHELL, R. & ALEXANDER, M. (1963). Lysis of soil fungi by bacteria. *Can. J. Microbiol.*, **9**, 169.

MORRIS, J. G. (1962). The synthesis of vitamins and coenzymes. In *The Bacteria*, 3. Ed. Gunsalus, I. C. & Stanier, R. Y. New York. Academic Press.

NOVAL, J. J. & NICKERSON, W. J. (1958). Decomposition of native keratin by *Streptomyces fradiae*. *J. Bact.*, **77**, 251.

PERLMAN, D. (1959). Microbial synthesis of cobamides. *Adv. appl. Microbiol.*, **1**, 87.

POLLOCK, M. R. (1962). Exoenzymes. In *The Bacteria*, **4**. Ed. Gunsalus, I. C. & Stanier, R. Y. New York. Academic Press.

POLLOCK, M. R. & RICHMOND, M. H. (1962). Low cyst(e)ine content of bacterial extracellular proteins; its possible physiological significance. *Nature, Lond.*, **194**, 446.

PRAMER, D. (1958). The persistence and biological effects of antibiotics in soil. *Appl. Microbiol.*, **6**, 221.

PRAMER, D. (1959). The status of antibiotics in plant disease control. *Adv. appl. Microbiol.*, **1**, 75.

PRAMER, D. (1961). Eradicant and therapeutic materials for disease control: antibiotics. *Recent Adv. Bot., Toronto*. University of Toronto Press.

RAINBOW, C. & ROSE, A. H. (1963). Editors, *Biochemistry of Industrial Microorganisms*. New York. Academic Press.

RANGASWAMI, G. & VIDYASEKARAN, P. (1963). Antibiotic production by *Streptomyces* in corn rhizosphere. *Phytopathology*, **53**, 995.

REYNOLDS, D. M. (1954). Exocellular chitinase from a *Streptomyces sp. J. gen. Microbiol.*, **11**, 150.

ROMANO, A. H. & SAFFERMAN, R. S. (1963). Studies on actinomycetes and their odors. *J. Am. Wat. Wks Ass.*, **55**, 169.

ROVIRA, A. D. (1962). Plant-root exudates in relation to the rhizosphere microflora. *Soils Fertil., Harpenden*, **15**, 167.

SCHMIDT, E. L. (1950). Soil microorganisms and plant growth substances. *Soil Sci.*, **71**, 129.

SCHMIDT, E. L. & STARKEY, R. L. (1951). Soil microorganisms and plant growth substances. II. Transformations of certain B-vitamins in soil. *Soil Sci.*, **71**, 221.

SILVEY, J. K. G. & ROACH, A. W. (1959). Laboratory culture of taste and odor producing aquatic actinomycetes. *J. Am. Wat. Wks Ass.*, **51**, 20.

SIZER, I. W. (1964). Enzymes and their applications. *Adv. appl. Microbiol.*, **6**, 207.

STARKEY, R. L. (1958). Interrelations between microorganisms and plant roots in the rhizosphere. *Bact. Rev.*, **22**, 154.

THAYSEN, A. C. (1936). The origin of an earthy or muddy taint in fish. *Ann. appl. Biol.*, **23**, 99.

THAYSEN, A. C. (1956). Food and fodder yeast. In *Yeasts*. Ed. Roman, W. The Hague. Junk.

VELDKAMP, H. (1955). A study of the aerobic decomposition of chitin by microorganisms. *Meded. LandbHoogesch. Wageningen*, **55**, 127.

WELSCH, M. (1962). Bacteriolytic enzymes from streptomyces. *J. gen. Physiol.*, **45**, 115.

WINTER, A. G. (1961). New physiological and biochemical aspects in the interrelationships between higher plants. In *Mechanisms in Biological Competition*. Ed. Milthorpe, F. L. New York. Academic Press.

# SIGNIFICANT CHEMOLITHOTROPHIC REACTIONS OF BACTERIA IN THE SOIL

H. G. SCHLEGEL

*Institut für Mikrobiologie der Universität, Göttingen*

## *INTRODUCTION*

During the course of scientific progress and the advancement of knowledge it often becomes necessary to redefine old terms. These changes in terminology become noticeable particularly in rapidly progressing fields such as genetics and biochemistry. The terms autotrophy, photosynthesis and chemosynthesis have undergone such changes but it is remarkable that to date these terms have retained almost all of their original meaning. Nevertheless, it has become necessary to introduce new terms for the sake of clarity. Since these old and new terms have been used in colourful mixtures in many publications, it seems appropriate to reiterate their general history.

Wilhelm Pfeffer (1897) used the terms 'autotrophs' and 'heterotrophs' as they are understood today: that is, organisms which are able to synthesize their cell substances from inorganic carbonate or from preformed organic substances respectively. In his paper 'Studien zur Energetik der Pflanze' (1892), he had already concerned himself with the problems of carbon dioxide assimilation using light energy (green plants) or using chemical energy (nitrifying bacteria); but he first used the terms photosynthesis and chemosynthesis in his textbook of plant physiology in 1897, 'In Hinsicht auf die betreibenden Energiemittel wird man also allgemein, je nach den obwaltenden Verhältnissen von Photosynthese, Thermosynthese, Chemosynthese, Elektrosynthese usw. reden'.[1]

The term autotrophic is unequivocal, although in combination with prefixes other than carbon dioxide, confusion can arise (vitamin- or auxoautotroph). Carbon-autotrophic organisms are those which are able to synthesize their various cell constituents utilizing carbon dioxide as the main source of carbon (Woods and Lascelles, 1954). In this sentence

[1] 'With respect to the sources of driving energy one could generally talk about photosynthesis, thermosynthesis, chemosynthesis, electrosynthesis etc., depending on the prevailing conditions' (Pfeffer, 1897).

the phrase 'which are able' must be emphasized since the ability to utilize carbon dioxide as the main carbon source is the determining characteristic; it is of minor importance that several autotrophs can occasionally grow with organic substrates. The biochemical pathway of $CO_2$ fixation in those autotrophic bacteria thus far investigated has been found to be identical with that responsible for $CO_2$ fixation in green plants. This pathway, the reductive pentosephosphate cycle or Calvin cycle, has become an integral part of the definition of carbon dioxide-autotrophy. 'Organisms capable of synthesizing all their organic matter from carbon dioxide possess both the heterotrophic and the autotrophic enzyme systems' (Elsden, 1962). This statement cannot be applied in the reverse sense.

Less unequivocal is the concept of chemosynthesis. This idea was developed in the work of Winogradsky from 1887 to 1896 and was used by Pfeffer with respect to the energy source. In his paper on iron bacteria Winogradsky (1922) coined the new term 'Anorgoxydanten'. Later both terms were refuted (Baas-Becking and Parks, 1927); the term chemosynthesis because it was illogical, since every organism performs a chemical synthesis, and the term 'inorgoxidants' because it was not sufficiently elastic. In fact, only the strict autotrophic bacteria could be termed inorgoxidants according to Winogradsky's definition. Thus, while the term photosynthesis is unequivocal, the term chemosynthesis has lost much of its significance. Since the time of Pfeffer, the term photosynthesis has retained the idea of energy conversion, or rather has regained it once more within the last few years, independent of whether or not the energy derived during the photochemical processes is utilized for the assimilation of carbon dioxide or of organic material. Chemosynthesis, however, no longer means 'energy production by oxidation of inorganic substances'.

The terms phototrophy and chemotrophy, as defined in 1946 (Lwoff *et al.*, 1946), as well as the derived terms litho- and organotrophy concerning the nature of the hydrogen-donor, correspond much better to recent metabolic findings. They emphasize the aspects of energy source and hydrogen-donor. These terms used to describe the different types of microbial nutrition do not pertain to the question of the derivation of cell carbon.

The importance of C-autotrophic micro-organisms with respect to processes in the soil is not directly related to $CO_2$ fixation as such. In comparison with $CO_2$ fixation by green plants, the yield of organic substances in these organisms is certainly minimal, and its quantitative value with respect to the entire carbon cycle in nature can be disregarded.

It is the energy source and the oxidation of the H-donors that are of interest in the study of soil microbiology.

The chemolithotrophic soil bacteria are extraordinarily important and have almost no competitors as far as the oxidation of inorganic compounds is concerned. Ammonia and nitrite appear to be oxidized to nitrate almost exclusively by the autotrophic nitrifiers; however, other bacteria and moulds may additionally participate in nitrification processes to a lesser degree (Hirsch, Overrein, and Alexander, 1961; Marshall and Alexander, 1962; Gunner, 1963). Reliable ecological investigations pertaining to the participation of micro-organisms other than the C-autotrophic nitrifiers are lacking.

Also, the oxidation of sulphur and its compounds appears to be performed by autotrophic thiobacilli. A considerable number of micro-organisms are, however, capable of oxidizing sulphur and it would require intensive ecological investigations to estimate the proportions of sulphur oxidation performed by thiobacilli and other micro-organisms in various natural habitats.

Chemolithotrophy on the basis of iron oxidation has so far been conclusively demonstrated only in the case of acidophilic ferrobacilli. In a neutral or alkaline medium, the non-biological iron oxidation is probably more significant.

A large number of micro-organisms, including *Azotobacter*, *Acetobacter*, the Enterobacteriaceae, *Rhizobium*, *Micrococcus* and others are capable of oxidizing molecular hydrogen. However, only a small group of bacteria termed Knallgasbacteria[2], is capable of carrying on a chemolithotrophic way of life. The most popular and most frequently investigated organisms are strains of the genus *Hydrogenomonas*. Hydrogen oxidizing strains of mycobacteria, nocardiae, streptomycetes, and micrococci have been isolated within the last 10 years, but have not yet been intensively investigated (reviewed by Eberhardt, 1965*a*).

## *COMBINATION OF CHEMOLITHO- AND AUTOTROPHY*

The possibilities for combination of the reactions involved in chemolithotrophic metabolism are much greater than one would generally imagine. The characteristic capabilities of a chemolithoautotrophic bacterium are the utilization of an inorganic compound as H-donor for energy production and carbon dioxide reduction.

Many examples of different and changing degrees of organotrophy

[2] The term Knallgas applies to the explosive mixture consisting of molecular hydrogen and oxygen.

and phototrophy are to be found in the various tissues of green plants while growing from seed to maturity. The colourless embryo or seedling is restricted to organotrophic nutrition while utilizing storage material *in vivo* or organic components from a nutrient medium *in vitro*. With light as the energy source, green plants are able to fix carbon dioxide and incorporate organic substances as well. Green algae such as *Chlamydobotrys* whose $CO_2$ fixation is not sufficient to synthesize cell material, additionally assimilate acetate in light (Pringsheim and Wiessner, 1961; Wiessner, 1962; Wiessner and Gaffron, 1964). The chemolithotrophic purple sulphur bacteria not only fix carbon dioxide, but also assimilate a large number of organic substrates, including glucose, fructose, glycerol, organic acids and amino acids (Thiele, unpubl.). *Athiorhodaceae* generally photoassimilate organic substances (Gest, 1963).

Phototrophy and chemotrophy are analogous ways of obtaining energy. Both processes lead to the production of ATP. According to current theories, the degree to which ATP may be utilized is independent of the mechanism of ATP production. ATP can be used for any energy-requiring chemical reaction which the cells are able to perform. Thus, one may expect to find chemolithotrophic organisms which combine an inorganic oxidation (for energy production) with the assimilation of organic substrates (Method 1) or perform a $CO_2$ fixation to an insufficient degree and which complement remaining requirements by means of the assimilation of organic substrates (Method 2). Finally, depending on its availability, these organisms may obtain their cellular carbon from either carbon dioxide or organic substrates but gain energy only from the oxidation of inorganic compounds (Method 3). Organisms whose metabolism incorporates these three methods of energy production and carbon assimilation have been found in nature.

*Method 1.* The possibility that organic carbon could be assimilated with the aid of a chemical (inorganic) reaction had been discussed by Lieske (1919) for the case of *Leptothrix ochracea*; he was referring to a mixotrophic metabolism.

This 'mixotrophic' way of life has been demonstrated in *Desulphovibrio*. Sulphate-reducing bacteria were previously reported to have been grown on purely mineral media without organic H-donors (Pont, 1939; Czurda, 1940; Butlin and Adams, 1947); one was thus tempted to classify *Desulphovibrio desulphuricans* in the group of hydrogen-oxidizing C-autotrophic bacteria. The sulphate-respiration was believed to yield energy necessary for autotrophic $CO_2$ fixation. The rate of sulphate-respiration, however, is high even if the cells do not grow. Thus by measuring the rate of sulphide production false conclusions concerning the growth rate were drawn. As has been shown by Stüven (1960*a* and *b*), acetate is incorporated during sulphate respiration with molecular hydrogen as H-donor. In spite of a very low efficiency with respect to $^{14}CO_2$ incorporation, he did not dare to conclude that *Desulphovibrio* cannot fix carbon dioxide autotrophically and thus cannot synthesize the bulk of its cell substance from $CO_2$. As finally observed by Mechalas and Rittenberg (1960), *Desulphovibrio desulphuricans*, during sulphur respiration with $H_2$ or incompletely oxidizable organic substrates as H-donors, synthesizes the major portion of its cellular material from yeast extract and obtains only 10 per cent of its required carbon from carbon dioxide. Thus, these authors furnished convincing evidence that one group of organisms performs the first of the three types of metabolism: the assimilation of organic materials with the aid of energy obtained by means of inorganic oxidation.

*Method 2.* Beijerinck (Beijerinck and Minkman, 1910) using a crude culture of denitrifying bacteria, observed the growth of micro-organisms in a simple mineral medium incubated under an atmosphere of nitrous oxide and hydrogen. He postulated a 'new kind of chemosynthesis' with molecular hydrogen as the H-donor and nitrous oxide serving as the H-acceptor. Kluyver and his co-workers (Kluyver, 1953; Verhoeven, Koster and van Nievelt, 1954; Verhoeven, 1956) succeeded in cultivating a bacterium which grew anaerobically in a hydrogen atmosphere with nitrate as the H-acceptor and carbon dioxide as a carbon source. However, after transferring the organisms to fresh medium growth ceased. Only when traces of yeast extract were added to the subcultures did the cells grow under the 'almost' chemolithotrophic conditions. Even the strain isolated by Beijerinck in 1910 was able to grow under chemolithotrophic conditions when yeast extract was added. To test the mechanism of autotrophic $CO_2$ fixation, Kornberg, Collins and Bigley (1960) grew *Micrococcus denitrificans* as a Knallgasbacterium in a mineral medium under a hydrogen-oxygen atmosphere containing carbon dioxide. $^{14}CO_2$ was incorporated into phosphorylated compounds and especially into 3-phosphoglyceric acid. Cell-free extracts catalysed the incorporation of $^{14}CO_2$ into 3-phosphoglyceric acid if ribulose-1·5-diphosphate or ribulose-5-phosphate and ATP were added. Thus, the functioning of the Calvin cycle seems to be sufficiently demonstrated in this case. Cells grown organotrophically with acetate do not contain the enzymes of the Calvin cycle. According to the results from our experiments performed with a strain isolated from garden soil, the growth rate of *M. denitrificans* is very low under strictly chemolithoautotrophic conditions with hydrogen as H-donor and oxygen or nitrate as H-acceptor. The cell yield was practically proportional to the amount of yeast extract added (Vogt, 1965; Banerjee, 1965).

When the cells were grown under a Knallgas atmosphere containing carbon dioxide and with small amounts of yeast extract, they contained hydrogenase and incorporated organic substrates mixotrophically. While under air the cells partially oxidized and partially assimilated yeast extract; under an atmosphere of hydrogen and oxygen they assimilated it completely. In the presence of yeast extract, carbon dioxide, hydrogen and oxygen, the cells obtained approximately two-thirds of their cell carbon from the yeast extract and only one-third by means of $CO_2$ fixation. The low growth rate under chemolithotrophic conditions is a result of the low activity of the enzymes of the reductive pentose cycle. *Micrococcus denitrificans* is unable to produce the bulk of its cellular carbon C-autotrophically although it contains the autotrophic enzyme system. Growth is dependent on supplementation by organic substances.

*Method 3.* Investigations concerning the simultaneous utilization of carbon dioxide and organic substrates, of the shift from chemolithotrophic to organotrophic metabolism and of the regulatory mechanisms involved have been started using Knallgasbacteria. Those Knallgasbacteria described until now are facultative chemolithotrophs. *Hydrogenomonas* strains H 1, H 16 and H 20 can grow chemolithotrophically with carbon dioxide as the sole carbon source as well as chemo-organotrophically with various substrates such as fructose, mono- and dicarboxylic acids, amino acids, alcohols and on complex media. Depending on the demand, they are able to produce energy by means of the oxidation of either hydrogen or organic substrates. The energy produced by each of these two reactions can be used either for the fixation of carbon dioxide or for the assimilation of organic substrates provided that the cells have formed the corresponding enzymes under suitable growth conditions. It is difficult to understand the regulation of the formation and function of the participating enzymes; as a phenomenon the regulation is only partly comprehended, and little is known about the causal factors involved. Since our group in Göttingen during the last few years has been intensively occupied with these questions, I intend to give a brief summary of these investigations. A comprehensive review of the physiology and biochemistry of Knallgasbacteria has already been written (Schlegel, 1965).

## *ENRICHMENT AND ISOLATION OF KNALLGASBACTERIA*

The aerobic, facultative chemolithotrophic, hydrogen-oxidizing bacteria (Knallgasbacteria) include members from various genera. Most of the strains which have been intensively investigated are Gram negative, polarly flagellated rods and belong to the genus *Hydrogenomonas*. Kaserer (1906) isolated *Bacillus pantotrophus*. In 1906, and since then, many 'species' have been described including *Hydrogenomonas flava*, *H. vitrea*, *H. agilis*, *H. carboxydovorans*, *H. facilis*, *H. ruhlandii* and *H. eutropha*. The *differentia specifica* are not always justified. Other typical Knallgasbacteria are found among the mycobacteria, some of which have been isolated from enrichment cultures with ethane, propane and natural gas (Foster, 1962; Lukins and Foster, 1963). Knallgasbacteria and mycobacteria are most easily isolated by the direct plating method on mineral agar and incubation under an atmosphere of hydrogen, oxygen and carbon dioxide. Nocardiae, streptomycetes (Takamiya and Tubaki, 1956; Hirsch, 1961) and cocci (Dworkin and Foster, 1957) are also capable of growing autotrophically with hydrogen as the energy source.

Spore-forming Knallgasbacteria have thus far been described only by Ruhland (1922; 1924) and by Belajewa (1954). New attempts to isolate bacilli have so far been unsuccessful (Eberhardt, 1966*a*, *b*).

In liquid enrichment cultures consisting of a mineral medium under hydrogen, oxygen and carbon dioxide, pseudomonads (*Hydrogenomonas*) predominate. The extent to which the partial pressure of the gas components, the temperature, the salt content, the hydrogen-ion-concentration and other environmental factors influence the results of the enrichment culture, still requires systematic investigation. In shaken cultures, *Hydrogenomonas* strains predominate which grow as homogeneous suspensions. Stationary cultures select bacteriogloea formers (Wilde, 1962).

Auxotrophic strains have not yet been isolated from natural habitats. Enrichments in vitamin-containing mineral media with inocula from 13 different locations did not result in the isolation of vitamin-requiring Knallgasbacteria (Schuster, unpubl.).

Apparently Knallgasbacteria are present in all soil samples which have thus far been investigated (Niklewski, 1910). It was only in beach sand that they could not be found (Grohmann, 1924). New investigations on their distribution in different soils and on their relative importance in the soil are still lacking.

## *SYNTHESIS AND RE-UTILIZATION OF STORAGE MATERIALS*

As far as is known, hydrogenomonads accumulate two intracellular storage materials: poly-$\beta$-hydroxybutyric acid (PHBA) and polyphosphates. Both are produced by the cell under conditions where energy as well as the corresponding substrates (C-source or phosphate) are available and growth and multiplication are limited by the lack of an additional factor. PHBA and polyphosphates can be re-utilized during metabolism in *Hydrogenomonas* and thus are true storage materials (Schlegel, 1962). The *Hydrogenomonas* strains H 1, H 16 and H 20 form PHBA when energy and carbon dioxide sources are present and when nitrogen or phosphorus, for example, are growth limiting (Schlegel, Gottschalk and Bartha, 1961; Wilde, 1962; Schlegel and Gottschalk, 1962).

Stored PHBA can be oxidized by the cells in an energy-producing reaction and can also be transformed into protein. PHBA-rich cells of *Hydrogenomonas* H 16 containing c. 60 per cent PHBA respire this storage product endogenously. Within four days, the $Q_{O_2}$ drops from 18 to 2·7. Ammonia appears in the medium only after complete consumption of PHBA. In PHBA-poor cells, the endogenous protein respiration with a $Q_{O_2}$ of 2·5 appears very early. The respiration of PHBA as well as that of protein facilitates the survival of the cells (Hippe, 1965). There is no doubt that in *Hydrogenomonas*, PHBA functions as storage material not only for energy production but also for protein synthesis under conditions which otherwise do not allow growth. This storage material is also of ecological value.

The accumulation of polyphosphates can be regarded as the most economic way of storing phosphate; no organic P-acceptors are required. Polyphosphates are always accumulated when enough phosphate is available for the cells. Polyphosphate-rich cells also grow in a phosphate-free medium for quite a while. The capability of storing phosphate may be of importance in the natural habitat where growth is limited to a varying extent by one or another factor (Kaltwasser and Schlegel, 1959; Schlegel and Kaltwasser, 1961; Kaltwasser, 1962). Although polyphosphate possesses energy-rich bonds, the amount of energy fixed in this way is surely of no importance. The highest amount of phosphate measured in *Hydrogenomonas* H 16 and H 20 corresponds to an amount of free energy which could be obtained from a hydrogen oxidation lasting only 10 seconds (Kaltwasser, 1962). Thus the storage of polyphosphate is certainly significant for the phosphate balance, but is irrelevant to energy storage.

## *THE SYNTHESIS OF PHBA AND THE CARBON PATHWAY*

PHBA synthesis in washed cell suspensions can be easily determined by measuring the increase in turbidity. This simple method facilitates preliminary experiments for the exploration of the pathway of PHBA synthesis from organic acids, carbon dioxide and sugars.

### *PHBA Synthesis from Organic Acids*

Most acids are assimilated by chemolithotrophically grown cells under air without a pronounced lag phase. With $\beta$-hydroxybutyric or lactic acid as substrate, the rate of synthesis is higher than under chemolithotrophic conditions with carbon dioxide as a carbon source. Crotonate and acetate are incorporated as total units into PHBA. After the assimilation of specifically $^{14}C$-labelled organic acids, the distribution of the radioactive carbon in the four C-atoms of the monomer of PHBA isolated from cells could be measured following systematic degradation. Lactate is incorporated after one decarboxylation, succinate after two decarboxylations (Gottschalk, 1964*a* and *b*).

These conclusions were drawn from experiments with chemolithotrophically grown cells and with cells which were adapted for three hours to the previously mentioned substrates. The $^{14}C$-labelled organic acids were then incorporated under a Knallgas-atmosphere. After a two-hour incubation period in the presence of 2-$^{14}C$-acetate, 96 per cent of the radioactivity was still found in C-atoms 2 and 4 of $\beta$-hydroxybutyrate derived from PHBA. The terminal oxidation via the tricarboxylic acid cycle is thus almost completely suppressed by Knallgas. The hydrogen oxidation supplies the energy necessary for the assimilation of organic substances.

### *PHBA Synthesis from Hexoses*

Fructose is the only sugar which is utilized by the wild types of strains H 16 and H 20. This hexose is degraded via the Entner-Doudoroff pathway (Gottschalk, Eberhardt and Schlegel, 1964). The mutant H 16 G$^{+}$ also utilizes glucose and uses the same pathway of degradation (Schlegel and Gottschalk, 1965). Investigations on the synthesis of PHBA from differently labelled $^{14}C$-glucoses led to the remarkable result that even in cells which were grown for many generations on fructose or glucose, the enzymes of the reductive pentose-phosphate cycle still participate in metabolism. The presence of the autotrophic enzyme system in heterotrophically grown cells had already been shown autoradiographically by Hirsch, Georgiev and Schlegel (1963*a*, *b*), and enzymatically by Gottschalk, Eberhardt and Schlegel (1964).

The incorporation rates of radioactive carbon derived from 2-$^{14}C$-, 1-$^{14}C$, and U-$^{14}C$-glucose into the PHBA of glucose-grown cells of H 16 G$^{+}$ were in the ratio of 100:16:65 respectively. These results do not agree with the concept that the cleavage products, pyruvate and 3-phosphoglyceraldehyde, of the 2-keto-3-desoxy-6-phosphogluconic acid-aldolase reaction are directly utilized without other intermediate reactions for PHBA synthesis. If this were true, the atoms C 1 and C 4 of glucose would be eliminated when acetyl-CoA is formed from pyruvate. The participation of other metabolic pathways, for example the Embden-Meyerhof scheme or phosphoketolase reactions can be excluded (Schlegel, Gottschalk and Schindler, 1962; Schindler, 1964). An exception is the reductive pentose-phosphate cycle. Even after eight transfers on glucose, cells of *Hydrogenomonas* strain H 16 G$^{+}$ still contained a remarkable activity of ribulose-diphosphate-carboxylase (that is 11 mU compared to 135 mU/mg. protein in chemolithotrophically grown cells). Presumably 1-$^{14}C$-ribulose-5-phosphate is formed from 1-$^{14}C$-glucose and the 2-keto-3-desoxy-6-phosphogluconic acid cleavage product, 3-phosphoglyceraldehyde, by a transketolase reaction. Ribulose-5-phosphate is further converted via ribulose-diphosphate to 3-$^{14}C$-3-phosphoglyceric acid and finally to 2-$^{14}C$-acetyl-CoA. These reactions are shown in Fig. 1. The participation of the pentose-phosphate cycle in glucose metabolism indicates that a strict separation of autotrophic and heterotrophic reactions is not possible. All enzymes present in the cell participate in cell metabolism insofar as their function is not impaired by specific regulatory mechanisms, for example allosteric inhibition.

### *PHBA Synthesis from Carbon Dioxide*

The function of the reductive pentose-phosphate cycle in Knallgasbacteria has already been indicated from the results of investigations with *Hydrogenomonas facilis* (Bergmann, Towne and Burris, 1958; McFadden, 1959). When cells of strains H 16 and H 20 synthesizing PHBA from carbon dioxide and molecular hydrogen were exposed to $^{14}CO_2$ for some seconds, $^{14}C$-labelled 3-phosphoglyceric acid, hexosemonophosphate, ribose-5-phosphate, dihydroxyacetone-phosphate and phosphoglycolic acid are found in the alcohol extracts; after a period of one minute, organic acids are also labelled (Hirsch, 1963; Hirsch, Georgiev and Schlegel, 1963*a*, *b*). The presence of the enzymes ribulose-diphosphate-carboxylase and phosphoribulokinase have been demonstrated (Gottschalk, 1964*c*). These observations indicate that the reductive pentose-phosphate cycle participates in the synthesis of PHBA from carbon dioxide. However, the question remained as to which intermediary product served as the source of acetyl-CoA.

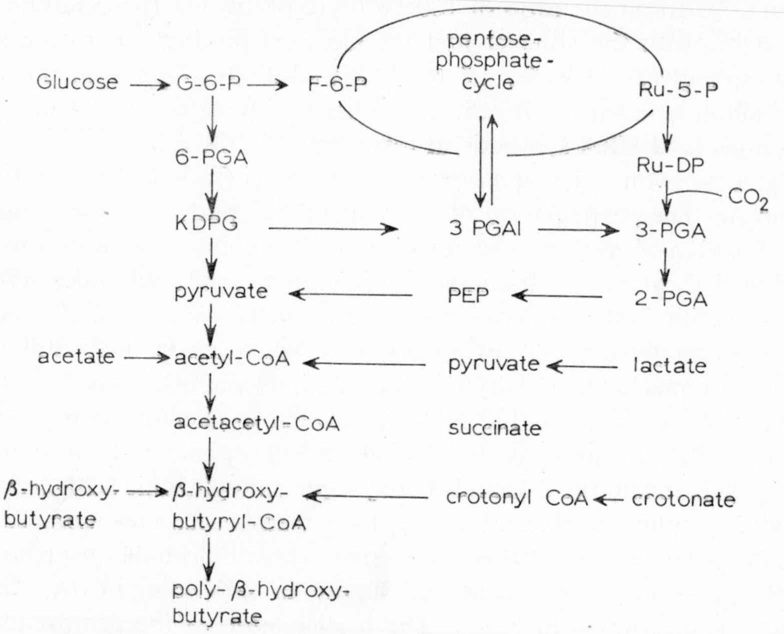


Fig. 1. Synthesis of poly-β-hydroxybutyric acid from glucose grown cells of *Hydrogenomonas* H 16 G+ which still contain the autotrophic enzyme system. The pathways from $CO_2$ and organic acids are also included in this scheme.

PHBA and acetate which were isolated from cells after a quite short incorporation of $^{14}CO_2$ (8 sec.), were already uniformly labelled (Gottschalk, 1964*c*). Therefore, in the synthesis of PHBA from carbon dioxide and hydrogen, only those reaction sequences could be involved which lead to uniformly labelled acetate. Uniformly labelled acetate might have been derived from intermediary compounds by means of phosphoketolase reactions. With the aid of an optical enzyme test (acetylation of p-nitro-aniline through phosphotransacetylase and arylaminetransacetylase), it was shown that strain H 16 does not contain phosphoketolase. No acetylation of p-nitro-aniline was found with either fructose-6-phosphate, ribose- or with ribulose-5-phosphate (Schlegel, Gottschalk and Schindler, 1962; Schindler, 1964). On the other hand the enzymes involved in the transformation of 3-phosphoglyceric acid into acetyl-coenzyme A (phosphoglyceratemutase, enolase, pyruvate-kinase and pyruvate-dehydrogenase) were found to be present and sufficiently active (Gottschalk, 1964*c*; Schindler, 1964). As a result of the exclusion of other reaction pathways the synthesis of PHBA from carbon dioxide must therefore occur via 3-phosphoglyceric acid, 2-phosphoglyceric acid, phosphoenolpyruvate, pyruvate and acetyl-CoA (Fig. 1).

The synthesis of acetoacetyl-CoA from acetyl-CoA is measured by the oxidation of $NADPH_2$ in the presence of $\beta$-hydroxybutyryl-CoA-dehydrogenase. It is not known in either H 16 or in other PHBA-accumulating bacteria whether malonyl-CoA also participates in the synthesis of acetoacetyl-CoA or whether, as in *Escherichia coli* or *Clostridium kluyveri*, the syntheses of lower and long chain fatty acids occur independently of each other (Goldman, Alberts and Vagelos, 1963). Experiments concerning the synthesis of polymers from $\beta$-hydroxybutyryl-CoA have not yet been carried out with *Hydrogenomonas*.

## *INDUCTION OF ORGANOTROPHIC SYNTHESIS*

If fructose is added to a suspension of chemolithotrophically grown cells of *Hydrogenomonas* H 16 and the suspension is incubated under air, the enzymes necessary for the uptake and utilization of fructose are

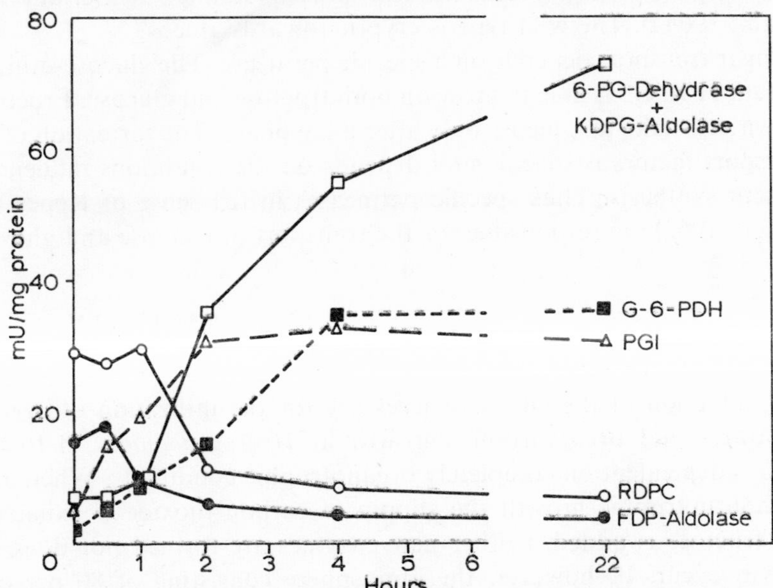


Fig. 2. Changes in the enzyme activities of chemolithotrophically grown cells of *Hydrogenomonas* H 16 $G^+$ during adaptation to fructose.

Cells were grown in a mineral medium under an atmosphere consisting of hydrogen, oxygen and carbon dioxide. Fructose was added and the gas mixture replaced by air at zero time. After different periods of time, samples were taken, centrifuged, washed and frozen. Cell free extracts were prepared from these cells by means of a Hughes press (Gottschalk, Eberhardt and Schlegel, 1964).

induced (Gottschalk, Eberhardt and Schlegel, 1964). Cells grown chemolithotrophically take up fructose only after a lag phase of 10 min. Subsequently, the activity of several enzymes is changed (Fig. 2). The activities of phosphoglucose-isomerase and glucose-6-phosphate-dehydrogenase increase first; then the formation of the enzymes of the Entner-Doudoroff system follows. After approximately 5 hours at 30° these enzymes had reached their maximal activity. The synthesis of these enzymes is accompanied by a drop in the activity of ribulose-diphosphate-carboxylase and fructose diphosphate-aldolase. However, even after many transfers onto fructose, there remains a residual activity of ribulose-diphosphate-carboxylase corresponding to approximately 6 per cent of that of chemolithotrophically grown cells.

The wild type *Hydrogenomonas* H 16 utilizes fructose, but no other sugars. Hexokinase present in cells grown on fructose also phosphorylates glucose; thus fructose-grown cells contain within the cell all enzymes necessary for glucose utilization.

Attempts to force a glucose oxidation by increasing the glucose concentration to 10 per cent remained unsuccessful. As shown by 'free space' experiments glucose is not transported into the cell interior (Gottschalk, 1964*d*). The wild type is cryptic towards glucose.

Sugar transport depends on a specific permease. The glucose-utilizing mutant H 16 $G^+$ is able to grow on both fructose and glucose. Fructose-grown cells take up glucose only after a lag phase. The formation of the transport factors is specific and depends on the conditions influencing protein synthesis. Thus specific permeases in the sense of Kepes and Cohen (1962) are responsible for the transport of fructose and glucose.

## *REPRESSION OF ENZYME FORMATION BY HYDROGEN*

The induction of the enzymes necessary for the utilization of organic substrates and organotrophic growth in *Hydrogenomonas* H 16 and H 20 is dependent on completely organotrophic conditions. When after chemolithotrophic growth the supply of carbon dioxide is exhausted and fructose is added, neither new enzymes are formed nor does cell growth occur. If, however, the atmosphere consisting of 80 per cent hydrogen and 20 per cent oxygen is replaced by air, growth starts immediately (Fig. 3). The enzymes of the Entner-Doudoroff system could not be demonstrated in cells which had been kept for four hours in the presence of fructose and under a hydrogen-oxygen atmosphere. Under air, however, the activity of phospho-glucose-isomerase, glucose-

6-phosphate-dehydrogenase, and the 6-phosphogluconic acid cleaving enzymes increased rapidly. The induced enzyme formation is completely suppressed by hydrogen (Gottschalk, 1965).

Even more remarkable is the observation that hydrogen suppresses the formation of the enzymes of the Entner-Doudoroff pathway in fructose-grown cells as well. The Entner-Doudoroff enzymes present are diluted and their specific activity decreases.

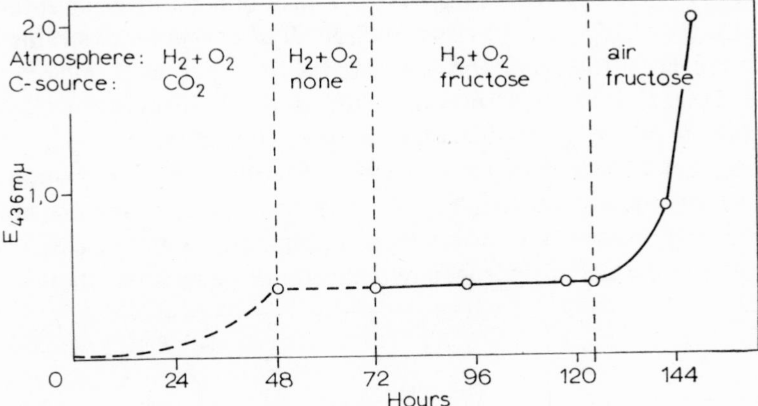


Fig. 3. Complete inhibition of fructose utilization by molecular hydrogen in *Hydrogenomonas* H 16.

*Hydrogenomonas* H 16 was chemolithotrophically grown in a mineral medium without bicarbonate (300 ml.) in an atmosphere of 80 per cent $H_2$ + 15 per cent $O_2$ + 5 per cent $CO_2$ for 48 hrs.; the gas atmosphere was then replaced by 80 per cent $H_2$ + 20 per cent $O_2$; 1·5 g. fructose was added from the side arm after 72 hrs.; the atmosphere was finally replaced by air after 125 hrs. The turbidity was determined in an Eppendorf photometer at 436 mμ (d = 1 cm.).

The 'hydrogen effect' is similar to the 'glucose effect' (Gale, 1943) and is a case of 'catabolite repression' (Magasanik 1961; 1964). However, it is differentiated from the 'glucose effect' by its consequences. The inhibition of enzyme induction and formation by glucose leads to the preferential consumption of that substrate which is more easily accessible for the cell. The 'hydrogen effect' prevents multiplication and growth. Here arises the curious situation in which an energy source—Knallgas—and an appropriate substrate—fructose—are available to the cells, but cannot be used.

*Hydrogenomonas* utilizes a substrate, whose components $H_2$ and $CO_2$ can be supplied separately. In the presence of both components growth is guaranteed, even in the presence of organic substrates. However, if only hydrogen is supplied and the corresponding carbon source ($CO_2$) is absent, fructose cannot be used.

The hydrogen effect is also observed with aspartate, glutamate, acetate and fructose, but not with lactate, pyruvate, crotonate or succinate.

## *RESPIRATORY CONTROL*

In microbiological publications, respiratory control is seldom discussed and apparently never mentioned in the title. According to text book opinion, a respiratory control is lacking in bacteria (White, Handler and Smith, 1964). However, as is generally known, the respiratory rate of bacteria is regulated by endergonic synthesis. This control mechanism, which aids metabolic economy, is very pronounced in chemolithotrophically grown Knallgasbacteria such as *Hydrogenomonas* strains H 1, H 16 and H 20 (Schlegel and Bartha, 1961*a*; Eberhardt, 1966*b*). The gas uptake of a washed suspension of strain H 16 under a $CO_2$-free atmosphere of hydrogen and oxygen is approximately 640 µl. gas/hr./mg. protein, but in the presence of carbon dioxide there is an uptake of 3000 µl. gas/hr./mg. protein (Fig. 4). Here carbon dioxide does not act catalytically, rather it is being fixed in substrate amounts. Since the ratio of the uptake of hydrogen and carbon dioxide under these conditions is not greater than 8, this nearly 5-fold increase in the oxidation rate must result from an acceleration of electron transport via the respiratory chain.

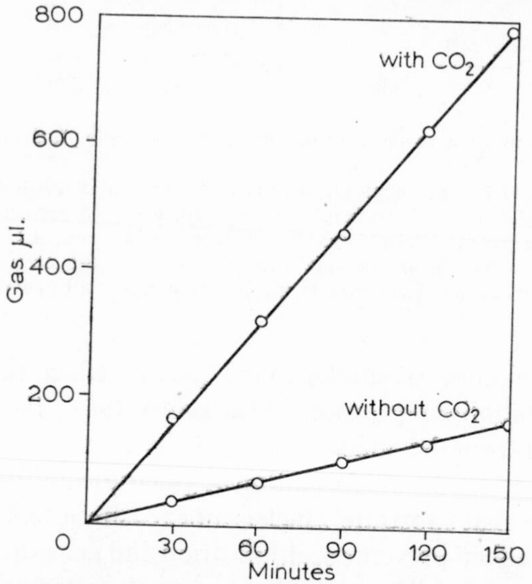


Fig. 4. $CO_2$ stimulated increase in the rate of $H_2$ oxidation in cells of H 16.

Chemolithotrophically grown cells were suspended in 0·066 M phosphate buffer (pH 7·0) and shaken in a Warburg flask at 30° in 95 per cent $H_2$ + 5 per cent $O_2$ (—$CO_2$) and 85 per cent $H_2$ + 5 per cent $O_2$ + 10 per cent $CO_2$. After Eberhardt (1965*b*).

Hydrogen oxidation is apparently very closely coupled with carbon dioxide fixation through the adenylic acid system. During the hydrogen oxidation without carbon dioxide—('Leerlauf')—very little energy is used. If, however, carbon dioxide fixation which requires extraordinary amounts of energy is made possible by the addition of carbon dioxide, hydrogen is oxidized at a maximal rate. It was not possible to accelerate hydrogen oxidation very drastically by the addition of organic substrates such as acetate, succinate and fructose. The increase in the rate of hydrogen oxidation amounted to only 10–30 per cent. This ineffectiveness of organic substrates is consistent with the fact that the synthesis of PHBA or other cell substances from organic acids or hexoses requires considerably less energy than that from carbon dioxide and hydrogen.

Inhibition experiments confirmed this conclusion (Schlegel and Bartha, 1961*b*). With $10^{-3}$M iodoacetate, which inhibits triosephosphate-dehydrogenase and ribulose-diphosphate-carboxylase and thus the reductive pentose-phosphate cycle (Rabin and Trown, 1964), the rate of hydrogen oxidation in the presence of $CO_2$ is lowered to the rate of the $CO_2$-free sample. Hydrogenase and other components of the respiratory chain were not inhibited by iodoacetate at this concentration. The inhibition of gas uptake by iodoacetate is overcome to a large degree by the addition of methylene blue.

Such a strict respiratory control is not known in other bacteria but should be expected to be present in other chemolithotrophic bacteria as well.

## *METABOLIC REGULATION IN CHEMOLITHO- AND ORGANOTROPHY*

The phenomena of enzyme induction and of repression indicate that the investigated *Hydrogenomonas* strains are basically chemolithoautotrophic. During growth with organic substrates under air, hydrogenase is also formed, although it usually has a lower specific activity. The enzymes of autotrophic $CO_2$ fixation are also partially retained during growth on those substrates thus far tested. These results obtained from three *Hydrogenomonas* strains can neither be regarded as representative for the entire genus *Hydrogenomonas* nor for all Knallgasbacteria, but the metabolic pattern is probably similar.

However, if we consider *Hydrogenomonas* H 16 as a representative of the metabolic type of Knallgasbacteria, it occupies a definite position in the ranks of different degrees of chemolithotrophy. Apparently different transition forms exist between the strict chemolithoautotrophic bacteria (such as *Nitrosomonas*, *Nitrobacter*, and most thiobacilli) and the organotrophic bacteria which only incidentally oxidize inorganic compounds. The nitrifiers refuse organic substrates. Thiobacilli incorporate perhaps glucose or other substrates to a slight degree, but are not able to grow on organic substrates. Indications concerning the existence of facultative chemolithotrophic transition types among the thiobacilli are becoming more frequent (Vishniac and Trudinger, 1962; London, 1963; Starkey, 1934*a* and *b*; Santer, Boyer and Santer, 1959). The facultative chemolithotrophic Knallgasbacteria are capable of utilizing organic substrates or hydrogen and carbon dioxide and apparently usually prefer inorganic rather than organic substrates. At the end of the scale is *Micrococcus denitrificans* which is also capable of $CO_2$ fixation as well as of obtaining energy through hydrogen oxidation, aerobically and anaerobically; however, its C-autotrophic capability is so low that it requires organic substrates. Moreover, it seems that in this organism the enzymes of both systems are strictly adaptive; hydrogenase as well as the key enzymes of autotrophic fixation are only formed when hydrogen is used as the sole hydrogen donor and carbon dioxide as the main carbon source; glucose or acetate completely suppress autotrophic abilities.

For a long time, biologists have been concerned with the question of the relationship between chemolitho- and organotrophy. The situation is analogous to the question of the relationship of photosynthesis and respiration in green plants. In both cases one and the same cell can obtain energy using different processes: by photophosphorylation or inorgoxidation or by oxidation of organic substrates. According to current concepts, both processes result in the production of ATP and reducing power. Studies on regulatory mechanisms indicate that repression and allosteric inhibition may also participate in the regulation of catabolic and anabolic processes in photo- and chemolithotrophic organisms. Induction and repression of enzymes as well as other information determine which substrate is preferentially utilized. Thus new aspects and new working hypotheses arise which may help to explain the strange abstinence of the strictly chemolithotrophic bacteria.

The problems related to auto- and heterotrophic $CO_2$ fixation have not yet been thoroughly investigated. The reductive pentose-phosphate cycle has been sufficiently demonstrated in most chemolithotrophic bacteria by autoradiography or by demonstration of the enzymes involved. Up to now, no C-autotrophic bacterium has been found which uses another system of $CO_2$ fixation. However, it is uncertain to what degree carbon dioxide is fixed via autotrophic and heterotrophic reactions by C-autotrophic bacteria and plants. Only in the case of *Thiobacillus denitrificans* has an estimation been made: 10 per cent of cell carbon from phosphoenolpyruvate carboxylation (Aubert, Milhaud and Millet, 1957).

Very little is known about the distribution of chemolithotrophic organisms in their natural habitat. Their presence in different soils can be better measured by their biochemical activities than by counting their numbers. According to our findings, the various strains isolated by the direct plating method are differentiated by many physiological characteristics. Most of the strains stopped growing after the second or third transfer; thus their physiological characteristics could not be determined. Conditions in the soil are different for each micro-environment. Imitating natural living conditions in the laboratory creates only one of a number of possibilities, and only those strains develop which easily adapt or are adapted to these conditions. Furthermore, it is not certain whether the strain growing in the laboratory is the dominant metabolic type in the soil. It remains to be seen whether the number of colonies grown on a certain mineral medium in a certain $H_2 + O_2 + CO_2$ atmosphere is comparable to the rate of $H_2$ oxidation or $^{14}CO_2$ fixation of a soil sample.

Ecological research requires extensive and reliable information about physiological and biochemical characteristics of organisms to be investigated. The spectrum of species and strains as well as their variability must be known. Since these requirements have not yet been realized, the study of the ecology of chemolithotrophic micro-organisms still remains to be developed.

## *ABBREVIATIONS USED IN TEXT AND GRAPHS*

| | |
|---|---|
| ADP | adenosinediphosphate |
| ATP | adenosinetriphosphate |
| CoA | coenzyme A |
| F-6-P | fructose-6-phosphate |
| G-6-P | glucose-6-phosphate |
| KDPG | 2-keto-3-desoxy-6-phospho-gluconic acid |
| NAD(P) | nicotinamide-adenine dinucleotide (phosphate) |
| NAD(P)$H_2$ | reduced NAD(P) |
| PEP | phosphoenolpyruvate |
| 2-PGA | 2-phosphoglyceric acid |
| 3-PGAl | 3-phosphoglyceraldehyde |
| 6-PGA | 6-phosphogluconic acid |
| PHBA | poly-$\beta$-hydroxybutyric acid |
| RuDP | ribulose-1·5-diphosphate |
| Ru-5-P | ribulose-5-phosphate |

## REFERENCES

AUBERT, J. P., MILHAUD, G. & MILLET, J. (1957). L'assimilation de l'anhydride carbonique par des bacteries chimioautotrophes. *Annls Inst. Pasteur, Paris*, **92**, 679.

BAAS-BECKING, L. G. M. & PARKS, G. S. (1927). Energy relations in the metabolism of autotrophic bacteria. *Physiol. Rev.*, **7**, 85.

BANERJEE, A. K. (1965). In preparation.

BEIJERINCK, M. & MINKMAN, D. C. J. (1910). Bildung und Verbrauch von Stickoxydul durch Bakterien. *Zentbl. Bakt. ParasitKde., Abt. II.*, **25**, 30.

BELYAEVA, M. Y. (1954). Die Assimilation molekularen Stickstoff durch Wasserstoffbakterien. *Uchen. Zap. bazan. gos. Univ.*, **114**, 13.

BERGMANN, F. H., TOWNE, J. C. & BURRIS, R. H. (1958). Assimilation of carbon dioxide by hydrogen bacteria. *J. biol. Chem.*, **230**, 13.

BUTLIN, K. R. & ADAMS, R. E. (1947). Autotrophic growth of sulphate-reducing bacteria. *Nature Lond.*, **160**, 154.

CZURDA, V. (1940). Zur Kenntnis der bakteriellen Sulfatreduktion. I. *Arch. Mikrobiol.*, **11**, 187.

DWORKIN, M. & FOSTER, J. W. (1957). Some new autotrophic hydrogen-utilizing bacteria. *Fedn. Proc.*, **16**, 176.

EBERHARDT, U. (1966*a*). Die Anreicherung von Knallgasbakterien. In *Anreicherungskultur und Mutantenauslese*. Ed. Schlegel, H. G., & Kroger, E. Stuttgart. Gustav Fischer Verlag.

EBERHARDT, U. (1966*b*). In preparation.

ELSDEN, S. R. (1962). *Photosynthesis and lithotrophic carbon dioxide fixation.* In *The Bacteria*, Vol. **3**, Ed. Gunsalus, I. C., & Stanier, R. Y. New York. Academic Press.

FOSTER, J. W. (1962). Hydrocarbons as substrates for microorganisms. *Antonie van Leeuwenhoek*, **28**, 241.

GALE, E. F. (1943). Factors influencing the enzymic activities of bacteria. *Bact. Rev.*, **7**, 139.

GEST, H. (1963). Metabolic aspects of bacterial photosynthesis. In *Bacterial photosynthesis.* Ed. Gest, H., San Pietro, A., & Vernon, L. P. Yellow Springs, Ohio. Antioch Press.

GOLDMAN, P., ALBERTS, A. W. & VAGELOS, P. R. (1963). The condensation reaction of fatty acid biosynthesis. II. Requirement of the enzymes of the condensation reaction for fatty acid synthesis. *J. biol. Chem.*, **238**, 1255.

GOTTSCHALK, G. (1964*a*). Die Biosynthese der Poly-β-hydroxybuttersäure durch Knallgasbakterien. I. Ermittlung der $^{14}C$-Verteilung in Poly-β-hydroxybuttersäure. *Arch. Mikrobiol.*, **47**, 225.

GOTTSCHALK, G. (1964*b*). Die Biosynthese der Poly-β-hydroxybuttersäure durch Knallgasbakterien. II. Verwertung organischer Säuren. *Arch. Mikrobiol.*, **47**, 230.

GOTTSCHALK, G. (1964*c*). Die Biosynthese der Poly-β-hydroxybuttersäure durch Knallgasbakterien. III. Synthese aus Kohlendioxyd. *Arch. Mikrobiol.*, **47**, 236.

GOTTSCHALK, G. (1964*d*). Verwertung von Fructose durch Hydrogenomonas H 16. II. Cryptisches Verhalten gegenüber Glucose. *Arch. Mikrobiol.*, **49**, 96.

GOTTSCHALK, G. (1965). Die Verwertung organischer Substrate durch Hydrogenomonas in Gegenwart von molekularem Wasserstoff. *Biochem. Z.*, **341**, 260.

GOTTSCHALK, G., EBERHARDT, U. & SCHLEGEL, H. G. (1964). Verwertung von Fructose durch Hydrogenomonas H 16 (L.). *Arch. Mikrobiol.*, **48**, 95.

GROHMANN, G. (1924). Zur Kenntnis wasserstoff-oxydierenden Bakterien. *Zentbl. Bakt. ParasitKde.*, *Abt. II*, **61**, 256.

GUNNER, H. B. (1963). Nitrification by *Arthrobacter globiformis*. *Nature Lond.*, **197**, 1127.

HIPPE, H. (1966). In preparation.

HIRSCH, P. (1961). Wasserstoffaktivierung und Chemoautotrophie bei Actinomyceten. *Arch. Mikrobiol.*, **39**, 360.

HIRSCH, P. (1963). $CO_2$-Fixierung durch Knallgasbakterien II. Chromatographischer Nachweis der frühzeitigen Fixierungsprodukte. *Arch. Mikrobiol.*, **46**, 53.

HIRSCH, P., OVERREIN, L. & ALEXANDER, M. (1961). Formation of nitrite and nitrate by actinomycetes and fungi. *J. Bact.*, **82**, 442.

HIRSCH, P., GEORGIEV, G. & SCHLEGEL, H. G. (1963*a*). Identification of early labelled products of $CO_2$-fixation by hydrogen bacteria accumulating poly-β-hydroxybutyric acid. *Nature Lond.*, **197**, 313.

HIRSCH, P., GEORGIEV, G. & SCHLEGEL, H. G. (1963*b*). $CO_2$-Fixierung durch Knallgasbakterien. III. Autotrophe und organotrophe $CO_2$-Fixierung. *Arch. Mikrobiol.*, **46**, 79.

KALTWASSER, H. (1962). Die Rolle der Polyphosphate im Phosphatstoffwechsel eines Knallgasbacteriums (Hydrogenomonas Stamm 20). *Arch. Mikrobiol.*, **41**, 282.

KALTWASSER, H. & SCHLEGEL, H. G. (1959). Nachweis und quantitative Bestimmung der Polyphosphate in wasserstoffoxydierenden Bakterien. *Arch. Mikrobiol.*, **34**, 76.

KASERER, H. (1906). Die Oxydation des Wasserstoffs durch Mikroorganismen. *Zentbl. Bakt. ParasitKde.*, *Abt. II*, **16**, 681.

KEPES, A. & COHEN, G. N. (1962). Permeation., In *The Bacteria*, Vol. **4**. Ed.Gunsalus, I. C. & Stanier, R. Y. New York. Academic Press.

KLUYVER, A. J. (1953). Some aspects of nitrate reduction. Symp. metabolismo microbiologico. *VI. Congresso Int. Microbiol.*, Roma.

KORNBERG, H. L., COLLINS, J. F. & BIGLEY, D. (1960). The influence of growth substrates on metabolic pathways in Micrococcus denitrificans. *Biochim. biophys. Acta*, **39**, 9.

LIESKE, R. (1919). Zur Ernährungsphysiologie der Eisenbakterien. *Zentbl. Bakt. ParasitKde.*, *Abt. II*, **49**, 413.

LONDON, J. (1963). *Thiobacillus intermedius* nov. sp. A novel type of facultative autotroph. *Arch. Mikrobiol.*, **46**, 329.

LUKINS, H. B. & FOSTER, J. W. (1963). Utilization of hydrocarbons and hydrogen by mycobacteria. *Z. allg. Mikrobiol.*, **3**, 251.

LWOFF, A. (1946). Nomenclature of nutritional types of microorganisms. *Cold Spring Harb. Symp. quant. Biol.*, **11**, 302.

MAGASANIK, B. (1961). Catabolite repression. *Cold Spring Harb. Symp. quant. Biol.*, **26**, 249.

MAGASANIK, B. (1964). Enzyme induction and catabolite repression. *6th Int. Congr. Biochem. Abstr.*, **9**, 680.

MARSHALL, K. G. & ALEXANDER, M. (1962). Nitrification by *Aspergillus flavus*. *J. Bact.*, **83**, 572.

MCFADDEN, B. A. (1959). Some products of $^{14}CO_2$ fixation by *Hydrogenomonas facilis*. *J. Bact.*, **77**, 339.

MECHALAS, B. J. & RITTENBERG, S. C. (1960). Energy coupling in *Desulfovibrio desulfuricans*. *J. Bact.*, **80**, 501.

NIKLEWSKI, B. (1910). Über die $H_2$-Oxydation durch Mikroorganismen. *Jb. wiss. Bot.*, **48**, 113.

PFEFFER, W. (1892). Studien zur Energetik der Pflanze. *Abh. sächs. Akad. Wiss.*, **18**.

PFEFFER, W. (1897). *Pflanzenphysiologie. 2. Aufl. Bd.*, **1**. Leipzig. Verlag W. Engelmann.

PONT, E. G. (1939). Association of sulphate reduction in the soil with anaerobic iron corrosion. *J. Aust. Inst. agric. Sci.*, **5**, 170.

PRINGSHEIM, E. G. & WIESSNER, W. (1961). Ernährung und Stoffwechsel von *Chlamydobotrys* (Volvocales). *Arch. Mikrobiol.*, **40**, 231.

RABIN, B. R. & TROWN, P. W. (1964). Inhibition of carboxydismutase by iodoacetamide. *Proc. Natn. Acad. Sci. U.S.A.*, **51**, 497.

RUHLAND, W. (1922). Aktivierung von Wasserstoff und $CO_2$-Assimilation durch Bakterien. *Ber. dt. bot. Ges.*, **40**, 180.

RUHLAND, W. (1924). Beiträge zur Physiologie der Knallgasbakterien. *Jb. wiss. Bot.*, **63**, 321.

SANTER, M., BOYER, J. & SANTER, U. (1959). *Thiobacillus novellus*. I. Growth on organic and inorganic media. *J. Bact.*, **78**, 197.

SCHINDLER, J. (1964). Die Synthese von Poly-β-hydroxybuttersäure durch *Hydrogenomonas* H 16: Die zu β-Hydroxybutyryl-Coenzym A führenden Reaktionsschritte. *Arch. Mikrobiol.*, **49**, 236.

SCHLEGEL, H. G. (1962). Bildung von Speicherstoffen durch Knallgas- und Purpurbakterien. *Beitr. Physiol. Morphol. Algen, Vorträge d. Dtsch. Bot. Ges. NF*, **1**, 167.

SCHLEGEL, H. G. & KALTWASSER, H. (1961). Veränderungen des Polyphosphatgehalts während des Wachstums von Knallgasbakterien unter Phosphatmangel. *Flora, Jena*, **150**, 259.

SCHLEGEL, H. G. & BARTHA, R. (1961*a*). 'Leerlauf'-$H_2$-Oxydation und 'Rückkoppelung' bei Knallgasbakterien. *Naturwissenschaften*, **48**, 414.

SCHLEGEL, H. G. & BARTHA, R. (1961*b*). Hemmungsanalytische Versuche zum Rückkoppelungseffekt bei Hydrogenomonas. *Z. Naturf*, **16b**, 777.

SCHLEGEL, H. G., GOTTSCHALK, G. & BARTHA, R. (1961). Formation and utilization of poly-β-hydroxybutyric acid by Knallgasbacteria (*Hydrogenomonas*). *Nature Lond.*, **191**, 463.

SCHLEGEL, H. G. & GOTTSCHALK, G. (1962). Poly-β-hydroxybuttersäure, ihre Verbreitung, Funktion und Biosynthese. *Angew. Chem.*, **74**, 342.

SCHLEGEL, H. G., GOTTSCHALK, G. & SCHINDLER, J. (1962). Biosynthesis of poly-β-hydroxybutyric acid by Knallgasbacteria (*Hydrogenomonas*). *8th Int. Congr. Microbiol. Montreal* A 7.7.

SCHLEGEL, H. G. (1965). Physiology and biochemistry of Knallgasbacteria. *Adv. Comp. Physiol. Biochem.*, **2**.

SCHLEGEL, H. G. & GOTTSCHALK, G. (1965). Verwertung von Glucose durch eine Mutante von *Hydrogenomonas* H 16. *Biochem. Z.*, **341**, 249.

STARKEY, R. L. (1934*a*). Cultivation of organisms concerned in the oxidation of thiosulphate. *J. Bact.*, **28**, 365.

STARKEY, R. L. (1934*b*). The production of polythionates from thiosulphate by microorganisms. *J. Bact.*, **28**, 387.

STÜVEN, K. (1960*a*). Beiträge zur Kenntnis der $CO_2$- und Lactatassimilation von *Desulfovibrio aestuarii* (van Delden) Kluyver and van Niel. *Arch. Mikrobiol.*, **36**, 31.

STÜVEN, K. (1960*b*). Beiträge zur Physiologie und Systematik sulfatreduzierender Bakterien. *Arch. Mikrobiol.*, **35**, 152.

TAKAMIYA, A. & TUBAKI, K. (1956). A new form of *Streptomyces* capable of growing autotrophically. *Arch. Mikrobiol.*, **25**, 58.

VERHOEVEN, W. (1956). Some remarks on nitrate and nitrite metabolism in micro-organisms. In *Inorganic Nitrogen Metabolism*. Ed. McElroy, W. D., & Glass B. Baltimore. Johns Hopkins Press.

VERHOEVEN, W., KOSTER, A. L. & VAN NIEVELT, M. G. A. (1954). Studies on true dissimilatory nitrate reduction. III. *Micrococcus denitrificans* Beijerinck a bacterium capable of using molecular hydrogen in denitrification. *Antonie van Leeuwenhoek*, **20**, 273.

VISHNIAC, W. & TRUDINGER, P. A. (1962). Carbon dioxide fixation and substrate oxidation in the chemosynthetic sulfur and hydrogen bacteria. *Bact. Rev.*, **26**, 168.

VOGT, M. (1965). Wachstumsphysiologische Untersuchungen an *Micrococcus denitrificans* Beij. *Arch. Mikrobiol.*, **50**, 256.

WHITE, A., HANDLER, P. & SMITH, E. L. (1964). *Principles of biochemistry*, 3rd edn. New York. McGraw-Hill.

WIESSNER, W. (1962). Kohlenstoffassimilation von *Chlamydobotrys* (Volvocales). *Arch. Mikrobiol.*, **43**, 402.

WIESSNER, W. & GAFFRON, H. (1964). Role of photosynthesis in the light-induced assimilation of acetate by *Chlamdobotrys. Nature Lond.*, **201**, 725.

WILDE, E. (1962). Untersuchungen über Wachstum und Speicherstoffsynthese von *Hydrogenomonas. Arch. Mikrobiol.*, **43**, 109–37.

WINOGRADSKY, S. J. (1922). Eisenbakterien als Anorg oxydanten. *Zentbl. Bakt. ParasitKde., Abt. II*, **57**, 1.

WOODS, D. D. & LASCELLES, J. (1954). The no man's land between the autotrophic and heterotrophic ways of life. *4th Symp. Soc. gen. Microbiol.* Ed. Fry, B. A. & Peel, J. L. Cambridge University Press.

# DECOMPOSITION OF CELLULOSE IN THE SOIL

A. A. IMSHENETSKY

*Institute of Microbiology, Academy of Sciences, Moscow*

The study of the microbiology of cellulose has passed through several important stages. Omeliansky (1895) was the first to use an elective medium to isolate a culture of mesophilic anaerobic bacteria which caused cellulose breakdown. Later, Hutchinson and Clayton (1919) described an aerobic cellulose bacterium *Spirochaeta cytophaga* having an unusual morphology. It was later found to belong to the myxobacteria. The following years saw the discovery of a number of other aerobic cellulose decomposing bacteria, many of them also belonging to the myxobacteria (Winogradsky, 1929; Krzemieniewska, 1937; Imshenetsky, 1953). Then came a series of investigations in which all cellulose decomposing bacteria, without exception, were found to produce the enzymes cellulase, which hydrolysed cellulose, and cellobiase which hydrolysed the cellobiose formed in the process of cellulose hydrolysis. It also became evident that all cellulose bacteria not only assimilated glucose formed from cellobiose hydrolysis, but were also capable of using glucose as a substrate (Pringsheim, 1912; Simola, 1931; Stanier, 1940; Fåhraeus, 1947). The formation of cellulose hydrolysis products has a great effect on the interrelations between the cellulose decomposers and other micro-organisms.

Within the last 20–30 years the number of bacteria, actinomyces and fungi which are known to decompose cellulose has increased sharply. Among the newly described species there are cultures that grow well on elective nutrient media containing cellulose as the sole source of carbon. However, the use of elective media has been questioned, since such media are far from natural, and in some cases prevent the discovery of new species. An analogous situation occurs with the nitrogen-fixing soil bacteria, where the use of media containing nitrogen, rather than nitrogen-free media, has revealed many new micro-organisms capable of active fixation of atmospheric nitrogen. This certainly applies to a number of cellulose bacteria which fail to grow on elective nutrient media containing cellulose as a sole carbon source. They will not grow unless the nutrient medium contains another carbon source, e.g. amino acids, vitamins, etc. Thus, by abandoning the principle of elective media we may discover new species.

The ability to decompose cellulose under aerobic conditions is possessed by numerous taxonomic groups of micro-organisms. Table 1

TABLE 1

*Taxonomic position of cellulolytic micro-organisms*

| Eubacteriales | | Actinomycetales | Myxobacteriales |
|---|---|---|---|
| *Aerobes* | *Anaerobes* | | |
| Cellvibrio | Bacteroides | Actinomyces | Cytophaga |
| Cellulomonas | Butyrivibrio | Mycobacterium | Sporocytophaga |
| Bacillus | Clostridium | | Sorangium |
| | Plectridium | | |

shows that aerobic cellulose micro-organisms are encountered among myxobacteria, mycobacteria, actinomycetes, vibrios, non-sporogenous bacteria and sporogenous bacteria. Thus, nearly every one of the major taxonomic groups contains representatives capable of cellulose decomposition indicating that convergent evolution has occurred. The cellulose resources of the earth are extremely large; the quantity of carbon contained in all of the cellulose amounts to $10^{15}$ tons. So, cellulose can be regarded as a principal source of carbon for micro-organisms. The capacity to produce cellulase has obviously been acquired by adaptation. The universal occurrence of cellulose and its accumulation under widely different natural conditions account for the physiological specialization observed in numerous micro-organisms. Such an ecological interpretation of the origin of cellulose decomposing bacteria is corroborated by the fact that within the same species cellulolytic and non-cellulolytic strains may be found. This applies in particular to *Butyrivibrio* (Bryant and Small, 1956).

It is interesting from the point of view of comparative physiology that if a representative of one or other taxonomic group acquires the ability to decompose cellulose, the rest of the properties typical for this group are retained. Thus, the cellulose-decomposing vibrios (*Cellvibrio*) have a typically vibrio morphology and developmental cycle, are very susceptible to desiccation, are capable of growing at comparatively low temperatures and require a highly humid environment. This also applies to myxobacteria, because the cellulose-decomposing myxobacteria differ in no way from the non-cellulolytic ones, except for their ability to decompose cellulose. For the cellulose micro-organisms to develop new properties, atypical of their systematic group, adaptation to new ecological conditions is necessary. I shall cite an example for illustration.

Aerobic cellulose-decomposing bacteria usually break down cellulose without the appearance of organic acids. This is particularly true for the Myxobacteriales, e.g. *Cytophaga*. It might be assumed theoretically that if anaerobic myxobacteria exist in nature, they must have a different physiology. Recently such a species, namely *Cytophaga succinicans*, was isolated by Anderson and Ordal (1961) from the rumen. This species differs from its aerobic counterpart, *Cytophaga*, in so far as, being anaerobic, it produces acetic and succinic acids as a result of cellulose decomposition.

The possibility of anaerobic myxobacteria being present in the soil is not ruled out. Routine methods, however, fail to detect them. Most of the cellulose in the soil is known to be decomposed by aerobic bacteria, actinomycetes and fungi. The anaerobic decomposition of cellulose in the soil is rather limited, this process being usually initiated by sporogenous bacteria which are found in soil in low numbers.

With regard to fungi which take part in cellulose decomposition, representatives of the following genera are encountered most frequently: *Stachybotrys*, *Dematium*, *Chaetomium*, *Stysanus*, *Microsporum*, *Rhizophlyctis*, *Fusarium*, *Myrothecium*, *Moniliopsis*, *Penicillium*, *Trichoderma*, *Phoma*, *Monotospora*. The exact numbers of cellulose decomposing fungi in the soil are as difficult to determine as the total numbers of soil fungi.

In studying the cellulose decomposing bacteria, investigators revealed a paradox. Some bacteria grew on cellulose and failed to grow on media containing glucose; however, cellulose could only be assimilated after its hydrolysis to glucose. This gave rise to the theory that cellulolytic bacteria oxidized cellulose to oxycellulose, and that an almost direct transformation of the cellulose decomposition products into humus occurred. As a matter of fact, such theories proved to be too complex, when it was shown that:

1. The failure of these bacteria to grow on nutrient media containing glucose is accounted for by the fact that during sterilization glucose produces toxic substances inhibiting the growth of cellulose-decomposing bacteria in the medium. On media containing glucose sterilized by filtration, bacterial growth was found to be good.

2. In cultures of either aerobic or anaerobic cellulolytic bacteria, glucose may accumulate. Occasionally, as seen in Fig. 1, the amount of glucose may be quite considerable.

3. It is possible to isolate from the cells of aerobic and anaerobic bacteria, as well as from fungus mycelium, an active cellulase.

Thus it has become quite apparent that irrespective of the systematic position of the micro-organism, the decomposition of cellulose begins

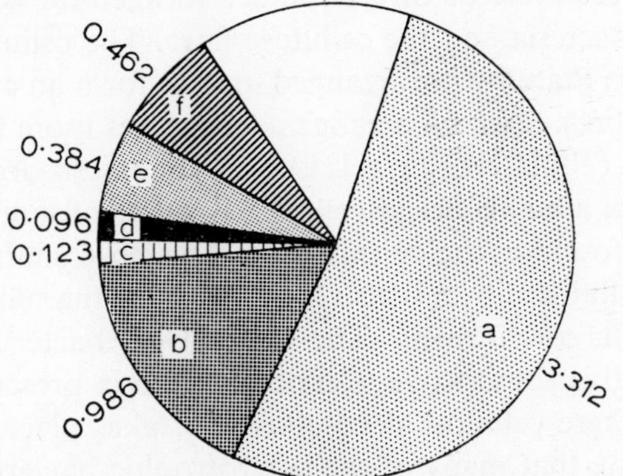


Fig. 1. The products of cellulose decomposition detected in cultures of thermophilic anaerobic bacteria.
(a) glucose (b) acetic acid
(c) butyric acid (d) formic acid
(e) lactic acid (f) carbon dioxide

with its hydrolysis by cellulase. The cellobiose formed is decomposed to glucose by a cellobiase. The cellulolytic bacteria usually utilize glucose, but there are some species which although they utilize cellobiose fail to assimilate glucose. Aerobic cellulolytic bacteria while consuming glucose synthesize cellular matter and capsular slime containing uronic acids and release carbon dioxide. Decomposition of 100 g. of cellulose yields 20 g. of bacterial matter. It is impossible to identify any other products.

Cultures of anaerobic bacteria, however, cause the fermentation of glucose and cellobiose formed in cellulose hydrolysis with the formation of ethyl alcohol, propionic, acetic, butyric and lactic acids.

The fact that cellulose is always hydrolysed to glucose is of extreme ecological importance. Today it would be unreasonable to consider glucose as an unfamiliar carbohydrate for soil micro-organisms; so that from the ecological viewpoint to use nutrient media containing glucose is perfectly permissible. It should be added that apart from glucose, other substances incorporated in soil with plant remains, such as hemicellulose, starch, pectin, etc., are also decomposed and form monosaccharides. The hydrolytic enzymes released from inside the cells usually produce the soluble products of polymer hydrolysis in larger quantities than are required by the organisms causing such hydrolyses. This applies to proteases, amylases and, particularly, cellulase (Plate 1A). Cellulose, however, is much more difficult to hydrolyse than other substances, for there must be direct contact between the cells of cellulose-decomposing bacteria and the cellulose fibre. The cellulolytic bacteria, as can be seen in Plate 1B, are arranged so as to form an envelope around the cellulose fibres. Such an arrangement secures more favourable conditions for the cellulase being released by the micro-organisms. At the point of contact a highly active cellulase is usually found; normally this enzyme is not found in the culture fluid. The close contact between the cells and the cellulose fibres is also favourable for the subsequent utilization of the glucose formed. The cellulolytic bacteria have certain advantages in this respect over the other bacteria present in the soil in those places where cellulose decomposition takes place. This does not mean, of course, that many of the heterotrophic bacteria fail to utilize any of the products of cellulose hydrolysis. If a piece of linen textile is put into the ground, as suggested by Vostrov and Petrova (1961) and after some time treated with ninhydrin, the material is found to give a highly positive reaction for amino acids. The more intense the cellulose decomposition, the greater is the amount of synthesized protein (Plate 1C). Microbiological analyses show that this protein is synthesized by both cellulolytic and non-cellulolytic bacteria.

It is known that one of the factors which may limit the utilization of the products of cellulose breakdown is a lack of available nitrogen. Under such conditions the growth of nitrogen-fixing micro-organisms is favoured. When *Sporocytophaga* and *Azotobacter* grow simultaneously on cellulose it is possible to observe (Plate 1D) cellulose fibres enveloped by the dividing cells of *Azotobacter*. Good growth of *Azotobacter* can also be obtained in symbiosis with aerobic cellulose decomposing bacteria by inoculating the two organisms into appropriate media (Plates 1E and 1F). In such symbiotic cultures molecular nitrogen is fixed following the utilization of nitrates contained in the nutrient medium.

It is also necessary to ask whether the glucose and cellobiose formed by the cellulose-decomposing bacteria during the decomposition of plant remains in the soil are consumed not only by the cellulolytic bacteria but also by other micro-organisms. If it does happen, on what scale does this process occur in the soil? The general problems of the ecology of soil micro-organisms have been discussed in comprehensive papers by Thornton (1956) and by Alexander (1964). Discussed below are only some special problems relating to metabiosis. If the environment

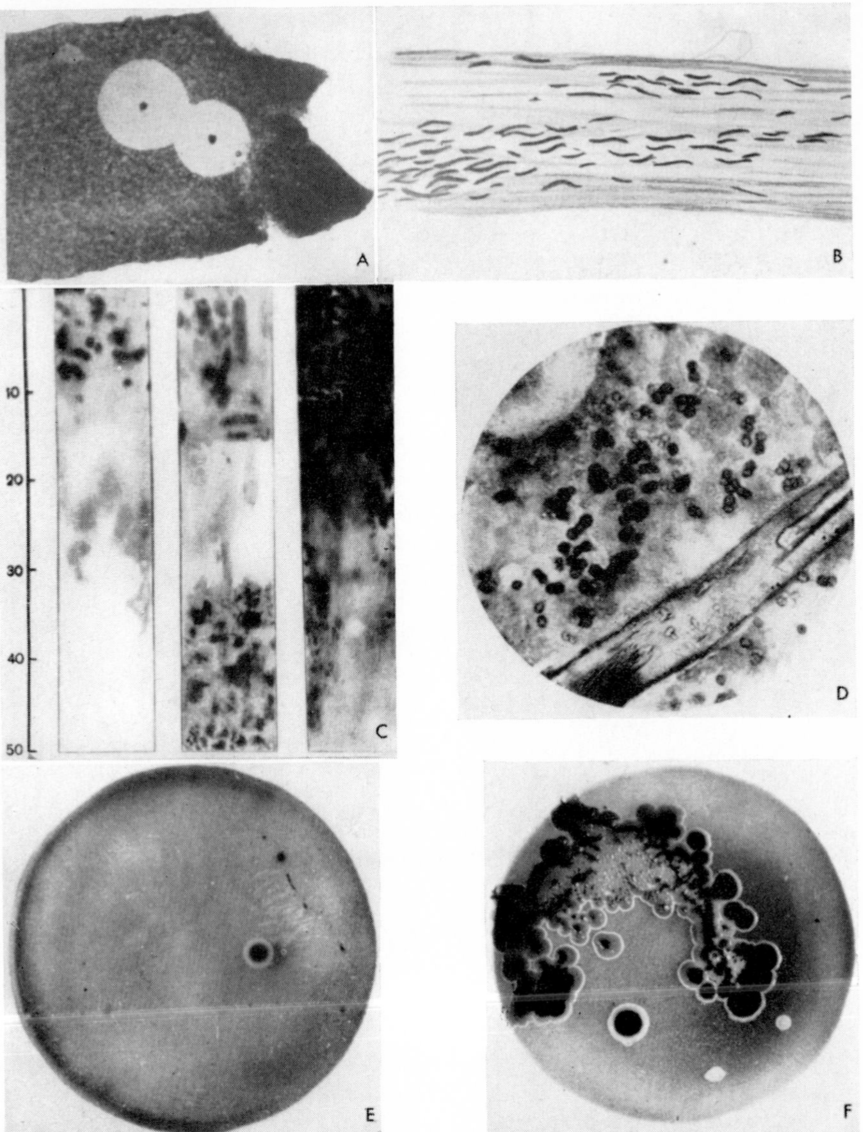


Plate 1. (A) the zones of hydrolysis around colonies of anaerobic cellulose bacteria. (B) *Cytophaga* cells arranged along cellulose fibres. (C) Pieces of textile destroyed by cellulose decomposing bacteria in the soil. (D) Cells of *Azotobacter* multiplying on cellulose together with aerobic cellulose decomposing bacteria (*Sporocytophaga*). (E) Multiplication of *Azotobacter* in a mineral medium containing cellulose. (F) Multiplication of *Azotobacter* in a mineral medium containing cellulose, in the presence of *Sporocytophaga*.

favours the development of cellulolytic bacteria, then more hydrolysis products are formed than they can consume themselves. In such cases these products can be utilized by other species, provided that nitrogen is available in the soil. The possibility of such metabiotic relationships in the soil is underestimated. The fact that soluble carbohydrates can be utilized by other micro-organisms can be proved without much difficulty with the aid of appropriate elective culture methods. Thus, if a yeast assimilating glucose alone (e.g. *Debaryomyces disporus*) is added to a pure culture of *Sporocytophaga*, both direct counts and viable counts show that the yeast has multiplied. Fedorov (1940) showed that straw introduced into the soil leads to higher crop yields due to nitrogen fixation, although this can be observed only in the second or third year. In the first year the soil microflora utilizes nutrients in the soil, which results in reduced yields. Recently it has been established by Erofeeff and Vostrov (1964) that the introduction of straw into the surface soil layers creates conditions that favour uniform decomposition of the straw and uniform nitrogen fixation. In such cases the crop yields do not diminish as is usually the case when straw is placed in the deeper soil layers.

As for the anaerobic decomposition of cellulose, the conditions for the development of a symbiotic microflora are even more favourable than in the case of aerobic decomposition of cellulose. Mesophilic anaerobes are always accompanied by sporogenous and non spore-forming bacteria, which actively consume ethyl alcohol, various organic acids, and the products of cellulose hydrolysis. In the case of thermophilic anaerobes the cultures are usually found to be spore-forming bacteria alone. The micro-organisms accompanying the anaerobic, cellulolytic bacteria enrich the medium with amino acids, vitamins and other growth factors, reduce the oxidation-reduction potential of the medium and diminish the quantity of organic acids produced. Thus, cellulose decomposition in the soil is a symbiotic process and the products formed in cellulose decomposition are the principal sources of carbon and energy for the overwhelming number of saprophytic micro-organisms inhabiting the soil.

The problem of the microbiological decomposition of cellulose from different plants is of considerable interest. The cellulose synthesized by *Acetobacter xylinum* decomposes at the same rate as that of higher plants. The more the latter is lignified, the slower is its decomposition rate. By reducing the content of lignin in the wood by alkali treatment, the decomposition of sawdust by anaerobic cellulose decomposing bacteria results in the formation of alcohol and acids. Some recently discovered bacteria are capable of lignin decomposition, but their relationship with the cellulolytic micro-organisms is little known as yet. Cellulose subjected to chemical treatment is found in some cases to become less resistant and in other cases more resistant to attack by micro-organisms. Thus, cellulose subjected to etherification or coated in polymeric films decomposes at a slower rate in the soil.

With regard to the geographical distribution of cellulolytic bacteria and fungi inhabiting the soil, it must be pointed out that numerous species of cellulolytic myxobacteria, e.g. *Sporocytophaga* and *Cytophaga*, as well as vibrios (*Cellvibrios*) and some other micro-organisms, are cosmopolitan, having been discovered in many different areas and in all of the continents. Thus, the distribution and activity of cellulolytic micro-organisms appear to be affected more by ecology than by geography.

Cellulolytic micro-organisms in the soil remain active even at comparatively low temperatures, e.g. 8–10°. The optimum temperature for their activity is between 20° and 30°. This is in full agreement with the fact that the myxobacteria and vibrios are neither thermophilic nor thermotolerant. The anaerobic cellulose bacteria encountered in the soil are also mesophilic. When thermophilic anaerobes are discovered in the soil they have usually originated from manure or peat.

The process of cellulose decomposition is confined to the surface of the soil, the decay of cellulose being most intensive in the 0–20 cm. layer. This is corroborated by the fact that aerobic cellulose bacteria show intensive growth only at an $r_H$ equal to 18–20. It is worth noting that *Sporocytophaga* was observed to grow very slowly on pieces of filter paper placed at the bottom of extremely tall test tubes containing liquid media. As regards the anaerobic bacteria, the $r_H$ values assigned to them are usually too low. This is due to the release of hydrogen during their growth, which quickly reduces the $r_H$ value of the nutrient medium in which the bacteria are growing. Having eliminated such technical difficulties, we have found that the anaerobic decomposition of cellulose may begin at an $r_H$ between 14 and 17.

The effect of soil reaction on the decomposition of cellulose has been studied in greater detail. The main data can be formulated as follows:

1. All cellulolytic myxobacteria and vibrios prefer either alkaline or neutral soils and are less frequently encountered in acidic soils. The optimum pH value for the aerobes varies between pH 6·0 and pH 8·5.
2. The anaerobic, cellulolytic bacteria have the same optimum pH values.
3. In acidic soils, especially in forest soils, the cellulose-decomposing fungi dominate the bacteria.

4. The intensity of cellulose decomposition is more affected by aeration, moisture and the presence of available nitrogen, than by the soil reaction.

The optimum soil humidity for bacterial decomposition of cellulose is about 60 per cent, although fungi and bacteria may initiate cellulose decomposition at a lower humidity; however, minimum humidity requirements needs further clarification. Thus, Feher (1946) discovered some cellulose-decomposing bacteria in the sands of the Sahara where there is virtually no rain. Novogrudsky (1946) observed *Penicillium* growing in soil where the humidity was about 3·3 per cent. Excessive humidity leads to the establishment of reducing conditions in the soil, which suppresses the aerobic decomposition of cellulose.

One of the most important factors is undoubtedly the quantity of available nitrogen. It is no coincidence that in spring and autumn, when the nitrates in the soil increase in quantity, cellulose decomposition intensifies. It is generally assumed that if the nitrogen content is below 1·2 per cent, cellulose decomposition stops, whereas if the nitrogen content increases to 1·7 per cent it increases. This accounts for the great importance of the symbiotic relationship of the cellulose and nitrogen-fixing bacteria.

Many ecological factors act jointly in the soil. If the number of cellulolytic micro-organisms is considered with reference to the depth of sampling, the picture will be similar to that represented in Table 2. As

TABLE 2

*The numbers of cellulose-decomposing micro-organisms in various horizons of a chestnut soil (according to I. L. Klevenskaia)*

| Sampling depth in cm. | Humus according to Tiurin (%) | Carbon (%) | Total nitrogen (%) | C:N ratio | Cellulose decomposing micro-organisms (thous. per g. of soil) |
|---|---|---|---|---|---|
| 0–20 | 2·04 | 1·18 | 0·125 | 9·4 | 13·0 |
| 20–40 | 1·02 | 0·59 | 0·077 | 7·7 | 9·6 |
| 40–60 | 0·65 | 0·38 | 0·061 | 6·2 | 1·0 |
| 60–80 | 0·33 | 0·22 | 0·045 | 5·0 | 0 |
| 80–100 | 0·27 | 0·16 | 0·032 | 5·0 | 0 |

can be seen, the number of micro-organisms decreases with depth, ranging from a maximum at the top to zero at a depth of 60 cm. The diminution of the number of micro-organisms is paralleled by a decreasing content of humus, carbon, total nitrogen and the C/N ratio. These data illustrate how the aeration and the content of cellulose and nitrogen influence the presence of cellulolytic bacteria in the soil.

The species of bacteria, actinomyces and fungi capable of cellulose decomposition are very numerous, these species having adapted themselves to different ecological conditions. Therefore, it may be assumed that cellulolytic micro-organisms would be detected in a wide range of soils. Table 3 presents data on the distribution of cellulolytic micro-organisms in soddy-podzolic, chernozem, grey-desert, dark chestnut and upland soils. To support these data one may cite counts of cellulolytic bacteria for different soils in numerous countries. As seen in the table, only in the far north (Kotelny Island) could neither bacteria nor fungi capable of cellulose decomposition be identified in the soil.

TABLE 3

*The distribution of cellulose-decomposing micro-organisms in various soils*

| Place of sampling | Soil | Horizon | Growth around the pieces of soil (% colonized) | | Author |
|---|---|---|---|---|---|
| | | | Bacteria | Fungi | |
| Kotelny Island | Polar Desert | 0–1 | 0 | 0 | V. A. Mirsoeva |
| Perm area | Soddy-podzolic cultivated | $A_1$ | 32 | 56 | E. N. Mishoustin and E. Z. Tepper |
| Moscow area | Soddy-podzolic cultivated | $A_1$ | 75 | 90 | E. Z. Tepper |
| Lugansk area | Chernozem fallow | $A_1$ | 70 | 60 | E. V. Runov |
| Voronezh area | Chernozem cultivated | $A_1$ | 24 | 50 | V. A. Mirsoeva |
| Azerbaidzhan | Serozem fallow | $A_1$ | 38 | 34 | A. N. Naumova |
| Central Asia | Dark chestnut ploughland | 0–10 | 16·3 | 53 | Z. F. Tepliakova |
| Zaaliiskoe Alatau | Virgin forest upland | 0–12 | 18·6 | 26 | Z. F. Tepliakova |

The fact that cellulolytic micro-organisms are found universally does not mean that the nature of the soil fails to influence the quantitative and qualitative composition of the cellulose-decomposing microflora.

Thus, in the soddy-podzolic soils in the northern areas of the U.S.S.R., the fungi and actinomycetes are prevalent, whereas the bacteria are less frequent. In the chernozems of the southern areas *Sporocytophaga* is common, the cellulose decomposition in the chernozems being more rapid than in the serozems (grey-desert soil).

The type of soil is usually not as important as the changes which accompany the cultivation of soil. The loosening of the soil in the process of its cultivation, the addition of fertilizers and other factors have a marked effect on the cellulolytic microflora. This becomes quite apparent if one examines the data cited in Table 4 and Table 5.

The data in these tables refer to the quantities of cellulolytic bacteria and fungi in virgin and cultivated soils. Only those results of microbiological soil analyses were compared which belonged to the same soil type. The analyses were all made at the same time and involved similar techniques. These data prove beyond doubt that soil cultivation causes a sharp increase in the numbers of cellulolytic micro-organisms; however, the numbers of bacteria usually increase more than those of the fungi. These data hold equally for the soddy-podzolic soil, the chernozem sampled at different localities and the serozem.

An increase in the total number of cellulose-decomposing organisms is not the only result of cultivation. According to Mishustin and Prokoshev (1949), cultivation causes qualitative changes in the cellulolytic microflora. *Sporocytophaga* and *Cytophaga*, which form yellow pigments, increase in quantity, sometimes as much as three or four times. The number of mesophilic and thermophilic anaerobic cellulose-decomposing bacteria also rises. The latter points to the occurrence of manure in the soil. The intensity of cellulose decomposition is much greater in cultivated soils.

In conclusion I would like to emphasize some ecological problems connected with the biology of cellulolytic micro-organisms that need further investigation:

1. The search for new cellulolytic micro-organisms in nature, particularly such species that fail to grow in strictly elective media.

2. Bringing to light the metabiotic relationships existing between cellulolytic and other micro-organisms, especially those which are capable of nitrogen fixation.

3. Development of quantitative methods for determining the activity of cellulolytic micro-organisms in the soil.

4. The effect of humidity, pH and oxidation-reduction potential on the cellulose-decomposing micro-organisms during their development in the soil as well as under pure culture conditions.

TABLE 4

*The numbers of cellulose-decomposing micro-organisms in cultivated and uncultivated soils*

| Place of sampling | Soil | Horizon and depth in cm. | Growth around the pieces of soil (% colonization) | | Micro-organisms (thousands per 1 g. of soil) | | | | Author |
|---|---|---|---|---|---|---|---|---|---|
| | | | Bacteria | Fungi | Total | Bacteria | Actinomyces | Fungi | |
| Moscow area Forest | Soddy-podzolic | $A_1$ | 9 | 37 | | | | | V. A. Mirsoeva |
| Moscow area Experimental farm | Soddy-podzolic cultivated | $A_1$ | 69 | 76 | | | | | E. P. Gromyko |
| Siberia Kolundinskaia steppe | Chernozem | $A_1$ | | | 11·3 | 4·9 | | 64 | I. L. Klevenskaia |
| | Chernozem after cultivation | $A_1$ | | | 47·2 | 24·2 | | 23 | |
| | Chernozem | 0–10 | | | 28·6 | 4·5 | 8·1 | 16 | |
| | Chernozem after cultivation | 0–10 | | | 32·0 | 24·0 | 4·0 | 4 | |
| Borisoglebsk area | Chernozem virgin | 0–20 | 17 | 17 | | | | | O. I. Pushkinskaia |
| | Chernozem ploughland | 0–15 | 98 | 70 | | | | | |

TABLE 5

*The numbers of cellulose-decomposing micro-organisms in other cultivated and uncultivated soils*

| Place of sampling | Soil | Horizon and depth in cm. | Growth around the pieces of soil (% colonization) | | Micro-organisms (thousands per 1 g. of soil) | | | | Author |
|---|---|---|---|---|---|---|---|---|---|
| | | | Bacteria | Fungi | Total | Bacteria | Actino-myces | Fungi | |
| Voronezh area | Chernozem virgin | 0–10 | 25 | 100 | | | | | O. I. Pushkinskaia |
| Kamennaja steppe | Chernozem ploughland | 0–15 | 65 | 100 | | | | | |
| Central Asia | Chernozem ploughland | 0–13 | 18·0 | 36·3 | | | | | Z. F. Tepliakova |
| Zailiiskoe Alatau | Chernozem ploughland | 0–10 | 40·6 | 51·0 | | | | | |
| Azerbaidzhan Milskaia steppe | Serozem virgin | 0–20 | 16 | 8 | | 1 | | 8 | A. N. Naumova |
| | Serozem lucerne | 0–20 | 32 | 60 | | 4 | | 48 | |
| | Serozem cotton | 0–20 | 100 | 32 | | 6 | | 35 | |

## *REFERENCES*


ALEXANDER, M. (1964). Biochemical ecology of soil microorganisms. *A. Rev. Microbiol.*, **18**, 217.

ANDERSON, R. L. & ORDAL, E. Y. (1961). *Cytophaga succinicans* sp. n., a facultatively anaerobic, aquatic myxobacterium. *J. Bact.*, **81**, 130.

EROFEEFF, N. S. & VOSTROV, I. S. (1964). The use of straw as a fertilizer. *Izv. Akad. Nauk SSSR Ser. Biol.*, **5**, 668.

FÅHRAEUS, G. (1947). Studies in the cellulose decomposition by *Cytophaga*. *Symb. bot. upsal.*, **9**, 3.

FEDOROV, M. V. (1940). The influence of *Azotobacter* on the nitrogen balance of the soil and yield of agricultural plants upon fertilization of the soil with straw. *Microbiologiya*, **9**, 541.

FEHÉR, D. (1946). Der Wüstenboden als Lebensraum. *Communs bot. Inst. Hungar. Univ. Sopron*, **10**, 1.

GROMYKO, E. P. (1958). Vlijanie glubokoĭ vspashki podzolistoĭ pochvy na pochvennuiu mikrofloru. Voprosy pochvennoĭ mikrobiologii. (The effect of deep ploughing of podzolic soils on the soil microflora. Problems in soil microbiology.) *Trudy Inst. Mikrobiol. latv. Akad. Nauk*, **7**, 19.

HUTCHINSON, H. B. & CLAYTON, I. (1919). On the decomposition of cellulose by an aerobic organism (*Spirochaeta cytophaga* n. sp.). *J. agric. Sci., Camb.*, **9**, 143.

IMSHENETSKY, A. A. (1953). *Mikrobiologija tselliulozy.* (*The microbiology of cellulose.*) Moscow. Acad. Sci. USSR.

KLEVENSKAJA, I. L. (1960). Vlijanie obrabotki pochvy na mikrofloru iuzhnykh chernozemov Kulundinskoĭ stepi. (The effect of soil cultivation on the microflora of the southern chernozems of the Kulundinsk steppes.) *Trudy Inst. Mikrobiol. Akad. Nauk SSSR*, **7**, 180.

KRZEMIENIEWSKI, H. (1937). Die Zellulosezersetzenden Myxobacterien. *Bull. int. Acad. Pol. Sci. Lett. Cl. Sci. Math. Nat. Ser. B. Sci. Nat.*, 11.

MISHUSTIN, E. N. & PROKOSHEV, V. N. (1949). Izmenenie sostava pochvennoĭ mikroflory v rezultate dlitelnogo primenenija udobreniĭ. (Variations in the composition of the soil microflora as a result of protracted application of fertilizers.) *Mikrobiologiya*, **18**, 30.

MISHUSTIN, E. N. & TEPPER, E. Z. (1963). Vlijanie dlitelnogo sevooborota monokultur i udobreniĭ na sostav pochvennoĭ mikroflory. (The effect of protracted monoculture crop rotation and fertilizing on the composition of the soil microflora.) *Izv. timiryazev. sel'.-khoz. Akad.*, **6**, 85.

NAUMOVA, A. N. (1960). *O vlijanii zasolenija na mikrofloru pochvy. Fiziologija ustoichivosti rasteniĭ.* (*On the effects of salinity on the microflora of soil. Physiological resistance in plants.*) Moscow. Akad. Sci. USSR.

NOVOGRUDSKY, D. M. (1946). Microbiological processes in semi-desert soils. II. Lower limit of soil moisture needed for life activity of bacteria. *Mikrobiologiya*, **15**, 479.

OMELIANSKY, V. (1895). Sur la fermentation de la cellulose. *C. r. Acad. Sci., Paris*, **121**, 653.

PRINGSHEIM, H. (1912). Über den fermentativen Abbau der Cellulose. *Z. physiol. Chem.*, **78**, 266.

PUSHKINSKAJA, O. I. (1951). Materialy k kharakteristike mikroflory pochv dubovych lesov Tellermanovskogo opytnogo lesnichestva. (Data on the characteristic microflora of soils in oak forests of the Tellermanovski experimental forestry area.) *Trudy Inst. Lesa, Mosk.*, **7**, 158.

RUNOV, E. V. (1954). Mikroflora chernozemov pod lesnymi nasazhdenijami v

Derkulskoĭ stepi. (Microflora of chernozems under forest plantation in the Derkulskoy steppes.) *Trudy Inst. Lesa., Mosk.*, **15**, 182.

SIMOLA, P. (1941). Über den Abbau der Zellulose durch Mikroorganismen II. *Annls Acad. Sci. Fenn. Ser. A.*, **34**, 1.

STANIER, R. (1940). Studies on the cytophages. *J. Bact.*, **40**, 619.

TEPLIAKOVA, Z. F. (1952). Aerobnye tselliulozorazrushaiushchie mikroorganizmy pochv Kazakhstana. (Aerobic cellulose-decomposing micro-organisms in the soils of Kazakhstan.) *Trudy Inst. Pochv. Alma-Ata*, **1**, 32.

TEPPER, E. Z. (1963). Metody vyiavlenija mikrorganizmov avtokhtonnoĭ mikroflory na agarizovannykh sredakh. (Methods revealing microorganisms of the autochthonous microflora on agar media.) *Izv. timiryazev. sel'.-khoz. Akad.*, **3**, 228.

THORNTON, H. G. (1956). The ecology of microorganisms in soil. *Proc. R. Soc. Ser. B.*, **145**, 364.

VOSTROV, I. S. & PETROVA, A. N. (1961). Assay of biological activity of soil by various methods. *Mikrobiologiya*, **30**, 665.

WINOGRADSKY, S. N. (1952). *Mikrobiologija pochvy.* (*Soil microbiology.*) Moscow. Akad. Sci. USSR.

# DEGRADATION OF PESTICIDES BY SOIL BACTERIA

M. ALEXANDER

*Laboratory of Soil Microbiology, Department of Agronomy, Cornell University, Ithaca, New York, U.S.A.*

One of the many remarkable achievements of modern agricultural research is the introduction of specific pesticidal chemicals to do either what was heretofore a laborious task or what could not have been accomplished by any other means. These toxic compounds have been successfully applied in many endeavours directed at the control or elimination of pests affecting man as well as the plants and livestock that he uses for the purposes of feeding and clothing himself. Parallel to the increasing use of selective and non-selective chemicals for pest control, there has been an increase in concern with regard to the possible biological and biochemical effects of these pesticides and their fate in the environment.

Although the microbiologist investigating the degradation and fate of synthetic organic compounds in the soil ecosystem has many possible avenues of approach to the problem, only two aspects, both of which are of prime concern to soil microbiologists, will be examined in the present discussion. These two problems have served as the focus of our attention in investigations of pesticide destruction. One aspect is concerned with establishing why certain of these compounds often resist microbial decomposition and persist in nature for disturbingly long periods of time. These investigations are designed to determine the chemical, physiological and pedological bases for the inability of specific micro-organisms or the microbial community at large to metabolize individual compounds or entire classes of chemicals. The second problem occupying our attention is related to the development of an understanding of how the compounds that are degraded by bacteria are indeed destroyed. Such studies involve considerations of the metabolism of the pesticide and the identity of those intermediates which are important in determining the activity of toxicants in soil.

A specific bacterial transformation may assume prominence because it involves an activation, that is, conversion of a compound with little or no toxicity to one of higher potency. Microbial action upon a pesticide may also assume ecological prominence if it results in an inactivation, a process in which a toxic compound or one which may be potentially inhibitory is destroyed so that the toxic effect is eliminated from the habitat. Further, since pesticides frequently are members of classes of compounds with marked biological activity, metabolic conversions may occur involving the transformation of an inhibitory substrate into a product which exerts some beneficial influence upon higher plants, micro-organisms or members of the soil fauna; such reactions have been noted during the destruction of a number of pesticides.

Many advantages accrue from the long life of various pest control agents in soil or other environments. The beneficial influences typically are associated with a prolonged duration of control of unwanted organisms. From the operational as well as the economic viewpoint, such prolonged toxicities or long persistence periods are quite welcome to the agricultural scientist. At the same time, chemicals exhibiting a long persistence have a number of disadvantages associated with their use. For example, the long life in soil of a persistent herbicide might easily reduce the yield of susceptible plant species introduced in a crop rotation system. Another objectionable feature of the persistent material arises from the fact that plants sown into soil weeks, months or even years after the initial application of the persistent material are often found to contain the pesticide. The finding of these chemicals in the food or feed commodity raises a number of public health problems and not uncommonly leads to condemnation of the food or feed product. Moreover, persistent chemicals may enter the public health domain when the compound moves from the soil into water supplies, either upon leaching of the chemical through the soil or as a result of the washing into streams, rivers and lakes of soil particles carrying sorbed pesticides that retain their toxicities because of the failure of micro-organisms to bring about the inactivation.

Two general reasons may be advanced to account for the persistence in soil of synthetic chemicals. First, certain compounds apparently are not susceptible to microbial degradation or detoxication under any circumstances. Second, many chemicals foreign to the soil ecosystem, although potentially biodegradable, are rendered largely or totally unavailable to microbial or enzymatic degradation because of the influence of some environmental factor or interaction. Unfortunately, there is little experimental data upon which to base a meaningful discussion or upon which to establish criteria for differentiation between these two working hypotheses. For example, only a few non-biodegradable chemicals have been identified to date, and the specific structural characteristics of synthetic compounds that are associated with or which prevent microbial decomposition are, with rare exceptions, unknown. Such resistant substances have been termed *recalcitrant molecules* (Alexander, 1965). Moreover, few of the environmental factors or conditions associated with or determining the resistance of susceptible molecules to microbial degradation are known. In spite of the large body of literature demonstrating the role of a number of soil factors, meteorological conditions and agricultural practices in modifying pesticide persistence, the individual ecological determinants are not sufficiently defined to permit the delineation of precise environmental factors or physiological characteristics which determine a chemical's resistance to microbial attack.

Prudence dictates silence in the absence of sufficient or adequate experimentation. Yet both the call to adventure in ecological theorism and the pressing practical needs arising from current developments in pesticide technology and usage argue for attempting to explain the mechanisms of molecular recalcitrance, i.e., to account for the long life in soil of certain types of chemicals. Nevertheless, the suggestions advanced here must be considered only as first approximations, tentative working models upon which to build a more firm foundation to understand the mechanisms of molecular recalcitrance.

Among the possible reasons for there being no bacterial destruction of specific chemicals, the following can be cited: (*a*) enzymes capable of catalysing a change in the class of compounds represented by the specific pesticide in question may not exist, or at least there may be no enzyme that can effect a change of sufficient magnitude to result in an inactivation of the toxic agent; (*b*) enzymes to metabolize representatives of these classes of compounds may exist, but the specific substance which has pesticidal action may not penetrate into the organism which has the requisite enzymes, and the molecule is therefore considered to be non-biodegradable; (*c*) the class of compounds, of which the pesticide is a member, may be potentially metabolized by one or another of the bacteria or other soil inhabitants, but the compounds have been modified in such a way to obtain pesticidal effectiveness that the enzyme cannot combine with its potential substrate in order to carry out the inactivation or, alternatively, the enzyme is itself inhibited by the modified substrate or a product of its decomposition.

In our studies of the chemical characteristics associated with or determining the resistance of specific compounds to microbial degradation, the test substances are derivatives of substrates which are degraded rapidly by numerous bacteria. These investigations are designed to establish the chemical modifications required in order to convert a susceptible compound into a resistant one or alternatively the chemical features that will need to be modified or removed in order to make a resistant compound into one which is readily destroyed by the soil population.

The results demonstrate that a number of characteristics are associated with the slow decomposition of the substances which prior to modification had been attacked readily. The type of substitution and the number and position of the substituents on the molecule are of notable importance. For example, chlorophenols and chlorobenzoates are more resistant than the corresponding unsubstituted phenols or benzoates, which are quickly destroyed by many bacteria representing a variety of soil inhabiting genera (Alexander and Aleem, 1961; MacRae and Alexander, 1965). Chlorophenols have fungicidal properties, while substituted chlorobenzoates are widely employed as herbicides. It is also apparent from several sources that the introduction of a methyl group on the alkyl portion of certain molecules results in the metabolizable substrate becoming resistant to destruction (Alexander, 1965). It has likewise been possible to establish substituents which, when introduced on the benzene ring, make the resulting aromatic compound resistant to destruction. As indicated in Table 1, the amino-, methoxy-,

TABLE 1

*Degradation of monosubstituted benzenes by the soil microflora*

| Compound | Substitution | Days for ring cleavage |
|---|---|---|
| Benzoic acid | —COOH | 1 |
| Phenol | —OH | 2 |
| Aniline | $—NH_2$ | 4 |
| Anisole | $—OCH_3$ | 8 |
| Benzene sulphonic acid | $—SO_3H$ | 16 |
| Nitrobenzene | $—NO_2$ | $>64$ |

sulphonate, and nitro- groups confer increasing degrees of resistance of the benzene ring to destruction. On the other hand, phenol and benzoic acid are easily destroyed by the soil population, suggesting that the hydroxyl- and carboxyl- groups favour decomposition, in agreement with other observations on aromatic hydrocarbons.

The importance of the number of substituents has been demonstrated in investigations in which it has been shown that the dichlorobenzoates are far more resistant and persist for longer periods in suspensions of soil organisms than the monochlorobenzoates (MacRae and Alexander,

1965). Similarly, it appears that the diaminobenzenes are generally less readily utilized than the monoaminobenzenes.

The significance to biodegradability of the position of the substituent can be illustrated by an examination of monochlorophenols. The soil population readily brings about the destruction of *o*- and *p*-chlorophenol, but *m*-chlorophenol is quite resistant to ring cleavage. Similarly, phenoxy herbicides with chlorines only in the *ortho* and *para* positions have a short life and exhibit a moderate period of persistence when tested by bioassay procedures, while phenoxy herbicides having a chlorine in the *meta* position are persistent and can be expected to inhibit susceptible plants several months after the time of their application to soil (Alexander and Aleem, 1961; Burger, MacRae and Alexander, 1962). Kameda, Toyoura and Kimura (1957) carried out a similar study to determine the effect of position of substituents on the susceptibility of benzoic acids to degradation by a number of soil pseudomonads. They showed that *p*-hydroxybenzoate is utilized by many more *Pseudomonas* strains than *o*- or *m*-hydroxybenzoates, whereas *o*- and *p*-methoxybenzoates supported the growth of a number of the isolates although none utilized *m*-methoxybenzoate.

When a mixed soil population is provided with substituted benzoic acids and the time recorded for destruction of the aromatic ring, the effects on degradation of the type and position of the substituent dramatically reveal themselves (Table 2). For example, introduction of the

TABLE 2

*Degradation of substituted benzoic acids by the soil microflora*

| Substitution | Days for ring cleavage | | |
|---|---|---|---|
| | *ortho* | *meta* | *para* |
| —COOH | 2 | 8 | 2 |
| —OH | 2 | 2 | 1 |
| —$NH_2$ | 2 | $>64$ | 8 |
| —$OCH_3$ | 4 | 16 | 2 |
| —$SO_3H$ | $>32$ | $>32$ | $>32$ |
| —$NO_2$ | 8 | $>32$ | 4 |

Unsubstituted benzoic acid: 1 day

sulphonate group markedly retards microbial destruction, whereas neither the hydroxyl group nor the second carboxyl group appreciably retards the decomposition. Considering the amino-, methoxy- and nitrobenzoates, on the other hand, a marked retarding influence of the substituent in the *meta* position is evident; an analogous effect is suggested among the dicarboxylic acids.

The reasons for the resistance conferred upon a compound by the addition of individual substituents to the molecule are as yet unclear. Since the original compound is often readily metabolized, the slow degradation might result from a change in permeability of the organism to the substrate or be attributable to a steric hindrance affecting the active enzyme; that is, an essential step in the degradation is retarded or prevented because the pesticide fails to reach the enzyme or because the enzyme is prevented from combining with the substrate. Such a steric effect may account for some of our observations on a soil *Flavobacterium* which cleaved the ether linkage between the phenolic and fatty acid moieties of a number of phenoxy herbicides; the decomposition of these compounds by the bacterium proceeded rapidly with phenoxybutyrate or phenoxy compounds having fatty acid side-chains with more than four carbon atoms, but the phenoxypropionate was metabolized quite slowly while the phenoxyacetate, in which the carboxyl group is close to the ether linkage, was not attacked at all by the bacterium (MacRae and Alexander, 1963). This suggests that the carboxyl interferes with the functioning of the ether cleaving enzyme.

Alternatively, the substituted compound may be altered to such an extent that the enzyme acting on the parent substance can effect no change on the daughter molecule. An effect of this type is particularly likely in view of the well-known specificity of enzymes. A number of observations with purified enzyme preparations provide evidence for this contention.

A metabolic deficiency which could account for the resistance of certain pesticides to destruction is related to a possible hindrance to the oxidation of those compounds which contain fatty acid or alkyl side-chains. The common mechanism for the catabolism of such substances is beta oxidation. If the substrate were changed in such a way as to prevent beta oxidation from occurring and if this were the only biochemical mechanism by which such compounds are degraded, then the modified substance would resist bacterial decomposition. For example, the non-biodegradability of a number of alkyl benzene sulphonates is associated with the presence of branches on the alkyl portion of the molecule, the branching probably hindering the beta oxidation sequence (Swisher, 1963). Similarly, the introduction into an organic substance of some characteristic which prevents the normal metabolic sequence from operating would undoubtedly result in a greater resistance in the chemical thus modified.

A hypothesis of this type may be invoked to account for the remarkable resistance to degradation of alpha-linked phenoxy herbicides. The data indicate that, whereas many of the omega-linked phenoxy compounds show a reasonably short persistence in soil, the corresponding compound containing the alpha linkage is typically resistant to microbial decomposition (Alexander and Aleem, 1961; Burger *et al.*, 1962); conceivably, the pesticides containing alpha-linked fatty acid side-chains cannot undergo beta oxidation, while the omega-linked herbicides are susceptible to degradation by this mechanism, explaining the differences in rates of detoxication.

At the present time, therefore, a number of observations have been made to show chemical characteristics associated with the resistance of pesticides to enzymatic degradation, but physiological explanations for these microbial deficiencies are still no more than tentative. Clearly, additional data and experimental models are needed in order to account for the resistance of certain pesticides to microbial destruction and to allow for a rational approach to the design of compounds which are either resistant or susceptible to microbial decomposition, the choice of relative degradability depending upon the specific economic, agricultural or public health requirements.

From a metabolic viewpoint, it should not be surprising that certain compounds persist for long periods in soil either because of the inherent structure of the chemical itself or because the conditions prevailing in the environment into which the substance is deposited do not allow for the decomposition. Modern investigations of microbial physiology and metabolism emphasize not the multitude of biochemical pathways and the vast differences between species but rather the few distinctly different metabolic mechanisms and the common anabolic and catabolic pathways. From arguments derived from the doctrine of comparative biochemistry and considering that comparatively few metabolic pathways account for most of the major processes of decomposition and mineralization, only a few common and widespread biochemical sequences would be expected in the bacterial community of the soil. Thus, should an individual compound or a structurally related group of pesticides be degraded by only one or not more than a limited few reaction sequences, it is not difficult to propose chemical structures which do not fit into the pattern of the existing pathways of degradation. For example, a synthetic alkane or fatty acid that cannot be metabolized by beta oxidation may, when introduced into soil, persist for astonishingly long periods since there may exist no biological agent capable of destroying the novel compound.

Since the topic of environmental factors associated with or determining the resistance to destruction of organic compounds has recently been reviewed (Alexander, 1965), only a few of the highlights will be considered.

Anaerobiosis is often associated with the long life of specific compounds in nature. Unfortunately, there is little information on the effect of oxygen deficiency or total anaerobiosis on pesticide transformation. It may be assumed, however, that many of these compounds will persist for long periods in the absence of oxygen, provided that biological inactivation is the major means of soil decontamination. This anticipated increase in resistance to detoxication under anaerobiosis may result from the biogenesis of toxins; e.g., the formation of $H_2S$ or aromatic inhibitors. Alternatively, the persistence of hydrocarbon pesticides may result from the need for molecular oxygen in certain enzymatic mechanisms involved in hydrocarbon metabolism, the oxygen entering into and appearing in the products of the particular reaction.

Adsorption of pesticides by soil colloidal matter will likewise often diminish the availability of the compounds to bacteria. An influence of adsorption has been demonstrated with many compounds serving as substrates for one or another of the soil bacteria, and it is probable that clays or organic colloids retard the inactivation of many pesticides in soil ecosystems. Similarly, sorption of extracellular enzymes participating in a detoxication sequence will probably result in a prolongation of the duration of toxicity in treated soils.

Furthermore, a pesticide that reaches a site in the environment into which micro-organisms are unable to penetrate or a locale which cannot be reached by the requisite enzymes will be effectively shielded from destruction. Unfortunately, micro-environmental influences upon micro-organisms and the significance of the micro-environment in modifying the susceptibility of organic substrates are still poorly understood (Alexander, 1964).

In view of the many natural substances that persist in soil for decades, centuries and occasionally millenia, what is most surprising is not the recent discovery that a few synthetic chemicals endure for long periods but rather that microbiologists have not realized until recently how widespread is the phenomenon of molecular recalcitrance.

Investigations of the metabolism of pesticides and products of their decomposition are of considerable theoretical significance, but such studies also have considerable applied importance. For example, it has been shown that bacteria have not one but rather two pathways for the degradation of certain compounds used for weed control such as 4-(2, 4-dichlorophenoxy)butyric acid. This herbicide, which itself has little phytotoxic activity upon suitable test plants, may be activated by certain bacteria (Taylor and Wain, 1962; Webley, Duff and Farmer, 1957). On the other hand, a strain of *Flavobacterium* rather than activating the herbicide converts it to a series of innocuous products (MacRae, Alexander and Rovira, 1963). One organism, therefore, may bring about a change which leads to environmental toxicity; another destroys the substance before its herbicidal potential is unveiled.

Several methods and experimental procedures have been employed in our investigations to demonstrate the microbial degradation of pesticides. The disappearance of the compound from a soil or medium is often not an adequate criterion for a microbial contribution to pesticide disappearance since many of the substances are lost by volatilization, photo-chemical processes or other non-biological reactions. Moreover, not even the time-tested criterion of bacterial growth in a medium containing the pesticide as the apparent source of carbon, nitrogen or phosphorus is an adequate basis upon which to conclude that the compound is being used for the purpose intended; growth in these media has often been observed even with no indications of detoxication or degradation. Such growth probably results from the utilization by the organism of contaminating substances in the medium, volatile nutrients which dissolve in the liquid or impure pesticide preparations. To overcome these limitations in the classical techniques of demonstrating substrate utilization by bacteria, several methods have been employed, all with the essential and appropriate controls. These include bioassay procedures, the evolution of radioactive $CO_2$ from soil treated with $^{14}$C-labelled pesticides, the liberation of chloride from chlorine-containing pesticides, spectrophotometric changes resulting from molecular modification and gas, paper and thin layer chromatography. Finally, in many but not all instances, the active species has been isolated. These isolates include strains of *Pseudomonas* and *Nocardia* metabolizing chlorinated fatty acids, an isolate of *Flavobacterium* decomposing a number of phenoxy herbicides and an *Arthrobacter* culture degrading 2,4-D.

One of the unexpected outcomes of our investigations was the finding that a bacterium incapable of using a pesticide as a carbon source for its growth was nevertheless quite capable of metabolizing the substance. This has been observed for a phenoxy herbicide like 4-chlorophenoxyacetic acid, and at least several of the organophosphorus insecticides probably are metabolized by bacteria unable to use them as sole carbon or phosphorus sources for proliferation. In the degradation of simple hydrocarbons, bacteria are also known to attack substrates which they cannot utilize as carbon and energy sources (Foster, 1962). It is not yet possible, however, to determine how many biodegradable compounds fail to provide the active bacteria with carbon, nitrogen or phosphorus in a form that will be assimilated and sustain growth.

These findings demonstrate one major shortcoming of the elective culture technique. A second shortcoming to classical enrichment procedures for obtaining the responsible soil inhabitants is related to the nutrition of the microflora. Investigators concerned with the decomposition of exotic substrates in soil and other environments have yet to devise a suitably selective enrichment technique for the specific isolation from nature of auxotrophs decomposing these odd chemicals. Thus, should all of the soil organisms degrading a pesticide require one or more growth factors, the simple enrichment culture, which is so effective in allowing for development of prototrophs, will not yield one or more of the auxotrophs that in nature catalyse the reaction.

Clearly, isolation of bacteria metabolizing pesticides is often not a simple, straightforward operation. Many of the chemicals are toxic either to micro-organisms or microbiologists. Frequently, the chemicals are volatile or are subject to non-biological degradation. Often, their water solubility is no more than a few parts per million. Coupled with such problems are the difficulties, cited above, of isolating the detoxifying auxotrophs from soil and the fact that the bacterium effecting the decomposition may not cleave the molecule in such a way as to provide itself with carbon in a form suitable to sustain its growth.

It is not surprising, consequently, that information on the microbiology of pesticides and the products formed in the bacterial degradations is sparse. For example, amitrole is readily degraded by the subterranean population, as shown by the release of $^{14}CO_2$ from soil treated with the labelled herbicide, yet micro-organisms cleaving the molecule and the fate of the compound remain unknown. Likewise, the high toxicity, volatility and low solubility of thiolcarbamates have served to deter investigations, but these herbicides also appear to be degraded by the microflora (MacRae and Alexander, 1965).

Despite the potential pitfalls, and even in the relative absence of guidelines for investigations of pathways of degradation of compounds which rarely have been examined by individuals better versed in metabolism than the soil microbiologist, some progress has been made. In general, however, the limited information is derived from investigations of model compounds supplied to individual bacteria in monocultural systems rather than from studies of the mixed microflora of a heterogeneous environment normally acting upon a wide spectrum of substrates.

In our studies of bacteria capable of degrading phenoxy herbicides and chlorophenols, a *Flavobacterium* was isolated which metabolized all $\omega$-linked 2,4-dichlorophenoxyalkanoic acids tested with the exception of 2,4-D, the acetic acid member of the series. The kinetics of substrate oxidation and results from sequential induction studies indicated a new mechanism for the degradation of these compounds, a reaction resulting in cleavage of the ether linkage (MacRae and Alexander, 1963). To establish that such a reaction mechanism indeed took place, the culture filtrates were extracted, methylated and the resulting methyl esters examined by gas chromatography (MacRae and Alexander, 1964). The results summarized in Table 3 demonstrate that the organism

TABLE 3

*Decomposition of ω-(2,4-dichlorophenoxy) alkanoic acids by a* Flavobacterium *sp.*

| Substrate | Product detected* |
|---|---|
| 3-(2,4-dichlorophenoxy)propionate | propionate |
| 4-(2,4-dichlorophenoxy)butyrate | butyrate |
| 5-(2,4-dichlorophenoxy)pentanoate | pentanoate |
| 6-(2,4-dichlorophenoxy)hexanoate | hexanoate |
| 7-(2,4-dichlorophenoxy)heptanoate | heptanoate |
| 8-(2,4-dichlorophenoxy)octanoate | octanoate |

* Characterized by gas chromatography

released the fatty acid corresponding to that bound in the side-chain of the phenoxyalkanoate, presumably by a cleavage of the ether linkage. The results are in contrast to those of Taylor and Wain (1962) who noted that bacteria in culture acted upon such compounds by $\beta$-oxidation, a process resulting in the sequential removal of 2-carbon fragments from the side-chain of the molecule. The anticipated metabolic products, many of which have been isolated, are shown in Table 4.

TABLE 4

*Anticipated products of the bacterial metabolism of phenoxyalkanoic acids*

| Substrate | β-oxidation | Ether cleavage |
|---|---|---|
| φO—$(CH_2)_6$COOH | φO—$(CH_2)_4$COOH<br>φO—$(CH_2)_2$COOH | φOH, $CH_3(CH_2)_5$COOH |
| φO—$(CH_2)_5$COOH | φO—$(CH_2)_3$COOH<br>φO—$CH_2$COOH | φOH, $CH_3(CH_2)_4$COOH |
| φO—$(CH_2)_4$COOH | φO—$(CH_2)_2$COOH | φOH, $CH_3(CH_2)_3$COOH |
| φO—$(CH_2)_3$COOH | φO—$CH_2$COOH | φOH, $CH_3(CH_2)_2$COOH |

φO designates the phenoxy moiety

Based upon these two pure-culture precedents, the reaction sequence in soil was examined (Gutenmann, Loos, Alexander and Lisk, 1964). A number of the phenoxy compounds were added to soil and the products characterized, but only two are here considered (Figs. 1 and 2). The data demonstrated that the decomposition, in this soil at least, proceeded by the β-oxidation mechanism.

Surprisingly, the decomposition of 2,4-D, which is one of the oldest and most widely used of the modern selective herbicides, is poorly

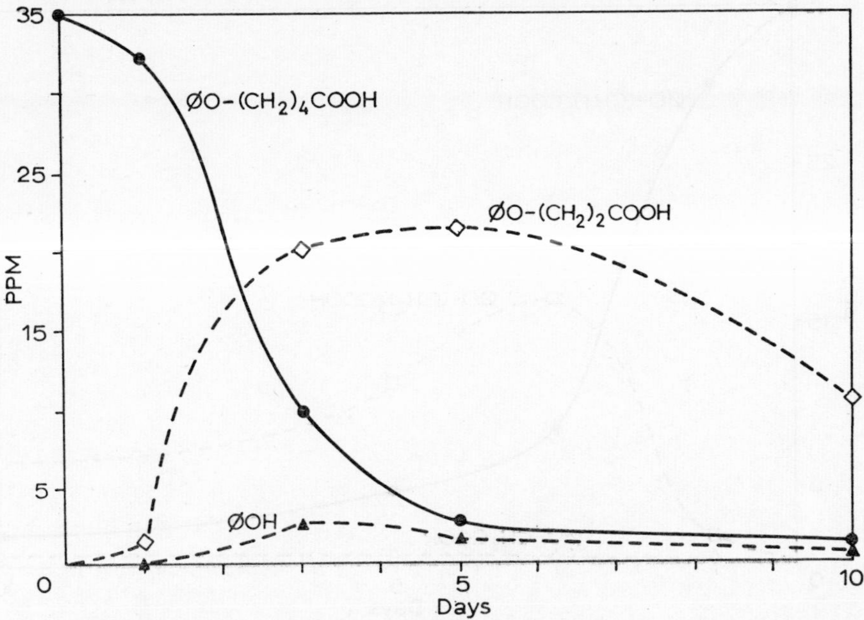


Fig. 1. Decomposition of 5-(2,4-dichlorophenoxy) pentanoic acid in Canfield silt loam. ØO represents the 2,4-dichlorophenoxy moiety.

understood. From soils treated with this herbicide, a strain of *Arthrobacter* was isolated which degrades 2,4-D and related compounds. Cells induced to metabolize 2,4-D oxidized 2,4-D, 2,4-dichlorophenol, 4-chlorocatechol and several other phenols without a lag phase, and the bacterium cleaved the respective benzene rings. In contrast to observations of others (Bell, 1960; Evans, Gaunt and Davies, 1961), there was no oxidation or metabolism of several hydroxy relatives of 2,4-D. During its growth on 2,4-D, the bacterium liberated a phenolic compound. This substance was extracted from the medium and identified as 2,4-dichlorophenol by gas chromatography, ultraviolet and infrared spectroscopy, and by certain characteristics of derivatives prepared from it. Another compound, as yet not fully characterized, has also been observed (Loos, Peters and Alexander, 1965). The formation of 4-chlorocatechol by a bacterium producing 2,4-dichlorophenol from another phenoxy herbicide has already been reported (MacRae *et al.*, 1963).

It has been shown that micro-organisms may act upon a pesticide in more than one way, one mechanism possibly involving an activation, other mechanisms resulting in detoxication or the destruction of a compound prior to the unmasking of its potential toxicity. It is also apparent that, by slight modification in the structure of a readily degradable

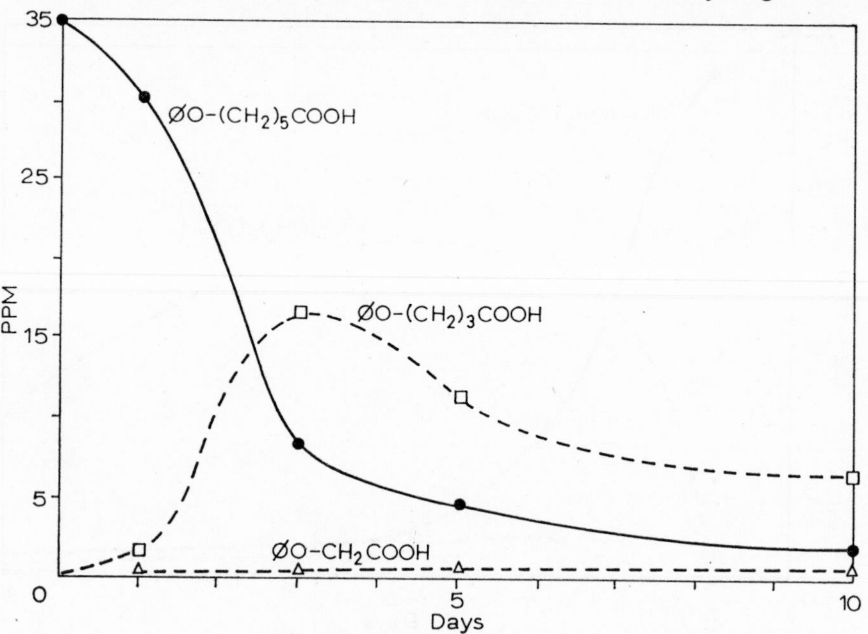


Fig. 2. Decomposition of 6-(2,4-dichlorophenoxy) hexanoic acid in Canfield silt loam. ØO represents the 2,4-dichlorophenoxy moiety.

molecule, a substance markedly resistant to microbial degradation can be obtained, such a structural change often being reflected in a long persistence of the new material in soil. The physiological explanations for the relationship between structure and decomposability are yet largely unclear, but the structural characteristics associated with phytotoxicity appear to differ from those determining resistance to biodegradation.

Pesticide degradation clearly offers an attractive line of investigation to the microbial ecologist concerned with an understanding of the biochemical changes occurring within the soil ecosystem. At the same time, the importance of pesticides in agriculture and public health should serve as a stimulus to engage in such studies. Whatever the cause and whatever the attraction, much more needs to be learned about the fascinating interplay between the soil community and the exotic chemicals introduced into the subterranean environment.

## *REFERENCES*


ALEXANDER, M. (1964). Biochemical ecology of soil microorganisms. *A. Rev. Microbiol.*, **18**, 217.

ALEXANDER, M. (1965). Biodegradation: problems of molecular recalcitrance and microbial fallibility. *Adv. appl. Microbiol.*, **7**, 35.

ALEXANDER, M. & ALEEM, M.I.H. (1961). Effect of chemical structure on microbial decomposition of aromatic herbicides. *J. agric. Food Chem.*, **9**, 44.

BELL, G. R. (1960). Studies on a soil *Achromobacter* which degrades 2,4-dichlorophenoxyacetic acid. *Can. J. Microbiol.*, **6**, 325.

BURGER, K., MACRAE, I. C. & ALEXANDER, M. (1962). Decomposition of phenoxyalkyl carboxylic acids. *Proc. Soil. Sci. Soc. Am.*, **26**, 243.

EVANS, W. C., GAUNT, J. K. & DAVIES, J. J. (1961). The metabolism of chlorophenoxyacetic acid herbicides by soil microorganisms. *Abst. Comm. 5th Int. Congr. Biochem., Moscow*, 306.

FOSTER, J. W. (1962). Hydrocarbons as substrates for microorganisms. *Antonie van Leeuwenhoek*, **28**, 241.

GUTENMANN, W. H., LOOS, M. A., ALEXANDER, M. & LISK, D. J. (1964). Beta oxidation of phenoxyalkanoic acids in soil. *Proc. Soil Sci. Soc. Am.*, **28**, 205.

KAMEDA, Y., TOYOURA, E. & KIMURA, Y. (1957). Metabolic activities of soil bacteria towards derivatives of benzoic acid, amino acids and acylamino acids. *Kanazawa Daigaku Yakugakubu Kenkyu Nempo*, **7**, 37. Cited in *Chem. Abst.*, **52**, 4081 (1958).

LOOS, M. A., ROBERTS, R. N. & ALEXANDER, M. (1965). Metabolism of 2,4-D by an *Arthrobacter* species. *Bact. Proc.*, 3.

MACRAE, I. C. & ALEXANDER, M. (1963). Metabolism of phenoxyalkyl carboxylic acids by a *Flavobacterium* species. *J. Bact.*, **86**, 1231.

MACRAE, I. C. & ALEXANDER, M. (1964). Use of gas chromatography for the demonstration of a pathway of phenoxy herbicide degradation. *Agron. J.*, **56**, 91.

MACRAE, I. C. & ALEXANDER, M. (1965). Microbial degradation of selected herbicides in soil. *J. agric. Food Chem.*, **13**, 72.

MACRAE, I. C., ALEXANDER, M. & ROVIRA, A. D. (1963). The decomposition of 4-(2,4-dichlorophenoxy)butyric acid by *Flavobacterium sp. J. gen. Microbiol.*, **32**, 69.

SWISHER, R. D. (1963). Biodegradation of ABS in relation to chemical structure. *J. Wat. Pollut. Control Fed.*, **35**, 877.

TAYLOR, H. F. & WAIN, R. L. (1962). Side-chain degradation of certain ω-phenoxyalkane carboxylic acids by *Nocardia coeliaca* and other microorganisms isolated from soil. *Proc. R. Soc. Ser. B*, **156**, 172.

WEBLEY, D. M., DUFF, R. B. & FARMER, V. C. (1957). Formation of a β-hydroxy acid as an intermediate in the microbial conversion of monochlorophenoxybutyric acids to the corresponding substituted acetic acids. *Nature, Lond.*, **179**, 1130.

# *DISCUSSION*

## THE PHYSIOLOGY OF SOIL BACTERIA

*Chairman: M. Alexander, Cornell University*

*Prof. H. Veldkamp.* Professor Schlegel, I noticed that when you grew *Hydrogenomonas* under heterotrophic conditions, then for many generations they kept 10 per cent of the $CO_2$ fixing enzymes. This does not seem to be very efficient. Do they use these enzymes? Is there any fixation of carbon dioxide under heterotrophic conditions?

*Prof. H. Schlegel.* We have evidence to show that the Calvin cycle goes on even during the oxidation of glucose, following experiments with glucose labelled in the 1st, 2nd and 6th positions. There was no other interpretation. Whether this is of any advantage to the organism, I do not know. There are some strains, e.g. *H. facilis* and *H. eutropha*, that lose their enzymes under these conditions, but these were isolated from normal soils. Perhaps the persistence of an autotrophic enzyme system is the property of strains isolated from soils where molecular hydrogen is very often produced; in soil where *Hydrogenomonas* occurs accidentally, having an autotrophic enzyme system would be of no advantage. Both Stanier and Snell collected strains of *Pseudomonas* from a pantothionate enrichment culture which have been shown to be *Hydrogenomonas eutropha.* Thus there may be several types, more strictly autotrophic ones and less strictly autotrophic ones. Firstly we must characterize these types and then we must investigate their distribution in different habitats.

*Dr. G. A. Zavarzin.* I should like to draw your attention to the question of whether certain types of bacteria do in fact exist. I am not sure whether we should classify organisms as lithotrophs or heterotrophs; rather we should speak about modes of life, because some organisms like *Hydrogenomonas* can change their mode of life. If we study the distribution of these modes of life among organisms, some interesting conclusions emerge. We can distinguish an autotrophic mode of life ($CO_2$ utilization) and a heterotrophic mode of life. The electron acceptors may be inorganic or organic and the organisms may be aerobic or anaerobic. There are 8 different combinations of these properties. Examples of such combinations are *autotrophic + inorganic electron acceptor + aerobic growth* e.g. *Hydrogenomonas* and the nitrifiers, and *autotrophic + inorganic electron acceptor + anaerobic growth*, e.g. *Thiobacillus.* Other combinations are rare, e.g. organisms which are autotrophic and yet oxidize organic compounds (*Bacillus formicicum* and *Pseudomonas oxalaticum*). All 8 combinations do exist, but there are other possible combinations which are forbidden. For instance, no-one can obtain acid-tolerant nitrifiers or organisms oxidizing iron under alkaline conditions. Of the 64 combinations of nutritional properties in the genus *Thiobacillus*, only 20 are possible. Of these, 19 have been discovered. The others are forbidden; they are impossible.

*Dr. N. Walker*. If one makes rigid definitions, one tends to create artificial barriers in respect of what is and what is not possible in the microbial world. For example, one can argue for a long time as to whether $CO_2$ is organic or inorganic.

*Prof. H. Schlegel.* I would not say that something is impossible. Ecological pockets may exist where a new method of obtaining energy may be realized.

*Dr. M. Alexander*. I don't agreé completely with you, Professor Schlegel. There are some reactions which, thermodynamically, are probably forbidden or, at least, very unlikely; an anaerobic nitrifier is probably impossible. Could Dr. Zavarzin say on what basis he feels other organisms are impossible?

*Dr. G. A. Zavarzin.* As far as the oxidation of iron under alkaline conditions is concerned, it is quite clear; the oxidized iron is unstable. Under acid conditions, nitrite is perhaps toxic.

*Dr. M. Alexander*. Your *perhaps* could be violated by Professor Schlegel's proviso that there is an ecological niche for an organism resistant to the toxic action of nitrite.

*Dr. G. A. Zavarzin.* It has not been possible to find such a niche.

*Dr. M. Alexander*. Maybe that is because the microbiologists do not know enough.

*Prof. D. Pramer*. There is no chemical reason to prevent nitrification at an acid pH. However, nitrite is more toxic at an acid pH, so that if a cell does oxidize ammonium to nitrite under these conditions, it must have a specialized system to render it resistant to nitrite.

*Prof. A. D. McLaren*. One must not be prejudiced by what one observes in pure culture. One can conceive that accumulated nitrite might be adsorbed on exchange sites of clay minerals (clay minerals have both positive and negative exchange sites) in a heterogeneous system. In other words, nitrite which is toxic in solution, might not be when adsorbed and hence, thermodynamically, the whole picture would be changed.

*Prof. D. Pramer*. We are all aware that you can get nitrification in soil at a much lower pH than you can in pure culture or enrichment culture. We can only find out why, if we try to isolate different strains of nitrifiers from nature. This is very difficult to do. We have tried and have isolated a *Nitrosomonas* that has an optimum pH in pure culture of about 7·5. It will not nitrify in pure culture below pH 6·0. Has anyone tried to isolate strains from acid soil to see if they have different pH optima?

*Dr. M. Alexander*. I do not believe that a nitrifier would be inhibited because of nitrite toxicity. When ammonia is oxidized, either the ammonium at acid pH combines with the nitrite and destroys it, or alternatively nitrite itself decomposes. Possibly we do not get nitrifiers at an acid pH because of the pH sensitivity of the group, or because we are using the wrong techniques.

*Prof. A. D. McLaren*. Dr. Alexander, I am not clear how you performed some of your pesticide degradation experiments. Were they done by perfusion or by incubating the material in a flask with the sample of soil?

*Dr. M. Alexander*. In some cases we used a soil suspension, in some instances soil in tumblers or cups. Pure culture work was done using normal methods.

*Mr. G. W. Hull*. Are we now beginning to think in terms of the synthetic activity of micro-organisms in relation to the pesticides we are adding to the soil?

*Dr. M. Alexander.* Pesticides are hazardous chemicals. However, they are the best weapons for controlling pests that man has ever devised. In order to live with the hazard and to maintain these weapons, we have to continually maintain our vigilance. We must avoid any possible hazard, either due to synthetic or degradative activities of the soil microflora, and be concerned with the possible persistence of pesticides which will increase the hazard in terms of plant uptake and appearance in milk and food. There is no evidence on the formation of complex molecules from pesticides in soil, which are themselves toxic, although some polymerization reactions do occur. I should add that chemical analyses are not sufficient to detect such compounds; we must also carry out bioassays. We have to live with pesticides; there are too many people to feed.

*Dr. H. L. Jensen.* I wish to defend what Gale said about the principle of microbial infallibility. He made a very important reservation, namely that though there might exist an organism, somewhere in the world, that would be able to oxidize any compound, it would have to be under the right conditions. Thus one reason why resistance occurs is because the ecological conditions will not permit the production of an enzyme to carry out a particular reaction. Furthermore, Gale never specified the rate at which these more or less resistant substances would be attacked.

*Dr. M. Alexander.* I am in agreement with the principle as a principle, not as a law of microbial infallibility. The rate of breakdown is obviously important since organic compounds have been shown to persist for over 2,000 years by radio-carbon dating. It is more than a mortal microbiologist can tolerate, to wait that long.

*Dr. H. B. Gunner.* May I add fuel to the fire which Dr. Jensen has started? The compound diazonon is very little soluble in water (c. 40 ppm.). We tried to dissolve it in hexane, ethyl alcohol, etc. At certain concentrations in ethyl alcohol, which would maintain it in solution in our culture media, we could get the organism to use the compound as a sole source of carbon.

We are sometimes misled in looking for breakdown of these recalcitrant compounds by imposing on them, only the role of a carbon source. We have found an *Arthrobacter* (?) which is capable of degrading phosphorothiolate, using it as a nitrogen, carbon, sulphur and phosphorus source *under the right conditions.* This organism uses phosphorothiolate as a source of sulphur and phosphorus without a very long lag phase, but when used as a source of carbon there is a very long lag phase. Thus this organism will use an otherwise recalcitrant compound as a source of sulphur, nitrogen and phosphorus, only when a readily available source of carbon is present in the medium.

Two conditions would seem to be necessary before recalcitrant compounds become available; (1), solubilization in aqueous media, and (2), the presence, together with the compound, of a readily available source of carbon.

*Dr. D. J. Greenwood.* I want to support Dr. Gunner's remarks about the faster decomposition of resistant compounds in the presence of additional very decomposable organic matter. We found that methionine was very resistant to decomposition, but when we added glucose, in about equal parts, then the methionine decomposed rapidly in the soil.

*Prof. D. Pramer.* When the alkyl aryl sulphonates were first introduced as detergents, they were recognized to be very resistant; they persisted in water and in soil. In recent years there have been increasing numbers of reports of the isolation of micro-organisms that are able to degrade these compounds. This is evidence of an evolutionary pattern. However, the way that you talk about this problem, Dr. Alexander, it seems that chemicals are recalcitrant, they are and always will be. I think that when strange chemicals become familiar, mutants will arise, capable of degrading them.

*Dr. M. Alexander*. I think we have a conflict of religions, rather than a conflict of facts. Most microbial ecologists and soil scientists are brought up to believe that any organic compound is capable of being degraded. We have, unfortunately, automatically extended this principle of faith to synthetic chemicals. I see no *a priori* reason to assume that it will be true. I would be willing to be convinced, but it seems to me to be very difficult to say that any compound which the organic chemist synthesizes will be degraded by a mutant or variant in soil, water or some other environment.

*Prof. D. Pramer*. Yes, but similarly there is no reason for them to persist.

*Dr. N. Walker*. The stability of meta-chlorine substituted compounds, is well known. The only instance I know of such a degradation is a claim in some early work by Audus that 2,4,5,T (2,4,5,trichlorophenoxyacetic acid) could be decomposed in a soil column, after the soil had been percolated with a solution of MCPA (2-methyl-4-chlorophenoxyacetic acid). I am trying to repeat this because I have failed, over a longer period of time, to get a direct enrichment of organisms to attack 2,4,5,T. Have you tried this?

*Dr. M. Alexander*. I have also failed to isolate an organism using 2,4,5,T. I feel that Audus' results are probably due to the fact that an organism which uses the phenoxyalkanoic acids (2,4-D or MCPA) might be able to degrade the side chain, but not get any energy from this degradation: the aromatic ring would remain in the soil. There has been some recent evidence that although organisms do not grow on certain compounds, they metabolize them, though possibly not completely. The activity that Audus observed with 2,4,5,T, which is contrary to field evidence, could be due to the fact that he built up a population which could degrade the side chain, but could not use it for growth. This would account for your failure and mine, to isolate an organism using the meta-substituted phenoxyacetic acid.

*Dr. H. L. Jensen*. I agree with the principle that meta-substitution increases resistance to decomposition. However, there has been another case reported of the degradation of a meta-substituted compound, although it was a nitro-substituted substance, i.e. meta-nitrobenzoic acid. Cartwright and King found that meta-nitrobenzoate could be degraded, although it was a much slower process than the degradation of the other isomers.

*Acad. A. A. Imshenetsky*. Is it possible to isolate cell free enzymes which degrade pesticides?

*Dr. M. Alexander*. There have been very few enzymes isolated so far, from pesticide degrading organisms. We have not been successful in isolating the enzyme degrading the ether linkages of these compounds. We have, however, found an enzyme liberating chloride from certain compounds.

*Dr. A. T. Bull*. When extracellular enzymes are attached to a bacterium, they may retain their activity. In wood destroying fungi, two types of extracellular enzymes occur, freely diffusing ones which account for the degradation of the materials in advance of the hyphae, and certain cellulolytic enzymes that remain attached to the hyphae. Cellulose, being an insoluble substrate, might possibly have an inactivating effect on the freely diffusing enzymes. By analogy, soil particles would do the same and so I wonder whether extracellular enzymes are of any significance in soil.

*Prof. N. A. Burges*. I think we are underestimating the intelligence of the micro-organisms. If you have substances like pectin or starch which can be split rapidly to give you a large number of readily available molecules, then the organism will be prepared to put out a large quantity of exo-enzyme. This will diffuse quite a long way, split the compound very rapidly and cause a temporary accumulation of relatively large amounts of usable products. The organism will grow well and will not mind if the 'waiting people' round the table get a little extra at the same time. However, if you take a compound like lignin or humic acid in which the initial cracking is very slow and difficult, the organism degrading it is not going to let the waiting neighbours get at the products, for it will need them all itself. Under these conditions, you will get a system where the organism stays close to the substrate. It will not waste its energy and run the risk of losing nutrients by producing large quantities of exo-enzymes; it will produce enzymes localized at the surface of the substrate. Cellulose decomposition may be intermediate between these two extremes.

*Prof. A. D. McLaren.* I would like to cite an observation made by Jones (*Proc. Vmt Exp. Stn*, 1912). He showed that when carrot tissue was attacked by *Erwinia carotovora*, there was a wave of exo-enzyme activity, 10 to 12 cells deeper into the tissue than the organisms themselves, indicating that the exo-enzymes attacked as a frontal army, so to speak, to degrade the tissue which then became susceptible to invasion by the organism itself. It is easy to consider this a model for the role of an exo-enzyme system in soil, but we must then ask why we cannot isolate exo-enzymes from the soil and the soil solution and crystallize them. One can conceive, as Waksman suggested, that the enzymes might be trapped in a humic type material. This is not far-fetched because Kachalsky (Biochem. J., 1965) has reported co-polymerization of the enzyme trypsin in polymaleic anhydride in which the trypsin molecules were trapped within a three-dimensional polymer network (analagous in this case to humus). The enzyme was fully active, but because one enzyme molecule was trapped at point A and another at point B, there was no cannibalism of one enzyme molecule by the other. These polymeric aggregates remained stable for months at a time.

May I also ask Professor Pramer a question? It has been found that in the gut of the clothes' moth, the enzyme capable of attacking the protein material requires a preliminary reduction of disulphide linkages in an alkaline reductive medium. I was therefore surprised to hear you say that an enzyme has been crystallized which could attack substances of this type. Does anyone know whether there are in soil, soil animals which can degrade wool and keratin-like materials, and whether this pure crystalline enzyme requires a reductive milieu in which it can function as a hydrolytic agent for the peptide bond, in the presence of disulphide linkages?

*Prof. D. Pramer.* I know nothing about soil animals consuming keratin. The information concerning crystallization of the enzyme has not been reported in the literature. It is a personal communication from Dr. Nickerson. As far as I know, a preliminary reduction is not required.

*Dr. R. C. W. Berkeley.* Professor Pramer, you mentioned that the chief products of chitin breakdown were the dimer chitobiose and the monomer acetylglucosamine. There has been work by Jeuniaux and Berger and Reynolds showing that higher oligosaccharides in this series can be isolated. Four-membered oligosaccharides have been obtained from *Streptomyces* cultures and recently I have identified the 5-membered sugar from a *Bacillus* digest. I think that we underestimate the ability of micro-organisms to decompose chitin. If you look carefully at the literature, there are records of vast numbers of organisms which are capable of decomposing this substance.

*Dr. H. Potgieter.* Most people talk about chitinase without reference to the purity of the enzyme. In most cases, preparations also contain chitobiase and other enzymes.

*Dr. G. Fåhraeus.* Academician Imshenetsky, you mentioned that there were two main pathways of cellulose decomposition, (a), the hydrolytic pathway, where you would expect cellobiose and glucose as intermediates and (b), the oxidative pathway where you would expect substances like polyuronides as intermediates. Our results, from work with *Cytophaga* spp., indicate that only the hydrolytic pathway is operative. Do you really think there are micro-organisms which use the oxidative pathway for the degradation of cellulose in accordance with Winogradsky's original theory?

*Acad. A. A. Imshenetsky.* It is possible to detect cellulase in different species of fungi and bacteria, indicating that the hydrolytic pathway is the main one. The oxidative pathway is a secondary system, possibly relying on the release of sugars following hydrolysis. It is possible to find large quantities of uronidase only in species of bacteria, e.g. myxobacteria, which produce large quantities of slime.

*Dr. A. T. Bull.* Another enzyme which deserves mention is cellobiose phosphorylase which has been detected in *Cellvibrio*. This is an enzyme which could be looked for more widely in cellulose decomposing organisms, particularly in those which are not able to utilize glucose. As far as I know, it has not been demonstrated in fungi. Perhaps it is sometimes a more efficient method since one ends up with phosphorylated glucose which can enter into subsequent metabolism.

*Prof. H. Veldkamp.* You mentioned the occurrence of *Cytophaga* in the rumen. This is a strictly anaerobic environment and I have never heard of the description of any obligate anaerobic *Cytophaga* spp., although facultative ones do occur.

*Acad. A. A. Imshenetsky.* Yes, they do occur.

*Dr. J. E. Satchell.* I was interested in Professor Veldkamp's suggestion that extracellular production of polysaccharides might be a protective device against predation by protozoa. What would be the mechanism involved and what evidence is there to support it?

*Prof. H. Veldkamp.* I don't think that there is very much evidence. Pathogenic species of bacteria are not so readily attacked by leucocytes when they form polysaccharides. This may be analagous to the situation with soil bacteria.

*Dr. O. W. Heal. Aerobacter aerogenes* is one of the favourite foods of small soil amoebae. When this bacterium is grown on an excess sugar medium, the large capsule produced retards the growth of the amoebae. This is also true for other capsulated bacteria and algae. Dr. Gray's slides showed colonies of bacteria in the soil that could have had capsules around them; this might retard the feeding of amoebae on these bacteria. This is probably a size effect since filamentous bacteria, e.g. *Bacillus cereus mycoides*, are not attacked by amoebae until the filaments fragment.

On the other hand, bacterial exudates may be a disadvantage to bacteria, in that they will attract protozoan predators. I have found that amoebae will remain active only in the presence of bacterial and yeast exudates. On control media, without these exudates, they encyst. This might be an example of probiosis.

# THE TAXONOMY OF SOIL BACTERIA

# THE TAXONOMY OF SOIL BACTERIA

RUTH E. GORDON

*Institute of Microbiology, Rutgers, the State University of New Jersey, U.S.A.*

## *INTRODUCTION*

To the microbiologist, the soil is a vast store of an infinite number and variety of micro-organisms engaged in a myriad of activities. Some decompose the wastes and tissues of man and animals and the tissues of plants; others dissolve inorganic substances. Some provide nutrients essential to plant life; others destroy these nutrients. Some have a major role in the production of food for man and animals; others cause food spoilage. Some invade the tissues of living plants and animals with results that range from beneficial to lethal. Studies of these and many other activities of soil micro-organisms have occupied microbiologists for two-and-a-half centuries and will doubtless do so for centuries to come.

A microbiologist investigating any of the soil bacteria and their activities needs to know, sooner or later, how these bacteria are described and named, how he can recognize them and other bacteria like them, and how he can organize his observations and communicate with other microbiologists. He soon realizes that certain strains appear more closely related than others and that some sort of an arrangement, or classification, of the micro-organisms is possible. This systematic arrangement, the basis of communication concerning the soil bacteria, is our topic for this session.

Among recent discussions of the general aspects of classification, based on broad experience and knowledge of its development and problems, are those of Cain (1962), Cowan (1962*a*, 1965), Cronquist (1964), Floodgate (1962), Mayr (1964), Sokal (1964) and Walters (1964), and I should like to comment on a few points made by some of these and other writers.

Cronquist (1964) concludes that 'all kinds of data are potentially useful (to taxonomy)', and that 'the system should be based on all available evidence'. It is, indeed, true that those of us who attempt to describe and group soil bacteria should welcome all bits of information about all micro-organisms. We may find that any fact, any technique, will prove, in the end, to be useful. As knowledge continues to accumulate, the description and classification of micro-organisms continue to undergo change. The taxonomy of the soil bacteria is not static; the more comprehensive classifications are no more than progress reports.

Mayr (1964) both extends and counterbalances the point made by Cronquist when he says that 'the ever-new characters utilized by resourceful taxonomists merely supplement the characters used by the classical workers but do not replace them. Indeed, as is well known, the newer methods and characters only rarely lead to drastic changes in the recognition and arrangement of taxa, provided the original arranging had been done by a biologically thinking taxonomist.'

New information provides a test of the old. Current classification, the foundation of today's communication concerning soil bacteria, is a continuation of the observations of our scientific forbears. In some instances, these observations are being corrected, whilst in others they are being confirmed, just as the taxonomic observations we make today are subject to future correction or confirmation.

The bacterial classification of the future constitutes a third point for emphasis. In my opinion, Walters (1964) describes it well: 'We should face the fact that a single name—or even a code number or formula—may be preferable as a means of communication. I see nothing sacrosanct in the binomial convention; its convenience outweighs its disadvantages for higher organisms but does not necessarily do so in other groups. . . . We should treat taxonomy as the servant of the science, providing a basic framework of communication. This is an essential service and taxonomists should take some pride in trying to provide it.'

In contrast to studies of the soil fungi, which are usually generically and specifically identified, the systematic recognition of large numbers of different kinds of soil bacteria is possible today in only a very few laboratories (Burges, 1958). The entire working life of the bacteriologist may have to be devoted to the accumulation of the knowledge necessary for the classification of a single genus, yet his need for classification as a basis of communication is as important to him as it is to the mycologist. Although the binomial system may not be 'sacrosanct', it is still, despite all its faults, the best means of communication among workers in all fields of bacteriology, past and present.

As a benchworker, interested almost exclusively in a study of only four genera, burdened with too many cultures, and undoubtedly learning more and more about less and less, I had, after accepting this assignment, to seek a definition of soil bacteria. The kinds of bacteria in the soil are not distinct from those in water or air, neither are they distinct from those generally called agricultural bacteria nor from food and industrial bacteria. Many bacteria of concern in human or veterinary medicine and in fish, insect, or plant diseases are counterparts or close relatives of some soil bacteria. In general, the bacteria involved in problems of dominant interest in soil microbiology, such as transformations of carbon, nitrogen, sulphur, phosphorus, cellulose, lignin, and many other compounds, are not rare or specialized but are widely distributed in the microbial world and in current classifications (Alexander, 1961; Evans, 1963; McKenna and Kallio, 1964; Senez, 1962; Starkey, 1964).

During my search of the literature for an acceptable delimitation of the soil bacteria, I heard a biophysicist define his field as 'anything that is interesting' and decided that the great diversity of soil bacteria permits a similar description. To the microbiologist attempting to recognize and delineate them, the soil bacteria are all bacteria that are interesting and that are there.

## *PROGRESS IN CLASSIFICATION OF THE SOIL BACTERIA*

In the preparation of this report, I tried to get some idea from the current literature of our advance in describing and recognizing the interesting bacteria. Because of today's burgeoning number of reports, my own sweeping definition of the soil bacteria, and the press of other work, my survey is incomplete. I hope that all those authors whose reports I have been unable to include will accept a benchworker's sincere apologies.

Our progress in the classification of the various taxa of bacteria is by no means even. Undoubtedly many kinds of soil bacteria are still not in captivity. Starkey (1958) estimated that 'probably less than 10 per cent' of the bacterial population of the soil is recovered by plating procedures. Other techniques, therefore, such as Casida's (1962) method of isolating vitally stained micro-organisms directly from the soil, are necessary. The studies of Lochhead (1958) and his co-workers on growth-promoting substances, and those of Hungate (1947), his associates and others, recently reviewed by Bryant (1964), on the bacteriology of the rumen, are excellent examples of successful cultivation of strains with unusual requirements for nutrition and environment. The numbers and types of projects that must be undertaken before all the soil bacteria can be maintained and observed in the laboratory for taxonomic purposes are beyond prediction.

In addition to the unknown bacteria, there are about fifty genera described in *Bergey's Manual of Determinative Bacteriology* (Breed, Murray and Smith, 1957), that, insofar as I have been able to learn, have disappeared from current literature and from our culture collections. Unless authentic strains can be found, these genera should be relegated to the unknown bacteria.

At first glance, the Gram-negative, polar-flagellated bacteria present a challenge to taxonomists, the challenge of a cluttered room to a good housekeeper. The listing of 149 species of the genus *Pseudomonas* by Breed, Murray and Smith (1957) reflects the need of thorough, comparative study of the pseudomonads. The reports of Colwell and Mandel (1964), Davis and Park (1962), De Ley and Friedman (1964), Eddy (1962), Friedman and De Ley (1965), Park (1962) and Scopes (1962), who used deoxyribonucleic acid base composition, infrared spectra or a large number of other characteristics and techniques, indicated that the genera *Acetobacter*, *Acetomonas*, *Aeromonas*, *Comamonas*, *Pseudomonas*, *Achromobacter*, *Vibrio* and *Xanthomonas* are composed of very few species. Serological relationships among strains of *Pseudomonas*, *Achromobacter*, *Vibrio* and *Aeromonas* did not correspond to any taxonomic divisions (Hobbs, Cann, Gowland and Byers, 1964). By computer analysis, Eddy and Carpenter (1964) found strains of *Aeromonas punctata*, *Photobacterium* sp. and *V. comma* to be alike and Stocks and McCleskey (1964) assigned certain strains of *Pseudomonas*, *Protaminobacter* and *Vibrio* to the same species.

Response to the challenge of this taxon seems forthcoming, however, in the establishment of a large number of characteristics for the identification of *Pseudomonas fluorescens* (Rhodes, 1961) and of *P. aeruginosa* (Colwell, 1964), and in the enormous amount of work and experience manifest in papers on the *Pseudomonas-Achromobacter* group by Ayres (1960), Bullock (1964), De Ley (1960), Haynes and Rhodes (1962), Holding (1960), Shewan, Hobbs and Hodgkiss (1960) and many others.

The order Pseudomonadales also contains photosynthetic, autotrophic, heterotrophic, and other bacteria whose description and identification depend mainly on their fascinating, distinctive metabolism or morphology. The development of non-photosynthetic mutants of the strain of *Rhodopseudomonas spheroides* (Griffiths, 1962) and of heterotrophic strains from autotrophic thiobacilli (Johnstone, Townsend and White, 1961) suggest a closer relationship between these bacteria and others in the same order. The assignment of methane-oxidizing, nitrogen-fixing bacteria (*Methanomonas*) to the genus *Pseudomonas* was confirmed by Davis, Coty and Stanley (1964). Saunders, Campbell and Postgate (1964) found that the base composition of deoxyribonucleic acid of 30 strains of *Desulfovibrio desulfuricans* did not support the allocation of these strains to one species. An excellent study and review of the caulobacters by Poindexter (1964) disclosed their similarities to strains of *Pseudomonas* and *Vibrio* but recommended that the stalked forms be divided into two genera, *Caulobacter* and *Asticcacaulis*.

Dependability of flagellation, currently a major criterion for the separation of groups of bacteria, has been carefully investigated by Leifson (1963). According to his observations, the pseudomonads from soil and fresh water rarely showed mixed polar and peritrichous flagellation; aeromonads frequently showed mixed flagellation; and chromobacteria typically showed mixed flagellation. Among 400 cultures of pseudomonads and aeromonads from marine animals, 70 had mixed flagellation. Leifson (1954) also found that strains of *Acetobacter* which oxidize acetic acid (*Acetomonas*) had polar flagella. In spite of this morphological difference, De Ley and Schell (1962) considered that the physiological and biochemical similarities of strains of *Acetobacter* and *Acetomonas* demonstrated a very close relationship between the two genera. The acetic acid bacteria may represent a bridge between two major taxonomic groups. Rubenchik (1959) has proposed the assignment of the nitrogen-fixing *Azotobacter*, *Azotomonas* and *Beijerinckia* to the family Azotobacteriaceae. This suggests another infringement of the separation of groups of bacteria by type of flagellation. Exceptions are expected in microbiology.

Because of the agricultural significance of the rhizobia and the importance of host specific strains, serological methods are widely used in distinguishing strains (Alexander, 1961; Johnson and Means, 1963; Vintiková, Šrogl and Škrdleta, 1961). The classification based on host specificity is very useful and necessary. Another aspect of rhizobial classification, however, was investigated by Graham (1964) in a comparison of 100 different features of strains of *Rhizobium*, *Agrobacterium*, *Chromobacterium*, *Beijerinckia* and *Bacillus*. Graham found that the strains of *Chromobacterium*, *Bacillus* and *Beijerinckia* formed distinct groups; he confirmed the previously reported similarity of *R. trifolii* and *R. phaseoli* to *R. leguminosarum* and the inclusion of *A. radiobacter* and *A. tumefaciens* in the genus *Rhizobium* as *R. radiobacter*. He suggested the limitation of *Rhizobium* to three species (*R. leguminosarum*, *R. meliloti* and *R. radiobacter*) and the creation of a new genus *Phytomyxa* for the slowly growing root-nodule bacteria. Recognition of only two species of *Chromobacterium*, another genus of the Rhizobiaceae, was recommended by Sneath (1956) and Eltinge (1957).

The few recent papers I have seen on members of the family Achromobacteraceae (*Alcaligenes*, *Achromobacter*, *Flavobacterium*, *Agarbacterium* and *Beneckea*) were critical of its classification and stressed the necessity of further study (Colwell and Mandel, 1964; Hayes, 1963; Koontz and Faber, 1963; Málek, Radochová and Lysenko, 1963; Steel and Midgley, 1962).

Because of their wide distribution, rapidity of growth, and significance in medicine and public health, the enterobacteria have long been one of the most widely studied taxa. Their popularity gave rise to the dire prediction that if *Escherichia coli* were lost, half the bacteriologists would be unemployed. An immeasurable amount of work is reflected in the outline of the Enterobacteriaceae by Ewing (1963). Reports of Falkow, Ryman and Washington (1962) on the deoxyribonucleic acid base composition of members of the family and of Davis and Ewing (1964) on their lipolytic, pectolytic and alginolytic activities constitute examples of continued examination of the arrangement of the enterobacteria. The close relationship of the genus *Erwinia* to the enterobacteria was confirmed by Martinec and Kocur (1963), who recommended the limitation of *Erwinia* to two species. Another investigation by Martinec and Kocur (1961) and one by Colwell and Mandel (1965) corroborated the assignment of only one species to the genus *Serratia* (Ewing, Davis and Johnson, 1962).

Although Cowan (1962*b*) referred to the classification of the micrococci and staphylococci as an 'introduction to chaos', the careful, comparative work on the aerobic and facultatively anaerobic strains of the family Micrococcaceae reviewed by Cowan has produced good order in this taxon, at least to the uninitiated. The separation of the staphylococci from the micrococci by their ability to form acid anaerobically from glucose (Evans, Bradford and Niven, 1955) has been confirmed by Baird-Parker (1963), Cowan and Steel (1964) and others. The validity of *Staphylococcus aureus* has been generally accepted, and the description of *S. epidermidis*, the second of the two species assigned to the genus, was expanded by Jones, Deibel and Niven (1963). The proposed assignment of the obligately aerobic micrococci and the non-spore-forming sarcinae to six species of *Micrococcus* by Kocur and Martinec (1962) offered a useful basis for the recognition of the micrococci.

The family Lactobacillaceae has also been widely investigated; recent reports on the classification of this taxon show reasonable agreement. Studies of the antigenic and biochemical composition of the cell walls of the haemolytic streptococci, reviewed by Krause (1963), supported their accepted classification. A review of the enterococci by Deibel (1964) and reports by Barnes (1964), Rogers and Sarles (1964) and Sharpe (1964), reflected acceptance of the allocation of the enterococci to two species, *Streptococcus faecalis* and *S. faecium*. More recent work on the lactic acid cocci, reviewed by Reiter and Møller-Madsen (1963), has been concerned with the separation of the various species of streptococci and with the differentiation of the genera *Leuconostoc* and *Pediococcus*. The status of *S. lactis* and *S. cremoris* was unchallenged, but that of *S. diacetilactis* was still unsettled. The genus *Leuconostoc* was recognized, although the number and definitions of its species were not decided. The genus *Pediococcus* (Deibel and Niven, 1960), composed of the microaerophilic, Gram-positive cocci generally present in air and dust and of importance in various fermentation processes, still offered some problems in generic and specific definitions and in nomenclature (Clausen, 1964; Coster and White, 1964; Dobrogosz and DeMoss, 1963).

The specific identification of all but a few of 1,755 isolations of lactobacilli by Franklin and Sharpe (1964) offered ample proof of the value of the classification proposed by Rogosa and Sharpe (1959). Results of computer analysis of the data from 245 strains (Hauser and Smith, 1964) and a study of the nutritional requirements of 179 strains (Franklin and Sharpe, 1964), also confirmed Rogosa and Sharpe's classification.

Conn and Dimmick (1947) proposed the genus *Arthrobacter* for the aerobic soil micro-organisms previously assigned to the genus *Corynebacterium*. They were characterized in young cultures by pleomorphic rods, sometimes developing filaments and buds, and in older cultures by small coccoid forms. As originally described, these pleomorphic bacteria grew well on simple media, used inorganic nitrogen, and differed markedly from *C. diphtheriae*, the type species. Although the division of the genus *Corynebacterium* was generally welcomed, the genus *Arthrobacter* and its species have not been satisfactorily delimited (Zagallo and Wang, 1962).

Mulder's (1964*a*) report on the genus *Arthrobacter* demonstrates clearly some of the taxonomic difficulties involved. The Gram reaction and nutritional requirements are variable. Morphologically the arthrobacters bear a 'striking similarity' to strains of *Brevibacterium*, *Cellulomonas* and *Mycobacterium*, and have also been considered 'closely related' to the nocardiae. Some aid in defining the genus *Arthrobacter* may be forthcoming in the determination of the composition of the cell walls (Cummins, 1962; Gillespie, 1963*a*, *b*), and in the serological relationships (Katznelson and Mason, 1962).

When considering the genus *Bacillus*, I return to familiar territory. No one knows better than Smith, Gordon and Clark (1952), how much remains to be done.

The soil is generally recognized as the primary habitat of the clostridia, a large group of essentially saprophytic organisms. Most of the recent studies on the identification of species, however, concern the clostridia causing or associated with infections in man or animals. Among the few descriptions of other clostridia are reports on psychorophilic strains (Sinclair and Stokes, 1964), pectinolytic species (Ng and Vaughn, 1963) and the sulphate-reducing *Clostridium nigrificans* (Saunders, Campbell and Postgate, 1964). The listing of 93 species of clostridia by Breed, Murray and Smith (1957) and the frequent appearance of 'new' species in the literature emphasize the need of a thorough comparison of many strains.

The motile, spore-forming sarcinae were proposed as newcomers in the family Bacillaceae, with *Sporosarcina ureae* as the type species, because of their close relationship to the bacilli (MacDonald and MacDonald, 1962; Kocur and Martinec, 1963).

The actinomycetes, transitional forms between the simple bacteria and fungi and consisting of a large proportion of the total microbial population in certain soils (Alexander, 1961), are now subject to much taxonomic investigation. The studies of Cummins (1962) on the composition of the cell wall have been extended by others. Among these, Lechevalier and Lechevalier (1965) divided about 150 strains of aerobic actinomycetes into five families on the basis of morphology and chemical analysis of cell walls. Yamaguchi (1965), studying the components of the cell wall of 30 strains, also described five groups. Some of the other classifications of members of the order Actinomycetales, also recently proposed, were those of Baldacci (1962), Buchanan and Pine (1962), Couch (1963), Jones and Bradley (1964), McClung (1963) and Waksman (1961).

Studies on the separate genera of the actinomycetes, some of which are of medical and industrial importance, were too numerous to be included in this survey. The International Subcommittee on the Taxonomy of the Actinomycetes has undertaken an ambitious programme (Küster, 1964), and the accumulating knowledge and experience can be expected to result, eventually, in a reliable classification.

In a review of current work on the iron and manganese bacteria, Wolfe (1964) frankly described present-day knowledge of these bacteria as 'primitive'. 'Sketchy' perhaps might be a kinder adjective to apply to our knowledge of the orders Chlamydobacteriales, Hyphomicrobiales, Caryophanales, Beggiatoales, Myxobacteriales and Spirochaetales, since these micro-organisms are not familiar to most bacteriologists. Representatives of some of the genera assigned to these six orders have not been examined in pure culture. Others are classified only by their serology; stock cultures of others are very difficult to maintain; and growth of some is too sparse for biochemical analyses. Many more studies like the following are needed: Morrison and Edwards (1964), Mulder (1964*b*) and Okrend and Dondero (1964), of the *Leptothrix-Sphaerotilus* group; Leifson (1964), of the genus *Hyphomicrobium*; Burton and Morita (1964), of the genus *Beggiatoa*; Meyer (1962), of the genus *Cytophaga*; Nellis (1963), of the genus *Chrondromyces*; Dworkin (1962) and Brockman and Boyd (1963), of the genus *Myxococcus*; and Lewin (1965), of the genus *Saprospira*. Pringsheim, whose papers on some genera of three of these six orders were recently collected by Van Niel (1963), stressed the variability of these organisms and the desirability of co-ordinated studies of their morphology, ecology and biochemistry.

This brief survey of some recent reports on classification of the interesting bacteria demonstrates that certain groups have been well studied, that species have been reduced to manageable numbers by the comparison of many characteristics of many strains and that new information has confirmed taxonomic separations. In general, however, this survey is a bare outline of unfinished work. The fascination and the burden of today's bacterial taxonomy lie in the need for more and more investigation. One day, when all the work is completed, rapid identification of all micro-organisms present in a given sample of soil by some technique, perhaps similar to fluorescent antibody microscopy (Coons, Creech and Jones, 1941), may become reality.

## *SOME GUIDING CONCEPTS IN CLASSIFICATION*

Because of the widely acknowledged lack of a generally accepted definition of a bacterial species and of principles and rules for taxonomic investigation, perhaps my most useful contribution to this symposium would be the presentation of some workaday concepts. Since guiding rules and definitions are largely a matter of individual opinion, my co-workers and I evolved a few basic concepts that eventually led to a definition of a species (Smith, Gordon and Clark, 1952; Gordon and Mihm, 1962*a*). Our concepts and rules slowly and gradually emerged from a study of hundreds of strains of bacilli, mycobacteria, nocardiae and streptomycetes. We do not claim to have developed any new or startlingly different principles; most of these principles have been stated by many other workers, from Aristotle down to today's numerical taxonomists. Our studies did, however, confirm and renew the conclusions of others.

In agreement with many, but not all, taxonomists, my co-workers and I considered the species as the primary, basic and stable unit of classification. We believed that a strain should always belong to the same species and that a strain should not change from one species to another spontaneously or by treatment in the laboratory. A strain of *Nocardia asteroides*, for example, should be as readily recognized after 50 years of cultivation *in vitro* as when first isolated. If it is not, the description of the species, *N. asteroides*, is incomplete. Another aspect of our concept of a species was the conviction that the species identity of a strain should always be inherent in the strain itself and not in its source, history, the records of a culture collection or in some investigator's notebook.

Our concept of a species necessitated the acceptance of microbial variation as one of the facts of life or, as Pringsheim stated, as 'a property of the species' (Van Niel, 1963). Bacteria possess many characteristics of varying degrees of stability. Aware that a characteristic may be lost by a strain or not shared by all the variants of a strain or by all the strains of a species, in our description of a species we attempted to accommodate for bacterial variation by using as large a group as possible of the more reliable properties and by expecting some variation of the more dependable characteristics within the group.

These few beliefs resulted in our defining a species as a group of freshly isolated strains, of strains maintained *in vitro* for many years and of their variants, that have in common a set of reliable characteristics separating them from other groups of strains. In preparing a description of a species and in finding ways to recognize strains belonging to that species, we examined fresh isolates, old stock strains and as many of their variants as could be obtained. In our opinion the properties of strains persisting after years of cultivation in the test tube or, for example, after exposure to ultraviolet were useful criteria for defining the species.

In the characterization of a species we did not attempt to establish a rule concerning the number of strains to be studied, but did urge that as many strains as possible be observed and in as many different ways as possible. Representation of a species in nature may sharply limit the number of strains available. Only three strains apparently belonging to a distinct species of *Nocardia*, including Emmart's (1947) nocardin strain, have come to us during the past 14 years. At this rate, accumulation of 50 strains will require over 200 years. Unless an unexpected source of more strains is found, any description of this 'nocardin species' in the near future will admittedly be based on too few strains and therefore inadequate.

Except for the recommendation that the most stable properties of the strains be used to define a species, we did not suggest the kinds of characteristics to be studied. Criteria used for describing and identifying the strains of a species are dependent on the strains themselves and on the investigator's purpose, inclination, time and laboratory facilities. Experience convinced us, however, that a distinct species may be delineated by more than one group of reliable properties and that investigators observing totally unlike but stable characteristics will assign the same and similar strains to the same species. The validity of each species recognized and established today depends on the confirmation or disapproval of the workers of the future, undoubtedly by tests and observations now unknown. The constant development of new media and laboratory procedures limits the importance of the methods used by any one investigator in describing and identifying a species, but an insurance of the availability to microbiologists, present and future, of strains representing described species is a very important contribution.

The delineation of a species as a group of new strains, old strains and their variants makes the representation of a species by a single strain inadequate. To become acquainted with a particular species or to compare that species with others, an investigator needs to study a number of strains. He needs to study recently isolated strains, old strains, including the nomenclatural type or neotype, and a number of their variants if he is to acquire some knowledge of the variation occurring within the species. If I were selecting reference strains to represent *Nocardia asteroides*, I should select the most recently isolated strain available; it might resemble strain No. 739 (Gordon and Mihm, 1962*a*, Plate 3), that was obtained from a case of bovine mastitis and which formed a pinkish growth with an abundance of aerial hyphae, giving the growth a chalky white appearance. The old strains could be represented by No. 3318 (Gordon and Mihm, 1962*a*, Plate 4), which, according to Waksman's records, is Nocard's (1888) strain. On most media, cultures of this strain failed to form aerial hyphae visible to the unaided eye; the growth resembled that of a mycobacterium. A strain isolated from soil (No. 3045A) would probably be the next choice. Its cultures formed a goodly number of aerial hyphae, while its variant (No. 3045B) formed so few they could not be seen without a microscope. Strain No. 443(1), isolated from a patient by Conant at Duke University, would be another selection, because of its pigment and its ability to produce a variant thickly coated with aerial hyphae. A strain whose aerial hyphae segmented into chains of bead-like spores resembling those of the streptomycetes

(Gordon and Mihm, 1958), would probably complete the strains chosen to demonstrate morphological variability. Other strains would be selected to acquaint the recipient with some of the variation in physiological properties among strains of *Nocardia asteroides*. At the risk of being accused of choosing all the strains of the species in our collection, I should also suggest strains representing the groups that Magnusson (1962 and unpublished data), found among the strains of *N. asteroides* in his study of their sensitins. After an examination of these reference strains, the recipient would, in my opinion, have a far better knowledge of the species than if he had observed only the nomenclatural type or neotype strain. In his future taxonomic studies, he would be less likely to separate strains by variable criteria and would probably soon win membership in a 'Lumpers Club'.

With these few concepts in mind, i.e. the acceptance of the species as the basic unit of classification; the belief that species should be so defined that a strain cannot change from one species to another; the rule that a strain's identity should always be inherent in its cultures; the recognition of variability as a property of the species; and the resulting definition of a species as a group of newly isolated strains, old stock strains, and their variants that have in common a set of reliable characteristics separating them from other groups of strains, I should like to demonstrate one method of preparing descriptions of two species of streptomycetes.

Strains No. 3558 and No. 3560 of *Streptomyces rimosus* were among the first strains of streptomycetes I examined. A photograph of a culture of strain No. 3558 (Gordon and Mihm, 1962*a*, Plate 6) shows the normal, heavy, spreading, beige growth thickly coated with whitish aerial hyphae. Strain No. 3560 had the same appearance. Shortly after I had observed that these two strains possessed certain physiological properties that separated them from the other strains I had studied, a variant of strain No. 3560 was brought to the laboratory. Its growth was soft, as easily lifted with an inoculating loop as a culture of *Escherichia coli*, without aerial hyphae visible under the microscope and like the variant No. 3699 of strain No. 3558 (Gordon and Mihm, 1962*a*, Plate 6). This variant of strain No. 3560, however, had the same physiological characteristics that distinguished the parent strain and strain No. 3558 from the others examined at that time.

The few strains of *Streptomyces fradiae* first observed also had certain distinctive physiological characteristics. Their growth was yellowish brown, spreading, thickly coated with sporulating aerial hyphae and deep pink in colour, as illustrated by strain No. 3535 (Gordon and Mihm,

1962*a*, Plate 6). The growth of a variant (No. 3535–7b) of strain No. 3535 was soft, without aerial hyphae and resembled the growth of the variants of strains of *S. rimosus*. The variant of strain No. 3535, however, possessed the physiological properties that seemed diagnostic of strains of *S. fradiae* and that easily separated strain No. 3535–7b from the variants of strains of *S. rimosus*. As the number of similar observations increased, reliance on characteristics common to the parent and daughter strains seemed feasible in describing and identifying the species of streptomycetes.

## *METHODS*

The strains of *Streptomyces albus* and *S. fradiae* listed in Tables 1 and 4 respectively, and nine variants of strain No. 3535 of *S. fradiae* obtained by ultraviolet irradiation, were examined by the following procedures. Six of the nine variants of strain No. 3535 were received as dependent on one or two amino acids. Because descriptions of the media and methods are scattered throughout several earlier reports, they are all given here for convenience.

### *Acid-fastness*

Cultures grown on glycerol agar (peptone, 5 g.; beef extract, 3 g.; glycerol, 70 ml.; agar, 15 g.; tap water, 750 ml.; soil extract, 250 ml.; pH 7·0), for 5 days at 28° were stained by a modification of the Ziehl-Neelsen method. Air-dried smears were immersed in carbol fuchsin [10 ml. of saturated solution of basic fuchsin in 95 per cent (v/v) ethanol and 90 ml. of 5 per cent (w/v) aqueous solution of phenol]. After the carbol fuchsin had been heated and boiled for 5 mins., the slides were washed in water, dipped once in acid ethanol [3 ml. of concentrated HCl and 97 ml. of 95 per cent (v/v) ethanol], quickly washed in water, and counterstained with methylene blue [30 ml. of saturated solution of methylene blue in 95 per cent (v/v) ethanol and 100 ml. of 0·01 per cent (w/v) aqueous solution of KOH].

Soil extract was made from garden soil, rich in organic material. The soil was air-dried, crushed and sifted through a coarse sieve. Four hundred grams of this soil, mixed with 960 ml. of tap water, was autoclaved at 121° for 1 hr. and left in the unopened autoclave overnight. The cool extract was carefully decanted and filtered through paper. Measured amounts of the filtrate (usually 300 ml.), were autoclaved for 20 minutes at 121° and allowed to stand at room temperature for 2 weeks or longer. The clear supernatant was decanted as needed.

*Colonial morphology*

A tube of Bennett's agar [yeast extract, 1 g.; beef extract, 1 g.; N–Z Amine A (Sheffield Farms, New York, N.Y.), 2 g.; glucose, 10 g.; agar, 15 g.; distilled water, 1000 ml.; pH, 7·3] (Jones, 1949), and one of soil extract agar (peptone, 5 g.; beef extract, 3 g.; agar, 15 g.; tap water, 750 ml.; soil extract, 250 ml.; pH 7·0) were melted, cooled to 47° and inoculated from a 2–3 week culture in glucose broth (peptone, 5g.; beef extract, 5g.; yeast extract, 5g.; glucose, 5g.; distilled water, 1000 ml.; pH 7·0). One to three loopfuls of the broth culture, depending on the turbidity, were used as inoculum for each tube of agar. Approximately 1 ml. of each agar was pipetted onto a sterile glass slide inside a sterile, moist chamber and incubated at 28°. The slides were observed under the microscope at 3, 7 and 14 days for the appearance of the substrate hyphae, aerial hyphae and spores. These hyphae could be seen easily if the inoculum was sufficient to produce two or more colonies per field under the X 10 objective.

The sterile, moist chamber for the incubation of the slide cultures was a Petri dish, the bottom of which was covered with filter paper. A bent glass tube served as a rest for the microscope slide. After sterilization and the pipetting of the inoculated agar onto the slide, the filter paper was moistened with 2 or 3 ml. of sterile distilled water and kept moist during the period of incubation by the frequent addition of more sterile water.

*Decomposition of adenine, hypoxanthine, L-tyrosine, xanthine and casein*

Half a gram of adenine (Nutritional Biochemicals Corp., Cleveland, Ohio), was suspended in 10 ml. of distilled water, autoclaved, mixed thoroughly with 100 ml. of sterile nutrient agar (peptone, 5 g.; beef extract, 3 g.; agar, 15 g.; distilled water, 1000 ml.; pH 7·0), cooled to 45°, and poured into five Petri dishes. Care was taken to insure an even distribution of the crystals throughout the solidified agar. Each culture was streaked once across a plate, incubated at 28°, and observed at 14 and 21 days for the disappearance of the crystals underneath and around the growth. Plates of hypoxanthine, L-tyrosine and xanthine agars were prepared, inoculated and incubated in the same manner, with the exception of the use of 0·4 per cent (w/v) of xanthine.

Five g. of skim milk powder (Difco) in 50 ml. of distilled water and 1 g. of agar in 50 ml. of distilled water were autoclaved separately and cooled to 45°. The milk and agar were mixed and poured into five Petri dishes. Each culture was streaked once across a plate, incubated at 28° and examined for clearing of the casein underneath and around the growth at 7 and 14 days (Hastings, 1903).

A heavy inoculum was used in testing for the decomposition of adenine, casein, hypoxanthine, L-tyrosine and xanthine. Some cultures grew well on the five media but did not dissolve the casein or crystals except around the larger clumps of inoculum.

*Decomposition of urea and allantoin*

Ten ml. of a 15 per cent (w/v) solution of urea, sterilized by filtration, was added to 75 ml. of sterile urease broth [$KH_2PO_4$, 9·1 g.; $Na_2HPO_4$, 9·5 g.; yeast extract, 0·1 g.; phenol red, 0·01 g.; distilled water, 1000 ml.; pH 6·8 (Rustigan and Stuart, 1941)]. The mixture was pipetted aseptically into sterile plugged tubes in 1·5 ml. amounts and inoculated with actively growing cultures. An alkaline reaction after 28 days of incubation at 28° demonstrated decomposition of urea.

Rustigan and Stuart's broth was distributed in 3 ml. amounts in tubes containing *c.* 0·01 g. of allantoin, autoclaved and inoculated with actively growing cultures. Decomposition of the allantoin was indicated by an alkaline reaction after 28 days at 28°.

*Temperature of growth*

Slants of Bennett's agar or yeast dextrose agar (glucose, 10 g.; yeast extract, 10 g.; agar, 15 g.; distilled water, 1000 ml.; pH 7·0), were inoculated, quickly heated or cooled to the desired temperature in a water bath and then placed in a water bath at the same temperature inside a constant-temperature incubator. The water level and temperature of the water bath were carefully maintained. The cultures were examined for growth after 5 to 7 days at temperatures of 35° or above, and after 3 weeks at 10°.

*Survival at 50°*

Cultures were inoculated on slants of Bennett's agar or yeast dextrose agar, quickly heated to 50° in a water bath and then transferred to another bath at 50° inside a constant-temperature incubator. After 8 hr. the cultures were rapidly cooled, incubated at 28° for 21 days and inspected for growth.

*Utilization of citrate, malate and succinate*

Modifications of Koser's (1924) citrate agar were made by adding 2 g. of sodium citrate, calcium malate or sodium succinate to: NaCl, 1 g.; $MgSO_4.7H_2O$, 0·2 g.; $(NH_4)_2HPO_4$, 0·1 g.; $KH_2PO_4$, 0·5 g.; agar, 15 g.; distilled water, 1000 ml.; 0·04 per cent (w/v) solution of phenol red, 20 ml. The pH value of the citrate and succinate agars was adjusted to 6·8 before autoclaving, and the malate agar to 7·4. Utilization of the organic acid was established by the alkaline colour of the phenol red after 28 days of incubation at 28°.

*Nitrite from nitrate*

Cultures in nitrate broth (peptone, 5 g.; beef extract, 3 g.; $KNO_3$, 1 g.; distilled water, 1000 ml.; pH 7·0), were tested for the presence of nitrite after 5, 10 and 14 days of incubation at 28°. One ml. of each broth culture was withdrawn aseptically and mixed with 3 drops of each of the following two solutions: (1) sulphanilic acid, 8 g.; 5 N acetic acid (glacial acetic acid and water 1:2·5), 1000 ml. (2) dimethyl-d-naphthylamine, 6 ml.; 5 N acetic acid, 1000 ml. (Conn, 1951). The appearance of a red colour indicated the presence of nitrite. In the absence of nitrite after 14 days of incubation, nitrate was demonstrated by a red colour after the addition of 4–5 mg. of zinc dust to the tube previously tested for nitrite.

*Hydrolysis of starch*

One g. of potato starch was suspended in 5 ml. of cold distilled water; the suspension was added to 100 ml. of nutrient agar, autoclaved, cooled to 45°, carefully mixed and then poured into five Petri dishes. Duplicate plates were streaked with each culture and incubated at 28°. One plate was flooded with 95 per cent (v/v) ethanol at 5 days and the other at 10 days. After 15 to 30 minutes, the unchanged starch became white and opaque, while a clear zone underneath and around the growth measured the hydrolysis of the starch (Kellerman and McBeth, 1912).

*Acid production from carbohydrates*

Half a millilitre of a 10 per cent (w/v) aqueous solution of each carbohydrate, sterilized by autoclaving, was added aseptically to 5 ml. of sterile, inorganic nitrogen base agar [$(NH_4)_2HPO_4$, 1 g.; KCl, 0·02 g.; $MgSO_4.7H_2O$, 0·2 g.; agar, 15 g.; distilled water, 1000 ml. (Ayers, Rupp and Johnson, 1919)]. The pH value of this medium was adjusted to 7·0 before the addition of 15 ml. of a 0·04 per cent (w/v) solution of bromcresol purple). Cultures were examined for the acid colour of the indicator after 7 and 28 days of incubation at 28°.

## *RESULTS*

Cultures of the 21 strains of *Streptomyces albus* (Table 1), grown on glycerol agar formed branching filaments that did not retain carbol fuchsin. Their colonies were densely or loosely filamentous and the substrate hyphae of adjoining colonies intertwined. The aerial hyphae of some cultures were long, fairly straight and branching; those of others coiled into spirals; and some formed many short, side branches that were usually curled or twisted. Five of the strains sporulated sparsely and the others abundantly. The growth of the cultures on the yeast dextrose agar was light yellow in colour and was usually covered with white aerial hyphae that sometimes developed a greyish tinge.

TABLE 1

*Strains identified as* Streptomyces albus

| Laboratory No. | Name when received, source and strain name or number |
|---|---|
| A 14631 | *Actinomyces varsoviensis*; J. B. Routien, Chas. Pfizer & Co., Groton, Conn.; ATCC = American Type Culture Collection, Washington, D.C. (14631) |
| A 6860 | *Nocardia rangoonensis* (Erikson) Waksman & Henrici; ATCC (6860); NCTC = National Collection of Type Cultures, London (1678, pulmonary streptothrichosis) |
| 758 | *Nocardia* sp.; M. Wilson, Univ. of Melbourne (284743, blood of patient) |
| A 618 | *Streptomyces albus* (Rossi-Doria) Waksman & Henrici; ATCC (618); A. J. Kluyver; A. Krainsky |
| A 3004 | *S. albus*; ATCC (3004); S. A. Waksman; Pribram Collection, Vienna |
| 1182 | *S. albus*; H. J. Kutzner, Rutgers Univ. (8); CBS = Centraalbureau v. Schimmelcultures, Baarn; H. Schmid-Kunz (dental patient) |
| 1183 | *S. albus*; H. J. Kutzner (105); E. Baldacci |
| 1187 | *S. albus*; R. Hütter, Inst. f. Spezielle Botanik, Zurich (ETH 28420, pulmonary cyst) |
| 1205 | *S. albus*; H. A. Lechevalier, Rutgers Univ.; R. Pomerleau (Vache, blood of sick cow) |
| 3784 | *S. albus*; E. Baldacci, Univ. de Milano (82x, diseased bees) |
| 3848–3853 | *S. albus*; T. G. Pridham, U.S. Dept. of Agr., Peoria, Ill. (B 2435, B 2436, B 2438, B 2439, B 2440, B 2444); E. Baldacci (52x, 79x, 82x, 298x, 299x, $C_{13}R_5$; diseased bees) |
| 3854 | *S. albus*; T. G. Pridham (B 2235); CBS; P. Redaelli (actinomycosis) |
| 3863 | *S. albus*; R. Hütter (ETH 24454); J. Nicot |
| 3888, 3889 | *S. fradiae*; P. H. Gregory, Rothamsted Experimental Station (A 75, A 76; mouldy hay) |
| A 6852 | *S. gibsonii* (Erikson) Waksman; ATCC (6852); NCTC (4575); A. G. Gibson |

Some physiological properties of the 21 strains recognized here as *Streptomyces albus* are listed in Table 2. The cultures decomposed casein, hypoxanthine, tyrosine, allantoin and urea. Crystals of adenine were dissolved by only one strain, No. A 3004. The cultures grew at 50° but not at 10°; they utilized citrate, malate and succinate and were unable to hydrolyse starch. They formed acid from adonital, erythritol, galactose, glucose, lactose, maltose, mannitol, mannose, α-methyl-D-glucoside and xylose. Acid was not produced from dulcitol or raffinose, and by only 1 strain (No. 1187) from rhamnose and sorbitol. This

TABLE 2

*Comparison of physiological characteristics*

| Property | % positive strains | |
|---|---|---|
| | *Streptomyces albus* | *Streptomyces fradiae* |
| Decomposition of | | |
| Adenine | 5 | 100 |
| Casein | 100 | 100 |
| Hypoxanthine | 100 | 0 |
| Tyrosine | 100 | 100 |
| Xanthine | 81 | 0 |
| Allantoin | 100 | 0 |
| Urea | 100 | 0 |
| Growth at | | |
| 50° | 100 | 0 |
| 45° | 100 | 91 |
| 40° | 100 | 100 |
| 10° | 0 | 5 |
| Survival at 50° for 8 hr. | 100 | 91 |
| Utilization of | | |
| Citrate | 95 | 0 |
| Malate | 100 | 95 |
| Succinate | 100 | 100 |
| Nitrite from nitrate | 57 | 100 |
| Hydrolysis of starch | 0 | 100 |
| Acid from | | |
| Adonitol | 100 | 0 |
| Dulcitol | 0 | 0 |
| Erythritol | 100 | 0 |
| Glucose | 100 | 100 |
| Inositol | 57 | 0 |
| Lactose | 100 | 63 |
| Mannitol | 100 | 0 |
| Melibiose | 14 | 0 |
| α-Methyl-D-glucoside | 95 | 0 |
| Raffinose | 0 | 0 |
| Rhamnose | 5 | 0 |
| Sorbitol | 5 | 0 |
| Xylose | 100 | 100 |

group of reactions distinguished strains of *S. albus* from about 850 other strains of streptomycetes and nocardiae forming aerial hyphae, observed thus far.

Characteristics not shared by the 21 strains were decomposition of xanthine, reduction of nitrate to nitrite and acid production from inositol and melibiose (Table 3). The results of these 4 tests did not

TABLE 3

*Some variable characteristics of* Streptomyces albus

| Strain No. | Decomposition of xanthine | Nitrite from nitrate | Acid from | |
|---|---|---|---|---|
| | | | inositol | melibiose |
| 3784<br>A 14631<br>758, 1182<br>1205 | + | + | + | − |
| 3848<br>3849<br>3852 | + | + | − | − |
| A 3004<br>1187 | + | − | + | + |
| 3863 | + | − | − | − |
| 3854<br>3889 | − | + | − | − |
| 1183 | − | − | + | + |
| 3853 | − | − | − | − |
| Majority of the 21 strains | + | | + | − |

correlate; combinations of the reactions to two or more tests did not allocate the same strains to the same groups.

Filaments of the 23 cultures of *Streptomyces fradiae* (Table 4) cultivated on glycerol agar were usually long and branching. They did not retain the carbol fuchsin. The colonies of the 23 strains were densely or loosely filamentous and the vegetative hyphae of neighbouring colonies were interwoven. The aerial hyphae of 10 strains were long and straight; those of 4 strains were twisted into spirals; those of the other strains were short, sparse and gnarled. The conidia of 19 strains were abundant; 4 strains exhibited few, if any, conidia.

TABLE 4

*Strains identified as* Streptomyces fradiae

| Laboratory No. | Name when received, source and strain name or number |
|---|---|
| 3535 | *Streptomyces fradiae* (Waksman & Curtis) Waksman & Henrici; H. A. Lechevalier, Rutgers Univ. (barnyard soil) |
| 3554 | *S. fradiae*; J. Rouatt, Rutgers Univ. |
| 3556a, 3556b | *S. fradiae*; H. Umezawa, National Inst. of Health, Tokyo (117, 260) |
| 3697 | *S. fradiae*; C. W. Hesseltine, U.S. Dept. of Agr., Peoria, Ill. (NRRL B-1195); S. A. Waksman (3535) |
| 3739 | *S. fradiae*; J. J. Noval, Rutgers Univ. |
| 3883–3885 | *S. fradiae*; A. G. Kuchaeba, Acad. of Sciences of the U.S.S.R., Moscow [109(2), 109(3), 110] |
| A 11903 | *S. fradiae*; American Type Culture Collection, Washington, D.C. (11903); Inst. for Fermentation, Osaka (3123) |
| 1186 | *S. fradiae*; R. Hütter, Inst. f. Spezielle Botanik, Zurich (ETH 16803) |
| 1199, 1200 | *S. fradiae*; L. Silvestri, Univ. de Milano (PSAM 44, PSAM 61) |
| DW 74, DW 124, DW 128, DW 157, DW 165, DW 199, DW 208 | *S. fradiae*; D. Weiss, Rutgers Univ. (barnyard soil) |
| 3572 | *Streptomyces* sp.; K. Aiso, Shiba Univ. (320) |
| 3594 | *Streptomyces* sp.; M. P. Lechevalier, Rutgers Univ. (212, soil) |
| 3719 | *Streptomyces* sp.; G. Hagemann, Roussel Labs., Seine, France (ST59G) |

The 23 strains of *Streptomyces fradiae* had the following pattern of physiological reactions (Table 2): decomposition of adenine, casein and tyrosine; failure to attack hypoxanthine, xanthine, allantoin or urea; growth at 45° (two exceptions, Nos. 3883 and 3884) but not at 50° or 10°; survival at 50° for 8 hr. (two exceptions, Nos. 3884 and 1200); utilization of malate and succinate but not of citrate as carbon sources; reduction of nitrate to nitrite; hydrolysis of starch; acid formation from galactose, glucose, maltose, mannose and xylose but not from adonitol, dulcitol, erythritol, inositol, mannitol, melibiose, $\alpha$-methyl-D-glucoside, raffinose, rhamnose or sorbitol.

The 9 variants of strain No. 3535 of *Streptomyces fradiae* resulting from ultraviolet irradiation, grown on glycerol agar, formed long branching filaments or filaments of varying length. The filaments were not acid-fast. The colonies of the variants were densely or loosely filamentous. The substrate hyphae of adjoining colonies intertwined. Two strains did not exhibit aerial hyphae; the aerial hyphae of six strains were straight and branching; and those of the remaining strain branched and coiled. Six of the nine strains sporulated.

Physiological characteristics of the 9 variants are compared with those of the parent strain No. 3535 in Table 5. With the exception of survival at 50° for 8 hr. and acid from arabinose, galactose, lactose, mannose and xylose, the reactions of the nine variants were the same as those of the parent. Cultures of strain No. 3535 and its nine variants on dulcitol, erythritol, inositol, melibiose, α-methyl-D-glucoside, raffinose, rhamnose and sorbitol (not given in Table 5), did not yield acid. After

TABLE 5

*Physiological characteristics of variants of strain No. 3535 of* Streptomyces fradiae

| Property | Parent strain | Variants | | | | | | |
|---|---|---|---|---|---|---|---|---|
| | | 1, 2 | 3, 4 | 5 | 6 | 7 | 7A | 7B |
| Decomposition of | | | | | | | | |
| Adenine | + | + | + | + | + | + | + | + |
| Casein | + | + | + | + | + | + | + | + |
| Hypoxanthine | — | — | — | — | — | — | — | — |
| Tyrosine | + | + | + | + | + | + | + | + |
| Xanthine | — | — | — | — | — | — | — | — |
| Allantoin | — | — | — | — | — | — | — | — |
| Urea | — | — | — | — | — | — | — | — |
| Growth at | | | | | | | | |
| 50° | — | — | — | — | — | — | — | — |
| 45° | + | + | + | + | + | + | + | + |
| 40° | + | + | + | + | + | + | + | + |
| 10° | — | — | — | — | — | — | — | — |
| Survival at 50° for 8 hr. | + | + | — | + | + | + | + | — |
| Utilization of | | | | | | | | |
| Citrate | — | — | — | — | — | — | — | — |
| Malate | + | + | + | + | + | + | + | + |
| Succinate | + | + | + | + | + | + | + | + |
| Nitrite from nitrate | + | + | + | + | + | + | + | + |
| Hydrolysis of starch | + | + | + | + | + | + | + | + |
| Acid from | | | | | | | | |
| Adonitol | — | — | — | — | — | — | — | — |
| Arabinose | + | + | + | + | + | —* | + | — |
| Galactose | + | —* | + | + | — | + | + | + |
| Glucose | + | + | + | + | + | + | + | + |
| Lactose | + | + | + | + | — | — | + | — |
| Mannitol | — | — | — | — | — | — | — | — |
| Mannose | + | + | + | + | + | —* | + | — |
| Xylose | + | + | + | + | + | + | — | — |

* Positive reactions after about 8 years.

the nine variants had been maintained *in vitro* for about 8 years, they were tested again for the properties lost during irradiation. The variants gave the same reactions as previously, with the following four exceptions: variants 1 and 2 formed acid from galactose, and variant 7 from arabinose and mannose. Observation of 23 strains and nine variants of one strain of *Streptomyces fradiae* disclosed, therefore, that growth at 45°, survival at 50° for 8 hr., and acid production from lactose and xylose were less reliable for describing the species than the other characteristics listed in Table 2.

## *DISCUSSION*

This study of about 20 strains of each of two species of streptomycetes merely indicates one way in which each species may be described and recognized. Because each test or observation had to be applied to hundreds of strains, it was relatively simple and economical in terms of time and materials. Associated properties, shared by freshly isolated strains, old strains and their variants, were used to differentiate the species. A character dissociated from the other characters of a species (Table 3) was not regarded as useful in defining the species.

Under the conditions of this examination, morphological characteristics dividing strains of *Streptomyces albus* and *S. fradiae* from each other were not observed, coiling of aerial hyphae into spirals occurred in cultures of some strains of each of the two species.

The two combinations of physiological characteristics shared respectively by the strains of *S. albus* and *S. fradiae*, however, appeared to be distinctive and useful in describing and recognizing strains of the two species. For example, among the data in Table 2, growth at 50° and failure to hydrolyse starch gave correlating results and might be suggested as a presumptive test for strains of *S. albus*. Some strains of *Nocardia asteroides*, however, also grew at 50° and did not attack starch (Gordon and Mihm, 1962*b*). Strains of *N. asteroides*, on the other hand, did not decompose casein, tyrosine or hypoxanthine and did not form acid from adonitol, lactose, mannitol, $\alpha$-methyl-D-glucoside or xylose. Positive reactions of the 21 strains of *S. albus* to these eight tests separated them from *N. asteroides*. Another combination of properties divided strains of *S. albus* from those of *N. brasiliensis*, and another, from *N. caviae*; a comparative examination of about 850 strains of nocardiae and streptomycetes indicated that the combination or pattern of reactions shared by a high percentage of the strains of *S. albus* distinguished the species.

The distinctiveness of each set of reactions must, of course, be confirmed by the examination of many more strains. For example, the next strain that grows at 50° and fails to hydrolyse starch may also decompose casein, tyrosine and hypoxanthine, and have the other properties of *S. albus* (Table 2). Alternatively, the next strain that does not hydrolyse starch may have all the other characteristics of *S. albus* except growth at 50°. Twenty more strains whose reactions conform to those of *S. albus* may all decompose xanthine, thus raising the dependability of the property for describing the species; conversely, the next 20 strains may prove xanthine to be less useful than indicated by the first strains.

The search must continue for more reliable characteristics for the identification of species to replace the less dependable criteria. In certain cases, better tests for measuring apparently variable properties may be useful. The study of more strains and more characters, therefore, is expected to provide a background of knowledge and experience in the recognition of the various distinct species.

Because each of the two species *S. albus* and *S. fradiae* is represented here by only a relatively few strains, it is too early to discuss any problems of nomenclature. The named strains of streptomycetes in the larger collections and in the collections of other investigators interested in this taxon must be examined before the rule of priority and the assignment of species names to synonymy can be considered.

The conviction, that different investigators studying the same and similar strains and using the more stable characteristics of the strains will divide the strains into the same species, is strengthened by confirmation in this report of the study of *S. albus* by Pridham and Lyons (1961). Pridham and Lyons also studied and recognized as *S. albus* nine of the 21 strains assigned here to *S. albus* but by quite different criteria. Because we are, therefore, in agreement on the identity of nine strains of *S. albus*, I am reasonably certain that we shall agree on the identity of many more strains and that other workers, using still different observations, will also confirm the identity of *S. albus*.

This study was supported in part by research grant GB-2579 from the National Science Foundation, Washington, D.C., U.S.A.

## *REFERENCES*

ALEXANDER, M. (1961). *Introduction to Soil Microbiology*. New York. John Wiley & Sons.

AYERS, S. H., RUPP, P. & JOHNSON, Jr., W. T. (1919). A study of the alkali-forming bacteria found in milk. *Bull. U.S. Dep. Agric.*, **782**.

AYRES, J. C. (1960). The relationship of organisms of the genus *Pseudomonas* to the spoilage of meat, poultry and eggs. *J. appl. Bact.*, **23**, 471.

BAIRD-PARKER, A. C. (1963). A classification of micrococci and staphylococci based on physiological and biochemical tests. *J. gen. Microbiol.*, **30**, 409.

BALDACCI, E. (1962). Tendances actuelles de la classification des actinomycetes. *Annls Soc. belge Méd. trop.*, **4**, 633.

BARNES, E. M. (1964). Distribution and properties of serological types of *Streptococcus faecium*, *Streptococcus durans* and related strains. *J. appl. Bact.*, **27**, 461.

BREED, R. S., MURRAY, E. G. D. & SMITH, N. R. (1957). *Bergey's Manual of Determinative Bacteriology*. Baltimore. Williams & Wilkins.

BROCKMAN, E. R. & BOYD, W. L. (1963). Myxobacteria from soils of the Alaskan and Canadian arctic. *J. Bact.*, **86**, 605.

BRYANT, M. P. (1964). Some aspects of the bacteriology of the rumen. *Principles and Applications in Aquatic Microbiology*. Ed. Heukelekian, H. & Dondero, N. C. New York. John Wiley & Sons.

BUCHANAN, B. B. & PINE, L. (1962). Characterization of a propionic acid producing actinomycete, *Actinomyces propionicus*, sp. nov. *J. gen. Microbiol.*, **28**, 305.

BULLOCK, G. L. (1964). Pseudomonadales as fish pathogens. *Developments in Industrial Microbiology*, **5**. Washington, D.C. American Institute of Biological Sciences.

BURGES, A. (1958). *Micro-organisms in the Soil*. London. Hutchinson.

BURTON, S. D. & MORITA, R. Y. (1964). Effect of catalase and cultural conditions on growth of *Beggiatoa*. *J. Bact.*, **88**, 1755.

CAIN, A. J. (1962). The evolution of taxonomic principles. In *Microbial Classification, 12th Symposium of Soc. gen. Microbiol.* Ed. Ainsworth, C. G. & Sneath, P. H. A. Cambridge. Cambridge University Press.

CASIDA, Jr., L. E. (1962). On the isolation and growth of individual microbial cells from soil. *Can. J. Microbiol.*, **8**, 115.

CLAUSEN, O. G. (1964). The discovery, isolation, and classification of various $\alpha$-haemolytic micrococci which resemble aerococci. *J. gen. Microbiol.*, **35**, 1.

COLWELL, R. R. (1964). A study of features used in the diagnosis of *Pseudomonas aeruginosa*. *J. gen. Microbiol.*, **37**, 181.

COLWELL, R. R. & MANDEL, M. (1964). Adansonian analysis and deoxyribonucleic acid base composition of some Gram-negative bacteria. *J. Bact.*, **87**, 1412.

COLWELL, R. R. & MANDEL, M. (1965). Adansonian analysis and deoxyribonucleic acid base composition of *Serratia marcescens*. *J. Bact.*, **89**, 454.

CONN, H. J. (1951). *Manual of Methods for Pure Culture Study of Bacteria*. 12th ed., leaflet, **5**, 10. Geneva, N.Y. Biotech. Pub.

CONN, H. J. & DIMMICK, I. (1947). Soil bacteria similar in morphology to *Mycobacterium* and *Corynebacterium*. *J. Bact.*, **54**, 291.

COONS, A. H., CREECH, H. J. & JONES, R. N. (1941). Immunological properties of an antibody containing a fluorescent group. *Proc. Soc. exp. Biol. Med.*, **47**, 200.

COSTER, E. & WHITE, H. R. (1964). Further studies of the genus *Pediococcus*. *J. gen. Microbiol.*, **37**, 15.

COUCH, J. N. (1963). Some new genera and species of the Actinoplanaceae. *J. Elisha Mitchell sci. Soc.*, **79**, 53.

COWAN, S. T. (1962*a*). The microbial species—a macromyth? In *Microbial Classification, 12th Symposium of Soc. gen. Microbiol.* Ed. Ainsworth, C. G. & Sneath, P. H. A. Cambridge. Cambridge University Press.

COWAN, S. T. (1962*b*). An introduction to chaos, or the classification of micrococci and staphylococci. *J. appl. Bact.*, **25**, 324.

COWAN, S. T. (1965). Principles and practice of bacterial taxonomy—a forward look. *J. gen. Microbiol.* (In the Press.)

COWAN, S. T. & STEEL, K. J. (1964). Comparison of differentiating criteria for staphylococci and micrococci. *J. Bact.*, **88**, 804.

CRONQUIST, A. (1964). The old systematics. In *Taxonomic Biochemistry and Serology*. Ed. Leone, C. A. New York. Ronald.

CUMMINS, C. S. (1962). Chemical composition and antigenic structure of cell walls of *Corynebacterium*, *Mycobacterium*, *Nocardia*, *Actinomyces* and *Arthrobacter*. *J. gen. Microbiol.*, **28**, 35.

DAVIS, J. B., COTY, V. F. & STANLEY, J. P. (1964). Atmospheric nitrogen fixation by methane-oxidizing bacteria. *J. Bact.*, **88**, 468.

DAVIS, B. R. & EWING, W. H. (1964). Lipolytic, pectolytic and alginolytic activities of Enterobacteriaceae. *J. Bact.*, **88**, 16.

DAVIS, G. H. G. & PARK, R. W. A. (1962). A taxonomic study of certain bacteria currently classified as *Vibrio* species. *J. gen. Microbiol.*, **27**, 101.

DEIBEL, R. H. (1964). The group D streptococci. *Bact. Rev.*, **28**, 330.

DEIBEL, R. H. & NIVEN, Jr., C. F. (1960). Comparative study of *Gaffkya homari*, *Aerococcus viridans*, tetrad-forming cocci from meat curing brines, and the genus *Pediococcus*. *J. Bact.*, **79**, 175.

DE LEY, J. (1960). Comparative carbohydrate metabolism and localization of enzymes in *Pseudomonas* and related micro-organisms. *J. appl. Bact.*, **23**, 400.

DE LEY, J. & FRIEDMAN, S. (1964). Deoxyribonucleic acid hybrids of acetic acid bacteria. *J. Bact.*, **88**, 937.

DE LEY, J. & SCHELL, J. (1962). Lactate and pyruvate catabolism in acetic acid bacteria. *J. gen. Microbiol.*, **29**, 589.

DOBROGOSZ, W. J. & DEMOSS, R. D. (1963). Glucose dehydrogenase activity in *Pediococcus pentosaceus*. *J. Bact.*, **86**, 164.

DWORKIN, M. (1962). Nutritional requirements for vegetative growth of *Myxococcus xanthus*. *J. Bact.*, **84**, 250.

EDDY, B. P. (1962). Further studies on *Aeromonas*. I. Additional strains and supplementary biochemical tests. *J. appl. Bact.*, **25**, 137.

EDDY, B. P. & CARPENTER, K. P. (1964). Further studies on *Aeromonas*. II. Taxonomy of *Aeromonas* and C27 strains. *J. appl. Bact.*, **27**, 96.

ELTINGE, E. T. (1957). Status of the genus *Chromobacterium*. *Int. Bull. bact. Nomencl. Taxon.*, **7**, 37.

EMMART, E. W. (1947). A new tuberculostatic antibiotic from a species of *Nocardia*. A preliminary report. *Am. Rev. Tuberc. pulm. Dis.*, **56**, 316.

EVANS, W. C. (1963). The microbiological degradation of aromatic compounds. *J. gen. Microbiol.*, **32**, 177.

EVANS, J. B., BRADFORD, Jr., W. L. & NIVEN, Jr., C. F. (1955). Comments concerning the taxonomy of the genera *Micrococcus* and *Staphylococcus*. *Int. Bull. bact. Nomencl. Taxon.*, **5**, 61.

EWING, W. H. (1963). An outline of nomenclature for the family *Enterobacteriaceae*. *Int. Bull. bact. Nomencl. Taxon.*, **13**, 95.

EWING, W. H., DAVIS, B. R. & JOHNSON, J. G. (1962). The genus *Serratia*; its taxonomy and nomenclature. *Int. Bull. bact. Nomencl. Taxon.*, **12**, 47.

FALKOW, S., RYMAN, I. R. & WASHINGTON, O. (1962). Deoxyribonucleic acid base composition of *Proteus* and Providence organisms. *J. Bact.*, **83**, 1318.

FLOODGATE, G. D. (1962). Some remarks on the theoretical aspects of bacterial taxonomy. *Bact. Rev.*, **26**, 277.

FRANKLIN, J. G. & SHARPE, M. E. (1964). Physiological characteristics and vitamin requirements of lactobacilli isolated from milk and cheese. *J. gen. Microbiol.*, **34**, 143.

FRIEDMAN, S. F. & DE LEY, J. (1965). 'Genetic species' concept in *Xanthomonas. J. Bact.*, **89**, 95.

GILLESPIE, D. C. (1963*a*). Cell wall carbohydrates of *Arthrobacter globiformis. Can. J. Microbiol.*, **9**, 509.

GILLESPIE, D. C. (1963*b*). Composition of cell wall mucopeptide from *Arthrobacter globiformis. Can. J. Microbiol.*, **9**, 515.

GORDON, R. E. & MIHM, J. M. (1958). Sporulation by two strains of *Nocardia asteroides. J. Bact.*, **75**, 239.

GORDON, R. E. & MIHM, J. M. (1962*a*). The type species of the genus *Nocardia. J. gen. Microbiol.*, **27**, 1.

GORDON, R. E. & MIHM, J. M. (1962*b*). Identification of *Nocardia caviae* (Erikson) *Nov. Comb. Annls. N.Y. Acad. Sci.*, **98**, 628.

GRAHAM, P. H. (1964). The application of computer techniques to the taxonomy of the root-nodule bacteria of legumes. *J. gen. Microbiol.*, **35**, 511.

GRIFFITHS, M. (1962). Further mutational changes in the photosynthetic pigment system of *Rhodopseudomonas spheroides. J. gen. Microbiol.*, **27**, 427.

HASTINGS, E. G. (1903). Milchagar als Medium zur Demonstration der Erzeugung proteolytischer Enzyme. *Zentbl. Bakt. ParasitKde.*, **10**, 384.

HAUSER, M. M. & SMITH, R. E. (1964). The characterization of lactobacilli from cheddar cheese. II. A numerical analysis of the data by means of an electronic computer. *Can. J. Microbiol.*, **10**, 757.

HAYES, P. R. (1963). Studies on marine flavobacteria. *J. gen. Microbiol.*, **30**, 1.

HAYNES, W. C. & RHODES, L. J. (1962). Comparative taxonomy of crystallogenic strains of *Pseudomonas aeruginosa* and *Pseudomonas chlororaphis. J. Bact.*, **84**, 1080.

HOBBS, G., CANN, D. C., GOWLAND, G. & BYERS, H. D. (1964). A serological approach to the genus *Pseudomonas. J. appl. Bact.*, **27**, 83.

HOLDING, A. J. (1960). The properties and classification of the predominant Gram-negative bacteria occurring in soil. *J. appl. Bact.*, **23**, 515.

HUNGATE, R. E. (1947). Studies on cellulose fermentation. III. The culture and isolation of cellulose-decomposing bacteria from the rumen of cattle. *J. Bact.*, **53**, 631.

JOHNSON, H. W. & MEANS, U. M. (1963). Serological groups of *Rhizobium japonicum* recovered from nodules of soybeans (*Glycine max*) in field soils. *Agron. J.*, **55**, 269.

JOHNSTONE, K. I., TOWNSEND, M. & WHITE, D. (1961). Inter-species change in thiobacilli. *J. gen. Microbiol.*, **24**, 201.

JONES, K. L. (1949). Fresh isolates of actinomycetes in which the presence of sporogenous aerial mycelia is a fluctuating characteristic. *J. Bact.*, **57**, 141.

JONES, D., DEIBEL, R. H. & NIVEN, Jr., C. F. (1963). Identity of *Staphylococcus epidermidis. J. Bact.*, **85**, 62.

JONES, L. A. & BRADLEY, S. G. (1964). Phenetic classification of actinomycetes. *Developments in Industrial Microbiology*, **5**. Washington, D.C. American Institute of Biological Sciences.

KATZNELSON, H. & MASON, A. (1962). Serological relationships among the species of *Arthrobacter. Can. J. Microbiol.*, **8**, 588.

KELLERMAN, K. K. & MCBETH, I. G. (1912). The fermentation of cellulose. *Zentbl. Bakt. ParasitKde.*, **34**, 485.

KOCUR, M. & MARTINEC, T. (1962). Taxonomická studie rodu *Micrococcus. Fol. Biol., Prague*, **3**, 1.

KOCUR, M. & MARTINEC, T. (1963). The taxonomic status of *Sporosarcina ureae* (Beijerinck) Orla-Jensen. *Int. Bull. bact. Nomencl. Taxon.*, **13**, 201.

KOONTZ, F. P. & FABER, J. E. (1963). A taxonomic study of some Gram-negative, non-fermenting bacteria. *Can. J. Microbiol.*, **9**, 499.

KOSER, S. A. (1924). Correlation of citrate utilization by members of the colon-aerogenes groups with other differential characteristics and with habitat. *J. Bact.*, **9**, 59.

KRAUSE, R. M. (1963). Symposium on relationship of structure of microorganisms to their immunological properties. IV. Antigenic and biochemical composition of hemolytic streptococcal cell walls. *Bact. Rev.*, **27**, 369.

KÜSTER, E. (1964). Report on the activity of the subcommittee on taxonomy of the *Actinomycetes*, 1958–62. *Int. Bull. bact. Nomencl. Taxon.*, **14**, 1.

LECHEVALIER, H. & LECHEVALIER, M. P. (1965). Classification des actinomycètes aérobies basée sur leur morphologie et leur composition chimique. *Annls Inst. Pasteur, Paris.* (In the Press.)

LEIFSON, E. (1954). The flagellation and taxonomy of species of *Acetobacter. Antonie van Leeuwenhoek*, **20**, 102.

LEIFSON, E. (1963). Mixed polar and peritrichous flagellation of marine bacteria. *J. Bact.*, **86**, 166.

LEIFSON, E. (1964). *Hyphomicrobium neptunium* sp. n. *Antonie van Leeuwenhoek*, **30**, 249.

LEWIN, R. A. (1965). Isolation and some physiological features of *Saprospira* thermalis. *Can. J. Microbiol.*, **11**, 77.

LOCHHEAD, A. G. (1958). Soil bacteria and growth-promoting substances. *Bact. Rev.*, **22**, 145.

MACDONALD, R. E. & MACDONALD, S. W. (1962). The physiology and natural relationships of the motile, sporeforming sarcinae. *Can. J. Microbiol.*, **8**, 795.

MAGNUSSON, M. (1962). Specificity of sensitins. *Am. Rev. resp. Dis.*, **86**, 395.

MÁLEK, I., RADOCHOVÁ, M. & LYSENKO, O. (1963). Taxonomy of the species *Pseudomonas odorans. J. gen. Microbiol.*, **33**, 349.

MARTINEC, T. & KOCUR, M. (1961). Taxonomická studie rodu *Serratia. Fol. Biol., Prague*, **2**, 1.

MARTINEC, T. & KOCUR, M. (1963). Taxonomická studie rodu *Erwinia. Fol. Biol., Prague*, **4**, 1.

MAYR, E. (1964). The new systematics. In *Taxonomic Biochemistry and Serology*. Ed. Leone, C. A. New York. Ronald.

MCCLUNG, N. M. (1963). Nocardia and nocardiosis. *Acta tuberc. jap.*, **13**, 1.

MCKENNA, E. J. & KALLIO, R. E. (1964). Hydrocarbon structure: Its effect on bacterial utilization of alkanes. In *Principles and Applications in Aquatic Microbiology*. Ed. Heukelekian, H. & Dondero, N. C. New York. John Wiley & Sons.

MEYER, R. C. (1962). Studies on the cellulose-digesting cytophaga of the soil. *Diss. Abstr.*, **22**, 2152.

MORRISON, G. A. & EDWARDS, C. J. (1964). Growth of a *Leptothrix* strain in a chemically defined medium. *J. gen. Microbiol.*, **37**, 1.

MULDER, E. G. (1964*a*). Arthrobacter. In *Principles and Applications in Aquatic Microbiology*. Ed. Heukelekian, H. & Dondero, N. C. New York. John Wiley & Sons.

MULDER, E. G. (1964*b*). Iron bacteria, particularly those of the *Sphaerotilus-Leptothrix* group, and industrial problems. *J. appl. Bact.*, **27**, 151.

NELLIS, L. F. (1963). A taxonomic study of the genus *Chondromyces. Diss. Abstr.*, **23**, 3592.

NG, H. & VAUGHN, R. H. (1963). *Clostridium rubrum* sp. n. and other pectinolytic clostridia from soil. *J. Bact.*, **85**, 1104.

NOCARD, M. E. (1888). Note sur la maladie des boeufs de la Guadeloupe connue sous le nom de farcin. *Annls Inst. Pasteur, Paris*, **2**, 293.

OKREND, H. & DONDERO, N. C. (1964). Requirement of *Sphaerotilus* for cyanocobalamin. *J. Bact.*, **87**, 286.

PARK, R. W. A. (1962). A study of certain heterotrophic polarly flagellate water bacteria: *Aeromonas, Pseudomonas* and *Comamonas*. *J. gen. Microbiol.*, **27**, 121.

POINDEXTER, J. S. (1964). Biological properties and classification of the *Caulobacter* group. *Bact. Rev.*, **28**, 231.

PRIDHAM, T. G. & LYONS, Jr., A. J. (1961). *Streptomyces albus* (Rossi-Doria) Waksman et Henrici: Taxonomic study of strains labelled *Streptomyces albus*. *J. Bact.*, **81**, 431.

REITER, B. & MØLLER-MADSEN, A. (1963). Reviews of the progress of dairy science. B. Cheese and butter starters. *J. Dairy Res.*, **30**, 419.

RHODES, M. E. (1961). The characterization of *Pseudomonas fluorescens* with the aid of an electronic computer. *J. gen. Microbiol.*, **25**, 331.

ROGERS, C. G. & SARLES, W. B. (1964). Isolation and identification of enterococci from the intestinal tract of the rat. *J. Bact.*, **88**, 965.

ROGOSA, M. & SHARPE, M. E. (1959). An approach to the classification of the lactobacilli. *J. appl. Bact.*, **22**, 329.

RUBENCHIK, L. I. (1959). A contribution to the systematics of bacteria of the Azotobacteriaceae family. *Microbiology*, **28**, 328.

RUSTIGAN, R. & STUART, C. A. (1941). Decomposition of urea by *Proteus*. *Proc. Soc. exp. Biol., N.Y.*, **47**, 108.

SAUNDERS, G. F., CAMPBELL, L. L. & POSTGATE, J. R. (1964). Base composition of deoxyribonucleic acid of sulfate-reducing bacteria deduced from buoyant density measurements in cesium chloride. *J. Bact.*, **87**, 1073.

SCOPES, A. W. (1962). The infrared spectra of some acetic acid bacteria. *J. gen. Microbiol.*, **28**, 69.

SENEZ, J. C. (1962). Symposium on metabolism of inorganic compounds. I. Introduction. *Bact. Rev.*, **26**, 14.

SHARPE, M. E. (1964). Serological types of *Streptococcus faecalis* and its varieties and their cell wall type antigen. *J. gen. Microbiol.*, **36**, 151.

SHEWAN, J. M., HOBBS, G. & HODGKISS, W. (1960). A determinative scheme for the identification of Gram-negative bacteria, with special reference to the Pseudomonadaceae. *J. appl. Bact.*, **23**, 379.

SINCLAIR, N. A. & STOKES, J. L. (1964). Isolation of obligately anaerobic psychrophilic bacteria. *J. Bact.*, **87**, 562.

SMITH, N. R., GORDON, R. E. & CLARK, F. E. (1952). *Aerobic Sporeforming Bacteria*. U.S. Dept. Agric., Monograph, **16**.

SNEATH, P. H. A. (1956). Cultural and biochemical characteristics of the genus *Chromobacterium*. *J. gen. Microbiol.*, **15**, 70.

SOKAL, R. R. (1964). The future systematics. In *Taxonomic Biochemistry and Serology*. Ed. Leone, C. A. New York. Ronald.

STARKEY, R. L. (1958). Interrelations between microorganisms and plant roots in the rhizosphere, *Bact Rev.*, **22**, 154.

STARKEY, R. L. (1964). Microbial transformations of some organic sulfur compounds. In *Principles and Applications in Aquatic Microbiology*. Ed. Heukelekian, H. & Dondero, N. C. New York. John Wiley & Sons.

STEEL, K. J. & MIDGLEY, J. (1962). Decarboxylase and other reactions of some Gram-negative rods. *J. gen. Microbiol.*, **29**, 171.

STOCKS, P. K. & MCCLESKEY, C. S. (1964). Morphology and physiology of *Methanomonas methanooxidans*. *J. Bact.*, **88**, 1071.

VAN NIEL, C. B. (1963). *The Selected Papers of Ernst Georg Pringsheim*. New Brunswick, N.J. Rutgers Univ.

VINTIKOVÁ, H., ŠROGL, M. & ŠKRDLETA, V. (1961). A contribution to the serological typization of the rhizobia. *Fol. Microbiol., Prague*, **6**, 243.

WAKSMAN, S. A. (1961). *The Actinomycetes. II.* Baltimore. Williams & Wilkins.

WALTERS, S. M. (1964). Principles of taxonomy. In *Developments in Industrial Microbiology*, **5**. Washington, D.C. American Institute of Biological Sciences.

WOLFE, R. S. (1964). Iron and manganese bacteria. In *Principles and Applications of Aquatic Microbiology*. Ed. Heukelekian, H. & Dondero, N. C. New York. John Wiley & Sons.

YAMAGUCHI, T. (1965). Comparison of the cell-wall composition of morphologically distinct actinomycetes. *J. Bact.*, **89**, 444.

ZAGALLO, A. C. & WANG, C. H. (1962). Comparative carbohydrate catabolism in *Arthrobacter*. *J. gen. Microbiol.*, **29**, 389.

# TAXONOMY OF SOIL ACTINOMYCETES AND RELATED ORGANISMS

E. KÜSTER

*Department of Industrial Microbiology, University College, Dublin, Ireland*

The Actinomycetes play a significant role as soil organisms. It is their physiological behaviour rather than their quantitative occurrence in soil which entitles us to consider the Actinomycetes as a particular and important group of the soil microflora. By their capacity to attack and metabolize components of organic matter which are usually resistant to microbial decomposition, and their ability to produce particular metabolites, the Actinomycetes contribute to soil fertility to a considerable extent. The proportion of Actinomycetes in the total soil microflora varies between 10 and 70 per cent depending on the soil type, vegetation and other factors.

When we are speaking about Actinomycetes, we mean mainly Streptomycetes. However, many other types of mould-like, mycelia-forming bacteria have also been found in soil and other habitats. They are included in the order Actinomycetales. I do not want to discuss the controversy whether the Actinomycetes belong to the fungi or to the bacteria. At present, the majority of workers consider them to be bacteria and follow the International Code of Nomenclature of Bacteria and Viruses for their taxonomy and nomenclature.

In this paper I shall restrict myself to the generic level and do not want to consider the classification of species. This is a particular taxonomic problem, the solution of which is not easy. Many attempts and experiments, mainly with the genus *Streptomyces*, have been carried out successfully in the past and are still in progress, partly on an international basis, in order to produce a uniform description and classification of species.

The order Actinomycetales consists of several families with a number of genera. Various keys exist for the identification and classification of Actinomycetes. Each worker has his own idea about the most logical order of genera and their grouping into families. Unfortunately, we are not yet in a position to set up a key on a phylogenetic basis. We found

TABLE 1

*Families and genera of the Actinomycetales*

| | | | |
|---|---|---|---|
| Vegetative mycelium fragmenting into bacillary elements | Actinomycetaceae | | |
| | *Actinomyces* | | |
| | *Nocardia* | | |
| | *Micropolyspora* | | |
| | Dermatophilaceae | | |
| | *Dermatophilus* | | |
| Vegetative mycelium not fragmenting into bacillary elements | Streptomycetaceae | | |
| | *Micromonospora* | aerial mycelium absent | single spores on vegetative mycelium only |
| | *Thermoactinomyces* | | ,, ,, on ,, and aerial mycelium |
| | *Thermomonospora* | aerial mycelium present | ,, ,, on aerial mycelium only |
| | *Microbispora* | | pairs of spores on aerial mycelium only |
| | *Streptomyces* | | chains of spores on aerial mycelium only |
| | Actinoplanaceae | | |
| | *Microellobosporia* | | non-motile sporangiospores in club-shaped sporangia |
| | *Streptosporangium* | aerial mycelium present | ,, ,, in spherical ,, |
| | *Spirillospora* | | motile ,, in ,, ,, |
| | *Actinoplanes* | | ,, ,, in ,, ,, |
| | *Ampullariella* | aerial mycelium absent | ,, ,, in cylindrical ,, |
| | *Amorphosporangium* | | non-motile ,, in irregularly shaped sporangia |

the following system and key useful and convenient for our taxonomic work (Table 1).

It does not claim to be a final and conclusive one. There are for instance some arguments which suggest it would not be justifiable to separate families on their ability to fragment mycelium into bacillary or coccoid elements (Lechevalier, Solotorovsky and McDurmont, 1961; Gordon and Mihm, 1962). Here and in the other keys the classification is mainly based on morphological features, such as fragmentation into smaller units, presence of aerial mycelium, number and arrangement of spores, occurrence and shape of sporangia.

The first two families are distinguished from the other two by their fragmentation power.

The Actinomycetaceae with the genera *Actinomyces* and *Nocardia* were the first detected and described organisms which led to the creation of the name *Actinomyces*. Anaerobic *Actinomyces* were first isolated from pathological material. They are mainly pathogenic organisms, causing severe diseases in man and animals. One of the best known and most dangerous of these is actinomycosis in cattle. It is characterized by the formation of granules or so-called drusen in the tissue. Even as pathogenic organisms they have been found occasionally in farmyard manure and soil (Hvid-Hansen, 1951).

The most striking feature of *Actinomyces* is their pleomorphism. All forms may be observed. Rod forms predominate which resemble, and are arranged like, certain members of the genus *Corynebacterium*. With certain microaerophilic forms a filamentous-diphtheroid dimorphism is obvious (Jordan and Howell, 1965). It depends on the atmospheric conditions under which growth takes place. Cultivation under $CO_2$ favours the development of the diphtheroid form, whereas aerobic incubation favours the mycelial form. Three main groups, *A. israelii*, *A. bovis*, and *A. naeslundii*, are recognized and can be differentiated from each other by their morphological and biochemical characters (Pine, Howell and Watson, 1960), *inter alia* also by their cell-wall composition (Cummins and Harris, 1958).

The genus *Nocardia* comprises aerobic organisms forming a typical mycelium, the hyphae of which are filamentous and branching. Besides several pathogenic forms nocardiae are common saprophytic soil organisms which are distinguished by their particular biochemical behaviour. They are able to decompose and utilize substances which are usually resistant to microbial degradation and unavailable to micro-organisms such as higher paraffines, alkanes, heterocyclic N-compounds and others. Nocardiae exhibit a great variability, because of which they may be confused with related genera. Their taxonomic position is still doubtful. Nocardiae have been considered to be intermediates between *Mycobacterium* and *Streptomyces*.

The distinction between *Nocardia* and *Streptomyces* is often difficult. There are many examples where nocardiae form aerial mycelium and look like streptomycetes (Gordon and Smith, 1955; Bradley, 1959); *Streptomyces* strains, on the other hand, can lose their ability to form sporogenous aerial mycelium and consequently grow in a similar way to *Nocardia* (Williams and McCoy, 1953; Gordon and Smith, 1955). The loss of the capacity to produce aerial mycelium seems to be a kind of degeneration which can be restored under certain circumstances.

Gordon and Mihm (1957) summarize these observations as follows: *Nocardia* is distinguished from *Streptomyces* by the more frequent occurrence of non-sporulating aerial hyphae and from *Mycobacterium* by the presence of aerial hyphae. This separation is not satisfactory, for it does not allow a clear distinction of *Nocardia* from *Streptomyces* or *Mycobacterium*. The term aerial hyphae has been introduced by Arai and Kuroda (1959) for *Nocardia*, instead of the term aerial mycelium used in *Streptomyces*.

Many links, overlaps, and relationships exist between *Nocardia* and other genera (*Dermatophilus*, *Streptomyces*, *Mycobacterium* and others). It has been suggested that the genus *Nocardia* should be disregarded and combined with *Streptomyces* (Bradley and Anderson, 1958; Gordon and Mihm, 1962). A clear concept and definition of the genus *Nocardia* has not yet been established, and further studies are necessary to clarify it.

If we keep, and still use, the old system of classification, based on the presence or absence of fragmentation, *Micropolyspora* must be considered to belong to the Actinomycetaceae; it fragments into small units (Lechevalier *et al.*, 1961). In its mode of sporulation, on the other hand, it resembles members of the Streptomycetaceae. Chains of spores are formed on both the aerial and vegetative mycelium. The first strains were isolated from pathological material; later it was found that *Micropolyspora* is not uncommon in soil.

The Dermatophilaceae, containing the single genus *Dermatophilus*, fragment into *Sarcina*-like packets after formation of septa in several planes. The individual free cocci are often motile. After germination they produce fine, branching hyphae. For this reason *Dermatophilus* must be placed among the Actinomycetales, although it is distinctly different from the Actinomycetaceae (Gordon and Edwards, 1963; Gordon, 1964). It has been suggested that each spore is covered with a coat; the whole arrangement may be comparable to a sporangium containing only one sporangiospore. Strains of *Dermatophilus* are not soil organisms in the true sense. They are pathogenic dermatophytes, mainly isolated from skin lesions of sheep and other animals. They are mentioned here only for the sake of completeness.

Many workers use thermophilic properties as characters for taxonomy and classification. This is useful to a certain extent, but should not be used to define new genera. Ecological properties are secondary characters as far as taxonomy and classification are concerned, and should be employed, if at all, for the differentiation of species and lower taxa only. Thermophily is doubtless an ecological character and therefore unsuitable for application in a key of form-genera (Kosmatchev, 1959; Lechevalier *et al.*, 1961), even if some genera are exclusively thermophilic.

One of the wholly thermophilic genera is *Thermoactinomyces*. It occurs frequently in various environments. Occasional reports of mesophilic *Thermoactinomyces* have not been confirmed. The genus consists of only one species, *T. vulgaris*; the other described species have been rejected in a recent study (Küster and Locci, 1964), including the former type species *T. thalpophilus*.

*Thermoactinomyces* species differ from *Micromonospora* species by their ability to grow at higher temperatures and to form aerial mycelium. How far these properties are related and depend on each other is not yet known. An examination of this question would be interesting. This might be attempted by induction of aerial mycelium formation and/or thermophily in *Micromonospora* by special treatment and modification of cultural conditions; cf. experiments with mesophilic bacteria (Oates, Sneed Beers and Quinn, 1961; Sie, Sobotka and Baker, 1961). The cell-wall composition of these two genera differs; *Micromonospora* contains glycine as a major component which is completely absent from *Thermoactinomyces* (Becker, Lechevalier and Lechevalier, 1965). Whether this is due to the presence of aerial mycelium may be shown by further studies when technical difficulties in preparing separate vegetative and aerial mycelium have been overcome.

The other three genera form spores on the aerial mycelium only. They are differentiated by the number and arrangement of spores produced.

In *Thermomonospora* single spores usually occur on the aerial mycelium, either sessile or on short sporophores (Henssen, 1957). Occasionally two spores have also been found (Küster and Locci, 1963). This genus is completely thermophilic.

*Microbispora* is characterized by the formation of longitudinal pairs of spores which are attached almost directly to the hyphae of the aerial mycelium (Nonomura and Ohara, 1957). Lechevalier and Lechevalier (1957) also observed short sporophores, at the tip of which the spores develop; the strains under examination were designated as *Waksmania* at that time.

*Streptomyces* is by far the best known and largest genus of the Actinomycetales. It comprises a very great number of species, the classification and taxonomy of which is a serious problem which I do not want to discuss in detail. Conidia are usually arranged in chains of various length on the aerial mycelium. Single spores or chains of conidia are also occasionally produced on the vegetative mycelium, but are not always easily seen (Lechevalier and Lechevalier, 1965). The morphology of their sporophores is very characteristic. They can be straight, flexous, or spiral, showing loops of more or less compact spirals. Verticillate forms have been observed also.

The differentiation between the two families which do not fragment into small units, the Streptomycetaceae and. Actinoplanaceae is simple The latter are distinguished from the Streptomycetaceae by the occurrence of sporangia of various shapes which contain a fairly large number of sporangiospores. These are flagellated and motile in some genera. Members of the Actinoplanaceae are usually soil organisms; a few also occur in water, particularly those with flagellated spores.

Since the discovery of *Actinoplanes* (Couch, 1949, 1950), a number of other genera have been found recently which are differentiated by the shape of their sporangia and spores (Couch, 1963; Cross, Lechevalier and Lechevalier, 1963). The originally proposed name *Ampullaria* was replaced by *Ampullariella* (Couch, 1964) because the generic name *Ampullaria* had already been used to describe a member of the Fungi Imperfecti.

With most of the Actinoplanaceae the sporangia are completely filled with spores. An exception is *Microellobosporia*, within the sporangia of which two to five spores are linearly arranged. *Microellobosporia* may represent an intermediate or link between the two families (Lechevalier and Lechevalier, 1965). Its gross appearance is much like *Streptomyces* and therefore it may have been previously overlooked and mistaken for *Streptomyces*. By modern, refined methods and techniques, small differences in the morphology and biochemistry of the relevant genera have been detected.

The suggestion that there is a transition between families with and without sporangia may not be as wrong as it seems at first, if one examines the recent results of the study of the surface structure of *Streptomyces* spores. The spores of *Streptomyces* arranged in chains, as well as the separated, individual ones, are coated with a thin fibrous layer forming a sack partially surrounding the mature spore (Hopwood and Glauert, 1961; Rancourt and Lechevalier, 1964). As such, this fibrous outer layer of *Streptomyces* may be compared with the sporangial wall of *Microellobosporia* (Rancourt and Lechevalier, 1963). The outer wall remained intact around the chain of spores in the latter, while *Streptomyces* lost the ability to preserve their sporangia. The original sporangial wall breaks up and only their remains cover each spore. We may conclude that the occurrence of sporangia is not an exception in one particular family, but quite common and probably more widespread in other families than hitherto assumed. However, this is still hypothetical and further detailed studies are necessary to prove it.

Successful and promising attempts have been made recently to elaborate methods and to find other characters by which the various genera can be further distinguished. They are mainly employed in an attempt to clarify the doubtful taxonomic position of *Nocardia.*

A character which has been studied recently is phage specificity. Actinophages have been observed for a great number of *Streptomyces* species, but have also been isolated from *Thermoactinomyces* (Agre, 1961), *Mycobacterium* and *Nocardia* (Manion, Bradley, Zinneman and Hall, 1964). Most of them are polyvalent, i.e. lysing strains of different species or groups. Some phages, however, have been found to be monovalent, attacking only one or a few species of the same group or series (Kutzner, 1961). Bradley, Anderson and Jones (1961) came to the conclusion from their own studies and other reports that monovalent and strain-specific phages are of no value for classification, and at most useful for identification. On the other hand, they suggested that polyvalent phages may be usefully employed in the identification of genera.

Arai, Kuroda and Koyama (1963) developed a spectrophotometric method and found different absorption spectra which are characteristic for certain types of *Nocardia* and the closely related genera *Streptomyces* and *Mycobacterium.* They suggested that the different absorption patterns are a reflection of differences in cellular composition and concluded that nocardiae are intermediates between *Mycobacterium* and *Streptomyces* with overlaps in both directions. These results have not yet been confirmed completely.

Serological reactions have also been used to differentiate between genera (Kwapinski, 1964) and to type certain groups of species (Bowman and Weinhold, 1963; Cross and Spooner, 1963). Studies of this type were quite successful with *Mycobacterium*, *Nocardia*, and *Streptomyces*. A relationship seems to exist between the antigenic structure of the cell walls and their chemical composition (Cummins, 1962).

Besides the morphological differences, the examination of the chemical composition of the cell wall seems to be the most useful method to distinguish between genera. Based on the results previously obtained by Cummins and Harris (1958), and following the procedure outlined by Becker, Lechevalier, Gordon and Lechevalier (1964), Lechevalier and his co-workers (Becker *et al.*, 1965; Lechevalier and Lechevalier, 1965) examined a great number of representatives of the various genera. They observed a specific pattern in the presence or absence of certain sugars and amino acids and were able to separate the genera into four types.

The results shown in Table 2 correspond almost exactly with those obtained at the same time, and independently, by Yamaguchi (1965). Table 3 shows the genera in the same order as before with the corresponding type numbers.

It is obvious from these results that *Microellobosporia* and *Streptomyces* are closely related; they show the same cell-wall composition. This confirms the originally suggested relationship based on their morphology.

TABLE 2

*Grouping of Actinomycetes based on cell-wall composition according to Lechevalier (Becker* et al., *1965) and Yamaguchi (1965)*

| Major components | Lechevalier Type | Yamaguchi Type |
|---|---|---|
| Glycine<br>LL-DAP | I<br>Streptomyces | V<br>Streptomyces |
| Glycine<br>Meso-DAP | II<br>Micromonospora | III<br>Actinoplanes |
| Meso-DAP | III<br>Madurae | IV<br>Streptosporangium |
| Meso-DAP<br>Arabinose<br>Galactose | IV<br>Nocardia | II<br>Nocardia |
| Lysine<br>Galactose | | I<br>Actinomyces |

DAP $=\alpha,\varepsilon$-diaminopimelic acid.

TABLE 3

*Genera of Actinomycetales and the respective types of cell-wall composition*

| Genus | Lechevalier Type | Yamaguchi Type |
|---|---|---|
| *Mycobacterium* | IV | II |
| *Actinomyces* | | I |
| *Promicromonospora* | | I |
| *Nocardia asteroides* | IV | II |
| *Nocardia madurae* | III | |
| *Pseudonocardia* | IV | |
| *Micropolyspora* | IV | II |
| *Dermatophilus* | III | |
| *Micromonospora* | II | III |
| *Thermoactinomyces* | III | |
| *Thermomonospora* | IV | |
| *Microbispora* | III | IV |
| *Streptomyces* | I | V |
| *Microellobosporia* | I | V |
| *Streptosporangium* | II–III | IV |
| *Spirillospora* | II–III | IV |
| *Actinoplanes* | II | III |
| *Ampullariella* | | III |
| *Amorphosporangium* | II | III |

On the other hand, this method allows differentiation between genera which are difficult to distinguish morphologically. If the mode of fragmentation is disregarded, *Streptomyces* and *Micropolyspora* are differentiated by the length of their spore chains only. In such cases, what should one consider to be a short chain, and of how many spores should it be composed? The chemical examination of the cell wall and the determination of the isomeric forms of α,ε-diaminopimelic acid clarifies the situation.

By examining cell-wall composition, it is possible to distinguish between the atypical, morphologically similar strains of *Nocardia* and *Streptomyces* (Becker *et al.*, 1965). The large number of strains designated as *Nocardia* have been divided into two main groups, *asteroides* and *madurae*, which differ biochemically and morphologically. Once again the inhomogeneity of the nocardiae is obvious.

Besides the genera shown in the key, there are several generic names which I consider to be invalid for the following reasons:

a *Jensenia*, termed 'soil diphtheroids' by Bisset and Moore (1949) resembles *Mycobacterium* and *Nocardia* on the basis of various tests and reactions (Gordon and Mihm, 1961).

b *Pseudonocardia* (Henssen, 1957) is a thermophilic *Nocardia* or *Streptomyces*.

c *Polysepta* (Thompson and Bisset, 1957) resembles and is synonymous to *Dermatophilus* (Gordon, 1964).

d *Promicromonospora* is *Micromonospora*, the only difference being that spore formation on the vegetative mycelium starts at a very early stage of growth (Krasilnikov, Kalakautskii and Kirillova, 1961).

e *Waksmania* (Lechevalier and Lechevalier, 1957) is synonymous to *Microbispora*. There was a long controversy about the priority of these names which has been cleared up recently (Lechevalier, 1965).

f *Thermopolyspora* was originally created as a thermophilic genus (Henssen, 1957). *T. bispora* is identical with *Microbispora*. *T. polyspora* seems to be identical with *Streptomyces* according to the description. Since it was not growing in pure culture and is no longer available, it must be eliminated, following the rules of nomenclature (Becker *et al.*, 1965).

g *Streptoverticillium* (Baldacci, 1959), is a verticillate *Streptomyces* and should not be regarded as a special genus. In support of the findings of Jones and Bradley (1962) concerning actinophage susceptibility, Yamaguchi (1965) recently reiterated Baldacci's view and placed verticillate *Streptomyces* in a separate genus because lysine is present as a minor component in their cell walls.

h *Chainia* (Thirumalachar, 1955) and *Actinopycnidium* (Krasilnikov, 1962) are *Streptomyces* which are able to form sclerotia and pycnidia respectively under certain cultural conditions. The formation of sclerotia is not limited to any particular species and occurs quite frequently in the genus *Streptomyces* (Gattani, 1957).

i *Thermoactinopolyspora* species are thermophilic *Streptomyces* and *Micropolyspora* species according to their description (Craveri and Pagani, 1962).

j *Actinosporangium* (Krasilnikov and Tsi-Chen, 1961) is characterized by the formation of pseudosporangia, as a result of the combination of spores from several sporophores and the formation of individual spore clusters covered with a slimy substance. According to such a description it should be considered as a *Streptomyces*. Krasilnikov later (personal communication, 14th November 1963) placed it in the same family as *Streptomyces*, even though he originally designated this genus as a member of the *Actinoplanaceae*. Yamaguchi (1965) confirmed this latter view. Because of the cell-wall composition of *Actinosporangium*, he grouped it with his *Streptomyces*-type.

k *Macrospora* (Tsyganov, Zhukova and Timofeeva, 1963) is synonymous with *Microellobosporia* (Tsyganov, Zhukova and Timofeeva, 1964). The generic name is invalid for it has already been given to a fungus (Becker *et al.*, 1965).

The Actinomycetes, in the widest sense of the word, hold an intermediate position between bacteria and fungi. The possession of filaments, sometimes branching and/or fragmenting, indicates a relationship with other filamentous bacteria. The presence of a mycelium and the formation of sporangia, on the other hand, suggest a link with the fungi. Broad relationships exist between genera and even orders. A number of bacterial genera, with which members of the Actinomycetales are mainly confused, will now be considered very briefly.

a *Arthrobacter*, a member of the Corynebacteriaceae, occurs widespread in soil and sewage; it is morphologically characterized by the occurrence of rods with irregular cell forms in a young stage, which can sometimes develop filaments and true branching (Mulder, 1964). A significant character is the change from rod-shaped cells in the young stage to coccoid forms upon ageing. The genus *Arthrobacter* was erected to accommodate the soil corynebacteria (Conn and Dimmick, 1947). It is a genus containing pleomorphic organisms and as such is very similar to the genera *Mycobacterium* and *Nocardia* at certain growth stages.

b *Corynebacterium*, another genus of the same family, contains, besides the well-known species which are pathogenic to man and animals, a number of plant pathogens. Their rods are irregularly shaped, sometimes with characteristic swellings. Many of the soil corynebacteria are pleomorphic and may be confused with *Mycobacterium* and *Nocardia* when grown under certain conditions.

c Finally, the genus *Mycobacterium* is still occasionally considered to belong to the Actinomycetales. The mycelium is rudimentary or absent and branching occurs rarely. Acid-fastness is widespread among the mycobacteria. Saprophytic forms are widely distributed in soil. Pleomorphism occasionally occurs in this genus.

Pleomorphism seems to be the main reason for the difficulty in classifying doubtful strains. There are transitional forms and borderline cases with which the examination of classical morphological features fails. The three genera, *Corynebacterium*, *Nocardia* and *Mycobacterium*, are not morphologically clearly defined types. There are always overlaps and close relationships between one and the other, and not least with *Nocardia*. Even an examination of the cell-wall composition and antigenic structure confirms the close relationship between *Corynebacterium*, *Mycobacterium*, and *Nocardia* (Cummins, 1962).

A typical example is *Mycobacterium rhodochrous* which has been studied in detail by Gordon and Mihm (1957). Many strains, designated as *Mycobacterium*, *Nocardia*, and *Serratia* are synonymous with *M. rhodochrous*. Experts in the genera in question placed strains of *M. rhodochrous* differently into *Arthrobacter*, *Corynebacterium*, *Mycobacterium*, and *Nocardia*. This shows again that no sharp borderlines exist between these genera.

A further example is *Leptotrichia*, an oral filamentous bacterium (Davis and Baird-Parker, 1959). It is closely related to *Lactobacillus* in its metabolic behaviour and to *Nocardia* in its morphology. The amino acid pattern of its cell-wall composition resembles that of *Nocardia*, but the sugar pattern is similar to that of *Lactobacillus* and *Fusobacterium*.

All these considerations lead to much speculation on a phylogenetic and evolutionary scheme in which the Actinomycetales can be placed (Jensen, 1953; Hesseltine, 1960; Buchanan and Pine, 1962; Jones and Bradley, 1964). There exist many links and relationships with *Mycococcus*, *Propionibacterium*, *Lactobacillus bifidus*, *Arthrobacter*, *Corynebacterium*, and *Mycobacterium*.

In all these proposals *Nocardia* takes a central position, probably because of its doubtful taxonomy. All the characters which separate *Nocardia* from *Streptomyces* and *Mycobacterium* are not generally applicable to the wide range of *Nocardia*-like organisms, even if a type species of *Nocardia* be proposed (Gordon and Mihm, 1962). This leads one to ask whether *Nocardia* is a genus in the true taxonomic sense of the word. However, even if we do not recognize *Nocardia* as a genus, we do not overcome all the difficulties and problems which arise in the classification of these organisms. We are still unable to classify and determine all the transition forms and borderline cases which exist between genera and which we encounter so frequently in nature. It shows again that our conception and system of classification is entirely arbitrary and that we are still far away from a natural, phylogenetic arrangement of bacteria in general and of the Actinomycetales in particular. Our task as taxonomists should be to elaborate and devise methods which will permit us to define a genus as clearly as possible.

## REFERENCES


AGRE, N. S. (1961). Phage of the thermophilic *Micromonospora vulgaris. Microbiology*, **30**, 414.

ARAI, T. & KURODA, S. (1959). Preliminary taxonomic studies on some strains of *Nocardia. Rep. Inst. Food Microbiol., Osaka*, **12**, 77.

ARAI, T., KURODA, S. & KOYAMA, Y. (1963). Infrared absorption spectra of whole cells of *Nocardia* and related organisms. *J. gen. appl. Microbiol., Tokyo*, **9**, 119.

BALDACCI, E. (1959). Criteria for the improvement of the classification of Actinomycetes. *Int. Bull. Bact. Nomencl. Taxon.*, **9**, 81.

BECKER, B., LECHEVALIER, M. P., GORDON, R. E. & LECHEVALIER, H. A. (1964). Rapid differentiation between *Nocardia* and *Streptomyces* by paper chromatography of whole-cell hydrolysates. *Appl. Microbiol.*, **12**, 421.

BECKER, B., LECHEVALIER, M. P. & LECHEVALIER, H. A. (1965). Chemical composition of cell-wall preparations from strains of various form-genera of aerobic Actinomycetes. *Appl. Microbiol.*, **13**, 236.

BISSET, K. A. & MOORE, F. W. (1949). The relationship of certain branched bacterial genera. *J. gen. Microbiol.*, **3**, 387.

BOWMAN, T. & WEINHOLD, A. R. (1963). Serological relationships of the potato scab organism and other species of *Streptomyces. Nature, Lond.*, **200**, 599.

BRADLEY, S. G. (1959). Sporulation by some strains of *Nocardia* and *Streptomyces. Appl. Microbiol.*, **7**, 89.

BRADLEY, S. G. & ANDERSON, D. L. (1958). Taxonomic implication of actinophage host-range. *Science, N.Y.*, **128**, 412.

BRADLEY, S. G., ANDERSON, D. L. & JONES, L. A. (1961). Phylogeny of Actinomycetes as revealed by susceptibility to actinophage. *Devs ind. Microbiol.*, **2**, 223.

BUCHANAN, B. B. & PINE, L. (1962). Characterization of a propionic acid producing Actinomycete, *Actinomyces propionicus* sp. nov. *J. gen. Microbiol.*, **28**, 305.

CONN, H. J. & DIMMICK, I. (1947). Soil bacteria similar in morphology to *Mycobacterium* and *Corynebacterium. J. Bact.*, **54**, 291.

COUCH, J. N. (1949). A new group of organisms related to Actinomycetes. *J. Elisha Mitchell scient. Soc.*, **65**, 315.

COUCH, J. N. (1950). *Actinoplanes*, a new genus of the Actinomycetales. *J. Elisha Mitchell scient. Soc.*, **66**, 87.

COUCH, J. N. (1963). Some new genera and species of the Actinoplanaceae. *J. Elisha Mitchell scient. Soc.*, **79**, 53.

COUCH, J. N. (1964). The name *Ampullaria* has been replaced by *Ampullariella. Int. Bull. Bact. Nomencl. Taxon.*, **14**, 137.

CRAVERI, R. & PAGANI, H. (1962). Thermophilic microorganisms among actinomycetes in the soil. *Ann. Microbiol.*, **12**, 115.

CROSS, T. & SPOONER, D. F. (1963). The serological identification of Streptomycetes by agar gel diffusion techniques. *J. gen. Microbiol.*, **33**, 275.

CROSS, T., LECHEVALIER, M. P. & LECHEVALIER, H. (1963). A new genus of the Actinomycetales, *Microellobosporia*, gen. nov. *J. gen. Microbiol.*, **31**, 421.

CUMMINS, C. S. (1962). Chemical composition and antigenic structure of cell walls of *Corynebacterium, Mycobacterium, Nocardia, Actinomyces*, and *Arthrobacter. J. gen. Microbiol.*, **28**, 35.

CUMMINS, C. S. & HARRIS, H. (1958). Studies on the cell-wall composition and taxonomy of Actinomycetales and related groups. *J. gen. Microbiol.*, **18**, 173.

DAVIS, G. H. G. & BAIRD-PARKER, A. C. (1959). The classification of certain filamentous bacteria with respect to their chemical composition. *J. gen. Microbiol.*, **21**, 612.

Gattani, M. L. (1957). Production of sclerotic granules by *Streptomyces* species. *Nature, Lond.*, **180**, 1293.

Gordon, M. A. (1964). The genus *Dermatophilus*. *J. Bact.*, **88**, 500.

Gordon, M. A. & Edwards, M. R. (1963). Micromorphology of *Dermatophilus congolensis*. *J. Bact.*, **86**, 1101.

Gordon, R. E. & Smith, M. M. (1955). Proposed group of characters for the separation of *Streptomyces* and *Nocardia*. *J. Bact.*, **69**, 147.

Gordon, R. E. & Mihm, J. M. (1957). A comparative study of some strains received as nocardiae. *J. Bact.*, **73**, 15.

Gordon, R. E. & Mihm, J. M. (1961). The specific identity of *Jensenia canicruria*. *Can. J. Microbiol.*, **7**, 108.

Gordon, R. E. & Mihm, J. M. (1962). The type species of the genus *Nocardia*. *J. gen. Microbiol.*, **27**, 1.

Henssen, A. (1957). Beiträge zur Morphologie und Systematik der thermophilen Aktinomyceten. *Arch. Mikrobiol.*, **26**, 373.

Hesseltine, C. W. (1960). Relationships of the Actinomycetales. *Mycologia*, **52**, 460.

Hopwood, D. A. & Glauert, A. M. (1961). Electron microscope observations on the surface structures of *Streptomyces violaceoruber*. *J. gen. Microbiol.*, **26**, 325.

Hvid-Hansen, N. (1951). Anaerobic actinomyces (*Act. israelii*) in ground water. *Acta path. microbiol. scand.*, **29**, 335.

Jensen, H. L. (1953). The genus *Nocardia* and its separation from other Actinomycetales with some reflections on the phylogeny of the Actinomycetes. *6th Int. Congr. Microbiol. Roma*, 69.

Jones, L. A. & Bradley, S. G. (1962). Relationship of *Streptoverticillium* and *Jensenia* to other Actinomycetes. *Devs ind. Microbiol.*, **3**, 257.

Jones, L. A. & Bradley, S. G. (1964). Phenetic classification of Actinomycetes. *Devs ind. Microbiol.*, **5**, 267.

Jordan, H. V. & Howell, A. (1965). Nutritional control of cellular morphology in an aerobic actinomycete from the hamster. *J. gen. Microbiol.*, **38**, 125.

Kosmatchev, A. E. (1959). Importance of thermophilic properties in the classification of Actinomycetes. *Microbiology*, **28**, 938.

Krasilnikov, N. A. (1962). A new genus of ray fungus—*Actinopycnidium* gen. nov. of family Actinomycetaceae. *Microbiology*, **31**, 250.

Krasilnikov, N. A. & Tsi-Chen, J. (1961). *Actinosporangium*, a new genus of the Actinoplanaceae family. *Izv. Akad. Nauk. SSSR Ser. Biol.*, 113.

Krasilnikov, N. A., Kalakautskii, L. V. & Kirillova, N. F. (1961). A new genus of Actinomycetales, *Promicromonospora* gen. nov. *Izv. Akad. Nauk. SSSR Ser. Biol.*, 107.

Küster, E. & Locci, R. (1963). Studies on peat and peat microorganisms. I. Taxonomic studies on thermophilic Actinomycetes isolated from peat. *Arch. Mikrobiol.*, **45**, 188.

Küster, E. & Locci, R. (1964). Taxonomic studies on the genus *Thermoactinomyces*. *Int. Bull. Bact. Nomencl. Taxon.*, **14**, 109.

Kutzner, H. J. (1961). Specificity of actinophages within a selected group of streptomycetes. *Pathologia Microbiol.*, **24**, 170.

Kwapinski, J. B. (1964). Cytoplasmic antigen relationships among the Actinomycetales. *J. Bact.*, **87**, 1234.

Lechevalier, H. A. (1965). Priority of the generic name *Microbispora* over *Waksmania* and *Thermopolyspora*. *Int. Bull. Bact. Nomencl. Taxon.*, **15**, 139.

Lechevalier, H. A. & Lechevalier, M. P. (1965). Classification des Actinomycetes aerobies basée sur leur morphologie et leur composition chimique. *Annls Inst. Pasteur, Paris*, **108**, 662.

LECHEVALIER, H. A., SOLOTOROVSKY, M. & MCDURMONT, C. I. (1961). A new genus of the Actinomycetales: *Micropolyspora* gen. nov. *J. gen. Microbiol.*, **26**, 11.

LECHEVALIER, M. P. & LECHEVALIER, H. A. (1957). A new genus of the Actinomycetales: *Waksmania* gen. nov. *J. gen. Microbiol.*, **17**, 104.

MANION, R. E., BRADLEY, S. G., ZINNEMAN, H. H. & HALL, W. H. (1964). Interrelationships among mycobacteria and nocardiae. *J. Bact.*, **87**, 1056.

MULDER, E. G. (1964). Arthrobacter. In *Principles and Applications in Aquatic Microbiology*. Ed. Heukelekian, H. & Dondero, N. C. New York. John Wiley & Sons.

NONOMURA, H. & OHARA, I. (1957). Distribution of actinomycetes in the soil. II. *Microbispora*, a new genus of the Streptomycetaceae. *J. Ferment. Technol., Osaka*, **35**, 307.

OATES, R. P., SNEED-BEERS, T. & QUINN, L. Y. (1961). Induction of heat resistance by filtrates of thermophilic bacterial cultures. *Bact. Proc.*, 58.

PINE, L., HOWELL, A. & WATSON, S. J. (1960). Studies of the morphological, physiological, and biochemical characters of *Act. bovis*. *J. gen. Microbiol.*, **23**, 403.

RANCOURT, M. & LECHEVALIER, H. A. (1963). Electron microscopic observation of the sporangial structure of an Actinomycete, *Microellobosporia flavea*. *J. gen. Microbiol.*, **31**, 495.

RANCOURT, M. & LECHEVALIER, H. A. (1964). Electron microscopic study of the formation of spiny conidia in species of *Streptomyces*. *Can. J. Microbiol.*, **10**, 311.

SIE, E. H. C., SOBOTKA, H. & BAKER, H. (1961). Factor converting mesophilic into thermophilic microorganisms. *Nature, Lond.*, **192**, 86.

THIRUMALACHAR, M. J. (1955). *Chainia*, a new genus of the Actinomycetales. *Nature, Lond.*, **176**, 934.

THOMPSON, R. E. M. & BISSET, K. A. (1957). *Polysepta*, a new genus and sub-order of bacteria. *Nature, Lond.*, **170**, 590.

TSYGANOV, V. A., ZHUKOVA, R. A. & TIMOFEEVA, K. A. (1963). A new genus of Actinomycetes, *Macrospora* gen. nov. *Abstr. 3rd. sci. Symp. Inst. Antib., Leningrad*, 90.

TSYGANOV, V. V., ZHUKOVA, R. A. & TIMOFEEVA, K. A. (1964). Morphological and biochemical peculiarities of a new species, Actinomycetes 2732/3. *Microbiology*, **33**, 769.

WILLIAMS, A. M. & MCCOY, E. (1953). Degeneration and regeneration of *Streptomyces griseus*. *Appl. Microbiol.*, **1**, 307.

YAMAGUCHI, T. (1965). Comparison of the cell-wall composition of morphologically distinct Actinomycetes. *J. Bact.*, **89**, 444.

# NUMERICAL TAXONOMY AND SOIL BACTERIA

A. D. ROVIRA and P. G. BRISBANE

*C.S.I.R.O., Division of Soils, Adelaide, South Australia*

## *INTRODUCTION*

The importance of being able to classify individuals in any population is a feature common to all fields of ecology. The difficulties of a successful identification of soil and rhizosphere bacteria have led many workers to devise their own systems of classification, e.g. according to nutritional requirements (Lochhead and Chase, 1943), morphology and gelatin digestion (Conn, 1948), morphology, stain reaction and dye tolerance (Clark, 1940). Sperber and Rovira (1959) used Skerman's key of identification in Bergey's Manual (1957) to identify over 80 per cent of their isolates to the generic level; while Rouatt and Katznelson (1961) classified 306 soil, rhizosphere, and rhizoplane isolates into ten genera and found that *Arthrobacter* predominated amongst the soil isolates and *Pseudomonas* amongst the rhizosphere isolates.

However, the mere naming of isolates according to Bergey's Manual is not completely satisfactory, because organisms which resemble each other in only a few 'key' characters but differ widely in other characters will fall into the same genus. This is particularly true for the genera *Pseudomonas, Flavobacterium* and *Achromobacter* which tend to be 'dumping grounds' for the Gram negative bacteria which predominate in the rhizosphere.

It was for this reason that we decided to apply a slight modification of the numerical taxonomic method developed by Sneath (1957) to bacteria isolated from the rhizosphere (Brisbane and Rovira, 1961). This modified similarity index was called the affinity index and was calculated by the formula

$$\text{Affinity Index} = \frac{\text{Number of similar characters}}{\text{Number of characters studied}} \times 100 \text{ per cent}$$

In this initial application of the affinity index to 21 named cultures of probable soil origin and 43 cultures selected at random from 318 rhizosphere isolates, a broad group containing 31 of the 43 isolates and a smaller group of named cultures was obtained. The named cultures

*Rhizobium trifolii*, *R. meliloti*, *Agrobacterium radiobacter*, and *Xanthomonas campestris* fell within a group of rhizosphere isolates which were related to one another at or above 80 per cent affinity. Using the criterion of Liston, Weibe and Colwell (1963) that similarities (or affinities) greater than 75 per cent should exist between members of a single bacterial species, it appeared that about three-quarters of the rhizosphere isolates belonged to a single group related to the genera *Rhizobium* and *Agrobacterium*. These genera have subsequently been linked together into a single genus (Graham, 1964) on the basis of affinities. The remainder of the isolates formed several small groups apparently not related to any of the known cultures.

This method was then applied to 290 bacterial cultures recently isolated from the rhizospheres of wheat and subterranean clover (*Trifolium subterraneum*), and from non-cropped soil. Seventy-seven named cultures representing common genera in soil were included in the study to serve as 'markers' for any groups which may have been obtained. The results of this trial and an examination of relationships between tests are discussed in this paper.

## *METHODS*

### *Organisms*

a Named cultures. Seventy-seven named cultures were obtained from culture collections throughout Australia for comparison with fresh isolates. The organisms were: *Streptomyces* (1); *Nocardia*, (3); *Mycobacterium* (5); *Bacillus* (5); *Arthrobacter* (5); *Agrobacterium* (5); *Rhizobium* (17); *Chromobacterium* (2); *Brevibacterium* (1); *Serratia* (1); *Aerobacter* (5); *Escherichia* (4); *Pseudomonas* (14); *Xanthomonas* (2); *Flavobacterium* (2); *Achromobacter* (3); *Azotomonas* (1); and *Beijerinckia* (1). The number of strains or species of each genus used in this study are shown in parentheses.

b Rhizosphere isolates. These were obtained by selecting colonies at random from pour plates prepared with yeast extract—peptone—soil extract (YPS) medium (Bunt and Rovira, 1955) from rhizosphere samples of one- and two-month-old subterranean clover and wheat plants growing in field plots situated on Urrbrae loam (a red brown earth). Control soil (fallow) samples were obtained from neighbouring unplanted plots at the same time as the rhizosphere samples were taken. The rhizosphere samples were obtained by suspending roots with firmly adhering soil in 100 ml. sterile water, shaking on a wrist action shaker for 15 minutes, preparing ten-fold dilutions and plating out 1 ml. aliquots from each of the higher dilutions. Sixty colonies from each source were selected from suitable plates after two weeks' incubation at 27°, subcultured directly into semi-solid YPS agar, tested for purity, and those which were pure then used directly from the semi-solid agar for the tests described below. Two hundred and ninety of these original colony selections were suitable for use in the final analysis, 95 from wheat rhizosphere, 100 from clover rhizosphere, and 95 from fallow soil.

c Miscellaneous cultures. Fifteen unidentified cultures from various sources were included in the analysis.

*Tests*

The 37 tests which were performed on each culture included many of the classical tests used in the identification of bacteria and several which were aimed specifically at distinguishing isolates from different sources. All tests were rated as + or − and recorded on punch cards.

The tests were: 1—Presence of filaments; 2—Gram stain; 3—presence of rods; 4—presence of cocci; 5—presence of pleomorphic forms; 6—presence of branching; 7—heat resistance (80° for 10 min.); 8—motility; 9—fluorescence; 10—pigment on starch agar; 11—growth on glucose in two days; 12—growth on glucose in seven days; 13—response to amino acid supplement to glucose broth in two days; 14—response to amino acids in seven days; 15—response to yeast extract supplement to glucose-amino acid broth in two days; 16—response to yeast extract in seven days; 17—growth rate (turbidity rating of two or better after two days in yeast extract-peptone broth; 18—milk peptonization; 19—starch hydrolysis; 20—gelatin liquefaction; 21—ammonia production; 22—nitrite production from nitrate; 23—acid from glucose (aerobic); 24—acid from glucose (anaerobic); 25—acid from sucrose (aerobic); 27—arginine breakdown (Thornley, 1960*a*); 28—tetracycline sensitivity; 29—chloramphenicol sensitivity; 30—erythromycin sensitivity; 31—oleandomycin sensitivity; 32—penicillin sensitivity; 33—sulphafurazole sensitivity; 34—establishment on clover roots in sterile sand for 8 days to a level $> 10^2$ per root system; 35—establishment on wheat roots $> 10^2$ per root system; 36—establishment on clover roots $> 10^6$ per root system; 37—establishment on wheat roots $> 10^6$ per root system. Details of the media and methods of most of these tests are given by Brisbane and Rovira (1961).

*Computation*

a Comparisons between organisms. The relationships between all organisms were calculated on the basis of the number of characters different, e.g. with 37 tests, organisms with zero characters different have 100 per cent affinity, with 2 characters different 94 per cent affinity, with 4 characters different 89 per cent affinity, with 10 characters different 73 per cent affinity.

The computer compared each organism with every other organism, recorded the number of characters that were different, and printed out the numbers of the other organisms which had 0, 1, 2 . . . 10 characters different. These results were then sorted by hand to give the familiar triangles (Sneath, 1957) in which groups of related organisms show as densely shaded areas near the diagonal. To reduce the sorting and grouping of isolates to manageable proportions only highly-related organisms were grouped, viz. fewer than 6 characters different, or affinities of more than 83 per cent.

b Comparisons between tests. The relationship between tests were obtained by calculating both the chi values (standard normal deviate), and similarity indices between all tests using two groups of organisms, viz. the 290 soil and rhizosphere isolates and the 77 named cultures. The data were computed using the programme of Lange, Stenhouse and Offler (1965).

c Relationship between character and source. The correlation between the characters and source of the isolates was calculated using the Stenhouse–Lange programme. These correlations between character and source also served as a check on the agreement between the two sets of isolates from wheat and clover rhizosphere and fallow soil which were sampled one month apart.

## *RESULTS*

### *Comparisons between Organisms*

When the affinities between organisms were calculated on the basis of the numbers of differences between cultures and the results represented diagrammatically (Fig. 1), 168 of the 383 cultures formed 7 well-defined groups (A to G) with affinities of 86 per cent or greater within each group. Only 14 of the 77 named cultures grouped at the 86 per cent affinity level and hence served little purpose in helping to identify the various groups. Of the remaining cultures most showed affinities of 73 per cent or more with other organisms and acceptance of lower affinities would have resulted in many of these cultures forming groups and being included in a much enlarged diagram.

If the poor grouping of the named cultures is taken into account, then over 50 per cent of the isolates fell into groups, fallow soil and clover rhizosphere isolates more so than wheat rhizosphere isolates.

An examination of the percentage of positives for each test showed striking consistencies within groups and differences between groups (Table 1).

TABLE 1

*Percentage of positives in each test for seven Affinity Groups. Seventy seven named cultures and 290 isolates*

| Test | Group | | | | | | | Source | |
|---|---|---|---|---|---|---|---|---|---|
| | A | B | C | D | E | F | G | Named | Isolates |
| 1 | 4 | 6 | 13 | 11 | 0 | 8 | 100 | 10·4 | 21·4 |
| 2 | 4 | 89 | 77 | 58 | 94 | 0 | 0 | 22·1 | 53·4 |
| 3 | 100 | 100 | 100 | 87 | 83 | 100 | 100 | 97·4 | 89·7 |
| 4 | 4 | 6 | 10 | 29 | 89 | 0 | 0 | 10·4 | 21·0 |
| 5 | 40 | 89 | 79 | 33 | 0 | 62 | 40 | 48·1 | 44·5 |
| 6 | 0 | 67 | 28 | 9 | 0 | 8 | 70 | 14·3 | 23·4 |
| 7 | 12 | 6 | 0 | 2 | 0 | 8 | 0 | 35·1 | 5·1 |
| 8 | 88 | 0 | 38 | 11 | 0 | 92 | 0 | 58·4 | 27·9 |
| 9 | 0 | 6 | 3 | 0 | 6 | 62 | 0 | 14·3 | 3·8 |
| 10 | 8 | 11 | 23 | 11 | 22 | 0 | 0 | 14·3 | 21·7 |
| 11 | 28 | 83 | 0 | 2 | 0 | 100 | 100 | 59·7 | 26·6 |
| 12 | 64 | 100 | 10 | 11 | 6 | 100 | 100 | 88·3 | 42·1 |
| 13 | 44 | 17 | 8 | 4 | 6 | 100 | 10 | 59·7 | 25·2 |
| 14 | 56 | 11 | 28 | 12 | 22 | 100 | 60 | 66·2 | 42·4 |
| 15 | 24 | 28 | 72 | 40 | 67 | 8 | 10 | 44·1 | 51·4 |
| 16 | 20 | 83 | 95 | 69 | 89 | 0 | 50 | 45·5 | 64·8 |
| 17 | 24 | 56 | 23 | 4 | 6 | 100 | 30 | 77·9 | 33·8 |
| 18 | 4 | 33 | 13 | 20 | 83 | 69 | 100 | 29·9 | 34·1 |
| 19 | 4 | 89 | 62 | 33 | 78 | 0 | 100 | 29·9 | 49·7 |
| 20 | 0 | 83 | 13 | 27 | 89 | 100 | 100 | 49·4 | 46·6 |
| 21 | 28 | 0 | 13 | 2 | 6 | 92 | 0 | 64·9 | 22·8 |
| 22 | 28 | 28 | 21 | 22 | 6 | 8 | 0 | 42·9 | 26·2 |
| 23 | 8 | 6 | 0 | 2 | 0 | 85 | 100 | 48·1 | 16·6 |
| 24 | 0 | 0 | 0 | 0 | 0 | 15 | 20 | 24·7 | 3·8 |
| 25 | 0 | 0 | 0 | 2 | 0 | 8 | 10 | 6·5 | 2·1 |
| 26 | 0 | 0 | 0 | 2 | 0 | 0 | 0 | 6·5 | 1·7 |
| 27 | 12 | 0 | 5 | 0 | 0 | 92 | 0 | 33·8 | 7·6 |
| 28 | 92 | 100 | 100 | 100 | 100 | 100 | 100 | 93·5 | 96·2 |
| 29 | 48 | 100 | 97 | 96 | 100 | 0 | 0 | 67·5 | 79·3 |
| 30 | 36 | 100 | 92 | 93 | 100 | 0 | 0 | 50·6 | 68·3 |
| 31 | 8 | 83 | 67 | 73 | 94 | 0 | 0 | 19·5 | 46·2 |
| 32 | 4 | 28 | 8 | 38 | 0 | 0 | 0 | 15·6 | 18·6 |
| 33 | 60 | 100 | 97 | 93 | 100 | 62 | 10 | 85·7 | 80·3 |
| 34 | 100 | 100 | 100 | 27 | 83 | 100 | 100 | 85·7 | 73·4 |
| 35 | 96 | 78 | 90 | 7 | 22 | 100 | 100 | 58·4 | 56·2 |
| 36 | 96 | 100 | 87 | 11 | 78 | 100 | 100 | 87·0 | 70·3 |
| 37 | 92 | 94 | 69 | 0 | 28 | 100 | 100 | 66·2 | 52·4 |
| Number in group | 25 | 18 | 39 | 45 | 18 | 13 | 10 | 77 | 290 |

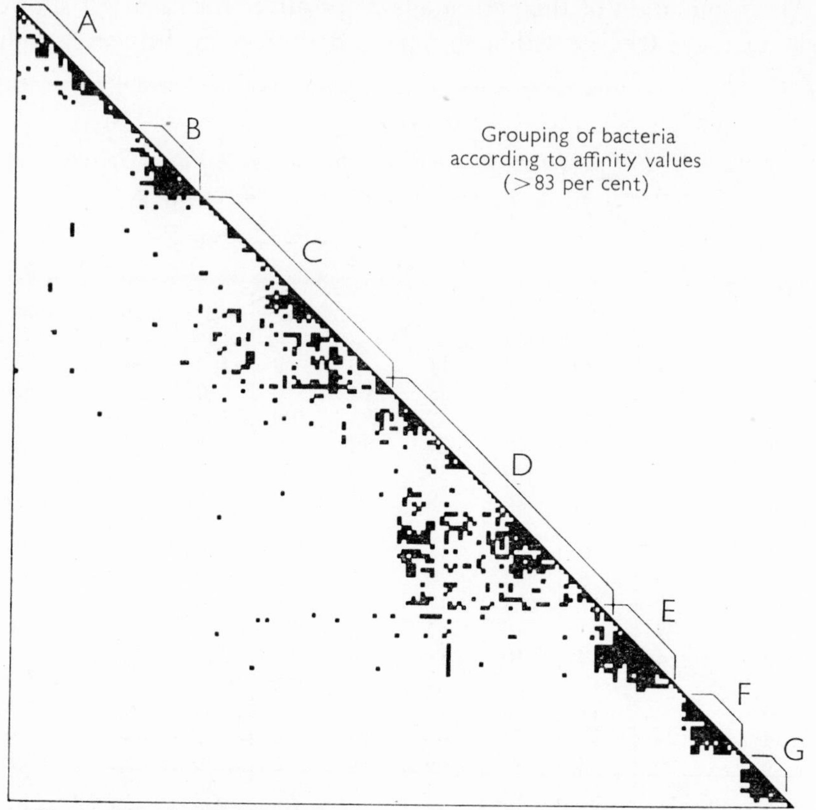


Fig. 1. Grouping of 168 cultures according to their affinities with each other.

From Table 1 it was possible to devise the dichotomous key shown below, by which 80 per cent of the 168 isolates could be correctly placed into the seven groups obtained by the affinity index method.

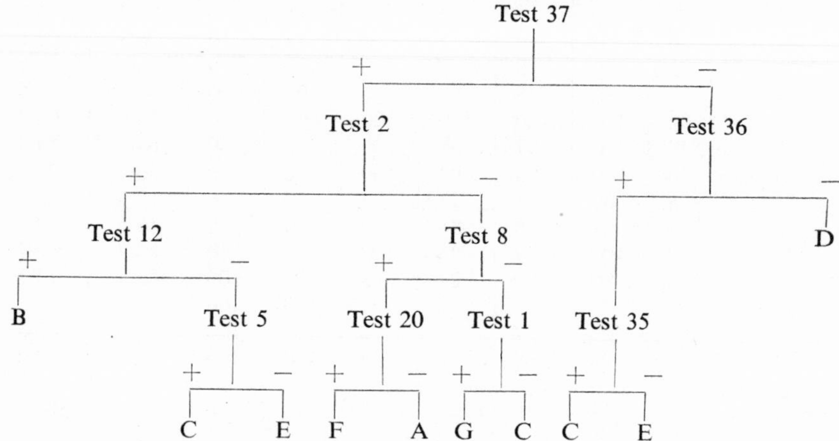

There was a tendency for isolates from a particular source to dominate certain groups (Table 2), e.g. clover (groups A and C), wheat (group G), fallow (groups D and E).

TABLE 2

*Distribution of bacteria within affinity groups according to source*

| Group | Wheat | Clover | Fallow | Named cultures |
|---|---|---|---|---|
| A | 1 | 13 | 8 | 2 { *Bacterium* (1 sp.)<br>*Mycoplana* (1 sp.) |
| B | 4 | 8 | 4 | 2 *Arthrobacter* (2 spp.) |
| C | 8 | 21 | 9 | 1 *Agrobacterium* (1 sp.) |
| D | 14 | 10 | 21 | — |
| E | 4 | 2 | 12 | — |
| F | — | — | 4 | 9 { *Pseudomonas* (7 spp.)<br>*Rhizobium* (1 sp.)<br>*Achromobacter* (1 sp.) |
| G | 7 | 2 | 1 | — |

*Relationships between characters*

From our previous experience and a consideration of the results shown in Fig. 1, it was decided that the 77 named bacteria and the 290 freshly isolated bacteria should be considered as two distinct ecological groups and these groups were treated separately when the relationships between characters were computed. It can be seen from Table 1 that the named and isolated bacteria differed in about one-third of their characters.

In any comparison between two characters the limits of the similarity or affinity values are set by the percentage of isolates positive for the character being considered. For example, if 50 per cent of the bacteria are positive for two characters A and B, the similarity index A:B can range from 0 to 100 per cent, but if the bacteria are 90 per cent positive to character C, then the similarity value A:C must lie between 40 per cent and 55·6 per cent. A more accurate estimate of the association between characters is given by the chi values; these have the added advantage that significance levels can be applied. Lange *et al.* (1965), have developed several computer programmes for taxonomic methods, which give both similarity and chi values. Table 3 illustrates a selection of the results obtained with these programmes. The similarity values between characters 3 and 28 must lie in the range 86 to 93 per cent because of the high proportion of positive reactions for each test, but

TABLE 3

*Correlations and similarity values between selected tests performed on 290 soil and rhizosphere isolates*

| Character | 3 (89·7) | 9 (3·8) | 26 (1·7) | 28 (96·2) | 30 (68·3) | 31 (46·2) | 35 (56·2) | 36 (70·3) |
|---|---|---|---|---|---|---|---|---|
| 3 | X | 4 | 2 | 88 | 62 | 43 | 56 | 68 |
| 9 | 1·1 | X | 0 | 4 | 4 | 5 | 5 | 5 |
| 26 | **0·7** | **0·4** | X | 1 | 0 | 1 | 1 | 1 |
| 28 | 1·8 | 0·6 | **1·9** | X | 71 | 48 | 56 | 68 |
| 30 | **1·0** | 0·3 | **2·3** | 4·9 | X | 67 | 34 | 45 |
| 31 | **0·4** | 1·1 | **1·1** | 3·1 | 10·5 | X | 27 | 34 |
| 35 | 2·2 | 1·1 | **0·7** | 1·3 | **5·1** | **2·9** | X | 62 |
| 36 | 1·7 | 2·1 | **0·5** | **0·8** | **3·9** | **2·3** | 6·5 | X |

The figures in parentheses represent the percentage of the 290 isolates which were positive for each character. Similarity values are to the right of the diagonal and chi values (standard normal deviate) are to the left of the diagonal. Negative associations are shown in bold type. Significance levels for chi are 2·0 (5 per cent), 2·6 (1 per cent) and 3·3 (0·1 per cent).

there was no significant association between these characters even though the similarity value was 88 per cent. On the other hand, the similarity value between characters 28 and 30 must lie between 65 per cent and 71 per cent and the similarity value obtained (71 per cent), represents a significant association between these two characters. Whilst chi values are preferable to similarity or affinity values, their use for isolate comparisons is made difficult by the arbitrary nature of the coding, a problem Sokal and Sneath (1963) refer to as 'column heterogeneity'. Also, the number of comparisons increases as the square of the number of characters considered, and the occurrence of significant associations due to random fluctuations becomes more certain with increasing numbers of comparisons (Stenhouse, personal communication). The identification of these spurious correlations is a very difficult problem.

The significant associations between the characters of the bacterial isolates and their source (chi>2 with at least one source), shown in Table 4, reveal that the variation between the sub-samples is as great as the variation between the sources; there is little difference between the behaviour of isolates from the rhizosphere of two plant species at the same age, as compared with the one plant species sampled at 4 and 8 weeks. Table 4 highlights what is probably the most important problem in this field at the present time, namely the difficulty of obtaining an adequate sample of the rhizosphere and soil bacteria. The testing

TABLE 4

*The relationship between sources and characters of isolated bacteria*

| Source | Chi values for various characters | | | | | | | | | | | | | | | | | | | | | | |
|---|---|---|---|---|---|---|---|---|---|---|---|---|---|---|---|---|---|---|---|---|---|---|---|
| | 1 | 3 | 4 | 5 | 8 | 9 | 11 | 12 | 15 | 17 | 18 | 20 | 23 | 25 | 26 | 27 | 31 | 32 | 33 | 34 | 35 | 36 | 37 |
| Wheat 1 | 2·7 | **2·6** | 1·2 | **3·8** | **1·1** | **1·4** | 0·5 | **0·2** | **1·9** | **0·9** | 2·0 | 0·0 | 0·9 | **1·0** | **0·9** | **0·9** | 0·0 | 2·5 | **1·1** | **3·7** | **2·7** | **2·4** | **1·4** |
| Wheat 2 | 0·6 | 0·5 | **0·8** | 1·4 | **0·4** | **0·6** | 2·5 | 2·8 | **1·1** | 1·5 | 0·8 | 1·4 | 3·4 | 0·0 | **1·0** | **0·9** | **1·3** | **1·1** | **2·2** | 0·6 | 2·2 | 1·8 | 1·8 |
| Clover 1 | **2·1** | 1·6 | 1·0 | 2·1 | 2·7 | 2·5 | **0·8** | 0·3 | **1·7** | 0·0 | **1·6** | **2·2** | **2·6** | **1·1** | **1·0** | **1·0** | **0·6** | **1·3** | 1·8 | 2·2 | 2·7 | 2·3 | 3·0 |
| Clover 2 | 0·4 | 1·1 | **2·4** | 0·0 | **1·0** | **1·5** | 0·6 | 0·0 | 3·8 | 1·6 | **1·6** | **1·0** | 0·3 | 4·3 | 3·7 | 0·7 | 0·0 | **1·7** | 0·3 | 0·8 | **0·3** | 0·2 | 0·0 |
| Fallow 1 | **2·0** | **2·0** | 3·0 | **0·7** | **0·1** | 0·9 | **1·6** | **1·6** | **3·0** | **2·7** | 1·2 | 0·5 | **2·5** | **1·1** | **1·0** | 2·6 | 2·1 | 0·4 | 0·1 | 0·0 | **0·9** | **0·2** | **1·6** |
| Fallow 2 | 0·3 | 1·4 | **1·1** | 0·9 | 0·0 | 0·1 | **1·2** | **1·2** | 4·0 | 0·3 | **0·6** | 1·3 | 0·5 | **1·0** | 0·2 | **0·3** | **0·2** | 1·3 | 0·8 | 0·1 | **1·0** | **1·7** | **1·7** |

Negative associations are shown in bold type. Significance levels for chi are 2·0 (5 per cent), 2·6 (1 per cent) and 3·3 (0·1 per cent).

TABLE 5

*The associations between various characters of isolated and named bacteria*

| Characters | 1 | 2 | 3 | 4 | 5 | 6 | 7 | 8 | 9 | 10 | 11 | 12 | 13 | 14 | 15 | 16 | 17 | 18 | 19 | 20 | 21 | 22 | 23 | 24 | 25 | 26 | 27 | 28 | 29 | 30 | 31 | 32 | 33 | 34 | 35 | 36 | 37 |
|---|---|---|---|---|---|---|---|---|---|---|---|---|---|---|---|---|---|---|---|---|---|---|---|---|---|---|---|---|---|---|---|---|---|---|---|---|---|
| 1 | X | | | | | 4·1 | | | | | | | | | | | | | | | | | | | | | | | | | | | | | | | |
| 2 | **3·7** | X | | 2·9 | | | | **3·3** | | 2·8 | | | | | | | | | | | | | | | | | | | | | | | | | | | |
| 3 | | **2·6** | X | | | | | | | | | | | | | | | | | | | | | | | | | | | | | | | | | | |
| 4 | **4·2** | 6·4 | *7·4* | X | | | | | | 3·0 | | | | | | | | | | | | | | | | | | | | | | | | | | | |
| 5 | | | 4·4 | **5·2** | X | | **3·3** | | | | | **2·6** | | | | | | | | **2·8** | | | | | | | | | | | | | | | | | |
| 6 | 9·9 | | | **4·8** | 3·2 | X | | | | | | | | | | | | | | | | | | | | | | | | | | | | | | | |
| 7 | | | | | | | X | | | | | | | | | | | | | | | 2·6 | | | | | | | | | | | | | | | |
| 8 | | **4·2** | | **3·5** | 3·4 | | | X | | | | | | | | | | | | | | | | | | | | | **2·6** | | | | | | 2·6 | | |
| 9 | | | | | | | | | X | | | | | | | | | | | | 2·6 | | 3·7 | | | | 2·9 | | **5·1** | **3·6** | | | | | | | |
| 10 | | | | | | | | | | X | | **2·7** | | | | | | | | | | | | | | | | | | 2·8 | | | | | | | |
| 11 | 3·4 | | | **3·0** | | 4·0 | | | | | X | 3·8 | | | | | 2·8 | | | | | | | | | | | | | | | | | | | | |
| 12 | | **2·6** | | **3·1** | | | | | | | 12·0 | X | | | | | | | | | | | | | | | | | | | **2·9** | | | | | | |
| 13 | | | | | | | | | | | | 4·4 | X | 2·7 | | | 4·0 | | | | 4·4 | | 2·7 | | | | 2·6 | | | | | | | 3·0 | | | |
| 14 | | **3·2** | | | | | | | | | | 3·6 | 8·4 | X | | | | | | | 2·9 | | 3·6 | | | | | | | | | | | | | | |
| 15 | | 2·6 | | | | | | | | | | | | | X | | | **3·0** | | | | | | | | | | | | | | | | | | | |
| 16 | | 3·8 | | | | | | | | | **2·7** | **4·5** | **3·2** | **4·6** | 6·2 | X | | **2·7** | | | | | | | | | | | 2·6 | | | | | | | | |
| 17 | | | | | | | | | | | 7·5 | 7·2 | 6·9 | | 5·3 | | X | | | | 3·4 | | | 2·6 | | | 2·7 | | | | | | | | | | |
| 18 | 2·9 | | | | **2·7** | | | **3·7** | | | 2·7 | | | | | | | X | | 5·3 | | **3·4** | | | | | | | **2·9** | | 2·8 | | | | | | |
| 19 | 3·4 | 3·3 | | | | 3·9 | | **2·6** | | | | | | | 2·8 | | 3·0 | 6·1 | X | | | | | | | | | | | | 2·8 | | | | **2·7** | | |
| 20 | 3·1 | | | | | | | **2·8** | | | 5·1 | 4·1 | | | | | 4·0 | 10·9 | 7·2 | X | | | | | | | | | | | | | | | | | |
| 21 | | | | | | | 2·9 | | | | 3·6 | 3·4 | 4·6 | 4·5 | | | 5·8 | | | 3·4 | X | | | 3·6 | | | 4·6 | | | | | | | 3·5 | 3·2 | | |
| 22 | | 2·7 | **2·6** | | | | | | | | | | 3·6 | | | | 3·4 | | | | 3·7 | X | | 3·6 | | | | | | | | | | | | | |
| 23 | 3·7 | **5·9** | | | | | | | | | 6·5 | 6·3 | | 4·0 | | | 3·2 | 4·2 | | 3·6 | | | X | | | | | | | | | | | | | | |
| 24 | 2·7 | | | | | | | | | | 3·5 | 2·7 | | | | | 3·4 | 2·7 | | | | | 6·7 | X | 2·9 | 4·0 | 3·1 | | | | | | | | 3·1 | | |
| 25 | 4·7 | | | | | 4·4 | | | | | 4·1 | 2·9 | | 2·8 | | | | | | | | | 5·5 | 5·9 | X | | | | | | | | | | | | |
| 26 | | | | | | | | | | | | | | | | | | | | | | | | | | X | | | | | | | | | | | |
| 27 | | | | | | | 2·8 | 2·8 | | | 3·0 | 3·0 | 3·3 | | | | 2·6 | | | | 4·7 | 2·6 | 2·6 | | | | X | | | **2·9** | | | | | 2·8 | | 2·9 |
| 28 | | | | | | | | | | | | | | | | | | | 2·7 | | | | | | | | | X | | | | | 3·0 | 4·3 | | | |
| 29 | **2·8** | 6·1 | | 3·0 | | | | | | | **6·5** | **5·5** | | | 2·8 | 3·9 | | | | | 3·2 | | **5·8** | | | | **3·5** | 6·6 | X | 5·1 | | | 3·0 | | | | |
| 30 | **2·8** | 7·6 | | 3·8 | | | | | | | **4·1** | **4·4** | **3·1** | 3·3 | 3·0 | 4·3 | | | | | 3·3 | | **7·3** | **2·9** | | | **3·3** | 4·9 | 9·9 | X | 3·6 | 3·0 | | | **3·1** | | |
| 31 | | 7·1 | | 4·2 | | | | | | | **3·6** | **4·1** | | **3·0** | | 3·7 | | | 3·6 | | 4·3 | | **5·1** | | | | | 3·1 | 7·4 | 10·5 | X | | | | **2·7** | | |
| 32 | | | | | | | | | | | | | **2·6** | **2·7** | | | | | | | | | | | | | | | 3·7 | 5·2 | 5·1 | X | | | | | |
| 33 | | 5·1 | | | | | | | | **3·0** | **3·9** | **3·8** | | **2·6** | | 3·0 | | | | | | | **5·7** | | | | | 6·0 | 7·3 | 8·8 | 7·2 | 2·8 | X | | | | |
| 34 | | **3·1** | | **3·8** | 3·0 | 2·8 | | | | | 4·6 | 4·4 | 2·8 | 3·1 | | | 3·6 | | | | 3·0 | | 4·2 | | | | 2·9 | | 3·2 | **2·9** | | **5·0** | | X | 4·2 | | |
| 35 | 2·6 | **3·5** | | **5·0** | 3·4 | 3·5 | | 3·8 | | | 5·5 | 5·8 | 3·8 | 3·5 | | | 3·9 | | | | 2·7 | | 5·4 | | | | 3·4 | | 4·7 | **5·1** | **2·9** | **3·7** | | 11·5 | X | | 3·0 |
| 36 | | | | | 3·1 | 3·3 | | | | | 4·6 | 4·7 | | | | | 4·3 | | 3·0 | | 2·6 | | | | | | 3·1 | | 2·7 | **3·9** | | **3·9** | | 6·4 | 6·5 | X | 4·7 |
| 37 | | **3·3** | | **4·0** | 3·8 | 3·9 | | 3·8 | | | 7·0 | 6·4 | 2·6 | 3·2 | | | 4·6 | | 2·9 | | 2·6 | | 3·7 | 2·6 | | | 3·7 | | 3·6 | **4·7** | **2·6** | **4·3** | | 7·5 | 9·8 | 11·6 | X |

of 50 pure cultures isolated from a population of several hundred million on a root system is liable to lead to gross sampling errors.

The significant associations between the various characters are given in Table 5. Only chi values greater than 2·6 (significant at the 1 per cent level) have been shown. Of the 64 associations within the named bacterial group, 35 had corresponding associations within the group of isolated bacteria.

## *DISCUSSION*

When Sneath (1957) published his idea of applying Adansonian principles and computer methods to the taxonomy of bacteria it appeared that this technique might overcome many of the difficulties of making taxonomic surveys of soil bacteria. Such surveys, which are so important in measuring changes in the balance of micro-organisms due to soil treatment, root growth, etc., are difficult because many of the 'key' or traditional diagnostic tests are of little value when applied to soil bacteria. The concept of carrying out many tests, giving them all equal weight and calculating the similarities between organisms on this basis, appeared to be one which would be very valuable in soil bacteriology.

To some extent, this application of numerical or computer taxonomy to soil and rhizosphere isolates has been successful; in both studies it has given distinct groups within which organisms were highly related to each other. However, in the survey reported in this paper about half the isolates did not fall into closely related groups which raises the problem of what to do with these organisms. One solution would be to lower the standards set for significant similarities to values similar to those used in other taxonomic studies, but with the number of isolates used in this study (383) it becomes physically impossible to hand sort them into the triangular arrangement used to show groupings.

If one could place most of the isolates into well-defined groups then it should be possible to use the 'median organism' concept of Liston *et al.* (1963), or the 'key method' of Gyllenberg (1963), to define the average organism within each group and then use these hypothetical 'average' organisms for the identification of fresh isolates. This may be too idealistic when studying bacteria isolated from the soil or rhizosphere on non-selective media and may best be applied to more limited ranges of isolates.

However, even with limited grouping it has been possible to show sufficient consistency within groups and differences between groups to devise a dichotomous key to enable a rapid sorting of fresh isolates into the appropriate groups. Although such a key could only be applied to the types of organisms used in this survey, it does point to the possibilities of devising diagnostic keys for collections of soil or rhizosphere isolates, provided a sufficient sample has first of all been grouped on the basis of affinity indices.

From Table 5 one may conclude that organisms which can establish in pure culture on clover and wheat roots (Tests 34 to 37) possess the following characteristics; Gram-negative, not cocci, pleomorphic, branching, grow on glucose in 2 and 7 days, respond to amino acid supplement at 2 and 7 days, grow rapidly, produce ammonia from peptone, produce acid from glucose, positive to the arginine test, chloramphenicol sensitive, erythromycin and penicillin resistant.

It is interesting to note that an ecological test such as the ability to establish at a high level on wheat roots is the primary character in the dichotomous key. The chi values (Table 5), showed that the ability of organisms to colonize wheat and clover roots was significantly associated with many characters. This means that a split on these ecological tests results in groups which are homogeneous for these characters.

Most of the success in the application of numerical taxonomy has been obtained when workers have used either well-defined type cultures representative of certain species or genera (Sneath, 1957; Liston *et al.*, 1963), or else restricted studies to a narrow range of freshly isolated cultures such as pseudomonads or xanthomonads (Hayes, 1960; Rhodes, 1961; Liston *et al.*, 1963; Shewan, 1963; Graham, 1964). When the technique has been applied to a wide range of organisms without any preselection of certain groups it has not been nearly so successful (Thornley, 1960*b*; Colwell and Liston, 1961). Thus we can conclude from experience already gained that the successful application of numerical taxonomy to soil bacteria will depend upon the use of narrow ranges of organisms, probably isolated by selective methods.

There still remains the problem of being able to detect ecological shifts in the soil microflora when one can study only a few hundred of the many hundreds of millions of organisms in the sample. To use unreplicated samples from these enormous populations is statistically unsound and is another argument for studying changes in stratified populations or studying organisms from a narrow environment, e.g. rhizoplane from a 1 mm. root segment rather than the entire rhizoplane–rhizosphere zone. Together with this concept of using a more limited spectrum of organisms one must stress the absolute necessity of studying replicate collections of isolates from each environment so that an estimate can be made of the variation within the one environment as well as the differences between environments. Wallace and King (1954) emphasized the importance of replication of samples and statistical analysis of results. In their study the nutritional requirements of the rhizosphere isolates were not significantly different from those of the soil isolates.

The application of the chi test to measure the relationship between the 37 tests used in this study has revealed several interesting associations between tests, some of which were predictable and others not so. On this basis it is possible to select those tests which have the most value in separating out the different groups of organisms. The different reactions to the various tests by the named laboratory cultures and the fresh soil and rhizosphere isolates reveal that these form two ecologically distinct collections of bacteria. This is probably because the named cultures have been repeatedly subcultured on laboratory media while the soil and rhizosphere isolates were transferred only twice on artificial media before testing. Sperber (1957) and others have shown that certain characters possessed by freshly isolated soil cultures, e.g. apatite solution, may be lost after two or three transfers on laboratory media. The stability in the characters of an organism in both soil and upon repeated subculture needs further investigation.

An examination of the association between character and source revealed little consistency for the samples selected. This was somewhat surprising in view of the numerous reports of qualitative differences between soil and rhizosphere bacteria. Although the number of isolates from each source would be considered adequate in most studies of this kind, the obvious lack in consistency of association between character and source indicates either that the samples were not typical of the rhizosphere or control soil, or else the sampling error discussed earlier had masked any difference.

## *ACKNOWLEDGEMENTS*

We wish to acknowledge the help given by Mr. J. Penny and Mr. N. Stenhouse of the C.S.I.R.O. Division of Mathematical Statistics for devising the computer programmes used in this study.

## *REFERENCES*

BERGEY'S MANUAL OF DETERMINATIVE BACTERIOLOGY (1957). 7th ed. Ed. Breed, R. S., Murray, E. D. G. & Smith, N. R. Baltimore. Williams & Wilkins.

BRISBANE, P. G. & ROVIRA, A. D. (1961). A comparison of methods for classifying rhizosphere bacteria. *J. gen. Microbiol.*, **26**, 379.

BUNT, J. S. & ROVIRA, A. D. (1955). Microbiological studies of some sub-antarctic soils. *J. Soil Sci.*, **6**, 119.

CLARK, F. E. (1940). Notes on types of bacteria associated with plant roots. *Trans. Kansas Acad. Sci.*, **43**, 75.

COLWELL, R. R. & LISTON, J. (1961). Taxonomic relationships among the pseudomonads. *J. Bact.*, **82**, 1.

CONN, H. J. (1948). The most abundant groups of bacteria in soil. *Bact. Rev.*, **12**, 257.

GRAHAM, P. H. (1964). The application of computer techniques to the taxonomy of the root nodule bacteria of the legumes. *J. gen. Microbiol.*, **35**, 511.

GYLLENBERG, H. G. (1963). A general method for deriving determination schemes for random collections of microbial isolates. *Ann. Acad. Sci. fenn. Ser. A.*, **69**, 5.

HAYES, P. R. (1960). *A study of certain types of pigmented marine bacteria with particular reference to the* Flavobacterium *and* Cytophaga *species*. M.Sc. thesis. Birmingham. University of Birmingham.

LANGE, R. T., STENHOUSE, N. S. & OFFLER, K. E. (1965). Experimental appraisal of certain procedures for the classification of data. *Aust. J. Biol. Sci.* (In Press.)

LISTON, J., WEIBE, W. & COLWELL, R. R. (1963). Quantitative approach to the study of bacterial species. *J. Bact.*, **85**, 1061.

LOCHHEAD, A. G. & CHASE, F. E. (1943). Quantitative studies of soil organisms. V. Nutritional requirements of the predominant bacterial flora. *Soil Sci.*, **55**, 185.

RHODES, M. (1961). The characterization of *Pseudomonas fluorescens* with the aid of an electronic computer. *J. gen. Microbiol.*, **25**, 331.

ROUATT, J. W. & KATZNELSON, H. (1961). A study of the bacteria on the root surface and in the rhizosphere soil of crop plants. *J. appl. Bact.*, **24**, 164.

SHEWAN, J. M. (1963). The differentiation of certain genera of Gram negative bacteria frequently encountered in marine environments. *Symposium on Marine Microbiology*. Ed. Openheimer, C. H. Springfield, U.S.A. Thomas.

SNEATH, P. H. A. (1957). The application of computers to taxonomy. *J. gen. Microbiol.*, **17**, 201.

SOKAL, R. R. & SNEATH, P. H. A. (1963). *Principles of numerical taxonomy*. San Francisco and London. Freeman.

SPERBER, J. I. (1957). Solution of mineral phosphates by soil bacteria. *Nature, Lond.*, **180**, 994.

SPERBER, J. I. & ROVIRA, A. D. (1959). A study of bacteria associated with the roots of subterranean clover and Wimmera rye grass. *J. appl. Bact.*, **22**, 85.

THORNLEY, M. J. (1960*a*). The differentiation of *Pseudomonas* from other Gram-negative bacteria. *J. appl. Bact.*, **23**, 37.

THORNLEY, M. J. (1960*b*). Computation of similarities between strains of *Pseudomonas* and *Achromobacter* isolated from chicken meat. *J. appl. Bact.*, **23**, 395.

WALLACE, R. H. & KING, H. DE L. (1954). Nutritional groups of soil bacteria on the roots of barley and oats. *Proc. Soil Sci. Soc. Am.*, **18**, 283.

# SIGNIFICANCE OF THE GRAM STAIN IN THE CLASSIFICATION OF SOIL BACTERIA

H. G. GYLLENBERG

*Department of Microbiology, University of Helsinki, Finland*

## *INTRODUCTION*

Since the early days of soil microbiology, the Gram stain has been a standard character used for bacterial classification. The widespread use of the Gram stain is primarily based on the view that it is a rapid and easy method for distinguishing between fundamentally different types of bacteria.

This view is supported by existing knowledge which suggests that Gram-positivity and Gram-negativity are due to structurally and chemically different kinds of cell walls (the walls of Gram-positive organisms are known to consist largely of mucopeptides and contain teichoic acids, whereas the walls of Gram-negative organisms are made from a lipoprotein-polysaccharide complex). However, the evaluation of the Gram reaction as a definite plus or minus, implying that the 'positive' and 'negative' attributes are mutually exclusive, is too simple. This is often the experience of the soil bacteriologist, who learns that the outcome of the Gram stain is not an easily interpretable 'yes or no' character. Particularly among soil bacteria, the outcome of the Gram stain depends upon the stage of cultural development. Since a sudden change from one kind of cell wall structure and composition to another is not very likely, a continuous spectrum of the amount of crystal violet retained must be supposed. Accordingly, of the two different 'Gram characters' (i.e. positivity and negativity), at least one of them must be a relative, quantitative character of the 'more or less' type.

This point of view, which supposes the Gram stain to be a relative measure, gives rise to some fundamental questions. How are we to define and estimate the transitional degrees of Gram reaction? What is the taxonomic significance of the Gram stain if evaluated in relative, rather than absolute terms?

This paper deals with the latter question, particularly with respect to soil bacteria. It should be emphasized that the study has been restricted to the heterotrophic non-sporeforming organisms.

## *METHODS*

### *Analysis of character correlations*

If one accepts the ideas upon which numerical taxonomy is based, then one must recognize that the existence of different taxa is due to the existence of specific character correlations. The taxonomic significance of the Gram reaction may thus depend on the existence of distinct correlations between the outcome of the Gram stain and other characters. The evaluation of character correlations in bacteria in statistically justified terms, requires treatment of a large and random collection of pure cultures. A useful method for establishing character correlations is provided by *factor analysis*. This is a technique which has been widely employed in psychology to quantify relationships between psychological tests computed on the basis of data recorded from a number of individuals. The study of character correlations amongst bacteria presents a very similar situation. The number of subjects (pure cultures), is very large when compared with the number of tests or characters and one is looking for the relation between the characters.

Principal component analysis, which is one particular kind of factor analysis (Harman, 1960) was applied to the soil isolates selected for study. The application of this method to pure cultures of bacteria has been described in more detail elsewhere (Gyllenberg, 1965*a*, 1965*b*, 1965*c*). Therefore, it is only necessary to say that the method reveals existing character correlations ('factors' or 'components') in order of significance, and supplies the weights of the various characters as diagnostic features of each 'factor' considered.

In the present work both qualitative and quantitative characters were employed. In the case of qualitative two-state characters which distinguish between two attributes, viz., A and not A, the positive attribute was scored 1, and the negative attribute 0. For all quantitative characters, the records were transformed to a scale from 0 to 1.

For performing the mathematical treatment the IBM 1620 computer (Department of Applied Mathematics, University of Helsinki) was employed.

### *Evaluation of the gram reaction*

Several methods for a quantitative evaluation of the outcome of the Gram stain have been described. For the present purpose, a semi-quantitative procedure described by Mittwer (1958) was used. This procedure is based on the fact that Gram stained bacteria are all decolourized if alcohol is applied for a sufficiently long time. Thus the Gram reaction can be described in terms of decolourization time.

The analysis was carried out using a filter-paper chromatography method (Mittwer, 1958). Small amounts of stained and iodine-treated cell suspensions were applied as spots to filter paper. The paper was placed in a jar dipping into 95 per cent ethanol. The ethanol ascended by capillarity passing over the spots and extracted dye from the stained cells. The procedure resulted in streaks of dye, the lengths of which were proportional to the degree of Gram-positivity of the cells in question. The most Gram-positive organisms showed the longest streaks. Absolute numerical values have not been assigned to the different cultures. Instead, a culture of *Staphylococcus aureus* has been used as a reference organism in all runs, and the streak length of each organism tested has been assessed in relation to the length of the streak given by *S. aureus*, which was scored as 1.

*The pure culture material and recorded characters*

About 200 isolates of soil bacteria were sampled at random for the study. However, since all sporeformers were excluded, the final pure culture material contained 176 cultures.

Thirty five different characters were considered. For the sake of brevity, the details of techniques and procedures are omitted. Particular attention was paid to the outcome of the Gram stain, which was evaluated semi-quantitatively both from young and old cultures, as well as qualitatively by ordinary microscopic examination. Other recorded characters were cell morphology (especially pleomorphism and motility), specific growth rate (determined with the aid of the biophotometer of Bonet, Maury & Jouan), nutritional requirements (Lochhead and Chase, 1943), the rate and degree of glucose oxidation (Warburg technique), the occurrence of yellow and orange non-diffusible pigments and a number of other common biochemical and physiological tests.

## *THE RESULTS OF PRINCIPAL COMPONENT ANALYSIS*

The principal component analysis was restricted to the eight first, and therefore most significant, character correlation patterns. These correlations are referred to as factors A to H. The outcome of the analysis for the four characters which were connected with the Gram reaction is presented in Table 1.

The data show that Gram-positivity, recorded either *qualitatively* or *quantitatively*, is a significant measure of factor A. Again, a low figure (short decolourization time) in the *quantitative* Gram stain is a measure

TABLE 1

*The weighting of the quantitative and qualitative Gram stains as measures of factors A to H. The most significant factor loadings are printed in bold type*

| Gram stain | Factors | | | | | | | |
|---|---|---|---|---|---|---|---|---|
| | A | B | C | D | E | F | G | H |
| Quantitative: 48 hours of incubation | **0·46** | −0·29 | −0·16 | −0·15 | **−0·43** | 0·24 | 0·12 | 0·08 |
| Quantitative: 240 hours of incubation | **0·46** | −0·12 | −0·23 | −0·12 | **−0·35** | 0·05 | 0·25 | −0·19 |
| Qualitative: scored *positive* | **0·60** | −0·03 | −0·20 | −0·15 | −0·03 | 0·25 | 0·25 | **−0·35** |
| Qualitative: scored *negative* | **−0·45** | 0·07 | 0·14 | 0·21 | −0·06 | −0·27 | −0·26 | **0·43** |

of factor E, whereas a negative outcome of the *qualitative* Gram stain is a significant indication of factor H. Moreover, it can be concluded from Table 1 that for five of the factors, viz., A, C, D, F, and G, rather good agreement exists between the quantitative and qualitative evaluation of the Gram reaction. These factors can be ranked according to the quantitative Gram reaction figures connected with them (the ranking would be: A, F and G, C and D). For the remaining factors (B, E, and H) the agreement between the quantitative and qualitative evaluation is not clear, but on the basis of the *quantitative* test, factors B and E would appear as the next members in the above ranking. With factor H, as already shown, microscopic examination pointed to a distinct Gram-negativity, but the quantitative method failed to indicate this.

Any explanation of these results remains speculative until experimental verification with other methods of study can be obtained. With this reservation in mind, a discussion may nevertheless be useful. Complete descriptions of the factors A to H are recorded in Table 2. Before examining this table in detail, it should be noted that factor H possesses a group of typical *Pseudomonas*-characters. If one accepts the view of pseudomonads as strictly Gram-negative organisms (totally lacking Gram-positive attributes), it should be concluded that factor H is connected with the occurrence of Gram-negativity and the definite lack of Gram-positivity. It follows that this strict Gram-negativity is recognized by the qualitative microscopic evaluation, but not by quantitative methods. Accordingly, the quantitative method only measures Gram-positivity, and because it seems to work well over a wide range of factors, it is justified to assume that Gram-positivity is a relative 'more or less' character.

It may be concluded that factors A to G probably represent different degrees of Gram-positivity, whereas factor H represents strict Gram-negativity. The highest and lowest degrees of Gram-positivity (factors A and E respectively), and strict Gram-negativity show significant correlations to other characters (Table 1).

In Table 2 the factors have been arranged in order of decreasing Gram-positivity. In order to make it possible to obtain a clear picture of the different character correlations, the original factor loadings have been converted into general statements. As can be seen, factor H is easily distinguished from the others, which suggests a distinct taxonomic and ecological significance for strict Gram-negativity. The gradual decrease in Gram-positivity from factor A to factor E is not reflected by corresponding gradual changes in other characters however, although both extremes are easily distinguished on the basis of a number of characters.

It is probable that some of the factors described in Table 2 are identical with those recognized in some other collections of bacteria, studied partly by examining other characters (Gyllenberg, 1965*a*, 1965*b*). This particularly concerns factors A, F, G, and H, but probably also factor C. The fact that highly similar character correlations are found in different collections of isolates provides evidence to support the reliability of the results.

## *MULTIFACTORIAL EFFECTS AND THE GRAM REACTION*

In order to determine the frequency of the various factors in the collection of isolates being examined, the factor pattern of each individual culture was investigated. This showed, as might be expected, that character combinations involving two or more of the described factors were much more frequent than combinations permitting the identification of only one factor. In view of the division of the factors into Gram-positive (A to G) and Gram-negative (H) suggested above, the occurrence and frequency of specific factor combinations was of particular interest.

The most frequent factor combinations are presented in Table 3, whilst the relative frequencies of every possible combination of two factors are recorded in Table 4. It is apparent from these data that a

TABLE 2

*Description of the character correlations A to H. The factors are arranged in order of decreasing Gram-positivity. Significant characters (according to the results of factor analysis) are indicated in italic.—Suggested Gram-negativity and taxonomic relationships are also indicated*

| Characters | Factors | | | | | | | |
|---|---|---|---|---|---|---|---|---|
| | A | G | F | D | C | B | E | H |
| Gram-positivity | *More* | More | More | Less | Less | Less | *Less* | None |
| Pleomorphism | *Frequent* | Some | None | Some | Some | None | None | None |
| Motility | None | May occur | None | None | None | May occur | May occur | *Occurs* |
| Pigments, indiffusible | None | None | May occur | *Occur* | *Occur* | None | May occur | None |
| $Q_{O_2}$ | High | Low | *Low* | High | Intermediate | High | Low | High |
| Growth rate | Intermediate | Intermediate | High | *Low* | High | Intermediate | Intermediate | High |
| Nutritional requirements | *Specific* | Complex | Complex | Simple | Simple | *Complex* | *Specific* | Simple |
| Fermentative metabolism | None | None | May occur | Occurs | Occurs | None | May occur | None |
| Oxidase production | None | None | None | None | None | May occur | May occur | *Occurs* |
| Resistance to penicillin | None | None | None | None | May occur | None | May occur | *Occurs* |
| Suggested: | | | | | | | | |
| Gram-negativity | No | No | No | Yes | Yes | Yes | Yes | *Yes* |
| Taxonomy | | A, G, F, and combinations | | D, C, B, E, and combinations to A, G, F | | D, C, B, E, and combinations to H | | H |
| | | Mycobacterium and mycococci<br>Nocardia<br>Corynebacterium<br>Brevibacterium | | Arthrobacter | | Arthrobacter<br>Agrobacterium<br>Alcaligenes<br>Flavobacterium<br>Aeromonas<br>Xanthomonas | | Pseudomonas |

particular affinity occurred between the 'most' Gram-positive factors A, F, and G. The other Gram-positive factors (B, C, D, and E) combined with the first mentioned factors, but also (factors B and E with particular frequency) with the Gram-negative factor H. Factors A, F, and G did not combine at all with factor H.

TABLE 3

*The most frequent factor combinations found in the individual cultures. Figures refer to numbers of cultures*

| | | | | | |
|---|---|---|---|---|---|
| AG | 14 | A | 5 | BH | 4 |
| G | 11 | B | 5 | EF | 4 |
| AFG | 10 | EH | 5 | BCF | 4 |
| H | 9 | BEG | 5 | ABFG | 4 |
| None | 9 | D | 4 | BF | 3 |
| BE | 8 | AB | 4 | ADG | 3 |
| FG | 7 | BG | 4 | BEH | 3 |

TABLE 4

*The relative frequencies of the various combinations of two factors. The figures indicate the numbers of cultures showing a given combination in per cent of the probable number which could be calculated from the frequency of both factors*

| | A | G | F | D | C | B | E | H |
|---|---|---|---|---|---|---|---|---|
| A | | | | | | | | |
| G | 124 | | | | | | | |
| F | 112 | 96 | | | | | | |
| D | 86 | 80 | 29 | | | | | |
| C | 100 | 56 | 100 | 33 | | | | |
| B | 62 | 55 | 80 | 56 | 100 | | | |
| E | 23 | 67 | 67 | 40 | 40 | 127 | | |
| H | 0 | 8 | 0 | 33 | 33 | 70 | 150 | |

The occurrence of all possible combinations of the factors A to G supports the interpretation that they have the Gram-positive attribute in common, and also suggests that Gram-positivity possesses taxonomic significance. Further a common character can be suggested for factors B and E, possibly even C and D, and H. By analogy this common character would be the Gram-negative attribute. The following model can then be suggested for the 'Gram characters' of the factors A to H, and, accordingly, for the soil bacteria included in the present study.

| Factors | Gram-positivity | Gram-negativity |
|---|---|---|
| A | (More) | (−) |
| G | More | − |
| F | More | − |
| D | Less | + |
| C | Less | + |
| B | Less | + |
| E | (Less) | + |
| H | None | (+) |

(The attributes which were found to be significantly correlated with other characters—cf. Table 1—are indicated in parentheses.)

This model provides an explanation of the phenomenon of Gram-variability. In the present study the quantitative Gram stain was performed when the cultures had been incubated for 48 and 240 hrs. Considerable variation was found with several cultures, but statistical analysis of all data did not show significant differences. Therefore both sets of data were included in the further analysis and considered as identical. The variation was thus included as 'within group' variance in the study of the effect of specific factor combinations on the outcome of the Gram stain. The results of statistical analysis showed that the factors A, F, and G, either alone or in whatever mutual combination, effected a *decrease* in Gram-variability, but that these factors in some combination with factors B and E effected an *increase* in Gram-variability. Factors B and E, either alone or together, even depressed the Gram-variability. This may show that the cause of Gram-variability is not the simultaneous occurrence of the positive and negative 'Gram characters' as such, but a specific combination of factors which lack the Gram-negative attribute with other factors which supply this element.

## *THE GRAM STAIN AND THE CLASSIFICATION OF SOIL BACTERIA*

This approach to the evaluation of the Gram stain is abstract and possibly provocative because most conclusions are rather speculative. Therefore, it seems necessary to restrict the final discussion to the data provided by the statistical methods employed.

The outcome of the Gram stain within the collection of 176 isolates

examined was found to possess considerable weight in three different character correlations (Table 1). The results involved were:
(A), long decolourization time (pronounced Gram-positivity),
(E), short decolourization time (weak Gram-positivity), and
(H), distinct Gram-negativity recognized by microscopic examination.
Because of their occurrence as specific links in significant character correlations these results can be considered to possess taxonomic significance.

However, one purpose connected with all classifications is the condensation of as much consistent information as possible within the basic classification. The Gram stain does not satisfy this requirement very well. The recognized alternative results of the Gram stain are not mutually exclusive; the distinction between alternatives E and H may be slight and character correlations involving a significant result of the Gram stain need not be found in all bacteria (Tables 3 and 4). Accordingly, the taxonomic significance of the Gram stain is restricted to limited groups of soil bacteria, e.g. very strictly Gram-negative organisms (pseudomonads and related organisms), and organisms showing very pronounced Gram-positivity (mycobacteria, mycococci and related forms). Most types of soil bacteria belong somewhere between these extremes, and in the characterization and classification of these bacteria, the Gram stain does not provide essential information concerning specific activities, ecological behaviour, and taxonomic relationships (Table 2).

## *REFERENCES*

GYLLENBERG, H. G. (1965*a*). An approach to numerical description of microbial populations. *Ann. Acad. Sci. fenn., Ser. A*, **81**, 1.

GYLLENBERG, H. G. (1965*b*). Character correlations of certain taxonomic and ecological groups of bacteria. A study based on factor analysis. *Ann. Med. exp. fenn.*, **43**, 82.

GYLLENBERG, H. G. (1965*c*). A model for computer identification of microorganisms. *J. gen. Microbiol.*, **39**, 401.

HARMAN, R. (1960). *Modern factor analysis*. Chicago. University of Chicago Press.

LOCHHEAD, A. G. & CHASE, F. E. (1943). Qualitative studies on soil bacteria. V. Nutritional requirements of the predominating soil flora. *Soil Sci.*, **55**, 185.

MITTWER, T. (1958). Semiquantitative evaluation of the Gram reaction. *Science, N.Y.*, **128**, 1213.

# NUTRITIONAL CLASSIFICATIONS OF SOIL BACTERIA AND THEIR VALUE IN ECOLOGICAL STUDIES

J. W. ROUATT

*Microbiology Research Institute, Research Branch, Canada Department of Agriculture, Ottawa*

## *INTRODUCTION*

It is now over twenty-five years since Lochhead and Taylor (1938), in the general introduction to a series of studies on the qualitative nature of the microflora of soils, observed that in soil microbiology considerable attention was directed towards processes in which micro-organisms were known to participate rather than towards an objective study of the micro-organisms themselves. Although much valuable data was gathered on biological processes known to occur in soil, such as ammonification, nitrification, nitrogen fixation and others, the organisms concerned had been studied largely because of their known functions. On the other hand, little attention was paid to groups of organisms whose functions were unknown but which undoubtedly comprised a large and very important proportion of the indigenous population of arable soils. An attempt was therefore made in our laboratories to strike a better balance by developing a 'biological' as contrasted with a 'biochemical' or 'functional' approach to the study of soil bacteria.

Investigations of the indigenous groups were hampered by a lack of satisfactory methods for their isolation and of suitable criteria for their identification. Thus, in contrast to those organisms concerned with known functions, they required for their isolation as non-selective a medium as possible in order that mutual interference be reduced to a minimum. By following systematic isolation methods the procedure was made quantitative and so permitted an estimation of the relative incidence of various qualitative groups.

In a series of investigations conducted on a non-selective basis Taylor and Lochhead (1938) demonstrated that, in a soil of definite type, there existed a surprisingly uniform balance between the various morphological and physiological groups of bacteria, even though the productivity was greatly altered by fertilizer treatment. The predominant soil bacteria were relatively inactive in pure culture and considerable divergences in biochemical action were shown by apparently closely related morphological forms.

In proximity to the growing plant, however, the bacterial equilibrium of the soil was found to undergo definite alterations, so that apart from increases in total numbers there was evidence of a selective action characteristic of all plants studied (Lochhead, 1940). Gram-negative short rods were found to be preferentially increased while Gram-positive short rods, coccoid rods and spore-forming bacteria were relatively suppressed. With regard to bacterial physiology, one of the outstanding effects of plant growth was to stimulate the development of metabolically active micro-organisms. Not only was there a notably greater proportion of motile forms and a pronounced increase in the incidence of chromogenic types, but also a higher incidence of proteolytic bacteria and of those able to ferment carbohydrate. These findings, when considered in conjunction with the numerical increase, pointed to a phenomenal stimulation of microbial activity with the shift in equilibrium in soil adjacent to the plant root.

While a classification of soil bacteria according to morphological and biochemical characters was considered an aid to the understanding of the kinds of bacteria inhabiting soil it provided little or no basis for assessing the significance of any change of equilibrium. Furthermore it had become apparent that the 'classical' biochemical tests commonly used in general taxonomic differentiation were inadequate for any rational grouping helpful to an understanding of the significance of the indigenous bacteria in soil.

Lochhead and Chase (1943) postulated that the equilibrium between various groups of organisms existing in any soil at any given time depended in large measure upon the availability of nutrients required for the growth of those organisms. Though special antagonisms and the presence of toxic factors may have distorted this relationship, in the main the relative incidence of a group of micro-organisms would be dependent upon the presence of necessary nutrients. A method was therefore developed for grouping soil bacteria according to their nutritional requirements. Following a preliminary system based on the use of three differential media (West and Lochhead, 1940), a more comprehensive procedure was proposed in which organisms were grouped according to growth response in seven media of different nutritional complexities (Lochhead and Chase, 1943). The procedure, representing a new approach to the grouping of soil bacteria, has been helpful in studying the microbial equilibrium in soil, not only in relation to season and soil treatment, but more particularly in relation to plant growth. It has also been the basis for research into the nature of the growth-promoting properties of soil.

## *METHODS OF STUDY*

The approach to the study of soil bacteria developed in our laboratory involved, among others, two important requirements; firstly, the use of as non-selective a medium as possible for isolation and secondly, the inclusion of quantitative as well as qualitative procedures. As the least selective medium available, soil extract agar (without added energy material), was used for plating. From representative plates, incubated for 14 days at 28°, colonial growth was systematically subcultured so that all colonies on a plate or sector thereof were taken (average of 100 for each plate) and stab inoculations made into soil extract semisolid agar (0·02 per cent $K_2HPO_4$, 0·01 per cent yeast extract, 0·3 per cent agar). This medium was found to give the highest percentage of viable transfers from the plates.

In a comparative study of the nutritional requirements of the isolates, seven media were used (Lochhead and Chase, 1943). These ranged from a simple basal glucose medium to those of increasing complexity. The major components of these seven media were as follows:

I. Basal glucose mineral salts medium.
II. Basal medium + amino acids.
III. Basal medium + growth factors.
IV. Basal medium + amino acids + growth factors.
V. Basal medium + yeast extract.
VI. Basal medium + soil extract.
VII. Basal medium + yeast extract + soil extract.

Subsequently, slight amendments were made with the substitution of vitamin-free casamino acids for the amino acid combination and the addition of vitamin $B_{12}$ to the growth factor medium (Stevenson and Rouatt, 1953). All media were dispensed in 5 ml. amounts. Transfers of each organism were made by loop inoculation from soil extract semi-solid agar cultures. Cultures were incubated at 28° for 5 days and the growth response of each isolate in the seven media recorded by assigning a turbidity value of 4 to the tube showing heaviest growth and rating the others by comparison. To avoid assigning too great importance to small variations, a difference of not more than two points was considered significant. The organisms were then divided into seven groups on the basis of their requirements which were indicated by their growth density in the nutritional media.

## *EXPERIMENTAL RESULTS*

Data relative to the incidence of the various nutritional groups of bacteria in soil in relation to fertility and season are presented in Table 1 (Lochhead and Chase, 1943).

TABLE 1

*Percentage incidence of nutritional groups of soil bacteria in relation to fertility and season*

| Nutritional Group | Soil N (infertile) | Soil X (fertile) | June sampling | October sampling |
|---|---|---|---|---|
| I. Grow in basal medium | 14·6 | 7·9 | 10·3 | 12·4 |
| II. Require amino acids | 8·4 | 12·1 | 10·3 | 9·9 |
| III. Require growth factors | 12·8 | 12·1 | 10·3 | 14·9 |
| IV. Require amino acids + growth factors | 17·0 | 7·3 | 16·6 | 7·5 |
| V. Require yeast extract | 9·4 | 22·4 | 13·7 | 18·1 |
| VI. Require soil extract | 7·0 | 3·0 | 6·3 | 3·7 |
| VII. Require yeast and soil extract | 29·2 | 32·1 | 29·1 | 32·3 |

One soil (N) had been impoverished by continuous cropping without fertilizer addition; the other (X) had been maintained at good fertility level by regular application of farmyard manure. In the fertile soil, organisms capable of developing in the basal medium, or in the media of known composition, groups I to IV, were less abundant than in poor soil, i.e. 39·4 per cent as compared with 52·8 per cent. On the other hand, forms for which the more complex ingredients of yeast and soil extract were necessary, groups V to VII, were relatively more numerous. Despite such differences, probably related to the higher content of organic matter in the better soil, the incidence of the different groups did not appear to reflect the pronounced difference in crop-producing capacity. In the June sampling, organisms requiring amino acids and growth factors for maximum growth were more abundant than in October, a result which appeared to be associated with the effect of an actively growing crop. In other respects few differences between the two sampling dates were noted. Lochhead and Chase (1943) also indicated that a correlation of nutritional requirements with morphological type did not reveal any clear-cut relationship, though they noted certain trends. Organisms with simpler requirements were, to a larger extent, spore-forming rods and Gram-negative non-sporing rods. Pleomorphic forms comprised a greater proportion of organisms with more complex nutritional needs.

Application of the method of nutritional grouping revealed that in rhizosphere soil profound and characteristic changes occurred in the equilibrium with respect to the bacterial nutritional requirements (Lochhead and Thexton, 1947; Wallace and Lochhead, 1949; Lochhead and Rouatt, 1955). The relative incidence of the various nutritional groups of bacteria in a non-rhizosphere and rhizosphere soil are shown in Table 2 (Lochhead and Thexton, 1947). The outstanding

TABLE 2

*Percentage incidence of nutritional groups of bacteria in non-rhizosphere and rhizosphere soil*

| Nutritional Group | Non-rhizosphere soil | Rhizosphere soil |
|---|---|---|
| I. Grow in basal medium | 12·0 | 22·5 |
| II. Require amino acids | 6·8 | 25·0 |
| III. Require growth factors | 23·1 | 15·0 |
| IV. Require amino acid + growth factors | 16·2 | 15·0 |
| V. Require yeast extract | 16·2 | 11·7 |
| VI. Require soil extract | 6·8 | 5·8 |
| VII. Require yeast and soil extract | 11·1 | 2·5 |

feature was that in the rhizosphere there was an increased percentage of organisms that required amino acids for maximum growth (group II), when compared with the non-rhizosphere soil. Also those groups of bacteria that were dependent upon the more complex nutrients provided by yeast extract and soil extract were relatively less abundant in the rhizosphere. This was especially true of those organisms that required certain unidentified substances in yeast plus soil extract. On the other hand, forms that were capable of maximum growth in the basal glucose-salts medium were relatively more abundant in the rhizosphere.

The effect of green manuring six cover crops on the relative incidences of different nutritional groups of bacteria was studied by Lochhead and Rouatt (1955). The 'rhizosphere effects' of the same crop plants were studied for comparison. The results indicated that incorporation of the plant materials exerted a much less pronounced effect on the balance between the nutritional groups than did the same plants when growing. The data pointed to shifts similar in kind to the rhizosphere effect in showing a trend toward higher proportions of bacteria with the simpler requirements and lower relative incidences of organisms needing more complex nutrients. In the rhizosphere the preferential stimulation of bacteria requiring amino acids for maximum growth was consistently noted in studies conducted in our laboratories over a period of 20 years with a wide variety of plants. These findings provided strong circumstantial evidence for the excretion of amino acids by plant roots. Direct evidence was obtained (Katznelson, Rouatt and Payne, 1955) which showed that when plant roots, grown in sand or sandy soil, were dried and then remoistened, appreciable amounts of amino acids and detectable amounts of reducing compounds were liberated. These excreted substances subsequently supported growth of amino acid-requiring bacteria. It was considered, therefore, that in field soil, subjected to frequent drying and remoistening, this phenomenon occurred, thus providing the rhizosphere microflora with nutrients rich in amino acids.

The grouping of soil bacteria according to their nutritional requirements indicated that there existed in soil a group of bacteria that depended for growth upon some essential factor or factors contained in extracts of soil not furnished by combinations of normally adequate nutrients. Lochhead and Thexton (1951) found that, for an important proportion, though not all of the bacteria dependent upon soil extract, the growth promoting effect of the latter could be replaced by vitamin $B_{12}$, then but recently discovered. Of 534 strains, isolated from a field soil on a non-selective basis, 41 required vitamin $B_{12}$ as an essential growth substance. It was further observed that other soil bacteria, with simple nutritional needs, were able to synthesize a factor whose nutrient effect on the organisms responding to the vitamin was related to the amount of vitamin $B_{12}$—active substance produced. From the findings reported it was apparent that the requirement for vitamin $B_{12}$ was shown by an important ecological group of soil bacteria. Subsequently ten types of bacteria for which vitamin $B_{12}$ acts as an essential nutrient were described (Lochhead and Burton, 1955). Three of the organisms were observed to be cocci and one a pleomorphic, curved, unbranched, filamentous form producing cocci in older culture. The remaining six types, representing approximately 80 per cent of the isolates studied were considered to belong to the genus *Arthrobacter*.

Other more nutritionally exacting bacteria for which vitamin $B_{12}$ was unable to replace soil extract, remained dependent upon unknown growth-promoting substances. A study of such fastidious organisms

(Lochhead and Burton, 1953) resulted in the isolation of a soil organism which when grown in a simple medium containing only inorganic salts and glucose was found to synthesize an essential growth factor that was nutritionally equivalent to soil extract in promoting the growth of an organism for which the latter was hitherto considered essential. The organism requiring the growth factor as well as that synthesizing it, both pleomorphic bacteria, were found to be undescribed species. They were considered to be members of the genus *Arthrobacter* and were named, respectively, *Arthrobacter terregens* and *Arthrobacter pascens*. Further investigations of the nature of the growth factor indicated that it was a previously unrecognized substance and it was referred to as the terregens factor (T.F.).

In an extension of studies on the incidence in soil of bacteria requiring growth factors and those elaborating growth-promoting substances, Cook and Lochhead (1959) compared organisms isolated by nonselective procedures from environments of different proximity to plant roots. Data on growth factor requirements by isolates from control soil, rhizosphere and rhizoplane of wheat are presented in Table 3. The

TABLE 3

*Percentage incidence of bacteria from control soil, rhizosphere, and rhizoplane requiring growth factors*

| Growth factor required | Control soil | Rhizosphere | Rhizoplane |
|---|---|---|---|
| Thiamin | 44·9 | 15·2 | 17·0 |
| Biotin | 18·7 | 6·1 | 7·0 |
| Pantothenic acid | 3·7 | 3·0 | 3·0 |
| Folic acid | 1·8 | 3·0 | 4·0 |
| Nicotinic acid | 5·6 | 6·1 | 5·0 |
| Riboflavin | 1·8 | 2·0 | 4·0 |
| Pyridoxine | 1·8 | 1·0 | 5·0 |
| Vitamin $B_{12}$ | 19·6 | 2·0 | 1·0 |
| Terregens Factor | 1·8 | $<$1·0 | 1·0 |
| p-Aminobenzoic acid | $<$0·9 | $<$1·0 | $<$1·0 |
| Choline | $<$0·9 | $<$1·0 | $<$1·0 |
| Inositol | $<$0·9 | $<$1·0 | $<$1·0 |
| One or more factors | 54·2 | 24·2 | 25·0 |

outstanding feature was the occurrence of a much higher proportion of organisms needing one or more growth-promoting substances in the control soil than was noted in the rhizosphere or rhizoplane. In all cases thiamin was found to be the factor most frequently required. In addition to this vitamin, biotin and vitamin $B_{12}$ were the most commonly needed growth substances by organisms from the control soil. In rhizosphere and rhizoplane, biotin and particularly $B_{12}$ were relatively much less important than in the control. Less obvious differences were noted in respect of other factors. Table 4 shows the growth factors produced

TABLE 4

*Percentage incidence of bacteria from control soil, rhizosphere, and rhizoplane synthesizing growth factors*

| Growth factor synthesized | Control soil | Rhizosphere | Rhizoplane |
|---|---|---|---|
| Thiamin | 28·0 | 61·6 | 68·0 |
| Biotin | 14·0 | 33·3 | 43·0 |
| Pantothenic acid | 32·7 | 71·7 | 74·0 |
| Folic acid | 26·2 | 58·5 | 61·0 |
| Nicotinic acid | 30·8 | 71·7 | 74·0 |
| Riboflavin | 27·1 | 72·7 | 76·0 |
| Pyridoxine | 18·7 | 56·6 | 58·0 |
| Vitamin $B_{12}$ | 14·0 | 20·2 | 27·0 |
| Terregens factor | 15·0 | 23·2 | 21·0 |
| One or more of 9 growth factors | 37·4 | 79·8 | 79·0 |

by isolates from control soil, rhizosphere, and rhizoplane of wheat. It was noted that for all factors capacity for synthesis was in all cases greater with bacteria from the rhizosphere and rhizoplane than with those from the control soil. Whereas 37·4 per cent of the control isolates were able to produce one or more growth factors under the conditions of the test, this ability was shown by 79·8 per cent and 79·0 per cent of those from rhizosphere and rhizoplane respectively. In both of the latter environments the greatest absolute percentage increases in vitamin-synthesizing bacteria were with organisms producing riboflavin and nicotinic acid. In the rhizosphere the greatest proportionate increases occurred with organisms producing pyridoxine and riboflavin, and in the rhizoplane with those forming pyridoxine and biotin. Further studies indicated that the rhizoplane organisms were capable of synthesizing a greater number of factors than those from the rhizosphere. The results supported previous reports of a higher level of microbial activity as the root surface is approached (Katznelson and Rouatt, 1957*a*; Katznelson and Rouatt, 1957*b*).

## *DISCUSSION*

Since the bacterial equilibrium in soil at any given time was thought to depend in large measure upon the availability of nutrients required for growth, the principle of grouping bacteria according to their nutritional needs was advocated. It was emphasized (Lochhead, 1952) that any system for the nutritional classification of soil bacteria was an arbitrary one, and the grouping of the organisms depended upon the observance of a rigid set of conditions with respect to the number and composition of the differential media, the time and temperature of incubation and the manner of assessing the growth response. Practical considerations were the chief factors in selecting the number of differential media used, since it was demonstrated (Lochhead and Chase, 1943), that there were wide divergencies in the individual requirements of members of the same nutritional group. Since the method was recognized as laborious and time consuming, considerable study was directed toward plating procedures with a series of solid media in attempts to obtain direct counts of organisms of the various nutritional groups. It was found not possible to develop such a rapid grouping method because of mutual interference between colonies which prevented any clear-cut differentiation on the basis of the media used.

The system revealed that in soil there were bacteria whose nutritional requirements varied from the simple to the very complex and also that the incidence rates of the groups were reasonably constant in soil of a given type. It also demonstrated wide differences in individual nutritional requirements between members of the same group. These results suggested that the indigenous soil bacteria may exercise highly specialized functions, such as the utilization and production of specific chemical compounds formed during organic matter transformations.

Studies of the 'rhizosphere effect' on the balance between different nutritional groups indicated two characteristic changes; firstly, the preferential stimulation of organisms requiring amino acids and secondly, the relative suppression of those dependent upon the complex nutrients provided in soil extract. In the rhizosphere the increased incidence of bacteria requiring amino acids for maximum growth raised interesting speculations as to the relation of this to plant root excretions, the nature of which at that time was little understood. While our results did not provide any direct evidence of excretion of amino acids, they were not inconsistent with the view that such products could be excreted in amounts sufficient to modify the microbial balance in the region of the plant root.

The differentiation of soil bacteria according to their nutritional requirements stimulated studies on the general vitamin requirements and the vitamin-synthesizing ability of the indigenous microflora. The findings indicated the potential of the indigenous soil bacteria for growth-factor synthesis, but did not establish that the organisms necessarily produce them in soil. However, there was no reason for doubting that circumstances could provide suitable conditions for production in soil. Since in the rhizosphere the numbers of organisms requiring growth factors, and even more particularly those with capabilities for the production of growth factors, may attain very high levels, it was suggested that growth factors be accorded far more consideration in studying plant-microbe interrelationships (Lochhead, 1958).

Studies in microbial ecology have consistently suggested a striving towards an equilibrium in any environment. Though changes in the bacterial equilibrium may be detected between morphological and certain physiological groups, it was considered that a more meaningful approach to the changes in balance was best investigated by a study of micro-organisms from the standpoint of their nutritional requirements. Methods suggested in these studies have proved helpful in certain directions.

Details of procedure are susceptible to modification and improvement, but it is felt that the general principles provide a useful tool for qualitative investigations of the bacterial flora of the soil and its relationship to plant growth.

## *REFERENCES*

COOK, F. D. & LOCHHEAD, A. G. (1959). Growth factor relationships of soil micro-organisms as affected by proximity to the plant root. *Can. J. Microbiol.*, **5**, 323.

KATZNELSON, H. & ROUATT, J. W. (1957*a*). Studies on the incidence of certain physiological groups of bacteria in the rhizosphere. *Can. J. Microbiol.*, **3**, 265.

KATZNELSON, H. & ROUATT, J. W. (1957*b*). Manometric studies with rhizosphere and non-rhizosphere soil. *Can. J. Microbiol.*, **3**, 673.

KATZNELSON, H., ROUATT, J. W. & PAYNE, T. M. B. (1955). The liberation of amino acids and reducing compounds by plant roots. *Pl. Soil*, **7**, 35.

LOCHHEAD, A. G. (1940). Qualitative studies of soil micro-organisms. III. Influence of plant growth on the character of the bacterial flora. *Can. J. Res. C.*, **18**, 42.

LOCHHEAD, A. G. (1952). The nutritional classification of soil bacteria. *Proc. Soc. appl. Bact.*, **15**, 15.

LOCHHEAD, A. G. (1958). Soil bacteria and growth-promoting substances. *Bact. Rev.*, **22**, 145.

LOCHHEAD, A. G. & BURTON, M. O. (1953). An essential bacterial growth factor produced by microbial synthesis. *Can. J. Bot.*, **31**, 7.

LOCHHEAD, A. G. & BURTON, M. O. (1955). Qualitative studies of soil micro-organisms. XII. Characteristics of vitamin $B_{12}$-requiring bacteria. *Can. J. Microbiol.*, **1**, 319.

LOCHHEAD, A. G. & CHASE, F. E. (1943). Qualitative studies of soil microorganisms. V. Nutritional requirements of the predominant bacterial flora. *Soil Sci.*, **55**, 185.

LOCHHEAD, A. G. & ROUATT, J. W. (1955*b*). Qualitative studies of soil microorganisms. XIII. Effect of decomposition of various crop plants on the nutritional groups of soil bacteria. *Soil Sci.*, **80**, 147.

LOCHHEAD, A. G. & ROUATT, J. W. (1955*a*). The rhizosphere effect on the nutritional groups of soil bacteria. *Proc. Soil Sci. Soc. Am.*, **19**, 48.

LOCHHEAD, A. G. & TAYLOR, C. B. (1938). Qualitative studies of soil microorganisms. I. General introduction. *Can. J. Res. C.*, **16**, 152.

LOCHHEAD, A. G. & THEXTON, R. H. (1947). Qualitative studies of soil microorganisms. VII. The rhizosphere effect in relation to the amino acid nutrition of bacteria. *Can. J. Res. C.*, **25**, 20.

LOCHHEAD, A. G. & THEXTON, R. H. (1951). Vitamin $B_{12}$ as a growth factor for soil bacteria. *Nature, Lond.*, **167**, 1034.

STEVENSON, I. L. & ROUATT, J. W. (1953). Qualitative studies of soil microorganisms. XI. Further observations on the nutritional classification of bacteria. *Can. J. Bot.*, **31**, 438.

TAYLOR, C. B. & LOCHHEAD, A. G. (1938). Qualitative studies of soil microorganisms. II. A survey of the bacterial flora of soils differing in fertility. *Can. J. Res. C.*, **16**, 162.

WALLACE, R. H. & LOCHHEAD, A. G. (1949). Qualitative studies of soil microorganisms. VIII. Influence of various crop plants on the nutritional groups of soil bacteria. *Soil Sci.*, **67**, 63.

WEST, P. M. & LOCHHEAD, A. G. (1940). Qualitative studies of soil microorganisms. IV. The rhizosphere in relation to the nutritive requirements of soil bacteria. *Can. J. Res. C.*, **18**, 129.

## *DISCUSSION*

### THE TAXONOMY OF SOIL BACTERIA

*Chairman: Dr. S. T. Cowan, National Public Health Laboratories, Colindale*

*Dr. S. T. Cowan.* Dr. Gordon remarked that 'Classifications are not permanent'; that is probably the truest thing that has been said here today. We all tend to think that the latest classification is the best classification and that it is going to last for all time, but it is not. It is going to be superceded as we gain more knowledge. We shall change our ideas and with those ideas we shall change our classification. This applies particularly to a manual like *Bergey's Manual.* I have seen so many times in papers, 'This organism is not in *Bergey's Manual*, therefore it does not exist'. It is not put in those words but it is implied. I can assure you that the *Bergey's Manual* trustees do not look at *Bergey's Manual* in that light. They compile that manual from the literature, and if organisms have never been described before, you cannot expect them to be in the manual. Neither can you assume, and you must not assume, that the classification in the current edition of *Bergey's Manual* is either correct or is never going to change.

Further confusion arises in the use of dichotomous keys. Dichotomous keys are not part of classification. Dichotomous keys are used for identification. This brings me back to the question—'What is taxonomy?'. Taxonomy is the description and examination of organisms and the dividing up and analysis of these organisms. Taxonomy can be divided into three parts. Firstly there is classification. Classification is the examination of cultures and the sorting of them so the likes are put on one side and unlikes on the other: those unlikes are then re-sorted until you are left with a series of groups. The second part of taxonomy is the naming or labelling of organisms; they may be given names or numbers; there are advantages in both. Finally the third stage is reached when you have a whole lot of unknown organisms and you want to identify them with those you have classified and named in the first two parts of what I call taxonomy. Dichotomous keys are extremely useful at the identification stage; they are no use at all when you are trying to classify.

Dr. Gordon also talked about species and she defined species in a way which horrified me a little. It really boiled down to this—'A species is what a competent taxonomist says is a species', i.e. that the newly isolated strains, the old ones in the culture collection and any old thing that we think is this same organism constitutes a species.

*Dr. R. E. Gordon.* Plus their variants.

*Dr. S. T. Cowan.* Yes, plus their variants. Those of you who know me, know that I do not believe in species.

In the various methods of classification that are being discussed today, a great deal of emphasis has been placed on morphology. I think this is because soil bacteriologists do not know very much about soil bacteria. We know rather more about our medical bacteria, partly because we have been dealing with them for a longer time and partly because they are easier to deal with. We have relatively little knowledge of morphology, but a lot more knowledge of their biochemical and physical reactions, pathogenicity, ecology, etc.

This leads me on to the Adansonian principle. Adansonian classification is not synonymous with numerical taxonomy. Numerical taxonomy is a statistical method of analysing data that has been collected Adansonially. Adanson was a taxonomist and he did have a classification, but he was not dealing with bacteria. The principle that Adanson used was to give equal weight to all the characters that he examined. Thus there is an Adansonian principle, not an Adansonian method.

I must mention briefly the use of numerical methods. Sneath, after he had carried out his analysis of the genus *Chromobacterium*, asked me if he could analyse the cultures in the National Collection of Type Cultures. You know the result. The gratifying feature, gratifying at any rate to some of the older bacteriologists, is that the answers that Sneath obtained were, more or less, the answers that we had before. There were a few differences: the cholera vibrio was put very close to the Enterobacteriaceae, and we had suspected this before. We had also suspected that certain *Pasteurella* spp. were closely related to the Enterobacteriaceae and the computer told us the same tale. However, the computer was confirming findings on our own data, so perhaps it was not quite as impartial as it might have been.

Professor Küster talked about a number of actinomycetes, but I am quite sure that he has only touched on the fringe of this topic. The actinomycetes are a horrible group of organisms. I am sure that up his sleeve he has hundreds of other species. I say this in the knowledge that the Bergey Manual Trust is publishing the *Index Bergeyana*, which is a list of about 25,000 to 50,000 names that have been used for bacteria. The section dealing with the actinomycetes, published in the *International Bulletin of bacteriological Nomenclature and Taxonomy*, is 40 to 50 pages long. What is the present position? How many of these species and genera are recognized?

*Professor E. Küster.* There are a number of new generic names which are similar to, even synonymous with, one or other of the old genera. *Jensenia* seems to be similar to *Mycobacterium* and *Nocardia. Pseudonocardia*, a thermophile, is synonymous with *Dermatophilus*. *Promicromonospora* is similar to *Micromonospora*, except that it forms spores on the vegetative mycelium at a very early stage of growth. *Waksmania* is synonymous with *Microbispora*. One species of *Thermopolyspora* is also synonymous with *Microbispora* and the other species is illegal because it was not grown in pure culture and is no longer available. *Streptoverticillium* is a verticillate *Streptomyces*. It is questionable whether we should put verticillate *Streptomyces* spp. into a different genus, although Yamaguchi agreed with Baldacci's view because he found that they had different chemicals in their cell walls. *Chainia* and *Actinopycnidium* are *Streptomyces* spp. which form sclerotia and pycnidia under particular growth conditions. The ability to form sclerotia is not restricted to any particular species; it is quite common among the streptomycetes. *Thermoactinopolyspora* is a thermophilic *Streptomyces*. *Macrospora* is synonymous with *Microellobosporia*. I feel that it is not useful to introduce new genera on the basis of very small differences between them.

*Dr. S. T. Williams*. Dr. Cowan mentioned the emphasis on morphology in the classification of soil bacteria. Much important information about the actinomycetes has been derived from cell wall analyses. Indeed, many doubtful genera, doubtful, that is, on morphological grounds, are also shown to be doubtful as a result of cell wall analyses. Thus species of *Chainia*, which morphologically resemble *Streptomyces* spp., although they form sclerotia, appear to fit into the genus *Streptomyces* as a result of cell wall analyses. There are several other genera where similar results have been obtained.

*Prof. N. A. Krasilnikov*. I think that a very important character for the delimitation of actinomycetes and proactinomycetes is pigment colour. The chemical composition of the pigments may vary. Some strains have anthocyanins whilst others possess actinorubin.

The proactinomycetes (*Nocardia*) are very interesting organisms. We have isolated strains from different soils of the USSR. Typically, *Nocardia* (*Proactinomyces*) fragments into rods and cocci. *Actinomyces* has a filamentous appearance. Some strains of *Nocardia*, after 2–5 transfers, change to typical *Actinomyces*. What are these organisms? Similarly, what are the organisms that are typical mycobacteria, but which change into *Actinomyces*?

*Dr. R. E. Gordon*. I do not know of any morphological characteristics that separate the genus *Nocardia* from the genus *Streptomyces*. *Nocardia madurae* does not fragment. Some strains of *Nocardia asteroides* form corkscrews. One variant of *Streptomyces rimosus* may be lifted from the agar with an inoculating needle as easily as a culture of *Escherichia coli*. It is flat and it fragments. One would certainly not put the parent and daughter strains in two different genera. It is impossible!

However, cell wall composition does separate *Nocardia asteroides*, *Nocardia brasiliensis*, *Nocardia madurae*, *Nocardia pelletieri*, *Nocardia vaccinium* and 2 or 3 other species from *Streptomyces albus*, *Streptomyces fradiae*, *Streptomyces somaliensis* and all the other *Streptomyces* spp. that we have tested.

I have not used visible pigmentation for the separation of species or genera, because I think it is much too variable. Detailed chemical studies might prove useful.

*Prof. E. Küster*. It is for these reasons that I pose the question, 'Is *Nocardia* a true genus?'! *Nocardia* overlaps with both *Mycobacterium* and *Streptomyces* and there are many strains that show characters of both; they can change when the cultural conditions change. They are intermediate.

*Prof. D. Pramer*. I hesitate to involve myself in this argument, but Professor Krasilnikov has referred to *Nocardia* and *Actinomyces*. It seems to me that the discussion has been concerned with *Nocardia* and *Streptomyces*. If I recall correctly *Actino-*

*myces* and *Nocardia* are differentiated on the basis of aerobic *versus* anaerobic and pathogenic *versus* non-pathogenic.

*Dr. R. E. Gordon.* Professor Krasilnikov uses *Actinomyces* for *Streptomyces*.

*Dr. H. L. Jensen.* It has been customary to talk about *Nocardia* as representing a transition between *Mycobacterium* and *Streptomyces*, but there is another group with which the nocardiae merge, the arthrobacters. In them the tendency to branch is often much more pronounced than in *Mycobacterium*. Indeed, the real, acid-fast mycobacteria rarely branch at all.

Mycobacteria are typically acid-fast. Nocardiae are sometimes more or less acid-fast, whilst other strains are non-acid-fast. Perhaps we have a double origin for the nocardiae. There are a few motile *Arthrobacter* spp. and a few motile *Nocardia* spp. but I know of no motile, acid-fast mycobacteria. Like Dr. Gordon, who knows no borderline between *Nocardia* and *Streptomyces*, I know no borderline between *Arthrobacter* and *Nocardia*.

*Dr. C. G. Dobbs.* When one identifies *Mucor*, fresh from the soil, the description never fits the classical description. One suspects that these organisms are not only mutating, but also fusing and anastamosing, perhaps in nature. It is a hopeless task to get any fixed classification therefore, because the organisms are probably changing faster than the descriptions are changing. I would like to know to what extent non-sexual fusions occur in bacteria and actinomycetes.

*Dr. R. E. Gordon.* Nocard's original strain of *Nocardia asteroides* has still got characteristics in common with freshly isolated strains of *Nocardia asteroides*. These characters separate them from all other strains of *Nocardia* and *Streptomyces* that I have examined.

*Dr. S. T. Williams.* There is certainly genetical evidence that strains of actinomycetes can fuse and that heterocaryosis can occur. Stable recombinants have been found in *Streptomyces* spp. There is also evidence that actinophages can carry genetic information from one strain to another.

*Prof. H. Veldkamp.* Dr. Gordon, the species concept in the higher organism is based partly on the ability of organisms belonging to a species to interbreed. We cannot use this criterion in bacteriology. You define species as a group of organisms which have in common a number of reliable characteristics. I feel that this is not a very satisfactory definition. Should we abandon the species concept in bacteriology until we can define bacterial species a little better?

*Dr. R. E. Gordon.* You mean that we should speak of groups of organisms or taxa?

*Prof. H. Veldkamp.* Yes, I agree; we have to be practical; we have to do something.

*Dr. R. E. Gordon.* You believe we should abandon the binomial system?

*Prof. H. Veldkamp.* Yes, that doesn't make very much sense either.

*Dr. R. E. Gordon.* I agree with Walters that the basis of communication in the future will be something different from the genus and species concept. Nevertheless, there are groups, and whatever we call them, they will still be very much the same.

*Dr. S. T. Cowan.* I have already said that I do not believe in species. I do not think that it is a very useful term, but I think that the concept is quite useful, as long as we are not too rigid. We must not, as we tend to do in bacteriology, tie species up with the nomenclatural type. Unfortunately, the nomenclature committee is stressing the use of the nomenclatural type concept. Now the type serves only to attach a name to one organism, one particular strain. It is left to the competence of the bacteriologist to say whether the other organisms are similar to that or not. My experience with bacteria is that if you do enough tests, you will never find two organisms alike. Therefore, for every strain you would have to create a new name and for every name you would have to have another type strain. This problem arose when Kaufmann wanted to have all serotypes recognized as species. If you accept that, you would have 120 serotypes of *Escherichia coli*, 800 serotypes of salmonellae and I don't know how many serotypes within *Klebsiella*, each with a different name. Dr. Gordon's idea of a population species is a much more realistic one than a nomenclatural type species (attaching a name to one strain). She would take a series of strains which had been worked over thoroughly and agree that they were a group of similar organisms; she would show, by picking out about 6 strains, the limits of the variability of the characters. It would not be essential for every strain to possess every character, either positive or negative. Indeed, I should like to see descriptions which said 'glucose fermentation-99', meaning that the odd strain would be negative, and 'motile-55', showing that there was great variability of that character.

*Prof. H. Veldkamp.* But there are thousands of variants. One bacterium in $10^7$ to $10^8$ is a mutant; pure cultures do not exist. How would you deal with them? When you grow an organism on a certain medium, you select the mutant which is best adapted to that environment and when you grow the same organism on another medium, you select another one.

*Dr. R. E. Gordon.* I did not intend to give the idea that I would study all the variants. I believe that variants should be used to give some idea of the amount of variation possible, not all the variation.

*Dr. T. Gibson.* A point which does not seem to have been mentioned is the great difficulty in classifying the dominant soil bacteria. It is a feature that seems to be common to the dominant organisms in the major natural habitats, including soil, water, seawater, etc. One gets strains varying in all sorts of directions without any really clear-cut groups or taxonomic species. They are not very active biochemically.

The bacteria which fall into nice, tidy groups are usually organisms which have become adapted to special conditions of life, e.g. in the tissue of an animal, in cheese or food; there one meets with great uniformity. In the genus *Bacillus* there are a great number of very clearly defined species, but when it comes to the aerobic spore-forming bacteria in soil, it is a very difficult matter to decide how to classify them. You find strains which resemble *Bacillus circulans*, or *Bacillus sphaericus*, or *Bacillus brevis*, or some others, and you would say that they are more or less intermediate between all of these well-defined species.

*Dr. T. R. G. Gray.* In connection with Dr. Gibson's remarks, I would like to take up something touched upon by the chairman. Dr. Cowan said that soil bacteriologists did not know very much about their organisms, at any rate when compared with what medical bacteriologists know about their bacteria. When I die, I hope I shall die only one death; when a piece of organic matter dies in the soil, it dies a thousand deaths, or perhaps more accurately, about $1 \times 10^8$ deaths, all of them possibly different. Using conventional methods, we cannot possibly cope with these enormous populations. We can only study a terribly insignificant proportion of them, and when we have done this all we can say is that at the moment in time when we sampled the soil, these particular organisms seemed to be important. From there, we can go on to investigate why these organisms might have been able to become important, even if only for a short time, to carry out autecological investigations.

We have been trying to accelerate the gathering of biochemical data for taxonomic purposes by using multipoint inoculation methods, whereby we can carry out about 500 tests in 20 to 30 mins. I don't think that this enables us to increase significantly the proportion of the microflora that we examine, but we can increase appreciably the amount of information that we know about some of the bacteria.

*Dr. P. J. Harris.* I was rather worried by the diagrams, shown in conjunction with Dr. Rovira and Mr. Brisbane's paper, where they compared a large number of rhizosphere isolates with type cultures. The type cultures seemed to go away and sulk in one corner. I fear that the organisms that the taxonomists are dealing with are not closely related with the things that we are getting out of the soil. The type cultures are organisms that have established their respectability; for one thing they will survive; they would not be type cultures if they did not survive. The fresh isolates that one gets from soil seem to have a tendency to shed characters like the trees in autumn. Should one, therefore, keep a new isolate for some time, until it has established its respectability, or should one start work as soon as one can and say 'I don't know what this organism is, but at least it's like what it was when I isolated it'?

*Dr. F. E. Clark.* I would like to emphasize that in most cases, isolates are quite stable, if we can get beyond the initial point of establishing them in culture. The cases that you mention are the exceptions. With some cultures the trouble is apt to be on the human side of the partnership with the test tube, and not the fault of the bacterium in the test tube.

*Dr. T. Mitchell.* I would like to comment on the clustering of the type cultures in Dr. Rovira and Mr. Brisbane's analysis. The number of characters that they tested for each strain was only 37. If you are making Adansonian analyses, you should have more characters, i.e. over 100. The tests that you use are also important, especially if you are dealing with soil isolates. If you take non-soil isolates for comparison and then use tests like nodulation of plant roots, it is unlikely that you will get a very good correlation between type cultures and fresh isolates.

*Mr. M. Goodfellow.* Dr. Rovira and Mr. Brisbane scored quantitative characters additively. When you use more than two or three characters and score them in this way, an imbalance may result. Consequently, whilst others have divided quantitative characters into 5 or 6 separate character states, they have not. This is one reason why only 37 characters were determined. I agree that the use of more tests might have provided some interesting results.

*Dr. H. B. Gunner.* As a microbiologist, to whom taxonomy is something better left to taxonomists, I have recently been impressed by reports from Mandel and others on the use of base ratios of microbial nucleic acids as a means of sorting out the genera. These reports seem to indicate that base ratios of microbial nucleic acids are much more stable than the ephemeral characteristics of morphology, motility, etc. Do other people feel that base ratios are useful?

*Dr. S. T. Williams.* There is an interesting piece of work *within* the genus *Streptomyces*, done by Silvestri, which led him to conclude from an analysis of base ratios, that all *Streptomyces* were one species.

*Prof. H. Veldkamp.* This has also been done on the genus *Bacillus.* It confirmed what the older taxonomists had already found.

*Dr. C. A. Fewson.* I think that many people working in the nucleic acid field would regard this as somewhat naive. Base ratios might be useful to establish very wide differences, but since the GC content depends on hundreds of thousands of individual nucleotides, one could easily get an averaging out from very different genomes, thus giving the same GC content.

*Dr. S. T. Cowan.* This is so. Staphylococci and micrococci have two quite different ratios.

*Mr. M. Goodfellow.* Every new test that appears is accepted as the key to the taxonomic lock. Base ratios fall into this category. They may be useful in some cases and not in others.

*Mr. G. W. Hull.* Can anyone tell us about the use of infra-red spectra of bacteria for diagnostic purposes? They should offer very considerable advantages for typing micro-organisms.

*Dr. S. T. Cowan.* I can answer that one because I was told, at the time the use of infra-red spectra was suggested, that I would soon be out of a job, that there would be nothing more for me to do. I still have a job.

There have been several papers describing the infra-red spectra of different bacteria, and it is certainly one method of identifying a particular strain, but the technique is laborious and it is difficult to get reproducible results.

*Mr. D. Baxby.* Classification is very important, but surely you must bear in mind that you have to identify organisms, and the fewer tests there are for this the better.

*Dr. M. Alexander.* We have always hoped that we would be able to find a diagnostic character that could be correlated either with biochemical activities or ecological relationships. Unfortunately, all the characteristics that we have ever examined, either from the biochemical or ecological points of view, have turned out to be the very characteristics that are lost in culture. I think that it is wishful thinking to say that it would be nice to have something that relates to the ecology or biochemistry of an organism. For the moment I would be very happy if the taxonomists would say 'This is the organism you have'; then we can go our own way.

*Dr. W. Gams.* Nutritional classifications have been used very widely to characterize the soil microflora and to gain some idea of ecological relationships in the soil. I get the impression that such classifications have been used so much that they have outlived their usefulness. Perhaps one should look for new criteria, further physiological requirements or potentialities. I was very impressed by the fact that Dr. Rovira and Mr. Brisbane used the establishment of bacteria on wheat roots as a character. I wonder, what are the physiological properties of the bacteria that allow this establishment? I cannot imagine that it is a growth factor requirement, for growth factors would not be present in sufficient quantities in the root environment.

*Mr. G. W. Hull.* Dr. Rouatt, do you think that co-ordination compounds of cobalt, other than vitamin $B_{12}$ may have great diagnostic importance?

*Dr. J. W. Rouatt.* I have had no experience with these compounds.

# BACTERIA IN THE ROOT REGION OF PLANTS

# PHYSIOLOGICAL STUDIES OF RHIZOSPHERE BACTERIA

J. MACURA

*Institute of Microbiology, Czechoslovak Academy of Sciences, Prague*

## *INTRODUCTION*

Micro-organisms are exposed to the influence of many factors in the soil. It is generally accepted that the numbers and types of soil micro-organisms and their activity are affected by the nature and availability of energy and nutrient sources, the physical, chemical and biological character of the environment and environmental conditions, e.g. humidity, temperature, aeration and others (Waksman, 1952). The effect of particular factors can vary to a great extent in various sites within the soil, which obviously contributes to the existence of micro-habitats. Moreover, all these particular factors are optimal for growth only in exceptional cases. Just as the microbial soil population varies in the incidence of types with different potentialities, the reaction of individual organisms is not always the same and continual changes are brought about in the amount, composition and activity of micro-biological populations in the soil environment. A dynamic equilibrium is, however, always attained, which is the result of the interaction between the environment and the microflora.

It is possible to distinguish two basic types of local environment of micro-organisms in the soil (Thornton, 1956). One type is found in the soil away from the direct influence of growing roots and its character is conditioned by the presence of organic residues, mainly of plant origin. The other basic type of environment is found in the vicinity of the roots, in the rhizosphere zone, and its existence is determined by the metabolic activity of the plant root system. As both basic types of environment differ in chemical and physical properties, the microbial population living therein varies also.

Many papers have been devoted to the study of micro-organisms in the rhizosphere. Surveys of these papers, as well as discussion on various aspects of the rhizosphere effect, are reported in several reviews

(Starkey, 1929, 1958; Katznelson, Lochhead and Timonin, 1948; Clark, 1949; Krasilnikov, 1958; Lochhead, 1959; Katznelson, 1965). Depending upon the approach and the aim of work, they are concerned with: (1) the establishment of the rhizosphere effect, (2) the colonization of roots by micro-organisms, (3) the effect of the rhizosphere microflora on the plant, (4) the control of the root or rhizosphere microbial populations. These different types of investigation seem to represent particular stages of the study of the rhizosphere effect.

The rhizosphere effect can be considered to have been established (Starkey, 1958). While in the study of quantitative and qualitative aspects of the rhizosphere effect a descriptive and analytical approach prevails, the study of root colonization by micro-organisms and the effect of these micro-organisms on plants represents a physiological stage of rhizosphere investigations. The ability of micro-organisms to colonize roots and affect the properties of their soil environment or plant growth is connected closely with their physiological properties and biochemical activity. Therefore, a more detailed knowledge of the physiological behaviour and biochemical expression of micro-organisms in this characteristic ecological niche, as well as of the properties of the rhizosphere environment, is necessary for the understanding of the interrelationships between plants and micro-organisms in the soil.

## *THE RHIZOSPHERE ENVIRONMENT*

Metabolic activity of roots and root exudates can be considered to be the main factors causing the rhizosphere effect and determining the properties of the rhizosphere environment because they supply the micro-organisms with available sources of nutrients. Although the products of decomposition of sloughed-off surface tissue and root hairs and microbial metabolites (Vágnerová and Vančura, 1962) can contribute to the nutrition of micro-organisms in the rhizosphere, the role of substances excreted by the roots seems to be more important (Macura, 1965). The composition of root exudates has been very intensively studied during the last few years (Kutáček, 1960; Börner, 1962; Woods, 1960; Rovira, 1962; Vančura, 1964). Sugars, organic acids, amino acids, glycosides, nucleotides and their bases, enzymes, vitamins, indole-derivates, phenolic substances and other substances have been identified. Their occurrence differs in various plants, according to the conditions of growth. Quantitative and qualitative changes have been established in the composition of root exudates during plant growth (Rovira, 1959; Vančura and Hovadík, 1965*a*, 1965*b*) and after foliar application of chemicals (Vraný, Vančura and Macura, 1962; Vraný, 1963, 1965).

However, less information is available on quantitative aspects of root exudates. Harmsen and Jager (1963) have found from 120–1,000 ppm. of carbon in soil immediately adjacent to the roots, 120–280 ppm. in the surrounding 1 cm. thick layer of soil and 0–40 ppm. in the more distant remaining soil. Meshkov (1961) established that the carbon content of root exudates of peas grown in nutrient solutions was 4–10 per cent (in maize exudates 1·7–2·3 per cent), of plant carbon. According to the data of Vančura (1964), the root exudates of barley and wheat seedlings represented 7–10 per cent of the dry weight of the aerial plant parts. The extent of the rhizosphere effect can be considerable (Papavizas and Davey, 1961), but it is difficult to express the amount of root exudation under natural conditions. Roots and root hairs of one plant can attain a considerable length (Dittmer, 1937) and therefore a great part of soil can be considered to be rhizosphere soil. However, organic substances are not released uniformly from all parts of the roots. In seedlings, the excretion of ninhydrin positive substances and reducing substances is concentrated near the root tip (Parkinson, 1955; Pearson and Parkinson, 1961; Čatská, 1965). Microbiological activity increases in this zone due to the effect of the root hairs enlarging the root surface area markedly. The properties of the environment vary, therefore, with the age of the plant and the physiological activity of its roots. The microbiological data on bacterial populations in the rhizoplane and in various root zones during plant growth are in good agreement with these conclusions (Vágnerová, Macura and Čatská, 1960*a*, 1960*b*; Vágnerová, 1965).

## *PHYSIOLOGICAL CHARACTERISTICS OF BACTERIA COLONIZING ROOTS*

The rhizosphere environment resembles an enrichment or elective culture. The substances liberated by roots, together with physical changes brought about by root activity in the rhizosphere, affect selectively the growth and development of various groups and types of micro-organisms. The mechanism by which the microbial root and rhizosphere populations build up remains obscure. In general, the organisms that predominate are those which are able, due to their physiological properties and metabolic potentialities, to react most rapidly to the specific conditions of the environment and make full use of them. A considerable amount of data exists which supports this assumption, indicating the higher physiological and metabolic activity of bacteria colonizing the roots.

As Starkey stated (1958), 'The mere fact that bacterial cells are more abundant in the rhizosphere than in the soil is evidence that they were more active in their natural environment, irrespective of their inherent physiological characteristics or what they did in the soil'. Nevertheless, it remains to be seen which properties or mechanisms enable certain micro-organisms to develop rapidly in the rhizosphere and to become dominant. The interesting data on the relatively higher incidence of ammonnifying, denitrifying, sugar fermenting, starch hydrolysing, methylene-blue and resazurin reducing bacteria (Katznelson and Rouatt, 1957; Macura, 1958*a*; Vágnerová, Macura and Čatská, 1960*a*, 1960*b*; Rouatt and Katznelson, 1961; Rouatt *et al.*, 1963) characterize the rhizosphere effect but cannot explain the reasons for the selection observed. Bacteria isolated from the rhizoplane grow more rapidly and abundantly than bacteria isolated from the rhizosphere or from the soil (Rovira, 1956; Rouatt and Katznelson, 1957; Macura, 1958*b*; Vágnerová *et al.*, 1960*a*, 1960*b*). The phenomenon was observed during the vegetative period of wheat (Vágnerová *et al.*, 1960*a*, 1960*b*): however, smaller differences in the incidence of rapidly growing strains were found between the isolates from the rhizoplane and the soil, than between the isolates from the rhizoplane and the rhizosphere. The rate of growth of various bacteria seemed to be correlated with their normal habitat. Thus the majority of rapidly growing strains of Gram-negative bacteria, which are characteristic of root populations, were isolated from the rhizoplane. Conversely, the majority of the rapidly growing strains of the Gram-positive cocci and spore-forming organisms were isolated from soil away from the roots. All the morphological groups varied in their nutritional requirements. The data on growth intensity of the rhizosphere and soil bacteria correspond with the rhizosphere phenomenon in nature, but it is evident that successful root colonization by certain types of micro-organisms is not only a result of their growth rate. Indeed it is only when the competing organisms are capable of utilizing a given substrate equally and are not affected differently by the physical properties of the environment or are not antagonistic to one another, that the growth rate can be decisive in determining which organism predominates.

The nutritional requirements of the micro-organisms are plainly very important in determining the rhizosphere effect. The predominance of bacteria requiring amino acids for their maximum growth and, in comparison with the soil bacterial population, the lower incidence of types requiring substances contained in yeast and soil extract, are characteristic of the rhizosphere effect. This was demonstrated by Lochhead and his colleagues (Lochhead and Thexton, 1947; Wallace and Lochhead, 1949; Lochhead and Rouatt, 1955; Rouatt and Katznelson, 1961) and confirmed by others (Macura, 1958*b*; Vágnerová *et al*., 1960*a*, 1960*b*; 1961; Rangaswami and Vasantharajan, 1962). The effect was most obvious on the root surface (Vágnerová *et al*., 1960*a*, 1960*b*; Rouatt and Katznelson, 1961), though still evident in the rhizosphere soil. This is ascribed to the influence of amino acids exuded by roots. It was also proved (Vágnerová, 1965) that on the roots of wheat seedlings growing in soil, the number of bacteria requiring amino acids increases from the basal portion to the tip of roots. The fact that during the continuous addition of root exudates to the soil the number of bacteria requiring amino acids increases markedly (Macura, 1965) supports the view that the accumulation of this bacterial group is a result of the higher content of amino acids in the environment.

The nutritional groups of bacteria are not uniform in their composition, the nature of the bacteria depending upon the source from which they were isolated. In the group of bacteria requiring amino acids, Gram-negative forms represented 72·0 per cent of the population isolated from the root surface, 48·3 per cent of the population isolated from the rhizosphere and only 26·8 per cent of the population isolated from the free soil. The opposite trend was observed for Gram-positive bacteria (Vágnerová *et al*., 1960*a*, 1960*b*). The incidence of bacteria utilizing glucose decreased as the distance from the roots increased. Soil isolates, however, utilized xylose better (Vágnerová, Vančura and Lasík, 1963). A higher incidence of bacteria capable of oxidizing glucose, acetate, and alanine more rapidly, was also found in the root zone (Zagallo and Katznelson, 1957; Katznelson and Bose, 1959). On the other hand, the relative incidence of bacteria utilizing p-hydroxybenzoic acid and benzoic acid was higher in the soil than on the roots (Vraný, 1960). The prevailing importance of energy and nutrient sources can be assumed, because no specific rhizosphere effect was observed in the occurrence of bacteria requiring vitamins and growth factors (Lochhead and Burton, 1956, 1957; Cook and Lochhead, 1959). However, indirect effects may occur when one of two bacterial strains is stimulated and suppresses or inhibits the growth of the other organism (Chan and Katznelson, 1961; Chan, Katznelson and Rouatt, 1963). In addition to this inhibiting effect, competition for nutrient sources or for limiting nutrients can occur (Marshall and Alexander, 1960; Finstein and Alexander, 1962).

### *ROLE OF THE ROOT EXUDATES IN ROOT COLONIZATION*

Since the excretion of organic substances by plant roots has been proved by various authors there is no doubt that root exudates cause both the quantitative and qualitative aspects of the rhizosphere effect. It is interesting that more attention has been paid to the study of the role of root exudates in processes of pathogenesis caused by root-infecting fungi and other plant pathogens (Schroth and Hildebrand, 1964), rather than to the study of the processes involved in the constitution of the root surface and rhizosphere microbial populations.

The addition of root exudates to liquid media increased the growth of micro-organisms isolated from the rhizosphere, soil and seeds (Rovira, 1956; Macura, 1958*b*) and affected the growth of mixed cultures of rhizosphere and soil bacteria (Chan, Katznelson and Rouatt, 1963). An appreciable development of bacteria, but not of fungi, was observed both in the liquid media enriched with root exudates and inoculated with a mixture of micro-organisms (Vágnerová, Vančura and Lasík, 1963), and in the soil enriched with root exudates (Rovira, 1956; Macura, 1965). It is also known that the germination of fungal spores is stimulated in the vicinity of roots and in media containing root exudates or their components (Čatská, 1965; Staněk and Lasík, 1965). The effect of root exudates on root pathogens is reviewed by Schroth and Hildebrand (1964).

As the selection and accumulation of bacteria in the rhizosphere is mediated by root exudates, differences in the utilization of root exudates by microbial populations isolated from the root surface, the rhizosphere, the soil and the seed coat might be expected. It has been shown (Vágnerová, Vančura and Lasík, 1963; Vágnerová, 1965) that sugars were utilized most rapidly by the seed coat and rhizosphere bacteria. Amino acids were utilized most rapidly by the microbial population isolated from the roots and rhizosphere, and most slowly by the seed coat population. Phenomena similar to the rhizosphere effect of plants were observed in these *in vitro* conditions. After the inoculation of media, a considerable development of bacteria growing in the basal medium took place, followed by an increase of bacteria requiring amino acids. The incidence of the latter group diminished towards the end of the experiment and the occurrence of bacteria requiring factors contained in yeast and soil extracts increased.

Evidence of the effect of root exudates on the development of micro-organisms in the rhizosphere was furnished by Staněk (1963) who established that the germination of *Ustilago zeae* chlamydospores was stimulated in the proximity of wheat roots; however, the germinated sporidia were destroyed by mycolytic bacteria.

In an attempt to gain more detailed data on the influence of root excretion on the microbial colonization of roots, we searched for a way to affect plant metabolism and therefore the composition of root exudates. The nutritional status of plants growing in the soil or nutrient solutions is reflected in the composition of rhizosphere microflora (Macura, 1958*a*, 1961), but in such cases both the environment of the plants and the micro-organisms are affected. To influence the plant without directly affecting the environment is possible by foliar application of chemicals. Foliar application can bring about both quantitative and qualitative changes in the rhizosphere population (Halleck and Cochrane, 1950; Ramachandra-Reddy, 1959; Venkata Ram, 1960; Horst and Herr, 1962; Vraný, Vančura and Macura, 1962). Another attractive feature of the method is the fact that certain substances can be absorbed by leaves, translocated within the plant and exuded by roots (Preston, Mitchell and Reeve, 1954; Linder *et al.*, 1958).

Foliar application seems, therefore, to be a suitable method for influencing the root population and a good basis for investigating the relation between root exudates and root colonization. It was found that changes were brought about in the number and composition of bacterial populations on the surface of wheat roots after the foliar application of urea, phosphate, growth regulators and antibiotics (Vraný, Vančura and Macura, 1962). Similarly, changes were observed in the quantitative composition of root exudates after chloramphenicol and tri-iodobenzoic acid application. When urea was applied, changes were found in the composition of the bacterial root population, in the ratio of bacteria to fungi (Vraný, 1963) and in the excretion of amino acids and sugars (Vraný, 1965). The differences in the composition of the bacterial population of the rhizoplane were more obvious when wheat was planted in nutrient solutions under sterile conditions and, concurrently with the foliar applications of urea, the medium was inoculated with a soil suspension; distinct differences were shown in the occurrence of nutritional groups of bacteria on roots of control and treated plants.

## *SEED AND SOIL BACTERIA IN RELATION TO ROOT COLONIZATION*

When studying the relation between physiological and biochemical potentialities of bacteria and their ability to colonize the roots, three approaches are possible: (1) investigating root colonization of plants grown aseptically by pure or mixed bacterial cultures, (2) tracing the fate of such strains that can be identified in culture or in another way (by means of fluorescent antibodies), and (3) comparing differences in the bacterial populations of roots of plants growing in the presence of different micro-organisms.

One of the approaches that we have chosen for studying the relation between the properties of bacteria and their ability to colonize the roots is to investigate the role of seed and soil bacteria in root colonization. Seed and soil bacteria differ in the occurrence of morphological groups, in nutritional requirements and growth activity (Wallace and Lochhead, 1951; Macura, 1958*b*; Vágnerová *et al.*, 1960*a*, 1961; Čatská *et al.*, 1963). Knowing the differences we can determine, according to the occurrence of various groups of bacteria on roots and in rhizosphere, which properties are the most decisive in root colonization.

Seeds have on their surface (and partly also inside) numerous micro-organisms, and the specific conditions for the development of these micro-organisms are created during the swelling and germination of seeds (Verona, 1963). Seed-borne bacteria can pass onto the roots (Rempe, 1951; Rovira, 1956; Macura, 1958) and if the inoculation of roots with the microflora of another source (soil) is excluded, then such populations develop quantitatively in accordance with the typical rhizosphere effect. Therefore, it has been concluded that the seed microflora constitutes the root population (Wallace and Lochhead, 1951; Rovira, 1956; Gyllenberg, 1957). The similarity in the species composition of the epiphytic microflora of seeds and roots has also been established (Pantos, 1955; Khudyakov and Voznyakovskaya, 1956). However, neither the incidence of the same bacterial species on the seeds and roots, nor the possibility of transfer of seed bacteria to the roots by the elimination of the soil microflora, prove the prevailing role of this microflora in the colonization of roots which continuously come in contact with soil micro-organisms during plant growth.

The composition of the bacterial population of the wheat rhizosphere remained very similar to the composition of the seed population in our experiments with plants growing from non-sterile seeds in nutrient solutions or sand (Macura, 1958*a*; Čatská *et al.*, 1963; Vágnerová, 1965). However, if soil bacteria were present (added with a soil suspension), the occurrence of the types growing in the basal medium increased and the rapidly growing soilborne strains accumulated. Furthermore, bacteria isolated from the soil grew more profusely in media enriched with root exudates than bacteria isolated from seeds.

Similar alterations were observed in plants growing in soil (Rouatt, 1959; Vágnerová *et al.*, 1960*a*; Čatská *et al.*, 1963; Vágnerová, 1965) and therefore it can be concluded that both seed and soil bacteria can participate in root colonization. However, because of the higher incidence of rapidly growing and metabolically more active types, it seems that soil bacteria play a more important part in root colonization. Similarly soil fungi contribute more to the build-up of the root population than seed-borne fungi (Peterson, 1958; Čatská *et al.*, 1960; Vágnerová *et al.*, 1961). The soil bacteria will have already colonized the spermatosphere during the seed germination and become dominant on the roots, competing with seed organisms.

In the colonization processes, the origin of bacteria is not so important as the properties they possess. The behaviour of *Azotobacter* and *Xanthomonas fuscans* in the rhizosphere can be cited as an example.

In contrast to many papers on seed inoculation with *Azotobacter* (Rubentchik, 1960), several authors have shown that *Azotobacter* does not occur on the root surfaces of various crop plants at all or occurs only in small numbers (Vančura *et al.*, 1959; Vančura and Macura, 1959); its incidence is higher in the rhizosphere than in free soil. The phenomenon is explained by the inhibitory effect of roots on *Azotobacter* (Krasilnikov, 1945; Metz, 1955). On the other hand, *Azotobacter* grew well in media containing root exudates of barley and wheat, though it did not occur on the roots of these plants (Vančura and Macura, 1961). It appears that *Azotobacter* does not colonize the roots, probably because it is not able to compete with the metabolically very active bacteria which colonize the root surfaces (Macura, 1962). Better survival on roots was observed with strains 'adapted' to these conditions (Vančura *et al.*, 1959), strains in which metabolic changes had been brought about, e.g. in the composition of the capsular polysaccharides (Vančura, 1960). But even in these cases, it is unlikely that the nitrogen fixed has a significant effect on the growth of the plant; however, it is not possible to eliminate the effect of physiologically active substances produced by *Azotobacter* (Vančura and Macura, 1960; Vančura, 1961). The recent data (Brown, Burlingham and Jackson, 1964; Rovira, 1965) confirm that the effect of *Azotobacter* on plants is due to growth substances, rather than fixed nitrogen. So, although rhizosphere conditions appear to be suitable for the growth of *Azotobacter*, these bacteria are not able to colonize this zone due to either the properties of the environment or to the antagonistic effects of other micro-organisms (Chan, Katznelson and Rouatt, 1963).

*Xanthomonas fuscans* was used as a model microbe for the investigation of root colonization in our experiments. Staněk and Lasík (1965) established that this bacterium, parasitizing the aerial parts of beans, occurs on the seeds of certain varieties and is capable of colonizing the roots in the initial stage of plant growth; however, it disappears from the rhizosphere usually after two weeks' growth. The alterations in the composition of the rhizoplane microflora were observed at the same time. The study of nutritional requirements of *Xanthomonas fuscans* carried out by Vančura (unpublished) has shown that this organism needs glutamic acid and is stimulated by yeast extract. The growth of *Xanthomonas fuscans* is retarded in the presence of root exudates while seed exudates stimulate its growth. This fact, together with the changes observed in the rhizosphere, suggests that the alteration in plant metabolism occurring during the transition from the cotyledon stage to the photosynthetic assimilation stage can be reflected in the type of root exudation occurring and in the type of root population that develops.

These examples cannot explain completely the mechanism causing the development of the rhizoplane and rhizosphere population. They show, nevertheless, that root colonization is the result of the interrelationships of environmental conditions, in the first place of root exudation and the properties of the micro-organisms, e.g. their growth and metabolic reaction to the environment.

## *CONCLUSIONS*

Accumulation and selection of microbial populations on plant roots and in their proximity, and the role of these populations in plant life, is one of the most attractive aspects of the rhizosphere phenomenon. The very nature of the phenomenon suggests that the decisive factor in root colonization is the environment, with which the properties of the respective micro-organisms can be connected. With respect to present data, it can be assumed that the nutritional factors and cell regulatory mechanism enabling maximum growth in a given environment determine the composition of the microbial rhizoplane and rhizosphere populations.

The nature and availability of energy and nutrient sources in the rhizosphere as well as in other environments determine the extent and composition of the microbial population (Gibson, 1957). In media in which a basal nutrient is the only limiting factor (e.g. carbon source), the increase in the biomass of the organism is proportional to the initial concentration of the basal nutrient (Monod, 1942). The concentration of substrate or specific nutrient, if it is low, can affect the specific growth rate; such conditions can be assumed to occur in the rhizosphere. Quantitative differences in the root population do not depend only on the amount of root exudates. The biomass resulting from one substrate unit can vary in different organisms (Bauchop and Elsden, 1963) and is related to ATP production and metabolic pathways of substrate catabolism.

In contrast to *in vitro* experiments, other features are characteristic of microbial growth under natural conditions of root colonization. Bacteria grow in mixed populations and in environments with mixtures of energy and nutrient sources. The cell regulatory mechanisms, by means of which the cell adjusts its state and activity so that it is in harmony with the environmental conditions (in particular the synthesis and activity of enzymes), may be affected under such conditions at different stages (Pardee, 1961). The microflora is subjected to various or changing conditions in time and space. Furthermore, the soil and rhizosphere environment is so complicated that it has not been fully defined hitherto and it cannot be predicted which enzymes will be synthesized under any given conditions. It is not possible to assume that some enzymes are indispensable for a particular organism and that others can remain without use at a given moment, becoming useful only under changed conditions. The data on the synthesis of enzymes in the soil which are not specific for an added substrate illustrate this principle (Drobník, 1955).

In an environment in which the growth of bacteria is limited by a deficiency of a particular nutrient, a preferential synthesis of an enzyme can occur which may diminish this deficiency. Urease activity in soil enriched with glucose was found to be higher than in control soil while soil with glucose and ammonium nitrogen added had a lower urease activity. Krammer (1957) showed that phosphatase activity was indirectly related to the phosphate content of the soil. On the other hand, several studies have shown that an increase of available energy results in a greater synthesis of enzymes involved in the degradation of substances relatively resistant to microbial attack. Humic acids are decomposed in the presence of glucose under laboratory conditions (Latter and Burges, 1961; Hurst, Burges and Latter, 1962; Mishustin and Nikitin, 1961). The increased decomposition of native soil organic matter has also been observed after glucose addition (Jansson, 1961; Macura *et al.*, 1963, 1965). Antagonism between nutrients can occur in the rhizosphere and can result in blocking the uptake or conversion of one nutrient into another.

Nevertheless, we have to admit the possibility of induction and repression of enzymes as factors affecting the activity of microbial populations in the rhizosphere. How are we to explain otherwise that healthy roots of growing plants are not decomposed by the action of proteolytic, pectinolytic, and cellulolytic micro-organisms living on their surface? Chaloupka, Křečková and Říhová (1963) established that the production of extracellular protease is inhibited by single amino acids. Natural inhibitors of some enzymes, e.g. cellulase, pectinase, amylase and others, are known to occur in plants (Kneen and Sandstedt, 1946; Bell, Aurand and Etchells, 1960; Mandels, Howlette and Reese, 1961; Bell *et al.*, 1962).

During the study of the rhizosphere phenomenon, the essential features of the interrelationships between micro-organisms and plant roots in the rhizosphere environment have been established. Although the data gained hitherto are of a general and schematic character, they have enabled us to characterize the rhizosphere environment usefully and have shown that the accumulation and selection of micro-organisms on the roots and in the rhizosphere is related to their physiological and biochemical properties. The basis of interactions between micro-organisms and roots in the rhizosphere is apparently biochemical. It is therefore necessary to increase our present knowledge of the physical and chemical properties of the rhizosphere environment, together with our knowledge of the physiological behaviour and biochemical expressions of the micro-organisms therein. As Alexander (1964), has emphasized the application of physiological and biochemical concepts and approaches have proved to be useful in studies of the ecology of soil micro-organisms. Rhizosphere studies seem to offer a suitable opportunity for the investigation of the role of cell regulatory mechanisms in the development and activity of natural microbial communities in a specific ecosystem. The elucidation of laws governing the colonization of roots by micro-organisms and the activity of these micro-organisms is imperative for understanding the function of the rhizosphere population in plant life and its control.

## *REFERENCES*


ALEXANDER, M. (1964). Biochemical ecology of soil microorganisms. *A. Rev. Microbiol.*, **18**, 217.

BAUCHOP, T. & ELSDEN, R. S. (1964). The growth of micro-organisms in relation to the energy supply. *J. gen. Microbiol.*, **23**, 457.

BELL, T. A., ETCHELLS, J. L., WILLIAMS, C. F. & PORTER, W. L. (1962). Inhibition of pectinase and cellulase by certain plants. *Bot. Gaz.*, **123**, 220.

BÖRNER, H. (1962). Liberation of organic substances from higher plants and their role in the soil sickness problem. *Bot. Rev.*, **26**, 393.

BROWN, M. E., BURLINGHAM, S. K. & JACKSON, R. M. (1964). Studies on *Azotobacter* species in soil. III. Effects of artificial inoculation on crop yields. *Pl. Soil*, **20**, 194.

CHALOUPKA, J., KŘEČKOVÁ, P. & ŘÍHOVÁ, L. (1963). Repression of protease in *Bacillus megaterium* by single amino acids. *Biochem. biophys. Res. Communs*, **12**, 380.

CHAN, E. C. S. & KATZNELSON, H. (1961). Growth interactions of *Arthrobacter globiformis* and *Pseudomonas sp.* in relation to the rhizosphere effect. *Can. J. Microbiol.*, **7**, 759.

CHAN, E. C. S., KATZNELSON, H. & ROUATT, J. W. (1963). The influence of soil and root extracts on the associative growth of selected soil bacteria. *Can. J. Microbiol.*, **9**, 187.

CLARK, F. E. (1949). Soil microorganisms and plant growth. *Adv. Agron.*, **1**, 241.

COOK, F. D. & LOCHHEAD, A. G. (1959). Growth factor relationships of soil microorganisms as affected by proximity to the plant root. *Can. J. Microbiol.*, **5**, 323.

ČATSKÁ, V. (1965). Colonization of wheat roots by fungi in relation to root excretion. In *Plant microbe relationships*. Ed. Macura, J. & Vančura, V., Prague. Publ. House, Cz. Acad. Sci.

ČATSKÁ, V., MACURA, J. & VÁGNEROVÁ, K. (1960). Rhizosphere microflora of wheat. III. Fungal flora of wheat rhizosphere. *Folia microbiol., Praha*, **5**, 320.

ČATSKÁ, V., VÁGNEROVÁ, K. & MACURA, J. (1963). Relations between the microflora of seeds and soil in colonization of roots. International Symposium. *Physiology, ecology and biochemistry of germination*. Greifswald.

DITTMER, H. A. (1937). A quantitative study of roots and root hairs of a winter rye-plant (*Secale cereale*). *Am. J. Bot.*, **24**, 417.

DROBNÍK, J. (1955). The splitting of starch by enzyme complex of soils. *Čs. Biol.*, **4**, 19.

FINSTEIN, S. & ALEXANDER, M. (1962). Competition for carbon and nitrogen between *Fusarium* and bacteria. *Soil Sci.*, **94**, 334.

GIBSON, J. (1957). Nutritional aspects of microbial ecology. In *Microbial ecology*, 7th Symp. Soc. gen. Microbiol., Ed. Williams, R. E. O. & Spicer, C. C. Cambridge. The University Press.

GYLLENBERG, H. G. (1957). Seasonal variation in the composition of the bacterial soil flora in relation to plant development. *Can. J. Microbiol.*, **3**, 131.

HALLECK, F. E. & COCHRANE, V. W. (1950). The effect of fungistatic agents on the bacterial flora of the rhizosphere. *Phytopathology*, **40**, 715.

HARMSEN, G. W. & JAGER, G. (1963). Determination of the quantity of carbon and nitrogen in the rhizosphere of young plants. In *Soil organisms*. Ed. Doeksen, J. & van der Drift, J. Amsterdam. North-Holland Publ. Co.

HORST, R. K. & HERR, L. J. (1962). Effects of foliar treatment on numbers of actinomycetes antagonistic to *Fusarium roseum* f. *cerealis* in the rhizosphere of corn. *Phytopathology*, **52**, 423.

HOVADÍK, A., VANČURA, V., VLČEK, F. & MACURA, J. (1965). Bacteria in the rhizosphere of red pepper. In *Plant microbes relationships*. Ed. Macura, J. & Vančura, V. Prague. Publ. House Cz. Acad. Sci.

HURST, M. H., BURGES, A. & LATTER, P. (1962). Some aspects of the biochemistry of humic acid decomposition by fungi. *Phytochemistry*, **1**, 227.

JANSSON, S. L. (1961). On the establishment and use of tagged microbial tissue in soil organic matter research. *Trans. 7th Int. Congr. Soil Sci.*, **2**, 635.

KATZNELSON, H. (1965). Nature and importance of the rhizosphere. In *Ecology of soil-borne plant pathogens. Prelude to biological control.* Ed. Baker, K. F. & Snyder, W. C. Los Angeles. University of California Press.

KATZNELSON, H. & BOSE, B. (1959). Metabolic activity and phosphate dissolving capability of bacterial isolates from wheat roots, rhizosphere and non-rhizosphere soil. *Can. J. Microbiol.*, **5**, 79.

KATZNELSON, H., LOCHHEAD, A. G. & TIMONIN, M. I. (1948). Soil microorganisms and the rhizosphere. *Bot. Rev.*, **14**, 543.

KATZNELSON, H. & ROUATT, J. W. (1957). Studies on the incidence of certain physiological groups of bacteria in the rhizosphere. *Can. J. Microbiol.*, **3**, 265.

KNEEN, E. & SANDSTEDT, R. T. (1946). Distribution and general properties of an amylase inhibitor in cereals. *Arch. Biochem.*, **9**, 235.

KRAMER, M. (1957). Phosphate-Enzym-Aktivität als Anzeiger des biologisch nutzbaren Phosphors im Boden. *Naturwissenschaften*, **44**, 1.

KRASILNIKOV, N. A. (1945). *Microbiological basis of bacterial fertilizer.* (In Russian.) Moscow. Publ. House Acad. Sci. U.S.S.R.

KRASILNIKOV, N. A. (1958). *Soil microorganisms and higher plant.* Moscow. Publ. House Acad. Sci. U.S.S.R.

KUTÁČEK, M. (1960). Liberation of substances from plant roots. *Přehl. zeměd. Lit.*, **9**, 1401.

LATTER, P. & BURGES, A. (1961). Experimental decomposition of humic acid by fungi. *Trans. 7th Int. Congr. Soil Sci.*, **2**, 643.

LINDER, P. J., CRAIG, J. C. Jr., COOPER, F. E. & MITCHELL, J. W. (1958). Movement of 2,3,6-trichlorobenzoic acid from one plant to another through their root systems. *J. agric. Fd Chem.*, **6**, 356.

LOCHHEAD, A. G. (1959). Rhizosphere microorganisms in relation to root disease fungi. In *Plant pathology, problems and progress 1908–1958.* Ed. Holton, C. S. *et al.* Madison. University of Wisconsin Press.

LOCHHEAD, A. G. & BURTON, M. O. (1956). Incidence in soil of bacteria requiring vitamin $B_{12}$ and the terregens factor. *Soil Sci.*, **82**, 237.

LOCHHEAD, A. G. & BURTON, M. O. (1957). Qualitative studies of soil microorganisms. XIV. Specific vitamin requirements of the predominant bacterial flora. *Can. J. Microbiol.*, **3**, 35.

LOCHHEAD, A. G. & ROUATT, J. W. (1955). The rhizosphere effect on the nutritional groups of soil bacteria. *Proc. Soil Sci. Soc. Amer.*, **19**, 48.

LOCHHEAD, A. G. & THEXTON, R. H. (1947). Qualitative studies of soil microorganisms. VII. The rhizosphere effect in relation to the amino acid nutrition of bacteria. *Can. J. Res., C.*, **25**, 20.

MACURA, J. (1958*a*). The rhizosphere microflora of sugar beet. *Folia microbiol., Praha*, **3**, 129.

MACURA, J. (1958*b*). Seed and soil bacteria in relation to the rhizosphere effect. *Folia microbiol., Praha*, **5**, 274.

MACURA, J. (1961). Bacterial flora of the root surface of wheat grown in nutrient solutions deficient in nitrogen and phosphorus. *Folia microbiol., Praha*, **6**, 279.

MACURA, J. (1962). Interrelations between soil microorganisms and plants. In *Advances in Biological Sciences.* Prague. Publ. House Cz. Acad. Sci.

MACURA, J. (1965). Interrelations between microorganisms and plant in the rhizosphere. In *Plant microbes relationships*, Ed. Macura, J. & Vančura, V. Prague. Publ. House Cz. Acad. Sci.

MACURA, J., SZOLNOKI, J. & VANČURA, V. (1963). Decomposition of glucose in soil. In *Soil organisms*, Ed. Doeksen, J. & van der Drift, J. Amsterdam. North Holland Publ. Co.

MACURA, J., SZOLNOKI, J., KUNC, F., VANČURA, V. & BABICKÝ, A. (1965). Decomposition of glucose continuously added to soil. *Folia microbiol., Praha*, **10**, 44.

Mandels, M., Howlett, W. & Reese, E. T. (1961). Natural inhibitors of cellulase. *Can. J. Microbiol.*, **7**, 957.

Marshall, K. C. & Alexander, M. (1960). Competition between soil bacteria and *Fusarium*. *Pl. Soil*, **12**, 143.

Meschkov, N. V. (1961). Total carbon content in root secretions of plants grown under the conditions of sterile cultures on permanent and exchanged nutrient solutions. *Proc. Acad. Sci., U.S.S.R., Ser. Biol.*, 352.

Metz, H. (1955). Untersuchungen über die Rhizosphäre. *Arch. Mikrobiol.*, **23**, 297.

Mishustin, E. N. & Nikitin, D. I. (1961). Susceptibility of humic acids to soil microflora. *Mikrobiologiya*, **30**, 841.

Monod, J. (1942). *Recherches sur la croissance des cultures bacteriénnes*. Paris. Herman et Cie.

Pantos, G. (1957). The principal forms and physiological properties of the bacteria in the rhizosphere of wheat and the interrelations between them and the plant. *Acta agron. hung.*, **7**, 37.

Papavizas, G. C & Davey, C. B. (1961). Extent and nature of the rhizosphere of *Lupinus*. *Pl. Soil*, **14**, 215.

Pardee, A. B. (1961). Response of enzyme synthesis and activity to environment. In *Microbial reaction to environment, 11th Symp. Soc. gen. Microbiol.*, Ed. Meynell, G. G. & Gooder, N. Cambridge. The University Press.

Parkinson, D. (1955). Liberation of amino acids by oat seedlings. *Nature, Lond.*, **176**, 35.

Pearson, R. & Parkinson, D. (1961). The sites of excretion of ninhydrin positive substances by broad-bean seedlings. *Pl. Soil.*, **4**, 391.

Peterson, E. A. (1958). Observations on fungi associated with plant roots. *Can. J. Microbiol.*, **4**, 257.

Preston, W. H. Jr., Mitchell, J. W. & Reeve, W. (1954). Movement of $\alpha$-methoxyphenylacetic acid from one plant to another through their root systems. *Science, N.Y.*, **119**, 437.

Ramachandra-Reddy, T. K. (1959). Rhizosphere microflora of pteridophytes. *Curr. Sci.*, **28**, 113.

Rangaswami, G. & Vasantharajan, V. N. (1962). Studies on the rhizosphere microflora of citrus trees. II. Qualitative distribution of the bacterial flora. *Can. J. Microbiol.*, **8**, 479.

Rempe, E. K. (1951). The microflora of the root system during growth of plants in water cultures. *Trudý Vses. n-issl. inst. s.-kh. mikrobiol.*, **12**, 56.

Rouatt, J. W. (1959). Initiation of the rhizosphere effect. *Can. J. Microbiol.*, **5**, 67.

Rouatt, J. W. & Katznelson, H. (1957). The comparative growth of bacterial isolates from rhizosphere and non-rhizosphere soils. *Can. J. Microbiol.*, **3**, 271.

Rouatt, J. W. & Katznelson, H. (1961). A study of the bacteria on the root surface and in the rhizosphere soil of crop plants. *J. appl. Bact.*, **24**, 164.

Rouatt, J. W., Peterson, E. A., Katznelson, H. & Henderson, V. E. (1963). Microorganisms in the root zone in relation to temperature. *Can. J. Microbiol.*, **9**, 227.

Rovira, A. D. (1956). Root excretions in relation to the rhizosphere effect. II. A study of the properties of root exudate and its effect on the growth of microorganisms isolated from the rhizosphere and control soil. *Pl. Soil*, **7**, 195.

Rovira, A. D. (1959). Root excretions in relation to the rhizosphere effect. IV. Influence of plant species, age of plant, light, temperature and calcium nutrition on exudation. *Pl. Soil*, **11**, 53.

Rovira, A. D. (1965). Effects of *Azotobacter*, *Bacillus* and *Clostridium* on the growth of wheat. In *Plant microbes relationships*, Ed. Macura, J. & Vančura, V. Prague. Publ. House Cz. Acad. Sci.

Rubentschik, L. J. (1960). *Azotobacter and its use in agriculture*. Kiev. Publ. House Acad. Sci. U.S.S.R.

Schroth, M. N. & Hildebrand, D. C. (1964). Influence of plant exudates on root-infecting fungi. *A. Rev. Phytopathol.*, **2**, 101.

Staněk, M. (1963). The germination of chlamydospores of the fungus *Ustilago zeae* (Beckm). Unger in the rhizosphere of maize. *Sb. čsl. Akad. zeměd. Věd, C*, **9**, 721.

Staněk, M. & Lasík, J. (1965). The occurrence of microorganisms parasitizing on the over-ground parts of plants in the rhizosphere. In *Plant microbes relationships*, Ed. Macura, J. & Vančura, V. Prague. Publ. House Cz. Acad. Sci.

Starkey, R. L. (1929). Some influences of the development of higher plants upon the microorganisms in the soil. I. Historical and introductory. *Soil Sci.*, **27**, 319.

Starkey, R. L. (1958). Interrelations between microorganisms and plant roots in the rhizosphere. *Bact. Rev.*, **22**, 154.

Thornton, H. G. (1956). The ecology of microorganisms in soil. *Proc. R. Soc., B*, **145**, 364.

Vágnerová, K. (1965). Properties of seed and soil bacteria with references to the colonization of roots by microorganisms. In *Plant microbes relationships*, Ed. Macura, J. & Vančura, V. Prague. Publ. House Cz. Acad. Sci.

Vágnerová, K., Čatská, V. & Macura, J. (1961). Composition and properties of bacterial and fungal flora of wheat rhizosphere. *Trans. 7th Int. Congr. Soil Sci.*, **2**, 568.

Vágnerová, K., Macura, J. & Čatská, V. (1960*a*). Rhizosphere microflora of wheat. I. Composition and properties of bacterial flora during the first stages of wheat growth. *Folia microbiol., Praha*, **5**, 298.

Vágnerová, K., Macura, J. & Čatská, V. (1960*b*). Rhizosphere microflora of wheat. II. Composition and properties of bacterial flora during the vegetation period of wheat. *Folia microbiol., Praha*, **5**, 311.

Vágnerová, K. & Vančura, V. (1962). Production and utilization of amino acids by various species of rhizosphere bacteria. *Folia microbiol., Praha*, **7**, 55.

Vágnerová, K., Vančura, V. & Lasík, J. (1963). The development of microorganisms of the root surface, rhizosphere and free soil in medium with root excretions. *Sb. čsl. Akad. zeměd. Věd, C*, **9**, 687.

Vančura, V. (1960). Composition of capsular polysaccharides of smooth and rough types of colonies of *Azotobacter chroococcum*. *Folia microbiol., Praha*, **5**, 100.

Vančura, V. (1961). Detection of gibberellic acid in *Azotobacter* cultures. *Nature, Lond.*, **192**, 88.

Vančura, V. (1964). Root exudates of plants. I. Analysis of root exudates barley and wheat in their initial phases of growth. *Pl. Soil*, **21**, 231.

Vančura, V. & Hovadík, A. (1965*a*). Composition of root exudates in the course of plant development. In *Plant microbes relationships*, Ed. Macura, J. & Vančura, V. Prague. Publ. House Cz. Acad. Sci.

Vančura, V. & Hovadík, A. (1965*b*). Root exudates of plants. II. Composition of root exudates of some vegetables. *Pl. Soil*, **22**, 21.

Vančura, V. & Macura, J. (1959). The development of *Azotobacter* in the oat rhizosphere and its effect on the yield. *Folia microbiol., Praha*, **4**, 200.

Vančura, V. & Macura, J. (1960). Indole derivates in *Azotobacter* cultures. *Folia microbiol., Praha*, **5**, 293.

Vančura, V. & Macura, J. (1961). The effect of root excretions on *Azotobacter*. *Folia microbiol., Praha*, **6**, 250.

Vančura, V., Macura, J., Fischer, O. & Vondráček, J. (1959). The relation of *Azotobacter* to the root system of barley. *Folia microbiol., Praha*, **4**, 119.

VENKATA RAM, C. S. (1960). Foliar application of nutrients and rhizosphere microflora of *Camelia sinensis*. *Nature, Lond.*, **187**, 621.

VERONA, O. (1963). Interaction entre la graine en germination et les microorganismes telluriques. *Annls Inst. Pasteur, Paris*, **105**, 75.

VOZNYAKOVSKAYA, L. M. & KHOUDIAKOV, Y. P. (1960). Species composition of epiphyte microflora of living plants. *Mikrobiologiya*, **29**, 97.

VRANÝ, J. (1960). Occurrence of bacteria assimilating benzoic acid and *p*-hydroxybenzoic acid in cereal rhizosphere and in soil. *Folia microbiol., Praha*, **5**, 116.

VRANÝ, J. (1963). Effect of foliar application of urea on the root microflora. *Folia microbiol., Praha*, **8**, 351.

VRANÝ, J. (1965). Effect of foliar application on the rhizosphere microflora. In *Plant microbes relationships*, Ed. Macura, J. & Vančura, V. Prague. Publ. House Cz. Acad. Sci.

VRANÝ, J., VANČURA, V. & MACURA, J. (1962). The effect of foliar application of some readily metabolized substances, growth regulators and antibiotics on rhizosphere microflora. *Folia microbiol., Praha*, **7**, 61.

WAKSMAN, S. A. (1952). *Soil microbiology*. New York. J. Wiley & Sons, Inc.

WALLACE, R. H. & LOCHHEAD, A. G. (1949). Qualitative studies of soil microorganisms. VIII. Influence of various crop plants on the nutritional groups of soil bacteria. *Soil Sci.*, **67**, 63.

WALLACE, R. H. & LOCHHEAD, A. G. (1961). Bacteria associated with seeds of various crop plants. *Soil Sci.*, **71**, 159.

WOODS, F. W. (1960). Biological antagonisms due to phytotoxic root exudates. *Bot. Rev.*, **26**, 546.

ZAGALLO, A. C. & KATZNELSON, H. (1957). Metabolic activity of bacterial isolates from wheat rhizosphere and control soil. *J. Bact.*, **73**, 760.

# PRE-INFECTION PHASES OF THE LEGUME SYMBIOSIS

G. FÅHRAEUS and H. LJUNGGREN

*Department of Microbiology, Agricultural College of Sweden*

## *INTRODUCTION*

Among soil bacteria, the rhizobia have the almost unique property of being able to escape competition with other soil organisms by occupying a very exclusive refuge inside the plant root. This is probably an ecological advantage to these bacteria, because their competitive abilities in many soils may be weak (see below). Survival during severe winter conditions may also be much better inside a nodule than in the soil, even in annual species (Pate, 1958*b*, Bergersen, Hely and Costin, 1963).

In the following pages, we shall look first at the partners in the symbiosis separately, continue with the interactions in the rhizosphere and finish with the invasion proper. The subsequent stages, including growth of the infection thread and nodulation and development of the nitrogen-fixing system, will not be covered in this review. Unfortunately, in much work on the legume symbiosis no clear distinction has been made between infection and nodulation. Although infection, in most cases, does result in nodulation, these two processes are nevertheless distinct; if only nodulation is recorded, some of the early reactions of the plant will pass unnoticed.

Few aspects of soil microbiology have been studied so extensively as the rhizobia-legume interrelationships. This is reflected in the large number of reviews which have appeared during the last decade (Nutman, 1956, 1959*b*, 1963, 1965*a*, *b*; Norris, 1956; Allen and Allen, 1958; Hallsworth, 1958; Schwartz, 1959; Raggio and Raggio, 1962; Schaede, 1962; Vincent, 1962; Balassa, 1963; Manil, 1963; Virtanen and Miettinen, 1963). We will frequently refer to these reviews instead of quoting original publications.

## *TECHNIQUES AND TERMINOLOGY*

The techniques used in our laboratory for those studies which will be reported here are mainly of two kinds; (*a*) methods for aseptic cultivation of seedlings on slides permitting direct microscopy of the growing roots, (*b*) a simple viscometric technique for studying the occurrence of polygalacturonase (PG) in the rhizosphere. Most of the details have been published earlier (Fåhraeus, 1957; Ljunggren and Fåhraeus, 1961). Some modifications of the slide technique were proposed by Nutman (1959*a*) and Sahlman and Fåhraeus (1963). A further modification ('dos-a-dos technique') which we have recently introduced might be useful for the study of some rhizosphere problems. In each culture tube seedlings of two different species are grown, each on a separate slide; the slides are put into the tubes in a back-to-back position with a bent glass rod between the slides to facilitate their handling.

The enzyme determined by the viscometric technique has been termed polygalacturonase (PG). Concurrent sugar determinations have not been made. It is not known, therefore, if it is identical with pectin depolymerase, PD (Starr, 1959; Wood, 1960). We have, however, exclusively used 'low-methoxyl pectin' as a substrate indicating that the enzyme is mainly PG Type I (Wood, 1960).

The preparation of the capsular material used for induction of PG activity and for transformation work involved repeated precipitation in 80 per cent ethanol overnight and deproteinization several times in chloroform and butanol, drying in a vacuum and filtration through bacterial filters. Presumably this very drastic treatment must have removed all living organisms.

The term infection is used in the sense of the establishment of a parasitic relation in the host and not in the wider medical sense which refers to the process leading to unhealthy conditions in the host. The term invasion is used as a synonym of infection, irrespective of whether the process is pathogenic or not.

The term virulence (= pathogenicity) is avoided because it often expresses the capacity of an organism to produce disease. Instead the term infectivity is used.

## *GROWTH OF PLANTS AND BACTERIA IN THE ABSENCE OF THEIR PARTNER*

### *The legume*

There is no indisputable example of any legume depending on rhizobia for its growth. Given a sufficient amount of ordinary mineral salts, including a source of combined nitrogen, most leguminous plants are easily cultivated even under aseptic conditions. In the absence of rhizobia and combined nitrogen, growth proceeds only as long as the nitrogen deposited in the seed suffices for the nutrition of the seedling. No fixation of atmospheric nitrogen has been observed under such circumstances.

Theoretically, it is possible that the fixation process could afford a better source of nitrogen than uptake from the soil. Nitrate must be reduced which seems to occur mainly in the green parts (Pate, Wallace and van Die, 1964) and requires a number of specific enzymes (Kessler, 1964). Nitrogen fixation in the nodules could therefore be a more economic process for the host. In fact, Roponen and Virtanen (1964), who re-examined an older claim by Castelli (1951) that *Hedysarum coronarium* was dependent on rhizobia for its nitrogen nutrition, found this plant grew much better with bacterial nodules than with combined nitrogen. This seems to be a very rare exception and Roponen and Virtanen have suggested that this result might have been due to salt toxicity.

A comparison of the amino acid composition of protein in nodulated and nitrate-grown plants was made by Nilsson, Korsan-Bengtsen, and Mellander (1954). No qualitative differences were observed, but nodulated red clover plants showed slightly higher concentrations of some amino acids. Similarly, Pate and Wallace (1964) found slightly different percentages of the amide fraction in uninoculated plants grown on different nitrogen sources.

*The rhizobia*

Before discussing physiological and ecological aspects, we will very briefly touch upon the taxonomy and variability of rhizobia. Taxonomic problems have been treated comprehensively in earlier reviews, for instance those of Allen and Allen (1958) and Jensen (1958). An interesting approach was made by Graham (1964*a*), using Adansonian principles. His results corroborated some older claims that the fast-growing clover, pea, and bean rhizobia should be united under a common species name *Rhizobium leguminosarum*, while *R. meliloti* and the closely related but non-infective *R.* (*Agrobacterium*) *radiobacter* should also have specific rank within the genus *Rhizobium*. The slow-growing lupin, soy-bean, and cow-pea rhizobia were referred to a second genus, *Phytomyxa*. The remaining genus in the family Rhizobiaceae, *Chromobacterium*, contained the more taxonomically remote forms.

The value of this division will have to be tested, particularly from a genetic stand-point. The position of *A. radiobacter*, for instance, has often been discussed and Allen and Allen (1958) argued against its inclusion in *Rhizobium*. In our following discussion the conventional cross-inoculation groups are retained with their common names, e.g. *R. trifolii* for clover bacteria, etc.

Genetic variation in *Rhizobium* may profoundly influence the interrelationships of rhizobia and legumes. The important properties of invasiveness and effectiveness are subject to mutation (Vincent, 1962). An old clover strain ('Bart A') which had lost its infectivity could be transformed so that it became infective again by treatment with DNA from an infective strain (Ljunggren, 1961). Mutation to ineffectiveness is common in soil (Nutman, 1946), though an increase in effectiveness has also been observed (Jordan, 1952). Recent work suggests that it is possible to transform rhizobia from one cross-inoculation group to another (Krasilnikov, 1941; R. Balassa, 1960; Lange and Alexander, 1961). Inter-generic transformation between *Rhizobium* and *Agrobacterium* was reported by Klein and Klein (1953), and Ljunggren (see Table 1).

TABLE 1

*Transformation in* Rhizobium *and related forms*

| Receptor strains | Donor strains | | | |
|---|---|---|---|---|
| | *R. trifolii* | *R. meiiloti* | *R.* sp. | *Agrobacterium tumefaciens* |
| *R. lupini* | | +[3] | | |
| *R. japonicum* | —[1] | | | |
| *R. trifolii* | +[4] | +[1, 5, 6,] | +[6] | |
| *R. leguminosarum* | +[1, 5] | +[5] | | +[2] |
| *R. meliloti* | +[1, 5, 6] | | +[6] | |
| *Agrobacterium radiobacter* | +[5] | +[5] | +[2] | +[2] |
| *Chromobacterium* sp. | +[5] | +[5] | | |
| *Bacillus polymyxa* | —[5] | —[5] | | |
| *Escherichia coli* | —[5] | —[5] | | —[2] |

\+ Successful transformation.
— No transformation.

[1] Krasilnikov (1941).
[2] Klein and Klein (1953).
[3] Balassa (1960).
[4] Ljunggren (1961).
[5] Ljunggren (unpublished).
[6] Lange and Alexander (1961).

Such genetic changes are interesting theoretically, but their significance under natural conditions in the soil seems questionable. Perhaps the possibility should be explored that a massive release of DNA from a nodule with effective rhizobia could induce transformation in a non-infective but more competitive strain in the soil. For example, it has been found that *A. radiobacter* strains are less sensitive to antagonistic micro-organisms than many rhizobia (van Schreven, 1964).

Like the legumes, the rhizobia are not dependent on their partner for survival: most rhizobia are easily kept in pure culture on relatively simple synthetic media, although it is generally agreed that they are unable to fix gaseous nitrogen under such conditions. Their nutrient requirements are not extraordinary. They can use a variety of nitrogen and carbon sources (Graham, 1964*b*), but cell wall constituents like cellulose, pectin or lignin cannot be utilized. This is important in any consideration of the invasive power of these bacteria.

Apart from ordinary mineral salts, trace elements and, in some cases, vitamins are needed. Much interest has recently centred upon the role of cobalt. A specific role for cobalt in the nitrogen fixation process has been proposed by several investigators (see Nicholas, 1963). Further, both rhizobia and legumes need cobalt irrespective of its possible role in nitrogen fixation (Kliewer, Lowe, Mayeux and Evans, 1964; Hallsworth, Wilson and Adams, 1965). The requirements for cobalt and molybdenum are evidently similar: they are both required for several processes in the living organism, but somewhat larger quantities seem to be specifically required for the nitrogen-fixing system.

It was shown by Burton and Lochhead (1952) that some rhizobia form vitamin $B_{12}$, whilst Fries (1962) has shown that legumes also produce this vitamin.

The vitamin requirements of rhizobia differ between strains, biotin being the vitamin most commonly needed. This was first shown by Nilsson, Bjälfve and Burström (1939) and by West and Wilson (1940). Recently, a specific role for biotin in nitrogen fixation by a *Pseudomonas* sp. was suggested (Proctor and Wilson, 1961). An almost unique case of biotin toxicity was studied by Murphy and Elkan (1963); this might give a clue to the role of biotin in cell metabolism. Other vitamins that have been found to stimulate growth of rhizobia are thiamin (mostly clover strains) (Nilsson, Bjälfve and Burström, 1938; Graham, 1963*b*) and pantothenic acid (Allen and Allen, 1950; Graham, 1963*b*). These requirements may influence the survival of rhizobia in the soil and the rhizophere (see below).

### *The distribution of rhizobia in soils in the absence of legumes*

Since the persistence of rhizobia in soil is of fundamental importance for the cultivation of legumes, it has been the subject of intensive study. Numerous tests have been made of the longevity of commercial cultures of rhizobia, some of which have been made with dried soil (Vincent,

1958; Jensen, 1961; Means and Erdman, 1963; Davis, 1963). The absence of microbial competition and the nearly optimal growth conditions in such cultures preclude accurate assessments of the behaviour of rhizobia in natural soils. For instance, lucerne bacteria survived lyophilization and storage under oil better than did clover bacteria (Means and Erdman, 1963), but they are more sensitive to soil acidity than the latter (Wilson, 1926; Jensen, 1943); and they are more often deficient in soils than clover rhizobia (Vincent, 1958; Nutman, 1963).

A possibly specific effect of soil pH is its influence on the ratio effective/ineffective strains. There is a high percentage of ineffective strains in poor soils (Allen and Allen, 1950; Thornton, 1952; Jones, 1963). The better survival of these strains could be due to their relatively high tolerance of aluminium and manganese ions (Holding and King, 1963).

Other soil conditions like high temperatures and desiccation (Marshall, 1964), may have a detrimental effect on free-living rhizobia. However, competition with other soil organisms for necessary nutrients and the action of antagonistic micro-organisms may be more important. Common soil fungi like *Aspergillus* (Robison, 1946) and *Fusarium* (Dorn, 1956) and bacteria, including *Streptomyces* species and *Bacillus* species may be active antagonists (Allen and Allen, 1950; Wieringa, 1963; van Schreven, 1964). Hely, Bergersen and Brockwell (1957) attributed difficulties in establishing *Rhizobium* in the legume rhizosphere to antagonism by other rhizosphere organisms. Here again large differences between strains belonging to different cross inoculation groups seem to exist. Cow-pea rhizobia were not very sensitive (Allen and Allen, 1950). Conflicting evidence is given for the slow growing *R. lupini* and *R. japonicum*: they were inhibited by a great number of antagonists (Allen and Allen, 1950) but Graham (1963*a*) found them to be little affected by selected antibiotics. Resistance to antibiotics (not streptomycin), in some mutant strains of pea, clover, and lucerne rhizobia was associated with ineffectiveness (Schwinghamer, 1964).

There are also reports of stimulation of rhizobia by various soil organisms (Krasilnikov, 1958; Vincent, 1962). It is also possible that substances unavailable to rhizobia in pure culture could be used by rhizobia in mixed symbiotic cultures. It was shown (Fåhraeus, 1949) that *Agrobacterium radiobacter* would develop vigorously in *Cytophaga* cultures with cellulose as the sole source of carbon. *Rhizobium* has not been studied in such an environment, but its reaction might be similar. Further, the need for vitamins would be met in such associations, since most aerobic cellulose decomposing bacteria are auxo-autotrophic; at least, thiamin is excreted in large amounts (Fåhraeus, 1947).

'Clover sickness' has sometimes been supposed to be due to phage action on clover rhizobia. Such hypotheses are not supported by the results of Kleczkowska (1957), though it is possible that ineffective mutants might develop in the presence of phage. Phages are of very common occurrence and are easily isolated from nearly all leguminous plant roots (Staniewski, Kowalski, Gogacz and Sokolowska, 1962).

A record of rhizobial ecology would be incomplete without mention of their synthetic abilities, which may have a positive influence upon other soil organisms. The formation of vitamin $B_{12}$ has already been mentioned. Rhizobia may also form a factor which stimulates nitrogen fixation in *Nostoc* (Table 2, after Bjälfve, 1962).

TABLE 2

*Nitrogen fixation in mixed cultures of* Nostoc *and rhizobia. Experiment in synthetic substrate with 200 mg. mannitol per 100 ml. No addition of nitrogen. Time 90 days (from Bjälfve, 1962)*

| Inoculation | Nitrogen mg. per 100 ml. |
|---|---|
| *Nostoc calcicola* | 0·97 |
| „ „ + *R. meliloti* | 2·50 |
| „ „ + *R. trifolii* | 5·16 |
| „ „ + *R. leguminosarum* | 4·71 |

Of agronomic interest is the profuse slime formation of many *Rhizobium* strains; this might play a part in stabilization of soil structure (Clapp, Davis and Waugaman, 1962).

## *INFLUENCE OF LEGUMES ON RHIZOBIA (RHIZOSPHERE EFFECT)*

### *The legume rhizosphere*

The competition between rhizobia and other micro-organisms may be expected to be more pronounced in the rhizosphere where the active secretion of nutrients from the growing roots (Rovira, 1962) gives higher microbial densities than in soil not in contact with roots. Here the legume rhizosphere will be considered, although rhizobia sometimes are stimulated as much in other rhizospheres (Krasilnikov, 1958).

Of potential interest is the observation that *Agrobacterium radiobacter* is greatly stimulated in grass rhizospheres (Starkey, 1958; Rouatt, Katznelson and Payne, 1960). We found this bacterium to be numerous in rhizospheres of the dune grass *Ammophila arenaria*. If bacteria of this type can be transformed to rhizobial strains, their occurrence in various rhizospheres merits further study.

The legume rhizosphere has in many comparative studies been found to harbour greater numbers of bacteria than non-legume rhizospheres (Clark, 1949; Krasilnikov, 1958; Rovira, 1961; Brown, 1961). However, this is not a general rule and depends on the species. Wallace and Lochhead (1949) found flax and oats rhizospheres to be very rich, and Kaunat (1963) found them more stimulatory to several bacterial groups than rhizospheres of clover or lupin.

The very large rhizosphere effects observed in many species, e.g. peas, are probably due to the release of soluble substances: vitamins, amino acids or amides, sugars, nucleotides or unidentified compounds (Rovira, 1962; Dehay and Care, 1958). Whole cells and tissue fragments may also be sloughed off and be available in the rhizosphere, but probably only at later stages in plant growth when compared with exudates (Rovira, 1962). It seems that the organic compounds released in this way might be more important for fungi, especially those capable of decomposing cell wall constituents.

The competition between rhizobial strains in the rhizosphere is a question of prime importance in legume agriculture. Nicol and Thornton (1941) first noted the difference in competitiveness of different rhizobial strains in the root zone. Later more detailed experiments were made, for instance by Vincent and Waters (1953) and others (see Vincent, 1962).

As mentioned above, field soils often harbour great numbers of ineffective rhizobia, and in some cases (Dart and Pate, 1959) it was found that the ineffective partner in a mixed inoculum competed more successfully than the effective one for infection sites on the host plants. However, the elegant experiments of Thornton and Kleczkowska (1950), followed by Read (1953), have shown that it is quite possible to secure a high proportion of effective nodules by introducing selected competitive and effective strains in sufficient numbers. Were this not so, the practice of field inoculation would be a very uneconomic enterprise.

*Inhibitory action of roots*

It is known that many higher plants, either as seeds before germination or in later stages, secrete substances inimical to micro-organisms (Woods, 1960) and legumes are not exceptional. Thompson (1960) and

Bowen (1961) showed that both *Trifolium subterraneum* and *Centrosema pubescens* secreted water-soluble and thermostable antibiotic substances active against several bacterial species, including rhizobia, while lucerne seed did not show such antibiotic activity. Turner (1955) adsorbed inhibitory substances secreted by clover roots and in this way enhanced nodulation. Similarly, Hely, Bergersen and Brockwell (1957) found stimulation of infection on burnt sites. In fact, some of the common practices of seed inoculation are devised with particular regard to this fact: the pelleting of seed is a suitable means for protecting rhizobia against toxic seed coat substances in *Trifolium subterraneum* (Brockwell, 1962).

Also some non-legumes secrete substances toxic to rhizobia. Examples were given by Rice (1964). *Aristida oligantha*, a dominant weed plant in Oklahoma, significantly decreased nodule formation in inoculated bean plants, apparently by antagonizing the introduced *Rhizobium* strain. Wide-spread occurrence of such plants would probably lead to a rapid decline of the rhizobial population. The active compounds from *Helianthus annuus* and other species were gallotannins and chlorogenic acid (Rice, 1965). Harmless compounds secreted by roots could also be converted by micro-organisms to toxic substances (Börner, 1960).

### *Specific stimulation of Rhizobium*

The above-mentioned substances are non-specific insofar as they will stimulate most micro-organisms. The question now arises: are rhizobia specifically stimulated by legumes and particularly by their potential host? Some evidence for this is found in earlier work (Wilson, 1940; Nutman, 1963), but often strains of different cross-inoculation groups seem to be stimulated to the same degree by one host plant (Krasilnikov, 1958; Dart and Mercer, 1964). Rovira (1961) found indications of a disproportionate increase of the clover bacteria when compared with the 'total bacteria' in the clover rhizosphere. This did not occur in grass rhizospheres. However, he comments: 'it is difficult to envisage a nutrient in the root exudate which will not be utilized by the general soil microflora yet will stimulate *Rhizobium*.'

Very specific compounds like eelworm hatching factors and zoospore attracting factors are, however, excreted by some plants (Rovira, 1962; Clayton and Lamberton, 1964). It seems likely that substances might be formed that will specifically attract *Rhizobium* strains to the roots of their host plants. In some preliminary experiments we used the above-mentioned 'dos-a-dos technique' to compare the attraction of rhizobia by two different plants, and we found a rather marked preference for

*Medicago lupulina* compared with *Trifolium repens* by a strain of lucerne bacteria, while a clover strain showed no marked preference for either plant. The results are somewhat in accordance with those obtained by Tuzimura, Watanabe and Shih (1963). More work along these lines must be made before definite conclusions can be drawn about the hypothetical attraction factors.

A possibly specific adhesion of rhizobial cells to the root hair wall will be discussed on p. 409.

In this connection, the host-synthesized 'nodulation factors', supposed to operate in the rhizosphere, should be considered. The definition of 'nodulation factors' is vague, because the effect could be on infection *or* nodulation *or* on the bacteria. It has been found that diffusible substances from the plant tops promote the infection of young seedlings (Thornton, 1929; Lie, 1964). Normally these substances pass down the sap stream, but they are active also if added to the surrounding medium. Rather simple amino compounds could be involved (Valera and Alexander, 1964). Raggio and Raggio (1962) showed that undefined factors from the shoot are not absolutely necessary for nodulation of excised roots; but they might still be stimulatory (Bunting and Horrocks, 1964).

A hypothetical nodulation or rather infection factor might act upon the rhizobia by promoting the formation of specific bacterial polysaccharides. The role of these will be discussed later. A nodulation-inhibiting factor, as for instance that reported by Elkan (1962), might then be an antagonist which reduces the formation or activity of the polysaccharide or the enzyme induced by it.

The reduced infection rate observed when the first nodule has appeared (Hiltner, 1900; Dunham and Baldwin, 1931; Nicol and Thornton, 1941; Virtanen and Linkola, 1947; Nutman, 1949, 1952, 1953, 1962) is probably an effect on root metabolism rather than on the bacteria. Root nodules contain auxins (Thimann, 1936; Pate, 1958*a*) and gibberellins (Radley, 1961). The auxins do not directly influence the infection when added to the medium, unless they are given in fairly large amounts, but gibberellic acid retarded infection of root hairs of *Trifolium glomeratum* even at $10^{-8}$M (Darbyshire, 1964). Perhaps nodules could inhibit further infections through secretion of gibberellin like compounds. The nodule factor causing chlorosis in soy-beans (MacCalla and Haskins, 1964) might be similar.

## *THE EFFECTS OF RHIZOBIA ON LEGUME ROOTS*

Although there may still be some doubt about a specific influence of legume roots on rhizobia, the converse effect is easily recognized. At least three different growth responses can be readily distinguished in susceptible roots. These are:

(1) Stimulated growth including 'curling' of root hairs.
(2) Growth of an 'infection thread' through root hair and cortex.
(3) Nodulation.

It is well known that these effects, although induced by the bacteria, are to a large degree dependent on other conditions, both internal (plant susceptibility), and external (the environment). These conditions will be considered in detail.

*Host susceptibility*

Owing to their genetic constitution, some plants are completely resistant to infection; this might be due to a single recessive gene (Nutman, 1956). Grafting a susceptible scion on a resistant stock did not change this pattern (Nutman, 1956; Tanner and Anderson, 1963), except in the case of *Trifolium ambiguum* (Evans and Jones, 1964). The resistance mechanism in a non-nodulating soy-bean line was the formation of diffusible inhibitory substances (Elkan, 1961).

Even in normal susceptible plants the root system is resistant during certain stages of its development. The most common points of entrance, the root hairs, are only infected when still growing, but on the other hand they must not be too young. The critical period is short. The first infections do not occur randomly, but on preformed sites along the roots (Nutman, 1956; Lim, 1963)

*Environmental effects*

A survey of the literature shows clearly that environmental conditions which are optimal for the growth of plant roots are also the best for infection. Any factors which restrict root development will restrict nodulation (Hallsworth, 1958). Temperature effects may be complex; curves showing two peaks for nodulation, as obtained by Pate (1962), are not easily explained, but the infection optimum may still lie at intermediate temperatures.

Nitrogen has been more studied than any other external factor influencing the infection process, but it is impossible to discuss this subject fully. It has been established that different sources of nitrogen act differently (Fred, Baldwin and McCoy, 1932). All sources of nitrogen stop infection at higher concentrations, but the amounts that are inhibitory vary within wide limits in plant species and even varieties of species (Hallsworth, 1958). Various hypotheses have been put forward to explain the nitrogen effects (see Raggio and Raggio, 1962).

In this context it is necessary to distinguish between invasion proper and nodule initiation. Hiltner (1900) was the first to discover the effects of nitrogen not only on nodulation, but also on the preceding stages of root hair curling and infection. Thornton (1936) and Nutman and co-workers have studied this question in greater detail. Gibson and Nutman (1960) found that very low levels of potassium nitrate delayed nodulation more than infection with the result that more nodules were obtained with low nitrate concentrations than in the controls without nitrogen. Darbyshire (1964) studied two clover species supplied with nitrate, nitrite, and ammonium ions in amounts as low as 10 $\mu$g N per seedling (c. 6 mg. $NaNO_3$ per litre). Nitrate and nitrite, but not ammonium ions, delayed nodulation. At higher concentrations, all salts reduced infection to about the same extent.

Ideas about the mechanism of the nitrate inhibition of nodulation are entirely speculative. A hypothesis was recently put forward by Tanner and Anderson (1964) placing emphasis on indole-3-acetic acid (IAA) and its role in infection and nodulation. They proposed that nitrite arising from reduction of nitrate reacts with IAA and reduces its concentration below limiting levels. The results of Nutman and co-workers cited above would then imply that IAA is more important for nodulation than for infection, a conclusion that seems to fit with the results reported below.

*Chemistry of root hairs*

Before discussing the effects of the rhizobia on root hairs, a few words should be said about the chemical composition of the hair wall and the growth of root hairs. The wall is mainly built up from two layers: an outer layer of randomly arranged cellulose fibrils, probably in a pectic matrix ($\alpha$-layer), and an inner layer of longitudinally oriented fibrils with little encrusting material ($\beta$-layer) (Belford and Preston, 1961; Cormack, 1962). The hair tip, where rapid growth occurs, contains only the $\alpha$-layer. In most plants the epidermal cells, including the root hairs, are also covered by a thin cuticle and a sheath, possibly pectic in nature (Cormack, 1962; Scott, 1963; Labrique, 1964). The sheath may be important for adhesion to soil particles (Jenny and Grossenbacher, 1963). The main chemical component of the cuticle, cutin, consists of polymeric hydroxy acids (Heinen, 1960; Baker and Martin, 1963; Baker, Batt and Martin, 1964).

The knowledge of the biochemistry of root hair growth is still very scanty. Recent reviews were given by Cormack (1962) and Wardrop (1962) who discuss some diverging hypotheses. One of these, first put forward by Ekdahl (1953), emphasizes the role of pectic enzymes, especially polygalacturonase, which may cause a continuous softening of the apical wall. This would account for the longitudinal extension of the hairs. Ekdahl's hypothesis is attractive, but has as far as we know not been explored further by plant physiologists.

Indole-3-acetic acid, which has such pronounced effects on root growth, has much less effect on root hair growth. It seems, however, to promote root hair elongation at low concentrations (Borgström, 1939; Ekdahl, 1960; Jackson, 1960; Stenz, 1962; Darbyshire, 1964).

*Morphological effects on root hairs*

The first visible effect of rhizobia (and their secretions) on legumes is the stimulated growth of the root hairs. Possibly also lateral root formation is promoted.

The effects on root hairs are probably multiple. First, both the formation and elongation of hairs is stimulated (Thornton and Nicol, 1936). For example, root hair numbers in lucerne were increased by 50 per cent up to more than 100 per cent in the presence of living bacteria or bacterial secretions. At the same time the length of the individual hairs could be doubled. These findings were confirmed by Stenz (1962) and Haack (1964). Haack also tested some non-legumes; she found an increase in root hair length of more than 100 per cent in *Oxalis valdiviensis* and *Epilobium parviflorum* due to the action of living rhizobia. In most non-legumes no significant stimulation was observed.

It is probable that these effects are due to IAA. However, Thornton (1936) found much greater elongation with living bacteria than anyone has found with IAA.

The second and more spectacular effect is the deformation of root hairs (Plate 1, Figs. 1–4). It is possible that this involves more than one reaction, viz. (*a*) the 'bending' or irregular swellings of various shapes, and (*b*) the 'curling' and formation of the 'shepherd's crook' (Plate 1, Fig. 8). The branching of root hairs (Plate 1, Figs. 5–7), which was observed in lucerne seedlings by McCoy (1932), and has been seen by us in several experiments as a result of the addition of bacterial filtrates to clover plants (Sahlman and Fåhraeus, 1962), may perhaps be looked upon as a specific effect. Branching near the base of the root hair, where the wall has already become hardened, probably involves the participation of cellulolytic enzymes (Cormack, 1962).

*Role of IAA*

The chemical compounds causing the curling reaction remain unidentified. It has frequently been postulated that IAA is the causative agent

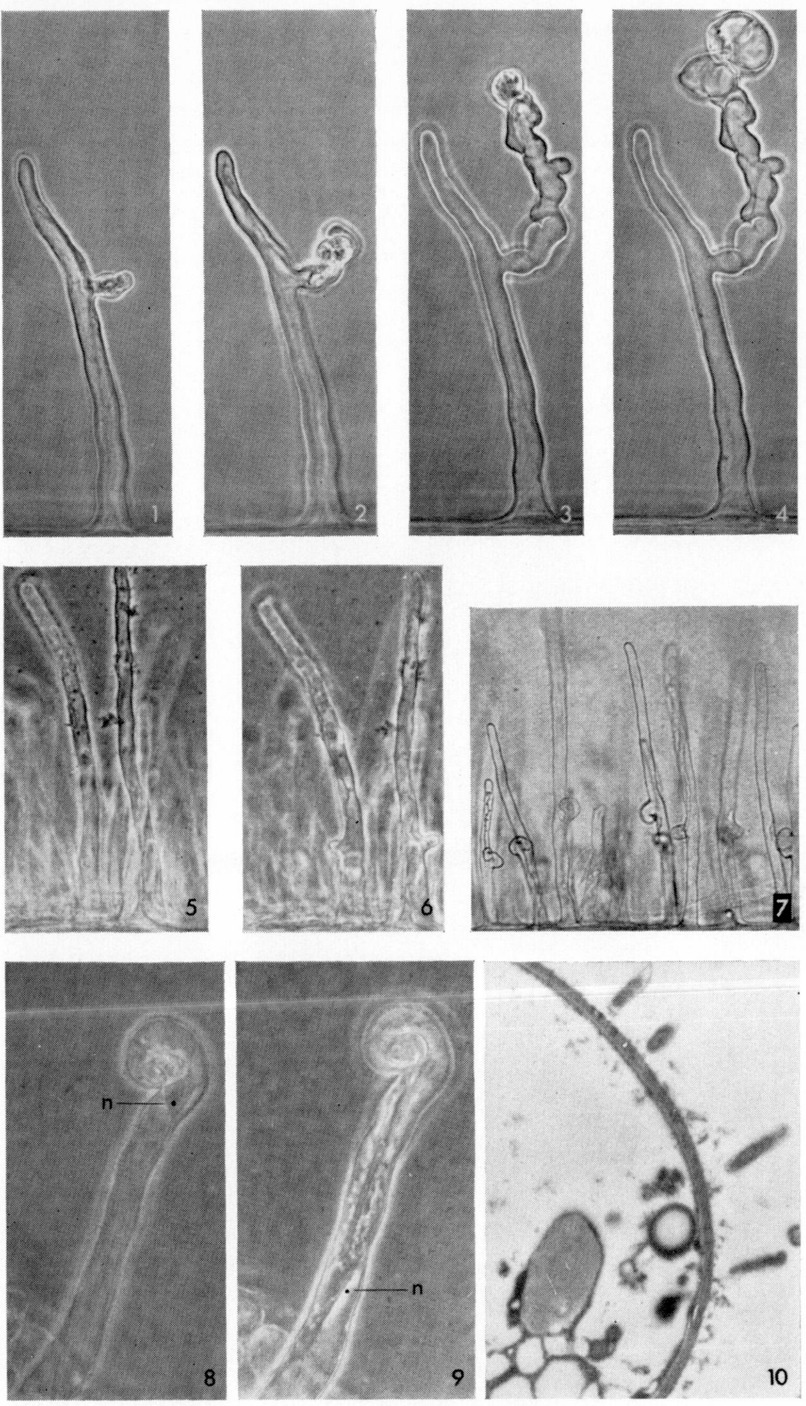


Plate 1. Description over page

Plate 1. Figs. 1–4. *Trifolium repens*. Successive deformation of a branched root hair under the influence of *Rhizobium trifolii* and its secretions. Plant inoculated, but no bacteria visible round the hair in 1 and 2. In 3 and 4, motile bacteria clearly visible. Photographs taken with a time lapse of (2) 4–5 hrs., (3) 24 hrs. and (4) 48 hrs. Phase contrast, ×450.

Figs. 5–6. *Trifolium repens*. Root hairs 4 and 8 hrs. after inoculation with *Rhizobium trifolii*. Branches initiated near the base of the hairs. Phase contrast, ×240.

Fig. 7. *Trifolium repens*. Short and curled root hair branches with several infection threads. Some of these have grown towards the hair tip, probably because the nucleus was situated in this part of the hair. Bright field, ×150.

Figs. 8–9. *Trifolium repens*. Formation of the 'shepherd's crook' and the beginning of infection. Photographs taken with an interval of 24 hrs. Note the position of the hair nucleus: before infection at the curl; after infection, just in front of the infection thread. Phase contrast, ×600. n = nucleus.

Fig. 10. *Trifolium parviflorum*. Electron micrograph from a thin section of the wall of an infected root hair. *Rhizobium* cells outside the hair are attached with one end to the mucilaginous cover of the root hair wall, in spite of the drastic treatment in the preparation of the section. ×7,000. (Photograph by K. Sahlman.)

but there is in our opinion very little evidence supporting this view. There are even several facts which make it extremely unlikely that IAA alone could have this effect. To sum up the present evidence,

(1) Experiments with several clover species and pure IAA at a large range of concentrations gave only negative results (Stenz, 1962; Sahlman and Fåhraeus, 1962; Darbyshire, 1964).
(2) A large variety of micro-organisms synthesize IAA (Roberts and Roberts, 1937; Katznelson and Sirois, 1961). None of these except rhizobia causes deformation of legume root hairs. Rhizobia like Bart A that have lost infectivity but still produce IAA (Kefford, Brockwell and Zwar, 1960) have no such effect.
(3) The curling reaction is more specific than has been thought (Haack, 1964). No such simple substance as IAA could possibly be so specific.

Curling is clearly a growth process, although somewhat abnormal. Like other growth processes it may be influenced by IAA, and IAA is perhaps a necessary but insufficient factor to account for root hair curling. An additional and more specific factor is apparently needed. This could, like the factor inducing PG formation reported below, be a specific polysaccharide fraction of the *Rhizobium* cells. However, we have not obtained a typical hair deformation with the purified material we used in studying the PG formation. The 'curling' factor may perhaps be sensitive to the chemical treatment used in the purification.

*Events at the cell surface*

The root hair curling has an obvious effect on those bacteria that are attached to the curled part of the cell surface because they may be trapped in the folds of the curled hairs. In the more or less closed chambers that result, various secreted compounds might be expected to accumulate and in this way be able to induce still larger effects. A relevant observation is that infections frequently arise at the borderline between two juxtaposed hairs (Fåhraeus, 1957; Haack, 1964; Darbyshire, 1964). Osmotic conditions may arise that balance the osmotic pressure from the expanding root hair, and the invasion proper may be initiated from these points of attack.

It has been postulated earlier that infection is preceded by an accumulation of rhizobia on the root hair at the infection site (Thornton, 1936), but other investigators have not observed any conspicuous numbers of bacteria at this point. Electron-microscopic studies show that single rhizobial cells become firmly attached to the root-hair wall suggesting a certain polar affinity of the cells (Sahlman and Fåhraeus, 1963)

(Plate 1, Fig. 10). These cells are of normal rod type. On the other hand, Dart and Mercer (1964) found indications of bacterial accumulation between the root epidermis and a sheath (cuticle ?), covering the root. They also observed very small flagellated swarmers which they believe are the true invaders. The 'flagella' are very reminiscent of the fimbriae studied in certain *Klebsiella* strains (Duguid, 1959). These were shown to cause adhesion of the bacterial cells to various structures, even root hairs, and the same function might be attributed to the similar cell appendages in *Rhizobium* swarmers.

*Formation of PG*

We have now strong evidence that rhizobia specifically induce the formation, in the host plant, of an enzyme which promotes infection. In a large number of experiments (Fåhraeus and Ljunggren, 1959; Ljunggren and Fåhraeus, 1959, 1961) it was found that polygalacturonase (PG) was formed in the host-bacteria system, and since cell-free extracts could replace living bacteria, it was quite clear that the enzyme was synthesized by the plant cells. According to Ekdahl (1953), PG is active in normal root hair elongation and thus the bacteria-induced formation is probably only an increased synthesis or activity of this enzyme. Since infection involves stimulated growth of the root hair, it may be concluded that increased PG activity is necessary before infection can take place. This is suggested by the fact that significantly higher PG activities could be demonstrated only when fully compatible bacteria were used. Examples are given in Tables 3 and 4.

TABLE 3

*Formation of polygalacturonase (PG) by* Trifolium repens *in association with* Rhizobium trifolii. *A 121111 and 226 are infective and Bart A and A 11 non-infective strains. Bart A. 2 and A 11.2 are infective and obtained from the latter by transformation (see p. 399). PG activity is expressed as per cent decrease in viscosity of 1 per cent (w/v) solution of low-methoxyl pectin in 24 hr (from Ljunggren and Fåhraeus, 1961)*

| *Rhizobium* strain | PG activity |
|---|---|
| — | 0·5 |
| Bart A | 2·1 |
| A 11 | 1·1 |
| A 121111 | 15·2 |
| 226 | 15·4 |
| Bart A.2 | 10·8 |
| A 11.2 | 11·3 |

TABLE 4

*Formation of polygalacturonase (PG) in associations of leguminous plants and nodule bacteria or capsular material from nodule bacteria. White clover, incubated 72 hr, lucerne 96 hr. PG activity expressed as per cent decrease in viscosity of a 1 per cent (w/v) solution of low-methoxyl pectin in 24 hr*

| Plant | Capsular material from | Living bacteria, strain No. | PG activity |
|---|---|---|---|
| *Trifolium repens* | — | — | 0·8 |
| ,, ,, | — | *R. trifolii* 226 | 21·0 |
| ,, ,, | *R. trifolii* 226 | — | 16·0 |
| ,, ,, | — | *R. meliloti* 27 | 1·2 |
| ,, ,, | *R. meliloti* 27 | — | 0·8 |
| *Medicago sativa* | — | — | 1·3 |
| ,, ,, | — | *R. meliloti* 27 | 31·9 |
| ,, ,, | *R. meliloti* 27 | — | 43·1 |
| ,, ,, | — | *R. trifolii* 226 | 3·6 |
| ,, ,, | *R. trifolii* 226 | — | 4·2 |

We are aware that the PG activities we have found are fairly small, but we do not believe that anything like the large activities shown by many fungi (Wood, 1960; Blackhurst and Wood, 1963), or plant pathogenic bacteria (Starr, 1959) are to be expected. There is probably, in the growing root hair tips, a very delicate balance between anabolic and catabolic processes involving pectic substances, and an uncontrolled PG activity would presumably lead to rapid destruction and plasmoptysis of the hair.

An interesting difference from plants attacked by pathogenic fungi seems to be that in these, it is primarily the formation of pectin methylesterase that is stimulated, not polygalacturonase (Ayers and Papavizas, 1965; Hancock and Millar, 1965).

In a recent publication by Krusberg (1960), it was suggested that PG is formed by plants as a response to infection by nematodes.

Further support for the idea of an essential role of PG in the infection process is given by experiments involving the addition of nitrogen (Fåhraeus and Ljunggren, 1959). Two hundred mg. $NaNO_3$ per litre, a concentration that reduces infection considerably in clover plants, also diminishes PG formation to a large extent. Lucerne plants responded only to somewhat higher nitrate concentrations. This is analogous with the findings of Hallsworth (1958) that the nodulation of lucerne plants was affected less than that of clover by increasing nitrogen additions.

Our present results indicate that the active compounds inducing PG formation are highly specific soluble substances which are secreted from the bacterial cells. Their general properties suggest that they are polysaccharides. Knowledge of the structure of capsular polysaccharides has been gained particularly through work with *Pneumococcus*. Their polysaccharides show great diversity and specificity, and similarities with rhizobial polysaccharides have been found. Probably the structure of rhizobial polysaccharides could account for the differences in infective properties of the bacteria. Some such polysaccharides have been studied (Humphrey and Vincent, 1959; Stacey and Barker, 1960; Dedonder and Hassid, 1964; Dudman, 1964), but the data are insufficient for any detailed comparisons to be made. Our PG hypothesis requires that the numerous cases of irregular infection within and between cross inoculation groups (Vincent, 1962; Bjälfve, 1963; Jessen, 1963) be satisfactorily explained by the specificity of bacterial polysaccharides and plant receptors. This still remains to be thoroughly investigated.

*Nuclear activity*

The effect of rhizobia on nuclear activity in the host cells is conspicuous. Earlier work showed the close affinity of the infection thread in the nodule to host cell nuclei (Allen and Allen, 1950). This was also illustrated in the recent work of Mosse (1964) and Sahlman (unpublished). The interactions of root hair nuclei and the young infection threads were described by Fåhraeus (1957), Nutman (1959) and Darbyshire (1964). It appears that a close contact between nucleus and infection thread is necessary for the growth of the latter. If the nucleus migrates away from the root hair tip, infection can no longer occur at this point. Also, if the cytoplasmic strand between nucleus and the tip of the growing infection thread is broken, growth is discontinued (Darbyshire, 1964), (see Plate 1, Figs. 8–9).

Wipf and Cooper (1940) noted the significance of disomatic cells for nodulation. The idea that the bacteria induce polyploidization in previously monosomatic cells was refuted by Trolldenier (1959). An unsolved problem is whether chromosome numbers may influence the original invasion of root hairs, so that infection occurs preferentially in hairs with disomatic nuclei. Even resting nuclei of disomatic cells can be recognized by their size (Wipf and Cooper, 1940), but nobody seems to have looked for this in root hairs.

Tetraploid varieties of red clover showed greater nodule numbers than diploid varieties (Weir, 1961), but in other investigations opposite results were obtained (Nilsson and Rydin, 1954; Ljunggren, unpublished). Because of its known effects on mitosis in plants, colchicine has been tested by many workers, and increased nodule numbers were recorded in several experiments (Bonnier, 1954; Migahid, El Nady and Abd el Rahman, 1959; Weir, 1961). Root hair growth and infection were not affected by colchicine (Darbyshire, 1964).

*Infection mechanism*

In the preceding paragraphs we have tried to describe the various steps leading up to invasion proper. There are two main hypotheses concerning the mechanism of invasion. One of these, tacitly accepted by most earlier investigators, could be called the penetration theory. This would imply that the rhizobia actually penetrate the cell wall and grow further through the root hair into the cortex. The cellulose lining of the infection thread is then interpreted as a structure laid down as a defence against the bacterial intruder (Schaede, 1962). The obvious difficulty with this hypothesis is that cell wall-dissolving enzymes have never been found in rhizobia.

A second hypothesis was put forward by Nutman (1956), explaining the infection as an invagination of the root-hair wall. It was founded mainly on negative evidence, but some recent morphological observations support Nutman's ideas (Bergersen and Briggs, 1959; Sahlman and Fåhraeus, 1963). Dart and Mercer (1964) argue that the cellulose mesh-work of the wall is so loose that the rhizobial swarmers which they have observed could readily penetrate through the meshes. However, this would, in our opinion, give a less localized type of invasion than has always been found.

A consequence of the invagination hypothesis would be that one should find other micro-organisms within the infection threads and perhaps in the nodules because, under natural conditions, the rhizobia must be accompanied by numerous other soil organisms, and there are no reasons to believe that only the rhizobia get trapped in the hair folds. Thus, even in quite healthy nodules, various bacterial types should be found, unless conditions within the nodules prevent the multiplication of such foreign organisms. Electron micrographs of nodules from plants grown together with *Rhizobium* and some additional easily characterized bacteria would give an answer to this question.

Summarizing, we now recognize the following successive steps leading to infection of root hairs:

(1) Multiplication of rhizobia in the rhizosphere. Their growth is promoted by exuded sugar, vitamins and amino acids, possibly also by more specific compounds, but they are exposed to severe competition by other micro-organisms, some of which might be antagonistic.
(2) Conversion of some tryptophan excreted by the roots to IAA.
(3) Stimulation of root hair growth through IAA.
(4) Deformation of the root hairs, probably by a specific substance from the rhizobia. IAA may be a necessary complement.
(5) Induction of PG formation through specific polysaccharides.
(6) Attachment of bacteria to root hairs through the mucilaginous sheath of the hairs, but possibly also by some polar affinity of the bacteria.
(7) Trapping of living bacteria in the hair folds produced by the bacterial secretions.
(8) Further accumulation of active substances in these folds.
(9) Increased cytoplasmic and nuclear activity in the hairs.
(10) Local invagination of the root-hair wall in a small number of hairs.

## *REFERENCES*


ALLEN, E. K. & ALLEN, O. N. (1950). Biochemical and symbiotic properties of the rhizobia. *Bact. Rev.*, **14**, 273.

ALLEN, E. K. & ALLEN, O. N. (1958). Biological aspects of symbiotic nitrogen fixation. *Handb. Pl. Physiol.*, **8**, 48.

AYERS, W. A. & PAPAVIZAS, G. C. (1965). An exocellular pectolytic enzyme of *Aphanomyces euteiches*. *Phytopathology*, **55**, 249.

BAKER, E. A., BATT, R. F. & MARTIN, J. T. (1964). Studies on plant cuticle. VII. The nature and determination of cutin. *Ann. appl. Biol.*, **53**, 59.

BAKER, E. A. & MARTIN, J. T. (1963). Cutin of plant cuticles. *Nature, Lond.*, **199**, 1268.

BALASSA, R. (1960). Transformation of a strain of *Rhizobium lupini*. *Nature, Lond.*, **188**, 246.

BALASSA, G. (1963). Genetic transformation of *Rhizobium*: A review of the work of R. Balassa. *Bact. Rev.*, **27**, 228.

BELFORD, D. S. & PRESTON, R. D. (1961). The structure and growth of root hairs. *J. exp. Bot.*, **12**, 157.

BERGERSEN, F. J. & BRIGGS, M. J. (1958). Studies on the bacterial component of soybean root nodules: cytology and organization in the host tissue. *J. gen. Microbiol.*, **19**, 482.

BERGERSEN, F. J., HELY, F. W. & COSTIN, A. B. (1963). Overwintering of clover nodules in alpine conditions. *Aust. J. biol. Sci.*, **16**, 920.

BJÄLFVE, G. (1962). Nitrogen fixation in cultures of algae and other microorganisms. *Physiologia Pl.*, **15**, 122.

BJÄLFVE, G. (1963). The effectiveness of nodule bacteria. *Pl. Soil*, **18**, 70.

BLACKHURST, F. M. & WOOD, R. K. S. (1963). Verticillium wilt of tomatoes—

further experiments on the role of pectic and cellulolytic enzymes. *Ann. appl. Biol.*, **52**, 89.

BONNIER, C. (1954). Action de la colchicine sur la symbiose *Rhizobium—Medicago sativa* et *Rhizobium—Trifolium pratense*. *Bull. Inst. agron. Stns. Rech. Gembloux*, **22**, 167.

BORGSTRÖM, G. (1939). Root hair formation as an auxin response. *K. fysiogr. Sällsk. Lund Förh.*, **9**, No. 1, 19.

BÖRNER, H. (1960). Liberation of organic substances from higher plants and their role in the soil sickness problem. *Bot. Rev.*, **26**, 393.

BOWEN, G. D. (1961). The toxicity of legume seed diffusates toward rhizobia and other bacteria. *Pl. Soil*, **15**, 155.

BOWEN, G. D. & ROVIRA, A. D. (1961). The effects of microorganisms on plant growth. I. Development of roots and root hairs in sand and agar. *Pl. Soil*, **15**, 166.

BROCKWELL, J. (1962). Studies on seed pelleting as an aid to legume seed inoculation. I. Coating materials, adhesives, and methods of inoculation. *Aust. J. agric. Res.*, **13**, 638.

BROWN, M. E. (1961). Stimulation of streptomycin-resistant bacteria in the rhizosphere of leguminous plants. *J. gen. Microbiol.*, **24**, 369.

BUNTING, A. H. & HORROCKS, J. (1964). An improvement in the Raggio technique for obtaining nodules on excised roots of *Phaseolus vulgaris* L. in culture. *Ann. Bot.*, **28**, 229.

BURTON, M. O. & LOCHHEAD, A. G. (1952). Production of vitamin $B_{12}$ by *Rhizobium* species. *Can. J. Bot.*, **30**, 521.

CASTELLI, T. (1951). Some considerations on the symbiotic microbe of *Hedysarum coronarium* L. In: *Contrib. Conf. Improvement of Pasture and Fodder Production in the Mediterranean Area*. Rome.

CLAPP, C. E., DAVIS, R. J. & WAUGAMAN, S. H. (1962). The effect of rhizobial polysaccharides on aggregate stability. *Proc. Soil Sci. Soc. Am.*, **26**, 466.

CLARK, F. E. (1949). Soil microorganisms and plant roots. *Adv. Agron.*, **1**, 241.

CLAYTON, M. F. & LAMBERTON, J. A. (1964). A study of root exudates by the fog-box technique. *Aust. J. biol. Sci.*, **17**, 855.

CORMACK, R. G. H. (1962). Development of root hairs in angiosperms II. *Bot. Rev.*, **28**, 446.

DARBYSHIRE, J. F. (1964). *A study of the initial stages of infection of clovers by nodule bacteria*. Ph.D. thesis. London. University of London.

DART, P. J. & MERCER, F. V. (1964). The legume rhizosphere. *Arch. Mikrobiol.*, **47**, 344.

DART, P. J. & PATE, J. S. (1959). Nodulation studies in legumes. III. The effect of delaying inoculation on the seedling symbiosis of barrel medic, *Medicago tribuloides* Desr. *Aust. J. biol. Sci.*, **12**, 427.

DAVIS, R. J. (1963). Viability and behavior of lyophilized cultures after storage for twenty-one years. *J. Bact.*, **85**, 486.

DEDONDER, R. A. & HASSID, W. Z. (1964). The enzymatic synthesis of a ($\beta$-1,2-)-linked glucan by an extract of *Rhizobium japonicum*. *Biochim. Biophys. Acta*, **90**, 239.

DEHAY, C. & CARE, M. (1958). Étude de la composition des excrétions radicellaires chez quelques légumineuses d'origine africaine. *C.r. hebd. Séanc. Acad. Sci., Paris*, **247**, 336.

DORN, M. (1956). Über den Einfluss phytopathogener Pilze auf die Entwicklung und Infektionskraft von drei *Rhizobium* Arten. *Zentbl. Bakt. ParasitKde., Abt. II*, **109**, 120.

DUDMAN, W. F. (1964). Immune diffusion analysis of the extracellular soluble antigens of two strains of *Rhizobium meliloti*. *J. Bact.*, **88**, 782.

DUGUID, J. P. (1959). Fimbriae and adhesive properties in *Klebsiella* strains. *J. gen. Microbiol.*, **21**, 271.

DUNHAM, D. H. & BALDWIN, I. L. (1931). Double infection of leguminous plants with good and poor strains of rhizobia. *Soil Sci.*, **32**, 235.

EKDAHL, I. (1953). Studies on the growth and the osmotic conditions of root hairs. *Symb. bot. upsal.*, **11**: 6.

EKDAHL, I. (1957). The growth of root hairs and roots in auxin and anti-auxin media. Unpublished work.

ELKAN, G. H. (1961). A nodulation-inhibiting root excretion from a non-nodulating soybean strain. *Can. J. Microbiol.*, **7**, 851.

ELKAN, G. H. (1962). Comparison of rhizosphere microorganisms of genetically related nodulating and non-nodulating soybean lines. *Can. J. Microbiol.*, **8**, 79.

EVANS, A. M. & JONES, D. G. (1964). Effect of graft and sexual hybridization on the nodulation of *Trifolium ambiguum* M.B. *Ann. Bot.*, **28**, 221.

FÅHRAEUS, G. (1947). Studies in the cellulose decomposition by *Cytophaga*. *Symb. bot. upsal.*, **9**: 2.

FÅHRAEUS, G. (1949). *Agrobacterium radiobacter* Conn as a symbiont in cellulose decomposition. *K. LantbrHögsk. Annlr*, **16**, 159.

FÅHRAEUS, G. (1957). The infection of clover root hairs by nodule bacteria studied by a simple glass slide technique. *J. gen. Microbiol.*, **16**, 374.

FÅHRAEUS, G. & LJUNGGREN, H. (1959). The possible significance of pectic enzymes in root hair infection by nodule bacteria. *Physiologia Pl.*, **12**, 145.

FRED, E. B., BALDWIN, I. L. & MCCOY, E. (1932). *Root nodule bacteria and leguminous plants*. Madison. Univ. of Wisconsin Press.

FRIES, L. (1962). Vitamin $B_{12}$ in *Pisum sativum* (L). *Physiologia Pl.*, **15**, 566.

GIBSON, A. H. & NUTMAN, P. S. (1960). Studies on the physiology of nodule formation. VII. A reappraisal of the effect of preplanting. *Ann. Bot.*, **24**, 420.

GRAHAM, P. H. (1963*a*). Antibiotic sensitivities of the root nodule bacteria. *Aust. J. biol. Sci.*, **16**, 557.

GRAHAM, P. H. (1963*b*). Vitamin requirements of root nodule bacteria. *J. gen. Microbiol.*, **30**, 245.

GRAHAM, P. H. (1964*a*). The application of computer techniques to the taxonomy of the root-nodule bacteria of legumes. *J. gen. Microbiol.*, **35**, 511.

GRAHAM, P. H. (1964*b*). Studies on the utilisation of carbohydrates and Krebs cycle intermediates by rhizobia, using an agar plate method. *Antonie van Leeuwenhoek*, **30**, 68.

HAACK, A. (1964). Über den Einfluss der Knöllchenbakterien auf die Wurzelhaare von Leguminosen und Nichtleguminosen. *Zentbl. Bakt. ParasitKde, Abt. II*, **117**, 343.

HALLSWORTH, E. G. (1958). Nutritional factors affecting nodulation. In *Nutrition of the legumes*. Ed. Hallsworth, E. G. London. Butterworth.

HALLSWORTH, E. G., WILSON, S. B. & ADAMS, W. A. (1965). Effect of cobalt on the non-nodulated legume. *Nature, Lond.*, **205**, 307.

HANCOCK, J. G. & MILLAR, R. L. (1965). Relative importance of polygalacturonate trans-eliminase and other pectolytic enzymes in southern anthracnose, spring black stem, and *Stemphylium* leaf spot of alfalfa. *Phytopathology*, **55**, 346.

HEINEN, W. (1960). Über den enzymatischen Cutin-Abbau. I. Mitt. Nachweis eines "Cutinase"-Systems. *Acta. bot. neerl.*, **9**, 167.

HELY, F. W., BERGERSEN, F. J. & BROCKWELL, J. (1957). Microbial antagonism in the rhizosphere as a factor in the failure of inoculation of subterranean clover. *Aust. J. agric. Res.*, **8**, 24.

HELY, F. W. & BROCKWELL, J. (1962). An exploratory survey of the ecology of

*Rhizobium meliloti* in inland New South Wales and Queensland. *Aust. J. agric. Res.*, **13**, 864.

HILTNER, L. (1900). Über die Ursachen welche die Grösse, Zahl, Stellung und Wirkung der Wurzelknöllchen der Leguminosen bedingen. *Arb. K. Gesundh-Amt. Biol., Abt.*, **1**, 177

HOLDING, A. J. & KING, J. (1963). The effectiveness of indigenous populations of *Rhizobium trifolii* in relation to soil factors. *Pl. Soil*, **18**, 191.

HUMPHREY, B. A. & VINCENT, J. M. (1959). Extracellular polysaccharides of *Rhizobium*. *J. gen. Microbiol.*, **21**, 477.

JACKSON, W. T. (1960). Effect of indoleacetic acid on rate of elongation of root hairs of *Agrostis alba* L. *Physiologia Pl.*, **13**, 36.

JENNY, H. & GROSSENBACHER, K. (1963). Root-soil boundary zones as seen in the electron microscope. *Proc. Soil Sci. Soc. Am.*, **27**, 273.

JENSEN, H. L. (1943). Nitrogen fixation in leguminous plants. IV. The influence of reaction on the formation of root-nodules in *Medicago* and *Trifolium*. *Proc. Linn. Soc., N.S.W.*, **68**, 207.

JENSEN, H. L. (1958). The classification of the rhizobia. In *Nutrition of the legumes*. Ed. Hallsworth, E. London. Butterworth.

JENSEN, H. L. (1961). Survival of *Rhizobium meliloti* in soil culture. *Nature, Lond.*, **192**, 682.

JENSEN, H. L. (1963). Relations de la plante hôte avec les *Rhizobium* du groupe *Lotus-Anthyllis*. *Annls Inst. Pasteur, Paris*, **105**, 232.

JONES, D. G. (1963). Symbiotic variation of *Rhizobium trifolii* with S.100. Nomark white clover (*Trifolium repens* L.). *J. Sci. Fd Agric.*, **14**, 740.

JORDAN, D. C. (1952). Studies on the legume root nodule bacteria. II. The production and behavior of colonial mutants produced by X-ray irradiation. *Can. J. Bot.*, **30**, 125.

KATZNELSON, H. & SIROIS, J. C. (1961). Auxin production by species of *Arthrobacter*. *Nature, Lond.*, **191**, 1323.

KAUNAT, H. (1963). Zum Problem der Spezifität der Rhizosphärenmikroflora von Kulturpflanzen. II. Mitt.: Wirkung der engen Rhizosphäre auf die Zahl der nichtsporenbildenden, sporenbildenden, anaeroben und oligonitrophilen Bakterien sowie Actinomyceten und Pilze. *Zentbl. Bakt. ParasitKde., Abt. II.*, **117**, 1.

KEFFORD, N. P., BROCKWELL, J. & ZWAR, J. A. (1960). The symbiotic synthesis of auxin by legumes and nodule bacteria and its role in nodule development. *Aust. J. biol. Sci.*, **13**, 456.

KESSLER, E. (1964). Nitrate assimilation by plants. *A. Rev. Pl. Physiol.*, **15**, 57.

KLECZKOWSKA, J. (1957). A study of the distribution and the effects of bacteriophage of root nodule bacteria in the soil. *Can. J. Microbiol.*, **3**, 171.

KLEIN, D. T. & KLEIN, R. M. (1953). Transmittance of tumor-inducing ability to avirulent crown-gall and related bacteria. *J. Bact.*, **66**, 220.

KLIEWER, M., LOWE, R., MAYEUX, P. A. & EVANS, H. J. (1964). A biological assay for cobalt using *Rhizobium meliloti*. *Pl. Soil*, **21**, 153.

KRASILNIKOV, N. A. (1941). The variability of root nodule bacteria. *Dokl. Akad. Nauk. SSSR*, **31**, 75.

KRASILNIKOV, N. A. (1958). *Soil microorganisms and higher plants*. Acad. Sci. U.S.S.R., Moscow.

KRUSBERG, L. R. (1960). Hydrolytic and respiratory enzymes of species of *Dithylenchus* and *Parathylenchus*. *Phytopathology*, **50**, 9.

LABRIQUE, J. P. (1964). Propriétés diélectriques de la membrane semi-perméable des poils absorbants radiculaires de *Raphanus sativus*. *C. r. hebd. Séanc. Acad. Sci., Paris*, **258**, 2164.

LANGE, R. T. & ALEXANDER, M. (1961). Anomalous infections by *Rhizobium*. *Can. J. Microbiol.*, **7**, 959.

LIE, T. A. (1964). *Nodulation of leguminous plants as affected by root secretions and red light*. Wageningen. Veenman & Zonen.

LIM, G. (1963). Studies on the physiology of nodule formation. VIII. The influence of the size of the rhizosphere population of nodule bacteria on root hair infection in clover. *Ann. Bot.*, **27**, 55.

LJUNGGREN, H. (1961). Transfer of virulence in *Rhizobium trifolii*. *Nature, Lond.*, **191**, 623.

LJUNGGREN, H. & FÅHRAEUS, G. (1959). Effect of *Rhizobium* polysaccharide on the formation of polygalacturonase in lucerne and clover. *Nature, Lond.*, **184**, 1578.

LJUNGGREN, H. & FÅHRAEUS, G. (1961). The role of polygalacturonase in root-hair invasion by nodule bacteria. *J. gen. Microbiol.*, **26**, 521.

MANIL, P. (1963). Les *Rhizobium* et la fixation symbiotique de l'azote. A propos de la taxonomie et de la classification des *Rhizobium*. Quelques données récentes sur le determinisme biochimique de la fixation. *Annls Inst. Pasteur, Paris*, **105**, 19.

MARSHALL, K. C. (1964). Survival of root-nodule bacteria in dry soils exposed to high temperatures. *Aust. J. agric. Res.*, **15**, 273.

MCCALLA, T. M. & HASKINS, F. K. (1964). Phytotoxic substances from soil micro-organisms and crop residues. *Bact. Rev.*, **28**, 181.

MCCOY, E. (1932). Infection by *Bact. radicicola* in relation to the microchemistry of the host's cell walls. *Proc. R. Soc., B*, **110**, 514.

MEANS, U. M. & ERDMAN, L. W. (1963). Longevity and efficiency of rhizobial cultures. *Proc. Soil Sci. Am.*, **27**, 305.

MIGAHID, A. M., EL NADY, A. F. & ABD EL RAHMAN, A. A. (1959). The effect of gamma radiation on bacterial nodule formation. *Pl. Soil*, **11**, 139.

MOSSE, B. (1964). Electron-microscope studies of nodule development in some clover species. *J. gen. Microbiol.*, **36**, 49.

MURPHY, S. G. & ELKAN, G. H. (1963). Growth inhibition by biotin in a strain of *Rhizobium japonicum*. *J. Bact.*, **86**, 884.

NICHOLAS, D. J. D. (1963). The biochemistry of nitrogen fixation. In *Symbiotic associations*. Ed. Nutman, P. S. & Mosse, B. 13th Symp. Soc. gen. Microbiol. Cambridge. Cambridge University Press.

NICOL, H. & THORNTON, H. G. (1941). Competition between related strains of nodule bacteria and its influence on infection of the legume host. *Proc. R. Soc., B*, **130**, 32.

NILSSON, P. E., KORSAN-BENGTSEN, K. & MELLANDER, O. (1954). Amino acid content of leguminous proteins as affected by genetic and nutritional factors. I. *Arch. Mikrobiol.*, **20**, 404.

NILSSON, P. E. & RYDIN, C. (1954). Studies on symbiotic nitrogen fixation by a new strain of tetraploid red clover (UO36). *Arch. Mikrobiol.*, **20**, 398.

NILSSON, R., BJÄLFVE, G. & BURSTRÖM, D. (1938). Über Zuwachsfaktoren bei *Bact. radicicola*. II. *K. LantbrHögsk. Annlr*, **6**, 299.

NILSSON, R., BJÄLFVE, G. & BURSTRÖM, D. (1939). Über Zuwachsfaktoren bei *Bact. radicicola*. V. *K. LantbrHögsk. Annlr*, **7**, 301.

NORRIS, D. O. (1956). Legumes and the *Rhizobium* symbiosis. *Emp. J. exp. Agric.*, **24**, 247.

NUTMAN, P. S. (1946). Variation within strains of clover nodule bacteria in the size of nodule produced and in the "effectivity" of the symbiosis. *J. Bact.*, **51**, 411.

NUTMAN, P. S. (1949). Nuclear and cytoplasmic inheritance of resistance to infection by nodule bacteria in red clover. *Heredity, Lond.*, **3**, 263.

NUTMAN, P. S. (1952). Studies on the physiology of nodule formation. III. Experiments on the excision of root-tips and nodules. *Ann. Bot.*, **16**, 79.

NUTMAN, P. S. (1953). Studies on the physiology of nodule formation. IV. The mutual inhibitory effects on nodule production of plants grown in association. *Ann. Bot.*, **17**, 96.

NUTMAN, P. S. (1956). The influence of the legume in root-nodule symbiosis. A comparative study of host determinants and functions. *Biol. Rev.*, **31**, 109.

NUTMAN, P. S. (1959*a*). Some observations on root-hair infection by nodule bacteria. *J. exp. Bot.*, **10**, 250.

NUTMAN, P. S. (1959*b*). Sources of incompatibility affecting nitrogen fixation in legume symbiosis. *Symp. Soc. exp. Biol.*, **13**, 42.

NUTMAN, P. S. (1962). The relation between root hair infection by *Rhizobium* and nodulation in *Trifolium* and *Vicia*. *Proc. R. Soc., B*, **156**, 122.

NUTMAN, P. S. (1963). Factors influencing the balance of mutual advantage in legume symbiosis. In *Symbiotic Associations*. Ed. Nutman, P. S. & Mosse, B. 13th Symp. Soc. gen. Microbiol. Cambridge. Cambridge University Press.

NUTMAN, P. S. (1965*a*). Origin and developmental physiology of root nodules. *Handb. PflPhysiol.*, **15**, 1355.

NUTMAN, P. S. (1965b). The relation between nodule bacteria and the legume host in the rhizosphere and in the process of infection. In *Ecology of soil-borne plant pathogens*. Ed. Baker, K. F. & Snyder, W. C. Berkeley. University of California Press.

PATE, J. S. (1958*a*). Studies of the growth substances of legume nodules using paper chromatography. *Aust. J. biol. Sci.*, **11**, 516.

PATE, J. S. (1958*b*). Nodulation studies in legumes. II. The influence of various environmental factors on symbiotic expressions in the vetch (*Vicia sativa* L.) and other legumes. *Aust. J. biol. Sci.*, **11**, 496.

PATE, J. S. (1962). Nodulation studies in legumes. V. The effects of temperature on symbiotic performances of bacterial associations of *Medicago tribuloides* Desr. and *Vicia atropurpurea* Desf. *Phyton, B. Aires*, **18**, 65.

PATE, J. S. & WALLACE, W. (1964). Movement of assimilated nitrogen from the root system of the field pea (*Pisum arvense* L.). *Ann. Bot.*, **28**, 83.

PATE, J. S., WALLACE, W. & VAN DIE, J. (1964). Petiole bleeding sap in the examination of the circulation of nitrogenous substances in plants. *Nature, Lond.*, **204**, 1073.

PROCTOR, M. H. & WILSON, P. W. (1961). Biotin in nitrogen fixation by a pseudomonad. *Z. allg. Mikrobiol.*, **1**, 175.

RADLEY, M. (1961). Gibberellin-like substances in plants. *Nature, Lond.*, **191**, 684.

RAGGIO, M. & RAGGIO, N. (1962). Root nodules. *A. Rev. Pl. Physiol.*, **13**, 109.

READ, M. P. (1953). The establishment of serologically identifiable strains of *Rhizobium trifolii* in field soils in competition with the native microflora. *J. gen. Microbiol.*, **9**, 1.

RICE, E. L. (1964). Inhibition of nitrogen-fixing and nitrifying bacteria by seed plants. *I, Ecology*, **45**, 824.

RICE, E. L. (1965). Inhibition of nitrogen-fixing and nitrifying bacteria by seed plants. II. *Physiologia Pl.*, **18**, 255.

ROBERTS, J. L. & ROBERTS, E. (1939). Auxin production by soil microorganisms. *Soil Sci.*, **48**, 135.

ROBISON, R. S. (1946). The antagonistic action of the by-products of a culture of *Aspergillus wentii* on the legume bacteria. *J. Bact.*, **51**, 129.

ROPONEN, I. E & VIRTANEN, A. I. (1964). Growth of *Hedysarum coronarium* L. with combined nitrogen. *Physiologia Pl.*, **17**, 146.

ROUATT, J. W., KATZNELSON, H. & PAYNE, T. M. B. (1960). Statistical evaluation of the rhizosphere effect. *Proc. Soil Sci. Soc. Am.*, **24**, 271.

ROVIRA, A. D. (1961). *Rhizobium* numbers in the rhizospheres of red clover and paspalum in relation to soil treatment and the numbers of bacteria and fungi. *Aust. J. agric. Res.*, **12**, 77.

ROVIRA, A. D. (1962). Plant-root exudates in relation to the rhizosphere microflora. *Soils Fertil., Harpenden*, **25**, 167.

SAHLMAN, K. & FÅHRAEUS, G. (1962). Microscopic observations on the effect of indole-3-acetic acid upon root hairs of *Trifolium repens*. *K. LantbrHögsk. Annlr*, **28**, 261.

SAHLMAN, K. & FÅHRAEUS, G. (1963). An electron microscope study of root-hair infection by *Rhizobium*. *J. gen. Microbiol.*, **33**, 425.

SCHAEDE, R. (1962). *Die pflanzlichen Symbiosen*. 3rd ed. Ed. Meyer, F. H. Stuttgart. G. Fischer.

VAN SCHREVEN, D. A. (1964). The effect of some actinomycetes on rhizobia and *Agrobacterium radiobacter*. *Pl. Soil*, **21**, 283.

SCHWARTZ, W. (1959). Bakterien- und Actinomyceten-Symbiosen. *Handb. PflPhysiol.*, **11**, 546.

SCHWINGHAMER, E. A. (1964). Association between antibiotic resistance and ineffectiveness in mutant strains of *Rhizobium* spp. *Can. J. Microbiol.*, **10**, 221.

SCOTT, F. M. (1963). Root hair zone of soil-grown roots. *Nature, Lond.*, **199**, 1009.

STACEY, M. & BARKER, S. A. (1960). *Polysaccharides of micro-organisms*. Oxford. Clarendon Press.

STANIEWSKI, R., KOWALSKI, M., GOGACZ, E. & SOKOLOWSKA, F. (1962). Susceptibility of *Rhizobium* strains to phages. *Acta microbiol. pol.*, **11**, 245.

STARKEY, R. L. (1958). Interrelations between microorganisms and plant roots in the rhizosphere. *Bact. Rev.*, **22**, 154.

STARR, M. P. (1959). Bacteria as plant pathogens. *A. Rev. Microbiol.*, **13**, 211.

STENZ, E. (1962). Über den Einfluss von Bakterienfiltraten und Wuchsstoffen auf Wurzelhaare. *Wiss. Z. Karl-Marx.-Univ. Lpz.*, **11**, 641.

TANNER, J. W. & ANDERSON, I. C. (1963). Investigations on non-nodulating and nodulating soybean strains. *Can. J. Pl. Sci.*, **43**, 542.

TANNER, J. W. & ANDERSON, I. C. (1964). External effect of combined nitrogen on nodulation. *Pl. Physiol.*, **39**, 1039.

THIMANN, K. V. (1936). On the physiology of the formation of nodules on legume roots. *Proc. natn. Acad. Sci. U.S.A.*, **22**, 511.

THOMPSON, J. A. (1960). Inhibition of nodule bacteria by an antibiotic from legume seed coats. *Nature, Lond.*, **187**, 619.

THORNTON, H. G. (1929). The role of the young lucerne plant in determining the infection of the root by the nodule-forming bacteria. *Proc. R. Soc., B*, **104**, 481.

THORNTON, H. G. (1936). The action of sodium nitrate upon the infection of lucerne root-hairs by nodule bacteria. *Proc. R. Soc., B*, **119**, 474.

THORNTON, H. G. (1952). The symbiosis between *Rhizobium* and leguminous plants and the influence on this of the bacterial strain. *Proc. R. Soc., B*, **139**, 171.

THORNTON, H. G. & KLECZKOWSKA, J. (1950). Use of antisera to identify nodules produced by the inoculation of legumes in the field. *Nature, Lond.*, **166**, 1118.

THORNTON, H. G. & NICOL, H. (1936). Stimulation of root-hair growth in legumes by sterile secretions of nodule bacteria. *Nature, Lond.*, **137**, 494.

TROLLDENIER, G. (1959). Polyploidie und Knöllchenbildung bei Leguminosen. *Arch. Mikrobiol.*, **32**, 328.

TURNER, E. R. (1955). The effect of certain adsorbents on the nodulation of clover plants. *Ann. Bot.*, **19**, 149.

TUZIMURA, K., WATANABE, I. & SHIH, C. F. (1963). Growth of two species of root-nodule bacteria living together in the rhizosphere of various crops. Ecological studies of root-nodule bacteria in soil. *J. Sci. Soil Manure, Tokyo*, **34**, 143.

VALERA, C. L. & ALEXANDER, M. (1964). Nodulation factors in the *Rhizobium*-legume symbiosis. *Bact. Proc.*, A51.

VINCENT, J. M. (1954). The root-nodule bacteria of pasture legumes. *Proc. Linn. Soc. N.S.W.*, **79**, 4.

VINCENT, J. M. (1958). Survival of the root nodule bacteria. In *Nutrition of the legumes*. Ed. Hallsworth, E. G. London. Butterworth.

VINCENT, J. M. (1962). Australian studies of the root-nodule bacteria. A review. *Proc. Linn. Soc. N.S.W.*, **87**, 8.

VINCENT, J. M. & WATERS, L. M. (1953). The influence of the host on competition amongst clover root-nodule bacteria. *J. gen. Microbiol.*, **9**, 357.

VIRTANEN, A. I. & LINKOLA, H. (1947). Competition of *Rhizobium* strains in nodule-formation. *Antonie van Leeuwenhoek*, **12**, 65.

VIRTANEN, A. I. & MIETTINEN, J. K. (1963). Biological nitrogen fixation. In *Plant Physiology*, **3**. Ed. Steward, F. C. New York and London. Academic Press.

WALLACE, R. H. & LOCHHEAD, A. G. (1949). Qualitative studies of soil micro-organisms. VIII. Influence of various crop plants on the nutritional groups of soil bacteria. *Soil Sci.*, **67**, 63.

WARDROP, A. B. (1962). Cell wall organization in higher plants. I. The primary wall. *Bot. Rev.*, **28**, 241.

WEIR, J. B. (1961). The effect of colchicine and indolyl acetic acid on diploid and tetraploid strains of red and white clovers in aseptic and pot culture. *Pl. Soil*, **14**, 187.

WEST, P. M. & WILSON, P. W. (1940). Biotin as a growth stimulant for the root nodule bacteria. *Enzymologia*, **8**, 152.

WIERINGA, K. T. (1963). Organismes isolés du sol des Apennins, producteurs d'antibiotiques envers diverses souches de *Rhizobium. Annls Inst. Pasteur, Paris*, **105**, 417.

WILSON, J. K. (1926). Legume bacteria population of the soil. *J. Am. Soc. Agron.*, **18**, 911.

WILSON, P. W. (1940). *The biochemistry of symbiotic nitrogen fixation*. Madison. Univ. of Wisconsin Press.

WIPF, L. & COOPER, D. C. (1940). Somatic doubling of chromosomes and nodular infection in certain Leguminosae. *Am. J. Bot.*, **27**, 821.

WOOD, R. K. S. (1960). Pectic and cellulolytic enzymes in plant disease. *A. Rev. Pl. Physiol.*, **11**, 299.

WOODS, F. W. (1960). Biological antagonisms due to phytotoxic root exudates. *Bot. Rev.*, **26**, 546.

# SANITATION OF SOIL BY MICRO-ORGANISMS

N. A. KRASILNIKOV

*Institute of Microbiology, Academy of Sciences, Moscow, U.S.S.R.*

## *INTRODUCTION*

Many crop plants and the soils that they grow in may be infested with harmful forms of micro-organisms, e.g. phytopathogenic bacteria and fungi, nematodes, viruses and other living organisms. Such contamination of soil by these microbial 'weeds' is often due to the violation of agrotechnical and agrobiological regimes or to the occurrence of unsuitable climatic conditions. In certain cases, the contamination of soil by pathogenic microbes may be so great, that these soils become useless from a practical point of view. Plant yields may be considerably reduced. For example, in England it has been estimated that up to £140,000,000 worth of crops are lost every year. Prasada (1965) reported that in India the loss of wheat alone was more than one million tons per annum. Similar losses are experienced in most other countries. According to the data supplied by FAO, the losses of corn due to pathogens may reach 33 million tons per annum. This is sufficient to feed 150 million people for one year. Further, it has been stated (International Congress for Plant Protection, Hamburg, 1957), that the losses due to pathogenic microbes and insects are one fifth of the total harvest for wheat, one sixth for beans and potatoes, and one half for apples. When a monoculture system is used, mass infection of plants is often observed in fields sown with perennial grasses, corn, cotton and other species of plants.

## *RESULTS*

In our country we experience great losses because of pathogenic microbes, e.g. in the cotton harvests in Central Asia. For the last 30 years in Usbekistan, the cotton wilt disease has been increasing year by year (Table 1). According to our observations, contamination of sierozem soils with fungi in the cotton fields in Usbekistan and Tadjikistan increased noticeably with each consecutive sowing of this plant. Microbial analyses of these soils showed a gradual increase in the count of the fungus causing wilt, *Fusarium vasinfectum* (Table 2).

TABLE 1

*The annual increase of wilt-disease of cotton, expressed as the percentage of infected plants*

| Year | 1937 | 1938 | 1959 | 1960 | 1961 | 1962 | 1963 |
|---|---|---|---|---|---|---|---|
| Infected plants | 1–3 | 1–2 | 10 | 22 | 30 | 46 | 42 |

TABLE 2

*Degree of infection of the soil with the fungus,* Fusarium vasinfectum *in monocultured cotton-fields*

| Sowing | Control soil | | Cotton sown soil | |
|---|---|---|---|---|
| | Total fungi | *F. vasinfectum* | Total fungi | *F. vasinfectum* |
| 1st and 2nd | 20–40 | 0–0·01 | 20–40 | 0–0·02 |
| 3rd | 15–30 | 0–0·05 | 20–40 | 1·5–5·0 |
| 5th | 40–60 | 0·1–0·2 | 60–80 | 20–40 |
| 6th | 30–40 | 0–0 | 100–200 | 30–40 |
| 7th | 50–60 | 0·01–0·05 | 100–200 | 50–60 |
| 8th | 50–70 | 0–0·2 | 180–200 | 50–80 |

Numbers of fungi are expressed in thousands/g. of soil.
N.B. The control soil was from the same field but from an area in which crop rotation was being practised.

It is apparent from this data that severe contamination of soil occurred after the 5th consecutive sowing of cotton in the 5th year. Contamination with the fungus *Fusarium vasinfectum* reached a maximum in the 8th year, when the fungal count was $8 \times 10^3$ propagules per g. of soil. We found a positive correlation between the increases in the number of pathogenic fungi in the soil and the percentages of cotton plants infected with wilt disease.

Similar results were obtained from studies on the infection of flax, clover and other plants grown in monoculture. Soils cultivated with these plants become more and more saturated with phytopathogens year by year. Table 3 shows the results of our analyses of soils over several years in experimental plots of the Timiryazeva Academy of Agriculture near Moscow, which have been established for many years with a flax crop.

The fungus *Fusarium lini* developed abundantly in soils repeatedly

TABLE 3

*Infestation of flax plants and soil with fungi*

| Year of sowing | Flax-monoculture—soil | | Plants sown | Normal soil | |
|---|---|---|---|---|---|
| | *F. lini* thousands/g. | Infection of flax (%) | | *F. lini* in thousands/g. | Infection of plant (%) |
| 1st year Flax | 0–0·1 | 0–0·02 | Flax | 0 | 0 |
| 2nd ,, ,, | 0·1–0·9 | 0–0·05 | Oats | 0 | 0 |
| 3rd ,, ,, | 2–3·5 | 3–5·5 | Clover | 0 | 0 |
| 4th ,, ,, | 5–10 | 10–20 | Clover | 0 | 0 |
| 5th ,, ,, | 20–50 | 30–40 | Clover | 0·5 | 0·1 |
| 6th ,, ,, | 60–80 | 50–60 | Wheat | 0 | 0 |

cultivated with flax over a long period, reaching a count of 50 thousand to 100 thousand propagules per g. of soil. This same soil, when cultivated with other plants, did not contain this pathogen or else it was observed only in rare cases.

It can be seen that the cotton plant grown in a sierozem, and the flax grown in a podsol, favoured the development and accumulation of pathogenic fungi of the genus *Fusarium* in the soil.

Soil is not only contaminated by wilt fungi. Appreciable contamination of soil with phytopathogenic fungi of the genera *Helminthosporium*, *Rhizoctonia*, *Verticillium*, etc. can be observed. Contamination of soil by bacteria pathogenic to man often occurs. Soils of towns, industrial centres, and other densely populated areas are often contaminated with bacteria of the coliform group. Certain fields may occur which are contaminated by the causative agent of Siberian ulcer (*Bacillus anthracis*); the accumulation of *Mycobacterium tuberculosis* in soil near hospitals and sanatoriums has been noted.

In all cases of contamination of soil by harmful micro-organisms, sanitary measures are essential to remove these pathogenic and phytopathogenic forms. In practice, methods for soil improvement do not always give the desired results. Soils may be treated with various chemicals; over the last few years pesticides, herbicides and fungicides have been used widely, together with methods involving complete or partial soil sterilization. It should be remembered, however, that it is only possible to carry out soil sterilization with small volumes of soil in greenhouses and seed beds or in small garden plots. Complete sterilization is never achieved and is not necessarily desirable since it destroys certain useful micro-organisms.

Application of pesticides often produces highly undesirable results. Wide-spread application and long-term use of pesticides or biocides leads not only to the poisoning of soils and the destruction of both harmful and useful organisms, but also to the poisoning of plants, wild animals and birds. They are also responsible for the poisoning of reservoirs and all the living creatures in them. Uncontrolled use of pesticides does more harm than good.

Moreover, pesticides often affect not only the pathogenic forms but also their antagonists. As a consequence, the soil does not improve: on the contrary, it becomes contaminated. The phytopathogenic forms, not finding competitors or inhibitors, begin to multiply and occur in the soil in much higher numbers than before the treatment.

As an example, I shall quote our data concerning analyses of soils treated with separate chemicals. Samples of sierozem soil from Tadjikistan and podsol soil from the Experimental Station near Moscow were inoculated with *F. vasinfectum* and *F. lini* respectively and then treated with simazine (5 mg./kg.), followed by a preparation of 2-4D (10 mg./kg.) or 3-chloracetate (300 mg./kg.). After a period of 5–10 days, the numbers of mycolytic bacteria in the soil were counted. The results are shown in Table 4.

TABLE 4

*The influence of chemical poisons on the process of soil contamination with pathogens. (bacteria in thousands and fungi in units/g.)*

| Chemicals | Dose of Chemicals | Sierozem soil | | Podsol soil | |
|---|---|---|---|---|---|
| | | Mycolytic Bacteria/g. soil | Fusarium vasinfectum/g. soil | Mycolytic Bacteria/g. soil | Fusarium-lini/g. soil |
| Simazine | 5 | 500 | 0–100 | 0–0·1 | 50000 |
| 2-4D | 10 | 1500 | 0–0 | 50000 | 0–0 |
| 3-chloracetate | 300 | 0 | 10000 | 0 | 80000 |
| Control soil | | 100000 | 0–0·1 | 150000 | 0–0 |

The results show that, under the experimental conditions, simazine inhibited the mycolytic bacteria which lyse the mycelium of *Fusarium lini*, as a consequence of which, the latter multiplied markedly in the podzol. 3-chloracetate completely inhibited the mycolytic bacteria, whereas 2-4D did not inhibit these bacteria.

Negative results from the use of chemical poisons has encouraged specialists to concentrate their attention on biological factors associated with the control of organisms harmful to plants. According to our observations microbial antagonism is a particularly effective means for the general improvement of soil and protection of plants. The phenomenon of antagonism is widespread in the microbial world, especially in the soil. Antagonists can accumulate in soil in millions or hundreds of millions per gram (Krasilnikov, 1958; Agre, 1964; Hussein, 1964; Tzi-Shen, 1961).

Antagonists nearly always exist in soil which are able to inhibit actively the growth of pathogenic bacteria and fungi. In cases where the antagonists develop abundantly in the soil and accumulate there in sufficiently large quantities, phytopathogenic forms do not develop. Because of this, the principle of soil improvement using micro-organisms has been established, i.e. the enrichment of soil with antagonists and the utilization of certain microbes for the control of other microbes. Is this useful in practical agriculture? I think so. There are experiments, although not many, which show that soils, artificially enriched with antagonists, contain no pathogenic bacteria. Such experiments were carried out by Bogopolski (1948, 1950) with the coliform organisms and by Afrikian (1951) with *Azotobacter* and the spore-forming bacterium *Bacillus cereus mycoides*. Krasilnikov (1944) observed the inhibition of staphylococci in soil enriched with antagonists. Arkhipov (1954) noted the death of *Bacillus anthracis* in the soil when bacterial antagonists had accumulated. Lastly, Gubkin (1963) observed the death of *Salmonella*.

The inhibition of phytopathogenic fungi in the soil by antagonistic microbes has been observed by many workers. Fungi such as *Helminthosporium*, *Fusarium*, *Phytophthora*, *Verticillium*, *Rhizoctonia*, *Phymatotrichum* and *Alternaria* can be inhibited and eliminated from the soil by bacteria and other antagonsitic micro-organisms (Krasilnikov, 1958; Stover, 1963; Baker, 1963; Alexander, 1964; Mitchell, 1963).

With regard to the question of whether it is possible to artificially enrich the soil with antagonists, the answer is decidedly positive. Two methods of enrichment of soils are possible:

1. The accumulation of antagonists with the help of plants.
2. The inoculation of appropriate antagonists into the soil.

Firstly plants are selected for crop rotation which encourage the development and accumulation of the antagonists. It is well known that plants differ in their ability to influence micro-organisms in the soil. Some plants favour the development of one group of microbial species whilst others attract and increase the growth of quite different organisms by means of root secretions. Certain plants favour the accumulation of phyto-pathogenic microbes, whereas others favour the growth of the antagonists. For example, in the sierozem soils of Central Asia under perennial cotton, the soil is enriched with the wilt-causing fungi, *Verticillium dahliae* and *Fusarium vasinfectum*. Lucerne, however, encourages the growth of mycolytic bacteria and other microbial antagonists, which inhibit the growth of these fungi. Thus, before the sowing of lucerne after a 7 year cotton culture, there were 10–100 cells of mycolytic bacteria per g., but at the end of the first year with lucerne (sown after cotton), the number had increased to 100–500 thousand/g. and after 2–3 years of lucerne cultivation to 10–100 million/g. Table 5.

TABLE 5

*Distribution of mycolytic bacteria in soil under cotton and lucerne in crop rotation. (millions/g. soil)*

| Region | Antagonists of *V. dahliae* | | | | Antagonists of *F. vasinfectum* | | | |
|---|---|---|---|---|---|---|---|---|
| | Lucerne | | | Cotton | Lucerne | | | Cotton |
| | 1st year | 2nd year | 3rd year | 7th year | 1st year | 2nd year | 3rd year | 7th year |
| Usbekistan Experimental Station STAZR | 0·1–0·5 | 1–15 | 10–50 | 0–0·01 | 0–0·2 | 15–30 | 20–50 | 0·01 |
| Field near Tashkent | 0·5–0·8 | 1·5–10 | 15–40 | 0·01 | 0·5 | 5–40 | 10–100 | 0·05 |
| Tadjikistan Experimental Station, Vaksh | 0·3–1·0 | 10–40 | 30–100 | 0·005 | 1·5 | 10–60 | 50–100 | 0·0 |
| Field near Kurgan Tube | 0·3–0·6 | 5–25 | 20–60 | 0·002 | 0·5 | 60 | 80–150 | 0·01 |

These data show that the degree of development of mycolytic bacteria is inversely proportional to the degree of development of the fungi that cause the infection. Cotton farmers have known for a long time that cotton wilt sharply declines after the inclusion of lucerne in crop rotation schemes for 2–3 years; this is a practical method of improving the fields.

In certain parts of the U.S.A., *Arachis* has been introduced into the crop rotation with cotton for soil sanitation purposes. *Arachis*, during development, inhibits and reduces the percentage of infected plants. Presumably *Arachis* favours the development of antagonists active against the wilt-causing fungi.

It is also possible to carry out soil improvement by means of suitable fertilizer treatment, mineral or organic. Voronkevich (1958) treated soil with lime, a mixture of lime and peat and manure. She reported a marked decrease in the soft rot bacterium, *Erwinia carotovora*, with a simultaneous increase of antagonistic actinomycetes. Similar observations were made by workers at the Rothamsted Experimental Station in England. According to their data, the introduction of chitin into the soil caused enrichment of the antagonists of the wilt disease fungus of peas, *Fusarium albo-atrum* (Rothamsted Experimental Station Report, 1963). This was also observed by Mitchell (1963) and Alexander (1964). They showed that the introduction of chitin or chitin-containing substances (mycelia of fungi, etc.) into the soil lead to the increased development of certain bacteria which produce the enzymes chitinase and laminarinase and consequently lyse the cell walls of phytopathogenic fungi, e.g. *Fusarium*, which contain chitin and laminarin. Sequeira (1962) added sugar and sugar cane to the soil. Both caused increased development of bacteria which inhibited the growth of fungi by causing lysis of their mycelia. Baker (1963) and Stover (1963) showed that application of organic matter to the soil increased the numbers of bacteria and actinomycetes which were antagonistic towards phytopathogenic fungi. Wierbicki (1961) reported the improvement of soil irrigated with sewage, the organic matter of the latter eliminating pathogenic bacteria from the soil. In such fields grazing cattle were not exposed to intestinal infection.

Our investigations show that specially composted microbial preparations of antagonists, bacteria or actinomycetes, inhibited the development of the phytopathogenic microflora in the soil. Composts can be prepared from peat mixed with soil. These substrates are inoculated with special isolates of antagonistic actinomycetes or bacteria, and incubated for 10–15 days. During this time the bacteria or actinomycetes germinate within the compost. After adding such a preparation to the soil the antagonists survive and develop to a greater degree. If the antagonists do not survive in the soil they will not produce the expected effects and such preparations will be worthless. Strains must be used which have the ability not only to inhibit the given disease-producing organism but also to survive and develop abundantly in the soil, particularly in the rhizosphere.

Preliminary experiments were carried out in pots and in special test-plots at experimental stations in Usbekistan and Tadjikistan; final experiments were carried out in commercial fields. In all cases where a good compost was established the results were positive; the infection with cotton wilt disease decreased by 40 to 70 per cent (Table 6).

TABLE 6

*The influence of compost preparations of actinomycete antagonists on the incidence of cotton wilt*

| Treatment | | Infected plants (%) | | Yield in g. × $10^2$/hectare |
|---|---|---|---|---|
| | | Cotyledon stage | Fruiting stage | |
| Control | | 74·4 | 19·1 | 16·4 |
| Compost treated with antagonistic strain number | 114 | 8·1 | 0·01 | 34·8 |
| | 160 | 10·7 | 0·05 | 35·1 |
| | 117 | 10·2 | 0·4 | 25·6 |
| | 66 | 18·4 | 2·0 | 18·2 |

The best effect was obtained with composts prepared from strains of actinomycetes No. 114 and No. 160. The percentage infection was minimal, and the harvest maximal (34·8-35·1 × $10^2$ g. per hectare). Microbial analyses of the soil with these treatments in the experiment showed that the organism causing wilt (*Fusarium vasinfectum*) had sharply declined in number. The count was 0 to 100 propagules/g. compared with the control soil where the count was 100 thousand to 500 thousand propagules/g. Such experiments were conducted by Kublanovska, Korenyako, Kuzina and Rasnitsina (Krasilnikov, 1958) and in recent years by Khodjibayeva (1965). Kublanovska tested composts with actinomycetes and these had just as effective results as the best fungicide at that time, granazan, in the control of *Verticillium* wilt of cotton. Rasnitsina used composts with mycolytic bacteria for the control of the wilt of pine seedlings in badly infected fields near Moscow. In control plots the loss of pine seedlings was over 80 per cent compared with the treated plots where the losses were from 10–15 per cent (Table 7). In our opinion the above data is sufficiently convincing to show the value of microbial methods for the improvement of soil.

TABLE 7

*The inhibition of wilt of pine seedlings by bacterial composts (calculated at the end of the second year of growth)*

| Treatment | Count of *Fusarium* spp. per g. of soil | Survival of Plants (%) | Plant height (cm.) |
|---|---|---|---|
| Control | 150,000 | 3 | 7·0–8·0 |
| Addition of | | | |
| mycolytic bacteria (strain 30) | 200 | 86 | 10·2 |
| ,, ,, (strain 18) | 0·4 | 88 | 12·1 |
| ,, ,, (strain 23) | 0·1 | 90 | 12·8 |
| Addition of actinomycetes | 0–100 | 85 | 10·8 |

Antagonists develop not only under experimental conditions in the laboratory, but also under natural conditions, directly in the soil. This is a fact beyond doubt. It is only necessary to use the antagonists skilfully to control pathogenic forms and remove them from soil. Further research is necessary, however, particularly in relation to the commercial value of the method under field conditions.

## *CONCLUSIONS*

Soil infestation with pathogenic fungi and bacteria has often been observed. In recent years, in many areas, noticeable increases in the degree of infestation of soil with harmful micro-organisms have been reported. As a result, mass infection of plants takes place and very poor harvests result. Infestation of soil with pathogens is often seen after monoculture of a crop has occurred in the field over a number of years. After 7–8 years of cotton cultivation, the quantity of *Fusarium vasinfectum* and *Verticillium dahliae* sharply increase and reach a maximum count of up to 80 thousand propagules per g. Their antagonists, bacteria or actinonycetes, sharply decrease or completely disappear. Similar changes can be observed in soil under monocultured flax or pine.

It is possible to remove pathogenic fungi and bacteria from soil with the help of microbial antagonists. It has been established that with the abundant development of antagonists in the soil, the phytopathogens sharply decrease and in some cases are completely destroyed. Of all the soil micro-organisms, the most effective antagonists of the phytopathogenic fungi (*Fusarium* and *Verticillium*) are the mycolytic, nonsporeforming bacteria and actinomycetes. Cultures of bacteria and actinomycetes have been isolated which actively inhibit the development of pathogenic microbes in the soil. Several methods for the practical use of these antagonists have been worked out. These methods are based upon two principles:

(a) the establishment of a crop rotation allowing the accumulation of antagonists in the soil,
(b) the production of special composts containing antagonists.

The use of these methods improves infected soil by removing pathogenic microbes.

## *REFERENCES*

AGRE, N. (1964). *Thermophilic ray fungi.* Thesis. Moscow. MGU.

ALEXANDER, M. (1964). Biochemical ecology of soil microorganisms. *A. Rev. Microbiol.*, **18**, 217.

AFRIKIAN, E. K. (1951). The composition of bacillar populations in soils under some plants. *Dokl. Akad. Nauk armyan. SSR*, **16**, 9, 14.

ARKHIPOV, V. V. (1951). On the possibility of the destruction of the causative agent of anthrax by planting cultivated grasses. *Veterinaria*, **3**, 33.

ARKHIPOV, V. V. (1954). On the problem of disinfection and sanitation of soils by plant cultivation. *Veterinaria*, **6**, 53.

BAKER, K. F. (1963). Control of phytopathogenic micro-organisms in soil by management practices. *Recent Progress in Microbiology.* Ed. Gibbons, N. E. Toronto. University of Toronto Press.

BOGOPOLSKI, M. D. (1948). The plant rhizosphere as a biological factor of the perishing of bacteria of the colon-paracolon group. *Mȳkrobiol. Zh.*, **10**, 1.

BOGOPOLSKI, M. D. (1950). Research on the bacteriostatic properties of the soil with regard to bacteria of the colon-paracolon group. *Mȳkrobiol. Zh.*, **12**, 67.

BRIAN, P. W. (1960). Antagonistic and competitive mechanisms limiting survival and activity of fungi in soil. In *The Ecology of Soil Fungi.* Ed. Parkinson, D. & Waid, J. S. Liverpool. Liverpool University Press.

GRIGORYAN, T. (1956). Antagonisticheksoe deistuie nekotorych pochvennych mikroorganizmov na *B. anthracis. Trudȳ turkmen. sel'.-khoz. Inst.*, **8**, 65.

GUBKIN, S. (1963). Zhiznesposobnost' salmonell i teoreticheskoe obosnovanie veterinaro-sanitarnykh meropriyatii pri salmonellezakh. *Trudȳ omsk. sel'.-khoz. Inst.*, **52**, 1.

HUSSEIN, A. (1964). *Actinomycetes of Egyptian soil.* Thesis. Moscow. State University of Moscow.

KHODJIBAYEVA, S. (1965). *Antagonistic actinomycetes in the control of cotton wilt by Verticillium.* Thesis. Moscow. State University of Moscow.

KRASILNIKOV, N. A. (1944). Biological methods of combating phytopathogenic microbes. *Mikrobiologiya*, **13**, 1.

KRASILNIKOV, N. A. (1958). *Soil microorganisms and higher plants.* Moscow. Acad. Sci. U.S.S.R.

MITCHELL, A. (1963). Lysis of *Fusarium* in laminarin amended soil. *Bull. Res. Coun. Israel*, **11**, 320.

PRASADA, I. (1965). *Report of the scientific congress*, Calcutta. University of Calcutta.

SEQUEIRA, L. (1962). Influence of organic amendments on survival of *Fusarium oxysporum* f. *cubense*. *Phytopathology*, **52**, 976.

STOVER, R. H. (1962). Fusarial wilt (Panama disease) of bananas and other *Musa* species. *Phytopathological paper*, 4. Kew. Commonwealth Mycological Institute.

STOVER, R. H. (1963). The use of organic amendments and green manures in the control of soil-borne plant pathogens. *Recent Progress in Microbiology*. Ed. Gibbons, N. E. Toronto. University of Toronto Press.

TUMARKIN, R. (1963). *Microbe antagonists of pathogenic bacteria as a means of soil improvement*. Thesis. Moscow. Acad. Med. Sci. U.S.S.R.

TZI-SHEN, U. (1961). *The biology of the orange group of actinomycetes*. Thesis. Moscow. Acad. Sci. U.S.S.R.

VORONKEVICH, I. V. (1958). The antagonism of micro-organisms in the soil and prospects for their use in the control of soil-borne casual agents of plant diseases. *Usp. sovremennoĭ Biol.*, **46**, 145.

WIERBICKI, T. (1961). Badania terenow nawadnianych wodami sciekowymi pod wzgledem higieniczno-sanitarnym. I. Znaczenie wykorzystania sciekow do nawadniania uzytkow rolnych i lesnych. *Acta Microbial. pol*, **10**, 425.

## *DISCUSSION*

### BACTERIA IN THE ROOT REGION OF PLANTS

*Chairman: D. Parkinson, The University of Waterloo*

*Prof. D. Parkinson.* Dr. Fåhraeus described the very intimate association of *Rhizobium* spp. with legume roots. The morphological effects of micro-organisms on living roots are only just beginning to be understood and the peculiar morphological effect of the rhizobia is surely extremely interesting. In this connection, the role of electron microscopy in studying microbial colonization of roots is becoming increasingly important. Many of you will probably remember the photographs, published in the California Agricultural Bulletin by Jenny and his colleagues, of the bacteria in the mucigel on roots.

Dr. Macura emphasized the role of the root exudates in the qualitative and quantitative expression of the rhizosphere effect. I think that he raised an important question with regard to rhizosphere ecology when he emphasized that the rhizosphere is a group of microhabitats, not a uniform microhabitat, that the situation in the root tip region may be ecologically very different from that in the crown of the root system. Also, he touched on the problems of foliar application of chemicals. This technique is a very powerful experimental tool for studying rhizosphere colonization and metabolism in the root region.

Professor Krasilnikov raised a number of very important questions with regard to biological control; he presented very clear-cut data on this problem. The effects of continuous crop treatment in building up pathogenic populations in soil is well known and presumably is, at least in part, an expression of the rhizosphere effect.

I would like to open the discussion with a question to Professor Krasilnikov. What methods did you use for counting mycolytic bacteria in the soils with which you were dealing?

*Prof. N. A. Krasilnikov.* I used a modification of the extinction dilution method. I grew cultures of *Fusarium vasinfectum* and *Fusarium lini* in tubes. Then I took the sample of soil to be analysed and dispersed it in water on a shaker. I prepared a series of dilutions from it and inoculated the different dilutions into the cultures of *Fusarium*. The mycelium was destroyed by those samples which contained mycolytic bacteria. By counting the tubes in which mycolysis occurred, I could calculate the most probable numbers of bacteria present.

*Prof. D. Pramer.* May I continue this line of questioning? How did you enumerate *Fusarium* in the soil?

*Prof. N. A. Krasilnikov.* I inoculated soil containing healthy flax plants with dilutions of the soil to be tested. I could then calculate the most probable number of *Fusarium lini* propagules by observing the number of flax plants which died.

*Dr. W. Gams.* What were these mycolytic organisms? Were they actinomycetes or bacteria? Have you discovered whether they dissolve the fungal cell wall, or do they simply act as antagonists?

*Prof. N. A. Krasilnikov.* They were bacteria belonging to different species of *Pseudomonas*, *Mycobacterium*, spore-forming bacteria, etc.

Microscopic pictures of the lysed mycelium were easy to obtain. In *Fusarium* the wall was destroyed, followed by the protoplast, perhaps some 10-20 hrs. later.

*Dr. H. J. Potgieter.* There is apparently a great deal of variation in the composition of the cell walls of fungi. I have tested *Fusarium solani.* Its cell walls can be destroyed easily and spheroplasts formed by using only 2 enzymes, namely a chitinase and a $\beta$ 1–3 glucanase. Other fungi like *Rhizoctonia* and *Neurospora* are not affected to the same extent. Consequently, the destruction of cell walls of different fungi will require different mycolytic bacteria.

*Prof. J. L. Lockwood.* I don't think we can say yet whether the lysis of fungi in soil is heterolytic or autolytic. There is some evidence that it is autolytic. We need not assume that it is always caused by cell wall decomposing enzymes from mycolytic bacteria.

*Dr. M. Alexander.* It is very difficult to see how autolysis or enzyme-induced autolysis could account for the enzymatic destruction of dead fungi.

*Dr. S. T. Williams.* Professor Krasilnikov, did you find that *Fusarium* chlamydospores were resistant to lysis?

*Prof. N. A. Krasilnikov.* Yes, and often. Mycolytic bacteria show specificity to the *Fusarium* spp. they attack. If you use the same strain of mycolytic bacteria with different species of *Fusarium*, you get different effects. Often the spores are resistant, but even they will be lysed if you use a strongly mycolytic strain. In such cases, the mycelium is more sensitive and is always lysed first.

*Dr. D. A. van Schreven.* How were the composts, treated with antagonists, added to soil? Were they spread over the soil or were they mixed with seeds? In what quantities were they added?

*Prof. N. A. Krasilnikov.* We used about 10 g. compost per kg. soil. It was necessary to use composts since pure cultures of bacteria and actinomycetes were usually inhibited in soil. In small scale laboratory experiments, pure cultures can be used. In these experiments we used about 1 ml. of a culture of mycolytic bacteria growing in a liquid medium, 2 or 3 days after inoculation. Each ml. of culture contained between 5 and 7 million mycolytic bacteria.

*Dr. A. J. Holding.* Dr. Macura, we support you wholeheartedly in the matter of the contribution of the seed microflora to the rhizosphere microflora. On the oat seeds we have examined, yellow fermentative organisms, often referred to as *Bacterium herbicola*, or related organisms, were dominant types. We have never been able to isolate these organisms from the oat rhizosphere. A similar situation was found in the case of clover; fermentative organisms were often found on the seed, but occurred rarely in the rhizosphere.

I would also like to ask you about the phenomenon of specificity in the rhizosphere. Does the growing plant have a different effect on the rhizosphere microflora than the root exudates, and does the root exudate material have a different effect on the soil microflora than any mixture of organic chemicals?

*Dr. J. Macura.* I think it is necessary to define the term specificity. Certainly, there is very strong specificity in the relationships between rhizobia and the Leguminosae and the relationships between certain plants and plant pathogens or root infecting fungi. However, I have never encountered any such specific relationship between saprophytic bacteria and plant roots. If the root exudates of different plants are not the same, then the roots will harbour a different microflora. However, I do not think that this is at all specific. All micro-organisms have certain needs; if the microbe needs a certain substance and that substance is not present, then it will not develop. Some of the experiments that I have described were carried out with root exudates obtained from plants, and some of them with a mixture of sugars, amino acids, organic acids and other substances that have been identified in root exudates. I have not been able to differentiate between the influence of natural root exudates and such mixtures because our data are schematic. We have only determined the occurrence of nutritional groups and morphological groups, and compared the growth intensities of isolated strains. Consequently, I don't think that I can answer your question on the basis of our data.

*Dr. D. A. van Schreven.* Dr. Macura, how do you distinguish the metabolic products which are excreted by the seeds, from those of the roots, especially in the early stages of growth?

*Dr. J. Macura.* I think Dr. Vančura can probably answer that.

*Dr. V. Vančura.* We plant seeds on filter paper and, before the first root appears, we elute the excreted products from the paper and analyse them. We cannot differentiate seed and root exudates after the appearance of the green parts of the germinating seedling. Such differentiation would be difficult unless one used isotopes for labelling the exudates. We obtain root exudates from plants grown in hydroponic culture.

*Dr. D. A. van Schreven.* If you transfer the young plant with the seed still attached to it, then the seed exudates will also be found in the hydroponic culture.

*Prof. A. D. McLaren.* A remark was made by our chairman about the observations of Jenny and Grossenbacher concerning the mucigel on roots. At the time of the Berkeley symposium a couple of years ago, the question was raised whether sterile roots have a mucigel, or whether the mucigel is produced by the bacteria in the rhizoplane. I would like to report that plants grown with sterile root systems possess a mucigel layer, but the amount is much less than when the root is non-sterile. We don't know where the extra mucigel is coming from, i.e. whether the organisms on the root produce it, or whether the organisms on the root induce the root to produce more mucigel.

A similar situation has been reported by Professor Krasilnikov. He observed that the amino acid content of a root system grown under sterile conditions is different from that of a root grown under non-sterile conditions. In particular, one or two amino acids essential for animal growth, including lysine, are more abundant in non-sterile roots. We have gone to a great deal of trouble to repeat this experiment and we find the same thing. There is, however, a question and that is whether something in the rhizoplane organisms causes an inhibition of protein synthesis, thereby building up a pool of free amino acids with no total increase in amino acids in the root, or whether there is a total increase in the amount of amino acids in the root, including these essential amino acids. The latter part of the question remains unanswered, but it seems to me that this kind of observation should be followed up. The implications are manifold, because if the organisms can influence the metabolism of the plant, so that it makes things it would normally make in different quantities, then this throws a great deal of light on the susceptibility of the plant to infection, resistance to infection, etc.

*Dr. M. Alexander.* As a first approximation, one usually assumes that there is a point in space or time when the plant excretes a substance stimulating, selectively or specifically, the infective *Rhizobium.* Peters, working in my laboratory, examined 7 *Rhizobium* strains, acting on a variety of host plants and found no selective, stimulatory substance in the rhizosphere of any of these plants, nor any selective adsorption or colonization of the roots of their homologous host plants. I would like to ask Dr. Fåhraeus if he can suggest how the bacterial polysaccharide induces polygalacturonase formation in the plant. Does the polysaccharide penetrate into the root, or do you think the enzyme is synthesized on the surface of the root?

*Dr. G. Fåhraeus.* It could be either way. The polysaccharides may enter the root (big molecules can enter roots), or may act at the surface. We believe that the polysaccharide enters the root cytoplasm and combines with the repressor of the enzyme; the enzyme will then be formed in larger quantities than in the normal root. Polygalacturonase is supposed to occur in normal root hairs, but the increased synthesis of this enzyme would cause the weakening of the pectin layer of the cell wall. We know that the very tip of the root hair is mainly built up of pectic substances; there is not much crystallized cellulose there. The bacteria could then enter, either through penetration or invagination. However, we don't know whether the polysaccharide acts only on the cytoplasmic surface or within the cytoplasm.

*Dr. J. S. D. Bacon.* Is the polygalacturonase in solution in the system that you are studying? Are there any other enzymes which might be liberated from the root, such as invertase or acid phosphatase?

*D. G. Fåhraeus.* Yes, the polygalacturonase is in solution. You find it in the rhizosphere solution around the roots. We have tried to find other enzymes, particularly cellulases, by means of the same viscometric techniques, but, using soluble cellulose derivatives, we could not find any. We have not looked for invertase or phosphatase.

*Dr. D. A. van Schreven.* The formation of nodules is inhibited by combined nitrogen. Is the formation of polygalacturonase also inhibited by combined nitrogen?

*Dr. G. Fåhraeus.* You get exactly the same inhibition. If you add combined nitrogen to the cultures, you do not get any polygalacturonase production. The effect of combined nitrogen could be primarily an effect on this system.

*Dr. J. S. D. Bacon.* Must the combined nitrogen be applied from the outside, or can one influence the root hairs through the plant?

*Dr. G. Fåhraeus.* Perhaps Dr. Nutman knows more about that than I do.

*Dr. P. S. Nutman.* The question is at what level the combined nitrogen has an inhibitory effect on polygalacturonase production. At very low levels combined nitrogen does not inhibit any of these processes; in fact it has an indirect stimulatory effect. As far as this stimulatory effect is concerned, applied nitrogen at low levels to the top of the plant does not have this effect.

*Dr. D. A. van Schreven.* During spraying of urea on the leaves of leguminous plants, I found that the number of nodules could be reduced quite markedly, so that this may be an effect from inside the root.

*Dr. H. Tribe.* Do you know of any property of their roots that could account for the Leguminosae being the only flowering plants to be affected by rhizobia?

*Dr. G. Fåhraeus.* This is a mystery. There are non-legumes which form analagous symbioses, but rhizobia are not involved. If you study *Alnus* you find the same, perhaps even more deformed, root hairs. However, I don't know any difference, anatomical or physiological, between legume roots and the roots of other plants that could account for this phenomenon.

*Dr. H. Tribe.* Is there any form of early attack of root hairs of non-legumes by rhizobia? Can they get half way, but not form a nodule?

*Dr. G. Fåhraeus.* There have been no reports of that. Perhaps it should be studied a little more. Haack has studied the effect of rhizobia on other plants and shown that you get elongation of the root hair, but no deformation. This might be an indole acetic acid effect. The type of deformation that you find in the legumes seems to be rare; it only occurs in the legume-*Rhizobium* associations and in the associations of trees, e.g. *Alnus*, with actinomycetes.

*Dr. M. Alexander.* Valera has recently reported a nodule inducing substance found in the cotyledons of legumes. Unfortunately, this substance is not restricted to the legumes. We also found a similar substance, at least behaving similarly, in coconuts, which I don't believe are classified as legumes!

*Dr. J. S. D. Bacon.* Does the branching of the root hairs always occur at the same distance from the tip of the root hair?

*Dr. G. Fåhraeus.* Branching occurs even in uninfected hairs, but it is much more common in plant systems inoculated with rhizobia. Typically, you get branching of the root hairs at about half the length of the hair. This is curious because you would expect the hair wall to be hard at that point since the cellulose must be crystallized and firm. Perhaps a cellulose decomposing enzyme is involved. We have tried to find cellulases, but we have not been successful.

*Dr. A. D. McLaren.* May I enlarge upon the penetration of large molecules into root hairs. The invagination of the root hair looks superficially like pictures of pinocytosis in animal cells. We tried to see if basic proteins would induce an invagination or pinocytosis in the root hairs. We have never been successful in getting any signs of such a phenomenon. On the other hand, one would hardly expect something like cellulase to be the answer, because this would not be sufficiently specific.

*Prof. D. Pramer.* Although you obtained no evidence for pinocytosis, did the protein enter the root?

*Prof. A. D. McLaren.* No, it did not.

*Prof. D. Pramer.* And yet animal viruses can get into plant roots and be translocated, although their molecular size and weight exceed those of your basic protein. The uptake of antibiotics, sulphur drugs, etc. is put to shame. This means that virus particles do not enter by pinocytosis either.

*Prof. A. D. McLaren.* We have made a detailed study of the uptake of protein molecules from sterile solutions by sterile root systems, and we have found that proteins are not taken up by healthy sterile root systems under these conditions. However, if a young plant is allowed to undergo a very minor incipient wilting, then allowed to recover and is exposed to proteins whilst it is in this state of mild 'sickness', then in 3 or 4 cases out of 10, the proteins will rise through the conductive elements and appear in the leaf. The work that was done with the uptake of viruses gave similar results, i.e. only occasionally did plants take up polio virus. We feel that in the cases in which protein does go up, there is probably a minor condition of entry of some kind, e.g. incipient wilting or abrasion of the root system. If the plant is very carefully nurtured, although protein may enter the root, it does not reach the shoot.

*Prof. E. L. Schmidt.* I had better comment on this since it is my work which is being quoted. The original work with mouse encephalitis virus was not done in this way, but was carried out in a soil environment, rather substantial amounts of virus being added to the soil system. There was no uniform uptake of the mouse virus by tomato plants. On the other hand, there was a certain but variable proportion of the plants which showed definite evidence of the virus molecule in their aerial parts by virtue of regular immunity tests. Later work was done in a sterile, non-soil environment with polio virus, and here there was some evidence of uptake, but less than with the mouse encephalitis virus. The conditions under which the plants existed in the pots in the soil, with roots only partially exposed, could involve some partial breakage of the root system. On the other hand, plants, as they exist in soil, do not always lead a sheltered life either, and it is very likely that these large molecules are taken up all the time.

More recently, we have examined the uptake of amino acids from the soil solution by intact plants, again from a sterile root environment. We have shown fairly conclusively that amino acids, if they are present near the root, can be taken up and used by the plant.

*Prof. A. D. McLaren.* I would like to confirm that observation. We have also shown that amino acids, including some sulphur amino acids, can be taken up and incorporated into plant proteins.

*Dr. P. S. Nutman.* As someone who has looked at very large numbers of root hairs of plants grown under what would normally be regarded as carefully controlled conditions, it is always a surprise to me to find that quite an appreciable proportion of root hairs suffer plasmoptysis spontaneously. If one cannot be sure that there are not ruptures of this kind, how can one be sure that one is dealing with a process such as uptake, or even exudation from the root in the real sense? Maybe in plants grown under sterile conditions (not in soil), many opportunities occur for entry of this kind.

*Prof. A. D. McLaren.* I would like to comment on that. We have grown plants sterilely in soil sterilized in an electron beam so that there was a minimum of physical and chemical alteration of the soil. The soil was inoculated with radioactive protein and with sterilized seeds. The radioactive protein did not go into the plants under these conditions. Presumably, it was bound by the exchange capacity of the soil. Similarly, amino acids entered only with great difficulty into sterile roots in sterile soil, again probably because of the exchange capacity phenomenon in the soil. However, if a sterile seedling was grown in sterile sand culture, then amino acids were taken up rapidly. Consequently, I think that it is very dangerous to extrapolate from results obtained in model systems like hydroponic sand culture, to the soil.

*Prof. E. L. Schmidt.* We obtained different results. We used a sterile soil system with a sterile root environment and the amino acids were taken up like a shot.

*Prof. A. D. McLaren.* What plant were you using?

*Prof. E. L. Schmidt.* Bean.

*Prof. A. D. McLaren.* That is very interesting. We were using barley and tomato and I think there is a reason for suspecting that the bean may be quite different. It has been shown that egg albumen enters legumes, e.g. broad bean, very readily and is transmitted to the leaf in such large amounts that, when extracted from the leaf, it can give an anaphylactic shock to a sensitized guinea pig. So I think that the uptake pattern of a legume may be quite different from that of a grass.

*Dr. J. S. Waid.* I would like to point out, in support of Dr. Nutman, that there are reports in the literature of the autolytic breakdown of cells in the root cortex of plants grown under aseptic conditions. This does not necessarily affect the uptake of nutrients at the apex of the root, where root hairs are present, but it does suggest the possibility of leakage from the older regions of the root.

*Mr. G. W. Hull.* I wonder if Dr. Fåhraeus would like to enlarge upon the idea of communication of information between different species of bacteria in the soil by means of DNA.

*Dr. G. Fåhraeus.* As I have said before, I think this is a very bold suggestion. The bacteria in the root nodules are not really alive, i.e. the bacteroids don't seem to be able to give rise to new bacteria. I wonder whether the DNA, which should be present in large amounts in the bacteroids, could have a transforming effect on the bacteria in the soil around the roots. Thus, related bacteria which occur in the rhizosphere might be transformed and become more competitive than the effective strain in the nodule. New strains of *Rhizobium* might be created from *Agrobacterium* strains, but this is very speculative; we have no evidence on this point.

*Dr. A. N. Barker.* Dr. Fåhraeus, you mentioned the stimulation of nitrogen fixation in *Nostoc* by *Rhizobium* and also suggested that this could be a feature of many other organisms. *Nostoc* can be stimulated by increasing the $CO_2$ in the atmosphere. Could this be the cause of the stimulation, the $CO_2$ coming from the respiratory processes of *Rhizobium*?

*Dr. G. Fåhraeus.* What I had in mind was the work of Carnahan and his colleagues. They have shown that in *Clostridium* the nitrogen fixing system can be resolved into two components, one a nitrogen activating factor and the other a hydrogen donating factor. In the legume association, we have two organisms which provide one of these factors each. We do not know if the rhizobia are the hydrogen donors and if the plants possess the nitrogen activating factor, or *vice versa*. However, in the case of *Nostoc*, we have an alga which can fix nitrogen, but only in small amounts. Possibly *Nostoc* has one of these factors in small, limiting amounts, and the bacteria that are added supply more of this factor and hence stimulate the fixation process. There are also other bacteria that can stimulate *Nostoc*, some of them to a greater extent, e.g. *Bacillus megatherium*. This bacterium was thought to be a nitrogen fixing bacterium, but it is probably not.

# THE GROWTH OF BACTERIA IN SOIL

# THE GROWTH OF BACTERIA IN SOIL

FRANCIS E. CLARK[1]

*Agricultural Research Service, Fort Collins, Colorado*[2]

## *INTRODUCTION*

The soil has long been a reservoir from which the taxonomist has described new species. It can be expected to remain such a reservoir for a long time to come. Above all, however, the soil with its innumerable inhabitants is a challenge to the microbial ecologist. Certainly it is a challenge to an amateur ecologist, to one at this moment burdened with the uneasy feeling that in the selection of his material he has chosen to ignore far too many facets of the growth of bacteria in soil. I plan to restrict my remarks to certain aspects of total microbial growth in soil and some phenomena attendant upon organic matter decomposition in soil. Hopefully, some of the data presented will be used as a basis for asking, but not for answering, why one or another species grows in a particular micro-site in soil and why soil organisms, individually or collectively, often fail to exhibit growth responses of some expected magnitude in given situations.

Attempting to discuss, even in a small part, the relationships between soil organisms and their food supplies is an ambitious undertaking. Many years ago Pfeffer remarked that the entire world and all the friendly and antagonistic relationships among different organisms are primarily regulated by the necessity for obtaining food. Microbial ecologists have expressed essentially this idea for 'the supply of food materials in soil can be said to be perennially inadequate' and 'there are many micro-organisms in the soil and they are nearly always hungry'.

In consequence of this ever-continuing struggle for food, the specializations developed among micro-organisms for utilizing energy-yielding materials have become enormous. Among the soil autotrophs, the specialization achieved is primarily that of successful exploitation of a substrate unavailable to most of the soil inhabitants. Among the soil heterotrophs, particularly among those engaged in the decomposition

[1] Chief Microbiologist, U.S.D.A., Fort Collins, Colorado.

[2] Contribution from the Soil and Water Conservation Research Division, Agricultural Research Service, U.S.D.A., in co-operation with the Colorado Agricultural Experiment Station, Fort Collins, Colorado.

of the plant and animal residues commonly returned to the soil, the specialization is more complex. It hinges not simply on the ability to use some specific material, for example glucose or cellulose, but on the ability to use a basically cosmopolitan substrate under the particular ecological conditions in which that substrate is encountered. In many instances the influential ecological factors are easily recognizable. In others the reasons why one or another micro-organism becomes more or less active or suddenly becomes dominant or suddenly disappears are much more difficult to recognize.

## *SOME ASPECTS OF ORGANIC MATTER DECOMPOSITION IN SOIL*

Studies on organic matter decomposition in soil frequently yield observations either difficult to interpret or open, initially at least, to controversial interpretation. Not uncommonly the phenomenon involved is given some designation of convenience. Thereafter such terms may become quite widely entrenched in the microbiological literature. Selected for discussion below are certain aspects of organic matter decomposition designated as the rate of addition effect, the volume effect, the aeration effect and the priming effect. Such a selection does not deny the existence of many other 'effects' as, for example, the drying effect, the particle-size effect and the successive-addition effect.

### *The rate of addition effect*

Within recent years, many microbiologists have reported that the percentage decomposition within unit time of an organic residue added to soil is inversely related to the rate of residue addition. Some illustrative data are shown in Table 1. Although the total output of carbon

TABLE 1

*Influence of rate of residue addition on residue decomposition*

| Alfalfa meal added | mg. $CO_2$ per 50 g. soil | | | % added C evolved as $CO_2$ | | |
|---|---|---|---|---|---|---|
| | 1 wk. | 2 wks. | 3 wks. | 1 wk. | 2 wks. | 3 wks. |
| 0 | 44 | 61 | 77 | — | — | — |
| 0·8% | 261 | 360 | 421 | 35·0 | 48·2 | 55·5 |
| 1·6% | 367 | 520 | 606 | 26·0 | 37·0 | 42·7 |
| 3·2% | 532 | 860 | 1007 | 19·7 | 32·2 | 37·5 |

dioxide is greater at higher rates of addition, the percentage of the added residue carbon evolved as carbon dioxide is lower. The rate effect has been described by van Schreven (1964) as follows: the higher the rate of residue addition, the longer the time required to accomplish a given percentage of decomposition. Applying van Schreven's statement to the data in Table 1, 37 per cent decomposition (added C evolved as $CO_2$), of alfalfa meal added at 0·8 per cent was accomplished in 8 days; at 1·6 per cent, in 14 days; and at 3·2 per cent, in 21 days.

In their first publication on the rate of addition effect, Broadbent and Bartholomew (1949) suggested that the smaller percentage decomposition at higher rates of addition might be caused by associated physical or biotic factors restricting microbial development in a given volume of soil. Subsequently, other writers also referred to over-crowding of the available living space and to aeration insufficiencies as being somehow involved.

That a shortage of microbial living space might help to explain why small amounts of added organic residues decompose more rapidly than do larger quantities seems relatively easy to investigate. One need only to provide more soil for a given quantity of organic residue. Such an experiment was established. Two grams of alfalfa meal were added to 50, 100, and 200 g. quantities of soil. The extent of residue decomposition during eight weeks of incubation, as revealed by carbon dioxide measurements, is shown in Table 2.

TABLE 2

*Influence of differing soil volumes on residue decomposition*

| 2 g. alfalfa meal added to | rate of addition | weeks of incubation | | | | |
|---|---|---|---|---|---|---|
| | | 1 | 2 | 4 | 6 | 8 |
| | | % added C evolved as $CO_2$ | | | | |
| 50 g. soil | 4% | 32·0 | 38·6 | 42·2 | 44·3 | 46·2 |
| 100 g. soil | 2% | 30·2 | 35·9 | 39·6 | 42·1 | 43·9 |
| 200 g. soil | 1% | 26·7 | 32·2 | 34·4 | 36·7 | 38·5 |

The results discount the importance, or at least any over-riding importance, of a space requirement in the decomposition of the added residues. They are apparently in contradiction to the rate of addition effect in that the lowest proportional decomposition was obtained with the lowest, not the highest, rate of residue addition. At least they suggest the desirability of altering the rate of addition rule to, 'The percentage decomposition within unit time of an organic residue added to soil is inversely related to the rate of residue addition, providing that the soil volume is held constant'.

*The volume effect*

Soil microbiologists have long recognized that comparisons of decomposition ratios are valid only when the same soil is used in all comparisons and when the incubation quantities are equal. With reference to organic matter decomposition, the volume effect can be described as the tendency for dissimilar quantities or incubation aliquots to show dissimilar decomposition ratios. In the great majority of decomposition experiments reported in the literature, the investigator has by-passed the volume effect simply by using a standard quantity of soil for any given experiment.

Different soils are likely to show the volume effect in differing degrees. The effect is often encountered in residue-amended soils but less commonly in unamended or control soil lots. Easily the most striking example of the volume effect thus far encountered by the writer was shown by an alluvial silt loam amended with 0·5 per cent alfalfa meal (Table 3). The magnitude of the volume effect in this particular soil was confirmed subsequently in two separate re-runs of the experiment.

TABLE 3

*Influence of size of incubation aliquot on decomposition*

| Soil* used per container | $CO_2$ evolved, mg. per container | | |
|---|---|---|---|
| | 1 wk. | 2 wks. | 3 wks. |
| 100 g. | 304 | 395 | 450 |
| | 310 | 405 | 454 |
| | 308 | 400 | 453 |
| 25 g. | 114 | 142 | 161 |
| | 113 | 143 | 165 |
| | 101 | 138 | 159 |

* Alluvial silt loam amended with 0·5% alfalfa meal.

In decomposition experiments involving added residues, the volume effect is usually negative. Only rarely is it positive. However, a positive volume effect is encountered frequently in experiments on nitrification in laboratory soil. In their review on soil nitrogen transformations, Harmsen and van Schreven (1955) observed that quite commonly in nitrification studies, nitrate accumulation is favoured by an increase in soil volume; also, that with soil quantity constant, nitrification in soil incubated in a deep layer is superior to that in soil incubated in a shallow layer; and that with soil quantities and surface/volume ratios constant, soil given vigorous aeration may show less nitrification than that given less vigorous aeration.

That greater nitrification may be achieved either by an increase in the size of the incubation sample or by a decrease in the surface/volume ratio is shown by the data presented in Table 4. These data reveal higher rates

TABLE 4

*Influence of differently sized incubation lots and of differently shaped incubation containers on rate of nitrification*

| Quantity of soil incubated | Type of container | Surface/volume ratio | $NO_3$–N, after 2 wks., ppm |
|---|---|---|---|
| 10 g. | Small bottle | 1·60 | 85* |
| 25 g. | Small bottle | 0·64 | 105 |
| 50 g. | Small bottle | 0·32 | 129 |
| 50 g. | Petri dish | 1·60 | 103 |
| 50 g. | Small bottle | 0·32 | 137 |
| 50 g. | Centrifuge tube | 0·12 | 146 |

* Each value shown is the average of 3 replicates.

of nitrification for soil lots that are undoubtedly less well aerated, insofar as their oxygen status is concerned. The results disagree with those published in textbooks of microbiology which show that full aeration, or atmospheric or even higher percentages of oxygen are required for the maximum rate of nitrification in soil. Such published emphasis on the desirability of full aeration, together with the apparently contradictory statements cited above from Harmsen and van Schreven (1955), prompted us to measure the influence of oxygen supply on the rate of nitrification in soil. Some representative data are shown in Fig. 1.

These findings are in agreement with earlier observations published by Amer and Bartholomew (1951). Even when the oxygen supply is reduced to as low as 10 per cent by volume, the nitrification rate remains fully comparable to that obtained in the presence of 21 per cent oxygen. Fig. 1, however, does not explain why a larger soil volume is more favourable to nitrification than a smaller soil volume.

If the $CO_2$ requirement for nitrification is examined, it is readily

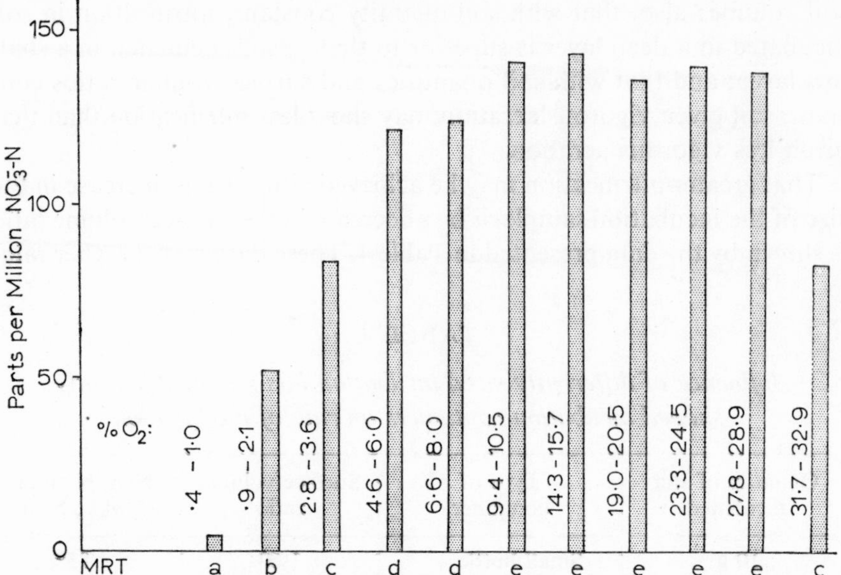


Fig. 1. Influence of differing oxygen concentrations on nitrate production in soil. MRT = multiple range test for significance at the 1 per cent level. Columns bearing the same letters do not differ significantly; those bearing a dissimilar letter differ significantly.

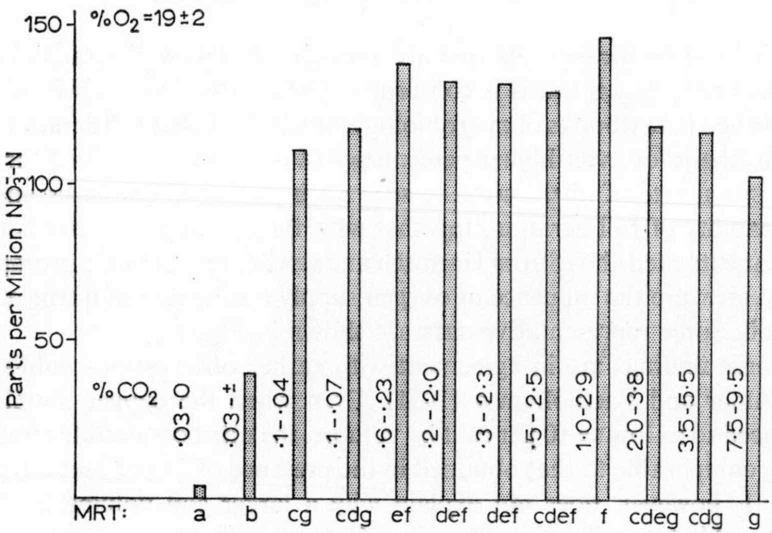


Fig. 2. Influence of differing carbon dioxide concentrations on nitrate production in silty clay loam (pH 7·7). MRT (see Fig. 1).

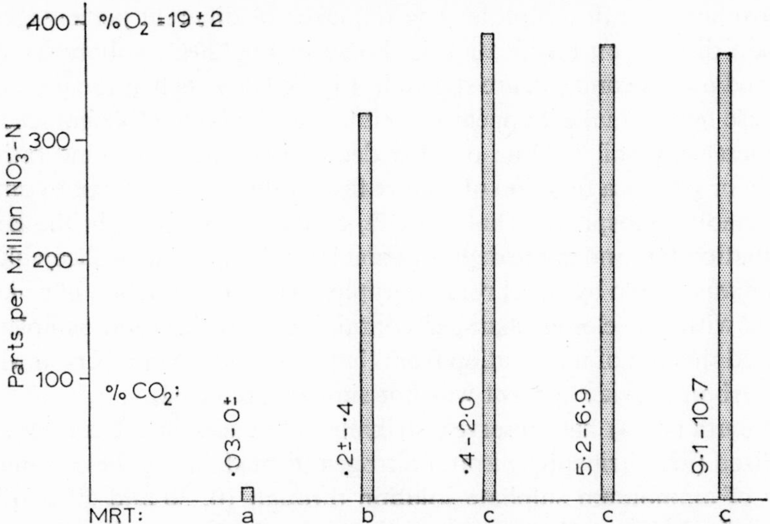


Fig. 3. Influence of differing carbon dioxide concentrations on nitrate production in silt loam (pH 6·5). MRT (see Fig. 1).

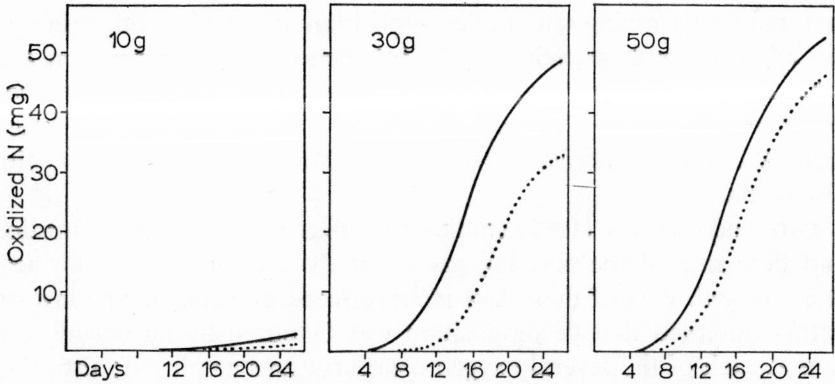


Fig. 4. Nitrification of ammonium sulphate in 10, 30 and 50 g. quantities of soil (Macura, 1964). ······ = nitrate N only. ——— = nitrite + nitrate N.

apparent that full aeration, in the sense of duplication of the epigeal atmosphere, is not desirable. The influence of different percentages of carbon dioxide on nitrification is shown in Fig. 2. Corroborative data secured on a second soil are shown in Fig. 3. Data such as are presented in these figures make it appear plausible that the favourable influence of an increasing soil volume or of a decreasing surface/volume ratio is partly or wholly a function of a more favourable carbon dioxide content in the soil atmosphere. That the $CO_2$ content was higher in the larger incubation lots and in the depths of soil lots with narrow surface/volume ratios was shown by gas chromatography. Also, introduction of a vial of alkali within a closed chamber containing a nitrification sample decreased the rate of nitrification from that observed in chambers in which the carbon dioxide content was not similarly reduced.

Macura (1964) has observed striking differences in the amounts of oxidized (i.e. nitrite plus nitrate) nitrogen formed during the continuous flow of ammonium sulphate solution through 10, 30 and 50 g. quantities of soil (Fig. 4). In experiments involving continuous flow of glycine solution, the rate of nitrification was also observed to increase with increase in soil volume. However, Macura and Kunc (1961) observed that the extent of glucose mineralization, based on total carbon dioxide production and using the continuous flow method, did not depend on the size of the soil sample or on the glucose concentration.

*The aeration effect*

Just as the aeration factor is involved in the volume effect on the rate of nitrification, so too does it appear to be involved with volume and other factors in determining rates of decomposition of organic residues in soil. An adequate understanding of the interactions between aeration and other factors in the mineralization processes in soil has not as yet been achieved, but noteworthy progress is being made. Posssibly one citation from the recent literature will suffice for the purposes of this discussion.

Parr and Reuszer (1962) studied the effect of oxygen concentration and flow rate of the aerating gas upon the decomposition of wheat straw in soil. Part of their data is reproduced in Table 5. The investigators observed that decomposition was favoured by increasing flow rate at each of the several oxygen concentrations employed; also, that decomposition was favoured by increase in oxygen concentration at any given flow rate. Nevertheless, the magnitude of the oxygen supply did not explain satisfactorily all aspects of their data. They pointed out that an aerating gas, A, of a certain volume per cent oxygen used for con-

TABLE 5

*Effect of oxygen concentration and flow rate on decomposition of wheat straw (Parr and Reuszer, 1962)*

| % $O_2$ in aerating gas | Flow rate, litres/hr. | mg. $O_2$ supplied, in 400 hrs. | mg. C as $CO_2$ in 400 hrs. | % decomposition of straw |
|---|---|---|---|---|
| 0·5 | 0·5 | 1248 | 302·5 | 29·1 |
| | 1·0 | 2496 | 314·5 | 30·3 |
| | 2·0 | 4992 | 320·9 | 30·9 |
| 1·0 | 0·125 | 624 | 311·6 | 30·0 |
| | 0·25 | 1248 | 323·7 | 31·2 |
| | 0·5 | 2496 | 330·7 | 31·9 |

stant aeration at a certain flow rate does not support the same amount of decomposition as does another gas, B, containing half as much oxygen and flowing at twice the rate of A, even though the same total amount of oxygen is supplied per unit time.

This is exemplified in Table 5. The amount of decomposition supported by 1 per cent $O_2$ flowing at $\frac{1}{4}$ litre per hr. is not equalled by that at half this concentration of oxygen flowing at twice the flow rate. Even doubling the total oxygen supply did not yield equivalent decomposition; quadrupling the supply, or providing $\frac{1}{2}$ per cent $O_2$ at 2 litres per hr. flow rate, did yield roughly equivalent output of carbon dioxide. Another discrepancy in their data was seen by Parr and Reuszer in the more rapid increase in decomposition (0·5 to 5 per cent $O_2$ levels) when the increases in flow rates were between the $\frac{1}{8}$ and $\frac{1}{2}$ litres per hr. than when they were above the $\frac{1}{2}$ litre per hr. flow rate. The authors believed this variation was only partly due to actual differences in oxygen supply. They suggested that it may have been partly caused by a flushing out of certain volatile toxic or inhibitory factors developing in soils undergoing active organic matter decomposition.

### *The priming effect*

The priming effect provides still another example wherein the observed data are difficult to interpret. This effect can be described as the tendency of an addition of fresh organic residues to soil to stimulate the decomposition of the native soil organic matter. It can also be described as the greater loss of soil organic matter from a soil receiving an organic amendment than from an untreated soil.

Explanations offered for the priming effect are almost as numerous as the experiments themselves. Among them are the following: (1) a more numerous microflora develops on components of the added residues and, as these components are exhausted, the micro-organisms are forced to feed on the soil organic matter; (2) fresh residues cause a more varied microflora to develop and there follows a pooling of enzymes that synergistically speed the breakdown of soil organic matter; (3) fresh residues provide an energy source or food base for the development of new microbial tissue which, once established, accomplishes more colonization and utilization of the soil organic matter than otherwise would be accomplished; (4) fresh residues promote the development of numerous new microbial cells which, because young cells possess great physiological vigour, are able to accomplish a more rapid decomposition of the soil organic matter.

Each of these explanations is more or less unsatisfactory. Rather than extol their virtues or point out how unrealistic they are from an ecological point of view, I prefer to condemn them *en bloc* because all of them place emphasis on changes in the soil microflora (that is, on its numbers, its physiological youth, or its communal enzyme pool), and in so doing ignore the fact that the substrate itself is changed, or more correctly, the conditions under which that substrate, the soil organic matter, is presented, are changed. These changes may involve aeration, reaction, accessory nutrients, growth factors and antagonisms, as well as diverse interactions between these factors. Admittedly the soil microflora does change, but the changes occur in response to some specific ecological modification in the environment.

In addition to the priming effect on organic matter decomposition in soil, there has been reported a priming effect of fertilizer nitrogen on release of soil nitrogen. Following the early work of Broadbent and Norman (1947), a number of workers have observed that the addition of fertilizer nitrogen to soil results in greater mineralization of soil nitrogen than occurs in unfertilized soil. Some data recently compiled by Broadbent (1965) are especially interesting and informative; therefore they will be cited in some detail.

As shown in Table 6, a nitrogen priming effect was obtained following addition of ammonium sulphate but not potassium nitrate. Calculation of the correlation coefficients for the relationship between untagged inorganic N and tagged organic N in one of the two soils employed showed that there was a high correlation where ammonium sulphate was the nitrogen source and no correlation where potassium nitrate was added. Broadbent (1965) suggested that such correlation might indicate preferential assimilation of ammonium nitrogen by soil organisms. He also suggested that an osmotic factor might be involved in nitrogen priming effects. The disquieting part of the supporting data (Table 7), was the failure of an equivalent salt concentration of calcium chloride to duplicate the priming effect obtained with potassium sulphate.

That increased mineralization of soil nitrogen occurs following addition of ammonium sulphate but not following potassium nitrate (Table 6), and following potassium sulphate but not following calcium chloride (Table 7), raises a question concerning the possible role of sul-

TABLE 6

*Effect of added tagged ammonium sulphate and potassium nitrate on mineralization and immobilization of nitrogen (Broadbent, 1965)*

| Days of incubation | $(NH_4)_2SO_4$ added, ppm. | | | $KNO_3$ added, ppm. | |
|---|---|---|---|---|---|
| | 0 | 100 | 200 | 100 | 200 |
| | Untagged inorganic N, ppm. | | | | |
| 0 | 6·3 | 6·6 | 6·4 | 7·2 | 5·0 |
| 10 | 17·3 | 25·3 | 25·9 | 16·7 | 19·0 |
| 30 | 27·5 | 34·6 | 37·1 | 28·2 | 32·0 |
| | Tagged organic N, ppm. | | | | |
| 0 | — | 1·4 | 1·9 | 1·5 | — |
| 10 | — | 15·9 | 17·4 | 1·3 | 2·7 |
| 30 | — | 17·4 | 19·2 | 2·0 | 2·3 |

TABLE 7

*Effect of potassium sulphate and calcium chloride on nitrogen mineralization in soil incubated at 24·5° for 30 days (Broadbent, 1965)*

| Salt added | Salt concentration, atmospheres | Increase in inorganic N, ppm. |
|---|---|---|
| $K_2SO_4$ | 0 | 10·4 |
| | 0·18 | 10·9 |
| | 0·90 | 14·4 |
| | 1·80 | 17·3 |
| $CaCl_2$ | 0 | 9·6 |
| | 0·18 | 9·9 |
| | 0·90 | 9·5 |
| | 1·80 | 9·0 |

phur in the nitrogen priming effect. Stotzky and Norman (1961) demonstrated that an addition of sulphur markedly stimulated the decomposition of glucose in a sandy soil. A portion of their data is reproduced in Fig. 5. They observed that a carbon: sulphur ratio of about 900 was required for the maximum rate of respiration, regardless of the levels of glucose and sulphur added. In view of this ratio they concluded that although the rate of organic matter decomposition may possibly be controlled by manipulation of the C:N or the C:P ratios, it is doubtful if the same could be accomplished with the C:S ratio. This conclusion was based largely on knowledge that the sulphur content of plant materials commonly added to soil provides C:S ratios substantially narrower than the ratio necessary for maximum rates of glucose oxidation. Without further investigation, it appears reasonable to assume that the C:S ratio required for the decomposition of the carbohydrate materials in plant residues should not be appreciably different from that required for the decomposition of glucose.

Recent work by Stewart and Porter (1964) has shown that such an assumption is not correct. Although these workers confirmed that sulphur provided at a C:S ratio of 900 permitted the maximum rate of glucose oxidation, they found that the sulphur requirement for maximum rate of cellulose decomposition was several times larger than that

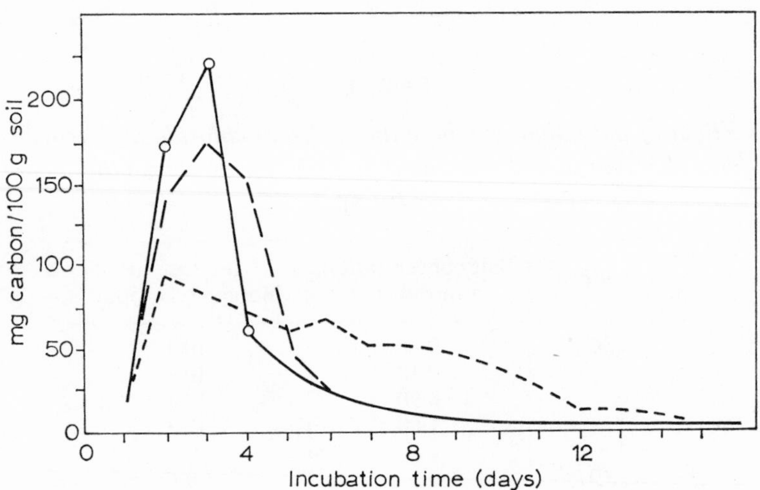


Fig. 5. Effect of added sulphur on daily rate of carbon dioxide production in soil treated with 2 per cent glucose (Stotzky and Norman, 1961). Sulphur added: none -----; 3·2 ppm — —; 8·0 ppm o———o.

for glucose. For cellulose, the C:S ratio needed to be 300 or even narrower (Fig. 6). The explanation that comes most quickly to mind is that dissimilar organisms differ materially in their sulphur requirements. However, even a single microbial species may differ in its sulphur requirements when utilizing different carbohydrates. Mandels and Reese (1957) observed that *Trichoderma viride* secreted roughly five times as much protein into the medium when grown on cellulose than when grown on glucose and that the quantity of protein in the culture filtrate was closely correlated to the cellulase content of the filtrate (Fig. 7).

Such observations as have been published make it appear reasonable to ask if the nitrogen priming effect obtained following addition of ammonium or potassium sulphate is due wholly or in part to the added sulphur. This possibility was investigated in the laboratory. In the two soils that were used, addition of sulphur caused no statistically significant increase in the amount of nitrogen mineralized during three weeks of incubation. Inasmuch as untagged urea was used as the applied nitrogen source, the accumulated data provide no information on biological interchange.

The possibility remains that biological immobilization of tracer nitrogen spares at least some non-tracer N from immobilization, and to the extent that this sparing action does occur, there is an apparent

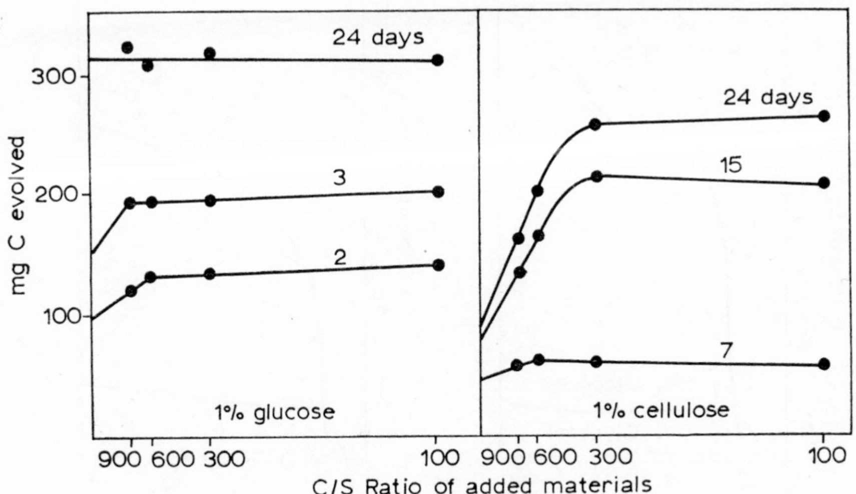


Fig. 6. Influence of differing C/S ratios on the mineralization of glucose and cellulose in soil (Stewart and Porter, 1964).

nitrogen priming effect. Certainly the data of Table 6, showing an appreciable conversion of applied inorganic nitrogen to organic nitrogen, suggests the possibility of a sparing action. One can easily imagine how an added nitrogen fertilizer may spare the immobilization of soil nitrogen. Assume that in an untreated soil, during the net mineralization of 30 ppm. of nitrogen, there is actually a gross mineralization of 60 ppm., but that 30 ppm. are re-immobilized. Net mineralization of soil nitrogen therefore appears as 30 ppm. If to such a soil there is added 60 ppm. of tagged fertilizer nitrogen, it can be assumed that the soil organisms will draw indiscriminately on the added N and the native soil N in order to satisfy their nitrogen requirements. After such indiscriminate withdrawal for immobilization purposes, there should remain 90 ppm. of nitrogen, 45 of which will appear as tagged N and 45 as untagged. Such data can be interpreted as indicating a nitrogen priming effect of 15 ppm., when in reality the net mineralization of soil nitrogen has not been changed at all.

In a recent paper, Sauerbeck (1963) has commented that the common interpretation of the priming effect may have become somewhat exaggerated, that workers may have been dazzled a little bit by the apparent elegance of isotope techniques. Another worker has recently remarked

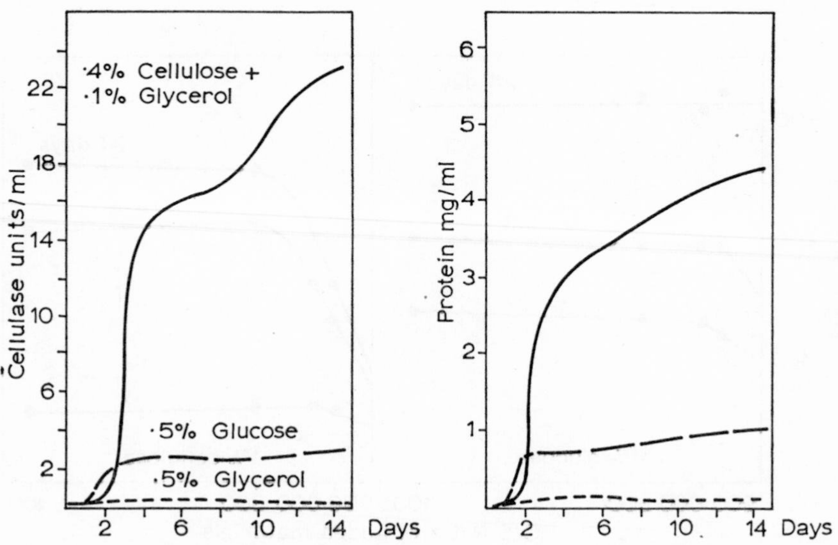


Fig. 7. Influence of carbon source on the production of cellulase and protein in the culture filtrate of *Trichoderma viride* (Mandels and Reese, 1957).

that questionable interpretations, through assiduous and persistent reiteration, are prone to acquire a spurious air of veracity. Such statements indicate that, at least to some workers, a satisfactory explanation of the priming effect has not yet been achieved. Although biological interchanges may be involved, the point believed especially worthy of emphasis is the extent to which the soil organic matter, viewed as a substrate for micro-organisms, is itself changed by the addition of the priming material. Although the ecologically critical change has not yet been defined, such definition is believed to be imminent. Possibly the explanation will be more complex than that involving the role of carbon dioxide in the volume effect on nitrification.

It is encouraging that in numerous current reports in which the microbial response to a given substrate is not of the expected order of magnitude, the authors have not been content simply to give the deviation some designation of convenience, but have successfully elucidated some of the determining factors involved. A recent publication by van Schreven (1964) provides a good example. In experiments involving the decomposition of plant residues in soil, it was found that mineralization of the carbon and nitrogen of the added residues was influenced not only by the N content, the C:N ratio, and quantity of added material, but was also dependent on whether the plant residues were in fresh chopped, dried chopped, or dried and ground condition. Van Schreven linked the observed changes to an increase in the C:N ratio of the water-soluble organic fraction upon drying and to the role of grinding in providing an increased surface exposure of the non-soluble carbonaceous compounds.

## *THE MULTIPLICITY OF MICROBIAL HABITATS IN SOIL*

The many variations encountered in measurement of microbial activities in soil emphasize that the soil constitutes a multiplicity of microbial habitats and any material in the soil capable of serving as an energy source for micro-organisms may be presented to them under an almost limitless number of conditions. It is well known that glucose if presented at 30° supports different microbial species than if presented at 60°. In similar fashion, moisture, pH, osmotic pressure, light, etc. can alter the relative availability of glucose to different species of soil micro-organisms. Likewise, secondary nutrients can be critical. Thus glucose added to soil without a supplementary nitrogen addition may encourage profuse development of *Azotobacter* species. With nitrogen added, a second species may become dominant; with nitrogen and phosphorus, a third species; with sulphur in addition, a fourth species; and so on with further additions. Knowledge concerning the effects of the soil physical environment and the mineral macro-nutrients on individual species is far from adequate, and that concerning the effects of micro-nutrients, accessory growth substances and the diverse array of biologically active compounds produced by the life in the soil is distressingly inadequate.

Nevertheless, enough is known of the number of factors that can be operative and of the number of interactions that are possible to permit the speculation that the number of ecological niches that exist in the soil must be in the thousands. It was with this realization that I chose to emphasize in the introduction that the soil is the habitat of innumerable microbial species, that it has long been an almost inexhaustible reservoir of new species for the microbial taxonomist. The ecological principle that no two species can occupy the same environmental niche, or that in nature complete competitors cannot co-exist, may be the parent material on which the microbial ecologist can build his edifices for a long time to come.

## *EPILOGUE*

Ecology has sometimes been defined as that branch of biology entirely abandoned to terminology. Ecology can also be defined as an art; specifically, as the art of talking about what everybody already knows about in a language that nobody understands. Microbial ecology has sometimes appeared to be the art of talking about what nobody really knows about in a language that everyone pretends to understand. The challenge in microbial ecology is to seek out the factors determining the growth of micro-organisms in their natural habitats and to talk about these factors in a language that everybody can understand.

## *REFERENCES*

AMER, F. M. & BARTHOLOMEW, W. V. (1951). Influence of oxygen concentration in soil air on nitrification. *Soil Sci.*, **71**, 215.

BROADBENT, F. E. (1965). Effect of fertilizer nitrogen on release of soil nitrogen. *Proc. Soil Sci. Soc. Am.*, **29**, 692.

BROADBENT, F. E. & BARTHOLOMEW, W. V. (1949). The effect of quantity of plant material added on the rate of decomposition. *Proc. Soil Sci. Soc. Am.*, **13**, 271.

BROADBENT, F. E. & NORMAN, A. G. (1947). Some factors affecting the availability of the organic nitrogen in soil, a preliminary report. *Proc. Soil Sci. Soc. Am.*, **11**, 264.

HARMSEN, G. W. & VAN SCHREVEN, D. A. (1955). Mineralization of organic nitrogen in soil. *Adv. Agron.*, **7**, 299.

MACURA, J. (1964). Application of the continuous flow method in soil microbiology. Proceedings of the 1962 Symposium, *Continuous Cultivation of Microorganisms*. Prague. Czechoslovak Academy Sciences.

MACURA, J. & KUNC, F. (1961). Continuous flow method in soil microbiology. II. Observations on glucose metabolism. *Folia microbiol., Praha*, **6**, 398.

MANDELS, M. & REESE, E. T. (1957). Induction of cellulase in *Trichoderma viride* as influenced by carbon sources and metals. *J. Bact.*, **73**, 269.

PARR, J. F. & REUSZER, H. W. (1962). Organic matter decomposition as influenced by oxygen level and flow rate of gases in the constant aeration method. *Proc. Soil Sci. Soc. Am.*, **26**, 552.

SAUERBECK, D. (1963). A critical evaluation of incubation experiments on the priming effect of green manure. *Technical Meeting on Use of Isotopes in Soil Organic Matter Studies*. Braunschweig.

SCHREVEN, D. A. VAN (1964). A comparison between the effect of fresh and dried organic materials added to soil on carbon and nitrogen mineralization. *Pl. Soil*, **20**, 149.

STEWART, B. A. & PORTER, L. K. (1964). Effect of sulfur on cellulose decomposition and nitrogen immobilization in soils. *Agron. Abstr.*, 26.

STOTZKY, G. & NORMAN, A. G. (1961). Factors limiting microbial activities in soil. II. The effect of sulfur. *Arch. Mikrobiol.*, **40**, 370.

# SPOREFORMING BACTERIA IN THE SOILS OF THE USSR

E. N. MISHUSTIN and V. A. MIRSOEVA

*Institute of Microbiology, Academy of Sciences, Moscow*

Sporeforming bacteria constitute an important part of the soil microflora. Their biology, ecology and systematics have been studied by a considerable number of workers (Conn, 1937; Knight and Proom, 1950; Smith, Gordon and Clark, 1952). Several groups of sporeforming bacteria have been investigated thoroughly in our laboratory. The results of the investigations have been reported in a number of publications (Gibson, 1944; Mishustin, 1947; Mirsoeva, 1959; Gromyko, 1957).

Our researches have shown that the species composition in different soils varies; further the species differentiation of sporeforming bacteria is difficult on normal bacteriological media. Therefore, considerable attention has been devoted to finding solid nutrient media permitting the identification of individual species of bacilli with less difficulty.

One of the best media has proved to be a mixture of beef-extract agar and malt agar in equal parts (pH about 7·0). On this medium a considerable number of *Bacillus* species are easily differentiated, according to their colony type. A long investigation into the *Bacillus* populations of the soils of the U.S.S.R. has enabled us to distinguish the species encountered most frequently. These are given in Table 1. The identification of sporeforming bacteria has generally been restricted to forms isolated from pasteurized soil suspensions (5 minutes at 80°).

The species in question are of different kinds and can be divided into several groups. This has been shown clearly with *B. mycoides*, which has different ecotypes, the characteristics of which are peculiar colony structure and variations in morphological and biochemical properties. The same is true of *B. subtilis*, *B. mesentericus*, *B. megaterium*, and other micro-organisms. In the table the most general features of the dominant soil bacilli are given, particularly in relation to their cell morphology and the structure of their colonies. It is necessary, however, to consider briefly some physiological peculiarities of the bacilli, significant for their ecology. To begin with, we shall analyse the relation of sporeforming bacteria to their sources of nitrogen.

The utilization of nitrogen-containing compounds allow us to distinguish the following two groups of bacilli:

I. *B. cereus*, *B. mycoides*, *B. virgulus* and *B. adhaerens*

These species develop very weakly, if at all, on ammonium salts and nitrates. They cannot use many amino acids as sources of nitrogen and carbon. They will multiply on some acids, e.g. arginine, if there are carbohydrates in the medium. Certain amino acids, e.g. asparagine, can serve as a source of both nitrogen and carbon. These micro-organisms multiply rapidly on peptone and various proteins, liberating amino acids and ammonia. Usually more nitrogen is liberated in the form of amino acids.

Generally speaking, then, this group of bacilli needs complex organic nitrogen-containing compounds and grow poorly or not at all with sources of inorganic nitrogen.

These micro-organisms are the dominant forms in northern soils where the mobilization of mineral nitrogen is slow.

II. *B. megaterium*, *B. mesentericus*, *B. subtilis*, *B. granulosus*, *B. gasificans*, *B. agglomeratus*

These species are capable of developing well on media containing ammonium and nitrate nitrogen as sole sources of nitrogen. Many amino acids may serve as a source of nitrogen and carbon for them. For this group of bacilli, proteins and peptones are also a good source of nutrients. Their decay leads to the accumulation of amino acids and ammonia in the medium, the former being generally produced in greater quantities.

The bacilli of this group (except for *B. agglomeratus*) are abundant in southern soils where mineralization is intense.

The micro-organisms in question can assimilate, as a source of carbon, a large number of carbohydrates and organic acids. Organic acids are usually accumulated when carbohydrates are fermented by bacilli. These organic acids are mainly lactic and acetic acids. Our investigations indicate that sporeforming bacteria require more vitamins than non-sporefoı ming bacteria. Further, bacilli multiply more slowly than non-sporeforming bacteria.

Some properties of the sporeforming bacilli which have been pointed out make it clear why it is chiefly the non-sporeforming bacteria that multiply on decaying vegetation in the early stages of its breakdown. Bacilli appear much later. This is confirmed by numerous observations of plant rhizospheres. In the rhizosphere, containing many exudates,

TABLE 1

*Characteristics of the dominant forms of sporeforming bacteria in the soil*

| Names of bacteria | Size (in $\mu$) | | Spore size (in $\mu$) | Spore characteristics | Colony characters on meat-peptone agar + malt agar |
|---|---|---|---|---|---|
| | Width | Length | | | |
| *Bacillus agglomeratus* | 0·5–0·6 | 1·2–2·6 | 0·5 × 1·0 | Spore formation is slow and does not occur on all the media. Spores egg-shaped and eccentric. | Small, greyish, mucoid or sometimes dry. Colony shape circular or sometimes star-like. |
| *Bacillus asterosporus* | 0·5–0·7 | 1·2–2·5 | 0·5 × 1·0 | Spore formation is slow and does not occur on all the media. Spores egg-shaped and eccentric. | Colonies identical with those of *B. agglomeratus*, but they produce gas from carbohydrates. |
| *Bacillus virgulus* | 0·3–0·6 | 4·0–10·0 | 0·6 × 1·2 | Spore formation is slow. Spores oval. | Circular, convex, small, with smooth or fringed edges, of greyish-yellow hue. Viscous. |
| *Bacillus mycoides* | 1·1–1·5 | 3·0–5·0 | 1·0 × 1·4 | Spores generally oval, central. | Rhizoidal, spreading widely over the medium. The structure of the rhizoidal strands is distinct in individual cultures. |
| *Bacillus cereus* | 0·9–1·1 | 2·5–5·0 | 0·9 × 1·5 | Spores egg-shaped, eccentric. | Large, flat, with granular surface. The edge is commonly irregularly serrate. Of greyish-white hue. |
| *Bacillus idosus* | 0·7–1·2 | 3·0–5·0 | 0·9 × 1·2 | Spores oval. | Rather large, filmy, dry, wrinkled. Sometimes of mucoid consistency, tuberous, of yellowish-grey hue. Colonies are easily removed with a loop from the agar surface. |

| | | | | | |
|---|---|---|---|---|---|
| *Bacillus granulosus* | 1·2–1·4 | 1·5–2·0 | 1·0 × 1·5 | Spores egg-shaped, eccentric. | Dry, convex, serrate, of greyish-white hue. Bacterial mass is easily removed with a loop from the medium surface. Old colonies form a thin wrinkled film. |
| *Bacillus megaterium* | 1·5–2·2 | 4·6–8·5 | 1·0 × 1·5 | Spores oval, polar or central. | Smooth, mucoid, brilliant, of milky-white hue. More seldom wrinkled with creamy-yellow hue. Edge of colonies sharply limited. |
| *Bacillus adhaerens* | 0·8–0·9 | 2·1–2·5 | 0·8 × 1·3 | Spores egg-shaped, eccentric or central. | Coarsely wrinkled, rounded, or with large laciniae, of whitish-grey hue. The colonies grow slightly into the agar. Small branches appear sometimes on the edge of colonies. |
| *Bacillus gasificans* | 0·6–0·8 | 1·6–2·4 | 0·9 × 1·5 | Spores egg-shaped, eccentric, causing the sporangium to swell. | Elevated, convex, or cupola-shaped, mucoid. Gas bubbles accumulate in the bacterial mass. The colonies are of greyish-white or yellow hue. |
| *Bacillus mesentericus* | 0·7–0·8 | 1·5–4·0 | 0·7 × 0·8 | Spores oval, eccentric. | Colonies of individual cultures are of different types. Often mucoid, wrinkled, or with thick cuticle, often petal-shaped. The surface is often farinaceous. Whitish-grey hue, sometimes brownish or pinkish. |
| *Bacillus subtilis* | 0·6–0·7 | 1·5–3·5 | 0·6 × 0·7 | Spores oval, eccentric. | Branching colonies, or with crenate edge. The surface is often convex, and exudes water. Microscopic analysis reveals rhizoidal growth on the edges. Colonies are most often of greyish-white hue. |

the conditions are more favourable for the multiplication of non-sporeforming bacteria. It is only when vegetation is senescent and the roots are dying that the numbers of bacilli begin to increase.

The introduction of sucrose as a substrate lead to the rapid multiplication of non-sporeforming bacteria (Plate 2). Bacilli began to increase in number only when the medium was enriched by the products of microbial activity, e.g. by proteins, vitamins, etc. In such cases, most of the bacilli were in the vegetative state. The introduction of peptone or protein as substrates speeded up the multiplication of sporeforming bacteria; their numbers increased sharply at the very beginning of the experiment. In our experiments, sand was used as a medium, moistened to 60 per cent of the water-holding capacity with Winogradsky's medium for nitrifying bacteria.

TABLE 2

*Changes in the populations of non-sporeforming and sporeforming bacteria after introducing different organic compounds into sand*

| Organic substance introduced into sand | Bacterial numbers | Number of days since the beginning of the experiment | | | |
|---|---|---|---|---|---|
| | | 7 | 14 | 28 | 56 |
| Sucrose | Total number of bacteria | 17·50 | 5·40 | 4·37 | 2·55 |
| | Number of sporeforming bacteria | 0·75 | 2·00 | 2·37 | 1·30 |
| | Number of spores | 0·38 | 0·34 | 0·28 | 0·24 |
| | Bacilli as a % of the total number of bacteria | 4·2 | 37·2 | 54·0 | 50·9 |
| | % bacilli present as spores | 50·0 | 16·7 | 11·6 | 18·2 |
| Peptone (0·5%) | Total number of bacteria | 10·82 | 0·65 | 3·55 | 2·97 |
| | Number of sporeforming bacteria | 5·82 | 4·00 | 2·70 | 2·92 |
| | Number of spores | 0·30 | 0·80 | 0·63 | 0·52 |
| | Bacilli as a % of the total number of bacteria | 53·7 | 61·5 | 76·3 | 98·3 |
| | % bacilli present as spores | 5·2 | 20·0 | 23·3 | 17·6 |

N.B. The numbers of bacteria are given in millions per g. sand.

Most of the vegetative cells of bacilli form spores at the time that the organic matter that is available to bacteria in the soil diminishes. We agree with Conn (1950) that the overwhelming majority of bacilli are

TABLE 3

*Relation of separate groups of micro-organisms in undisturbed and polluted soils*

| Indices | Undisturbed soils | | | | | | Polluted soils | | | | | |
|---|---|---|---|---|---|---|---|---|---|---|---|---|
| | June | July | July | Aug. | Sept. | Oct. | June | July | July | Aug. | Sept. | Oct. |
| Total number of bacteria | 0·93 | 0·24 | 0·24 | 0·52 | 1·20 | 0·74 | 27·60 | 3·90 | 2·96 | 1·52 | 3·95 | 1·06 |
| Total number of bacilli | 0·50 | 0·08 | 0·06 | 0·12 | 0·30 | 0·34 | 1·60 | 1·50 | 0·80 | 0·49 | 0·87 | 0·53 |
| Number of spores | 0·29 | 0·09 | 0·09 | 0·08 | 0·25 | 0·24 | 0·45 | 0·53 | 0·52 | 0·28 | 0·44 | 0·47 |
| % bacilli of the total number of bacteria | 53·7 | 33·3 | 25·0 | 23·0 | 25·0 | 46·3 | 5·8 | 38·4 | 27·0 | 31·3 | 82·0 | 50·0 |
| % spores of the total number of bacilli | 58·0 | 100·0 | 100·0 | 70·0 | 83·3 | 70·6 | 28·1 | 25·3 | 65·0 | 57·1 | 50·5 | 88·7 |
| % spores of the total number of bacteria | 31·2 | 37·5 | 37·3 | 16·1 | 28·3 | 32·4 | 1·6 | 13·6 | 17·5 | 17·8 | 11·1 | 44·3 |

N.B. The numbers of bacteria are expressed in millions per g. of soil.
The undisturbed and polluted soils were sampled at the same time.

in the form of spores in the soils in which there is a biological equilibrium. Table 3 gives the changes in the total numbers of bacteria, bacilli and spores in a sod-podzol soil near Moscow which in one case was undisturbed and in the other was polluted with town refuse. The bacteria and bacilli were counted using beef-extract agar. The number of spores was determined by dispersing the pasteurized soil suspension (80° for 5 minutes) in the same medium.

Evidently 60–100 per cent of the bacilli were present as spores in the undisturbed soil. The number of non-sporeforming bacteria was much larger in the soil polluted by non-proteinaceous organic matter. The number of bacilli was also increased slightly, most of them in the vegetative state. After most organic matter had decomposed, and the number of bacteria had decreased markedly, the bacilli formed spores again.

While analysing different soils of the U.S.S.R., the authors became convinced that the number of bacilli in the soil could change considerably in response to changes in the state of movable organic matter and weather conditions. These changes, however, are less marked than the changes in the numbers of non-sporeforming bacteria. Some examples of such changes in the numbers of spores in different soils are given below. The data obtained from the analyses of a chernozem in the Voronezh province are given in Table 4. It is evident that the water con-

TABLE 4

*Changes in the numbers of bacteria in the chernozem soils of the Voronezh province*

| Soil | Object of observation | Months | | | |
|---|---|---|---|---|---|
| | | May | June | July | August |
| Virgin steppe $A_0$ horizon | % Moisture content | 33·6 | 44·7 | 29·2 | 28·0 |
| | Total number of bacteria | 9·92 | 9·45 | 7·75 | 4·39 |
| | Number of bacilli | 4·84 | 5·48 | 1·49 | 1·32 |
| Virgin steppe $A_1$ horizon (0–10 cm.) | % Moisture content | 29·1 | 29·7 | 32·4 | 28·6 |
| | Total number of bacteria | 5·07 | 4·36 | 4·09 | 2·04 |
| | Number of bacilli | 2·82 | 1·71 | 1·66 | 1·44 |
| Cultivated soil, wheat sowing (0–10 cm.) | % Moisture content | 22·5 | 24·6 | 18·7 | 26·0 |
| | Total number of bacteria | 3·40 | 4·11 | 3·69 | 3·69 |
| | Number of bacilli | 1·25 | 1·92 | 1·12 | 1·28 |

N.B. The numbers of bacteria are expressed in millions per g. of soil.

tent was quite sufficient to support the development of bacteria in this case. In the cultivated chernozem, where there was hardly any addition of fresh organic matter to the soil, the numbers of bacteria, including bacilli, changed little during the summer period. Remains of deciduous herbaceous vegetation accumulated on the surface of the soil in the virgin steppe. Therefore, both the total numbers of bacteria and bacilli showed marked increases here in the first half of the summer period. Their number decreased considerably by autumn.

The next table shows the changes in the numbers of bacteria in the different soils of Kazakhstan near Alma-Ata. In the second half of the summer period, moisture decreased greatly in the grey and chestnut soils which were very poor in organic matter. This resulted in a sharp decrease in the number of bacteria, including spores. This confirms the idea that sporeforming bacteria are not permanently present as spores in the soil. In the latter case one would have expected their numbers to remain practically unchanged.

TABLE 5

*Changes in the numbers of the bacteria in the virgin soils of Kazakhstan $A_1$ horizon*

| Soils | Object of observation | Months | | | |
|---|---|---|---|---|---|
| | | April | June | August | October |
| Grey soils | % Moisture content | 21·2 | 15·2 | 1·6 | 4·6 |
| | Total number of bacteria | 8·20 | 3·50 | 8·00 | 1·10 |
| | Number of spores | 2·40 | 1·02 | 1·42 | 1·03 |
| Chestnut soils | % Moisture content | 26·4 | 19·7 | 6·5 | 6·5 |
| | Total number of bacteria | 4·70 | 4·10 | 2·00 | 1·60 |
| | Number of spores | 0·37 | 0·31 | 0·63 | 0·64 |

N.B. The numbers of bacteria are expressed in millions per g. of soil.

These data enable us to conclude that sporeforming bacteria take part in a certain stage of the mineralization of organic residues in the soil. The sporeforming bacteria are an active part of the soil microflora and exist as spores only when there is not enough organic matter in the soil.

Microbiological processes in different soil-climatic zones proceed with different intensities. Their intensity increases from northern to southern zones due to the improvement of hydrothermal conditions and

TABLE 6

*Approximate composition of the bacterial flora of different soils*

| soil | Total number of bacteria | Number of spores | % spores | % composition of bacilli | | | | | | | | |
|---|---|---|---|---|---|---|---|---|---|---|---|---|
| | | | | *Bacillus agglomeratus–Bacillus asterosporus* | *Bacillus mycoides* | *Bacillus cereus* | *Bacillus virgulus* | *Bacillus idosus* | *Bacillus megaterium* | *Bacillus subtilis–Bacillus mesentericus* | *Bacillus adhaerens* | *Bacillus gasificans* |
| Tundra. Virgin arctic soils | 2·00 | 0·004 | 0·2 | 50 | 0 | 0 | 0 | 0 | 0 | 0 | — | — |
| Taiga. Virgin podzol soils (forest) | 1·20 | 0·012 | 1·0 | 50 | 4 | 25 | 12·5 | 4 | 0 | 0 | — | — |
| Cultivated soils | 1·80 | 0·03 | 1·7 | 23 | 2 | 17 | 0 | 10 | 5 | 0 | — | — |
| Forest-meadow zone (sod-podzol soils and podzol soils) | | | | | | | | | | | | |
| Forest soils | 0·80 | 0·10 | 12·5 | 26 | 10 | 20 | 37 | 0 | 0 | 0 | — | — |
| Virgin meadow soils | 0·90 | 0·12 | 13·3 | 25 | 17 | 21 | 0 | 8 | 5 | 0 | — | — |
| Cultivated soils | 1·00 | 0·18 | 18·0 | 7 | 11 | 17 | 0 | 22 | 25 | 0 | — | — |

| | | | | | | | | | | | | |
|---|---|---|---|---|---|---|---|---|---|---|---|---|
| Meadow steppe and steppe (chernozem of central and southern zones) | | | | | | | | | | | | |
| Virgin soils | 2·20 | 0·70 | 31·7 | 4 | 0 | 4 | 0 | 64 | 17 | 0 | — | — |
| Cultivated soils | 3·00 | 1·00 | 33·3 | 5 | 0 | 4 | 0 | 70 | 20 | 0 | — | — |
| Dry and desert steppe (chestnut soils) | | | | | | | | | | | | |
| Virgin soils | 2·20 | 0·60 | 27·2 | 10 | 0 | 6 | 0 | 33 | 16 | 2 | — | — |
| Cultivated soils | 4·00 | 1·20 | 30·0 | 4 | 0 | 3 | 0 | 50 | 25 | 13 | — | — |
| Desert (grey soils) | | | | | | | | | | | | |
| Virgin soils | 2·50 | 0·75 | 30·0 | 8 | 0 | 6 | 0 | 40 | 26 | 8 | — | — |
| Cultivated soils | 4·00 | 1·50 | 37·5 | 4 | 0 | 6 | 0 | 50 | 26 | 13 | — | — |
| Saline | 3·50 | 1·20 | 34·3 | 4 | 0 | 4 | 0 | 30 | 34 | 7 | 4 | 4 |

N.B. The numbers of bacteria are expressed in millions per g. of soil.
Species enclosed in boxes are the most characteristic of the particular soil.
'O' refers to the probability of individual species being present, though not detected.

the higher biochemical activity of southern forms of bacteria which are adapted to life at higher temperatures (Mishustin, 1947). One might expect that this would affect the biology of the soil and, in particular, the relation between non-sporeforming bacteria and bacilli and the species composition of the latter as well. This has been confirmed (see below).

Table 6 summarizes a very great number of analyses of different soils. The data given are approximate, but significant. It can be seen that the absolute and relative numbers of bacilli increase in the soil of southern regions. Furthermore, if the number of bacteria is calculated per g. of organic matter in the soil (Table 7), a distinct increase in the numbers

TABLE 7

*Approximate numbers of bacteria in the organic matter of different soils*

| Soil | Total number of bacteria | Number of spores |
|---|---|---|
| Tundra. Virgin arctic soils | 40·0 | 0·08 |
| Taiga. Virgin podzol soils | 36·0 | 0·36 |
| Cultivated soils | 54·0 | 0·9 |
| Forest-meadow zone (sod-podzol soils and podzol) | | |
| Forest soils | 24·0 | 3·0 |
| Meadow virgin soils | 27·0 | 3·6 |
| Cultivated soils | 30·0 | 5·4 |
| Meadow steppe and steppe (chernozem of central and southern zones) | | |
| Virgin soils | 33·0 | 10·5 |
| Cultivated soils | 45·0 | 15·0 |
| Dry desert steppe (chestnut soils) | | |
| Virgin soils | 110·0 | 30·0 |
| Cultivated soils | 200·0 | 60·0 |
| Desert (grey soils) | | |
| Virgin soils | 125·0 | 37·5 |
| Cultivated soils | 200·0 | 75·0 |

N.B. The numbers of bacteria are expressed in millions per g. of organic matter.

of the soil bacteria that may be supported can be seen, i.e. an increase in the 'biogenous' state of the soil. The species composition also changes markedly. Each type of soil is characterized by its own significant groups of sporeforming bacteria. For instance, *B. mycoides* is present in high numbers in podzol and peat-podzol soils, while *B. virgulus* is only found in podzols in the forests. *B. mesentericus* and *B. subtilis* are widespread in grey and chestnut soils. These data reflect indirectly the state of

TABLE 8

Bacillus *species in soils at different altitudes* (*Ala-Tau, Kazakhstan*). ($A_1$ *horizon of virgin soils*)

| Soil | Altitude (in m.) | Total number of bacteria | Number of bacilli | % bacilli | % of different Bacillus species | | | | | |
|---|---|---|---|---|---|---|---|---|---|---|
| | | | | | *Bacillus agglomeratus* | *Bacillus mycoides* | *Bacillus cereus* | *Bacillus idosus* | *Bacillus megaterium* | *Bacillus mesentericus–Bacillus subtilis* |
| Grey soil | 500–600 | 3·78 | 1·05 | 27·7 | 2 | 0 | 3 | 43 | 29 | 22 |
| Chestnut soil | 850–1,100 | 4·68 | 0·61 | 13·0 | 2 | 0 | 13 | 52 | 18 | 14 |
| Deep chernozem, mountainous | 1,300–1,700 | 3·90 | 0·41 | 10·5 | 4 | 3 | 12 | 47 | 31 | 2 |
| Mountain-forest soil, dark-coloured | 1,700–2,100 | 2·80 | 0·19 | 6·7 | 8 | 3 | 11 | 50 | 22 | 0 |
| Mountain-meadow, chernozem-like, sub-alpine | 3,000–3,600 | 1·13 | 0·11 | 9·7 | 18 | 0 | 13 | 45 | 13 | 00 |
| Mountain-meadow, sod-semi-peat, alpine | more than 3,800 | 1·00 | 0·08 | 8·0 | 14 | 0 | 14 | 25 | 0 | 00 |

N.B. Average data are taken from a number of summer analyses.
The number of bacteria are expressed in millions per g. of soil.
Species enclosed in boxes are the most characteristic of the particular soil.

organic matter in different soils. The changes which are brought about by cultivation have a great effect on the species composition of the soil bacilli.

We have studied also the soils of several mountains of the Caucasus and of Central Asia. A vertical zonation of the soil microflora has been demonstrated analagous to the geographical zonation. The results of the analysis of the soils of the Ala-Tau mountain ridge are given in Table 8.

It is evident that the soils became poorer and poorer in micro-organisms towards the top of the mountain. The percentage of bacilli dropped appreciably, and the species composition changed in almost the same way as in the zone soil types. In the mountain soils the number of microbes decreased, which led to a weakening of mobilization processes. In particular, this had a remarkable effect on nitrification which decreased gradually as the altitude increased.

As mentioned previously, we calculate the number of bacteria per g. organic matter to characterize the 'biogenous' state of the soil. Such calculations for the Ala-Tau mountain soils are given in Table 9.

TABLE 9

*Approximate numbers of bacteria in organic matter in different soils*

| Soil | Altitude (in m.) | Total number of bacteria | Number of bacilli |
|---|---|---|---|
| Grey soil | 500–600 | 220·00 | 55·00 |
| Chestnut soil | 850–1,100 | 190·00 | 24·00 |
| Deep chernozem | 1,300–1,700 | 47·00 | 5·00 |
| Mountain-forest, dark-coloured | 1,700–2,100 | 56·00 | 3·80 |
| Mountain-meadow, chernozem, sub-alpine | 3,000–3,600 | 12·60 | 1·20 |
| Mountain-meadow, sod-semi-peat, alpine | not more than 3,800 | 6·00 | 0·50 |

N.B. The numbers of bacteria are expressed in millions per g. organic matter.

In conclusion, we should like to emphasize the fact that soil type is the main influence on the composition of the *Bacillus* population of the soil. Nevertheless, the effects of vegetation and cultivation are quite obvious. The data in Table 10 show the *Bacillus* species present in cultivated chernozem, in chernozem under forest, and in virgin soils. There

TABLE 10

*Distribution of bacilli in the profile of the chernozem soils of the Voronezh province*

| Soil | Horizon | Depth (in cms.) | Number (in millions per g. soil) | | | % composition of different *Bacillus* species | | | | | | |
|---|---|---|---|---|---|---|---|---|---|---|---|---|
| | | | Bacteria | Bacilli | % bacilli | *Bacillus agglomeratus* | *Bacillus mycoides* | *Bacillus cereus* | *Bacillus virgulus* | *Bacillus idosus* | *Bacillus megaterium* | *Bacillus subtilis–Bacillus mesentericus* |
| Virgin steppe | A (soddy) | 0–7 | 4·20 | 1·73 | 41·2 | 23 | 1 | 4 | 0 | 11 | 12 | 0 |
| | $A_1$ | 10–20 | 2·30 | 1·26 | 54·8 | 7 | 0 | 4 | 0 | 48 | 18 | 0 |
| | $A_2$ | 25–35 | 1·75 | 0·96 | 54·7 | 7 | 0 | 1 | 0 | 39 | 15 | 0 |
| | $B_1$ | 42–52 | 0·41 | 0·37 | 91·1 | 4 | 0 | 1 | 0 | 24 | 0 | 0 |
| | $B_2$ | 50–65 | 0·12 | 0·037 | 30·8 | 3 | 0 | 0 | 0 | 29 | 0 | 0 |
| Cultivated chernozem | A | 0–10 | 8·90 | 1·32 | 14·8 | 5 | 0 | 7 | 0 | 44 | 27 | 4 |
| | A | 10–20 | 6·60 | 1·47 | 22·3 | 10 | 0 | 4 | 0 | 45 | 21 | 1 |
| | $A_2$ | 30–35 | 1·91 | 1·14 | 59·6 | 4 | 0 | 0 | 0 | 35 | 12 | 0 |
| | $B_1$ | 47–52 | 0·18 | 0·17 | 94·4 | 0 | 0 | 0 | 0 | 31 | 0 | 0 |
| | $B_2$ | 70–75 | 0·13 | 0·12 | 89·5 | 0 | 0 | 0 | 0 | 22 | 0 | 0 |
| Forest zone | $A_0$ | litter | 53·60 | 0·70 | 13·1 | 12 | 1 | 11 | 1 | 60 | 13 | 0 |
| | $A_1$ | 0–20 | 2·30 | 0·80 | 34·7 | 5 | 6 | 10 | 1 | 63 | 12 | 0 |
| | $A_2$ | 25–35 | 1·50 | 7·20 | 48·0 | 4 | 0 | 9 | 0 | 48 | 8 | 0 |

are many common features here which characterize the chernozem (there are many cells of *B. idosus* and *B. megaterium*, while *B. subtilis*, *B. mesentericus*, *B. virgulus*, etc, are poorly represented). In addition, *B. mycoides* and *B. virgulus* appear in the soil under the forest. When the soil is cultivated *B. megaterium* begins to multiply, and cells of *B. subtilis* and *B. mesentericus* appear. The intensity of mineralization is evidently correlated with the multiplication of *B. megaterium*.

The data of Table 10 also demonstrate that all the bacilli do not penetrate the soil to an equal depth. The microbiological profile depends largely on the soil type. In general, some sporeforming bacteria, such as *B. idosus*, occur deep in the soil, while others, such as *B. mycoides* and *B. megaterium*, develop in soil layers nearer the surface.

## *CONCLUSIONS*

1. Sporeforming bacteria can be differentiated with difficulty on the normal bacteriological media. A medium is suggested which permits the determination of bacilli, according to the colony type.
2. The investigation of sporeforming bacteria, encountered in the main soil types of the U.S.S.R., has made it possible to identify the principal groups. The diagnostic features of these bacilli are reported.
3. The experimental material shows that the sporeforming bacteria multiply at the later stages of mineralization of plant remains, being correlated with the C/N ratio. The complex forms of nitrogen-containing compounds (protein, peptones) allow the rapid multiplication of sporeforming bacteria.
4. In soils in which the biological processes are at equilibrium, most of the bacilli are present as spores. The enrichment of the soil with fresh organic matter causes spore germination.

The number of bacilli in the soil is governed by variations in the climatic conditions and the organic compounds entering the soil.

5. The richness of different types of soil in bacteria, and in bacilli in particular, relates to the intensity of the mobilization processes which develop under certain hydrothermal conditions. As a rule, the number of bacteria (and also the absolute and relative contents of bacilli), is larger in soils being formed in warmer climates. These differences are more marked when the number of bacteria per g. organic matter are calculated.
6. Each soil type is characterized by particular groups of *Bacillus* species. Cultivation and other influences may change the composition of the *Bacillus* population slightly.

## *REFERENCES*

CONN, H. (1950). The identity of *Bacillus subtilis*. *J. infect. Dis.*, **46**, 341.

GIBSON, T. (1944). A study of *Bacillus subtilis* and related organisms. *J. Dairy Res.*, **13**, 248.

GROMYKO, E. P. (1955). Bacteria of the *Bacillus megaterium* group in the soils of the Soviet Union. *Mikrobiologiya*, **24**, 565.

KNIGHT, B. & PROOM, H. (1950). A comparative survey of the nutrition and physiology of mesophilic species in the genus *Bacillus*. *J. gen. Microbiol.*, **4**, 508.

MIRSOEVA, V. A. (1959). *Bacteria of the Bacillus subtilis, Bacillus mesentericus group*. Moscow. Academy of Sciences, USSR.

MISHUSTIN, E. N. (1947). *Ecologo-geographical changeability of soil bacteria*. Moscow. Academy of Sciences, USSR.

SMITH, N., GORDON, R. & CLARK, F. E. (1952). Aerobic sporeforming bacteria. *U.S. Dept. Agric. Monograph*, **16**, Washington.

# SOIL BACTERIA IN RELATION TO THE DEVELOPMENT OF POLDERS IN THE REGION OF THE FORMER ZUIDER ZEE

D. A. VAN SCHREVEN and G. W. HARMSEN[1]

*Rijksdienst voor de IJsselmeerpolders, Kampen, The Netherlands*

## *INTRODUCTION*

In 1932 the Zuider Zee was cut off from the sea by an enclosing dam and was renamed the IJsselmeer (IJssel-lake). Gradually the water of this lake became fresh. After the construction of the Wieringermeer polder in 1930 and the North-East polder in 1942, East Flevoland, the third IJssel-lake polder, emerged from the water in June 1957 and the construction of the dyke for the fourth polder (South Flevoland) is now in progress (Fig. 1).

Since the enclosing dam was not completed until two years after the Wieringermeer polder was drained, this polder was reclaimed from salt water. In the later reclaimed polders, however, the salt had already virtually disappeared from the soil by diffusion into the fresh water of the IJssel-lake. During the reclamation of a polder, a series of processes occurs by which the soft, water-saturated and unaerated soil becomes a normal arable soil. The changes which take place are physical (Smits, 1962), chemical (Zuur, 1962) and microbiological (van Schreven, 1962). The microbiological investigation of the polder, soils was undertaken by Dr. Harmsen until 1947 (Harmsen, 1932, 1934, 1935, 1940, 1944) and afterwards continued by the other author (van Schreven, 1951, 1962).

During the period that the soils were covered by the sea, sulphates present in the sea-water were converted into sulphides which combined with iron to form FeS, $FeS_2$ and polysulphides. When at a later stage the soils were drained these iron sulphides were exposed to the air and became oxidized to ferric hydroxide ($Fe(OH)_3$) and elementary sulphur, $S_2$. The sulphur was then oxidized still further to sulphuric acid. These processes were assisted by sulphur-oxidizing micro-organisms.

[1] Head of the Microbiological Laboratory of the Institute for Soil Fertility (Instituut voor Bodemvruchtbaarheid) in Groningen.

The most important species proved to be *Thiobacillus thiooxidans* (Quispel, Harmsen and Otzen, 1953). Most soils in the Wieringermeer polder contained ample stores of calcium carbonate. After drainage this combined with the sulphuric acid just referred to and was converted to gypsum, which played an important role in the conversion of sodium clay into calcium clay. In marine soils adsorbed calcium is replaced by sodium and magnesium to a considerable extent. Unlike calcium clay, this sodium magnesium clay is liable to collapse when wet. As a result of the formation of gypsum, calcium displaced the sodium in the

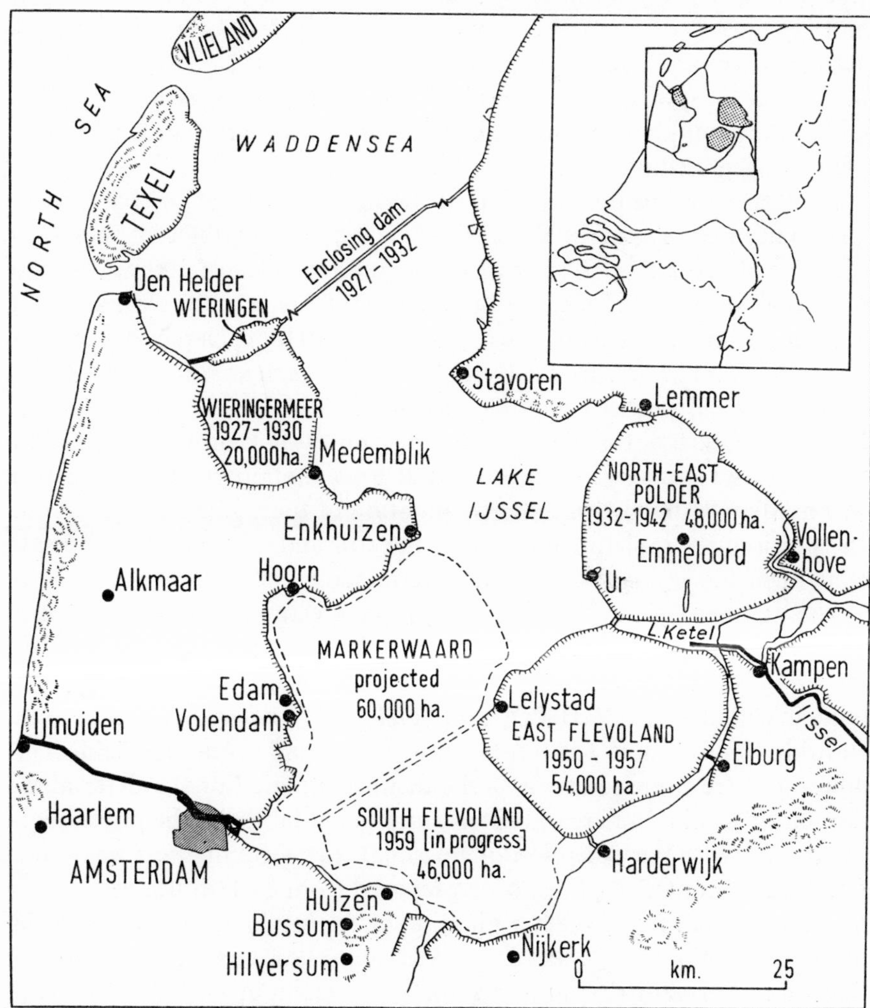


Fig. 1. The Ijssel lake polders (3 polders reclaimed, 1 polder in progress, 1 projected polder).

clay, converting it into normal clay in the course of a few years. For this reason, very few detrimental effects due to the unfavourable properties of exchangeable sodium were noticed in the Wieringermeer polder. However, there were a few lime-deficient soils which became highly acid when drained, due to the fact that sulphuric acid was formed in excess and was not neutralized.

## *METHODS OF STUDY*

In addition to total numbers of bacteria, the numbers of protein, starch and cellulose decomposers, azotobacters (principally *Azotobacter chroococcum*) and nitrifying organisms were determined. The presence of *Rhizobium* species was studied in field crops, in experimental fields and in soil samples which were planted with various kinds of leguminous plants in a greenhouse.

In addition to an investigation of the development of the bacteria in a large number of experimental fields, their growth in different soil types was also studied at a number of fixed sampling sites of 100 $m^2$. At the fixed sites, 40 borings for each sampling were taken. On the experimental fields the number of borings varied from 10 to 20 for each plot of between 9 and 30 $m^2$. The soil from all the borings at each sampling point was collected in large sterile copper tins or in clean plastic bags. The following day the soil from each sampling point was thoroughly mixed in the laboratory in large flame-sterilized iron containers. The fresh soil was used immediately for the determination of the numbers of bacteria. In addition, the moisture content of the soil and, if necessary, the salt content of the soil moisture were determined.

The numbers of nitrifying organisms were estimated by means of a dilution method; this involved determining the amount of nitrite or nitrate nitrogen formed in a nitrite and nitrate free sterilized sandy soil treated with $CaCO_3$, $KH_2PO_4$ and $(NH_4)_2$ $SO_4$, after incubation with 10-fold, 100-fold and 1,000-fold dilutions of soil from the field. The dilutions were prepared with sterile distilled water. For the determination of the total numbers of bacteria and the numbers of the physiological groups (with the exception of rhizobia), the plate method was used. For all the counts, 10 plates were prepared from each dilution.

*Synthetic media.* For the determination of the total numbers of bacteria sodium albuminate agar was used (Waksman, 1932). For the determination of the protein decomposers the same medium was used without glucose and in place of albumin, 1 g. of purified casein was added per litre of medium.

The medium used for the starch decomposers had the following composition: agar, 15·0 g.; insoluble starch (amylum triticum), 2·0 g.; $K_2HPO_4$, 1·0 g.; $(NH_4)_2SO_4$, 0·5 g.; $MgSO_4.7H_2O$, 0·5 g.; a little $CaCO_3$; a trace of $FeCl_3$; water, 1,000 ml.

For the cellulose decomposers the following medium was used: agar 15·0 g.; $K_2HPO_4$, 1·0 g., $MgSO_4.7H_2O$, 0·5 g.; $(NH_4)_2SO_4$, 0·5 g.; cellulose, 2·5 g.; water, 1,000 ml. The cellulose was prepared using the method described by Harmsen (1946).

The composition of the medium used for counting *Azotobacter* was as follows: agar, 15 g.; $K_2HPO_4$, 1·0 g.; $MgSO_4.7H_2O$, 0·5 g.; mannitol, 2·0 g.; glucose, 0·2 g.; $CaCO_3$, 1·0 g.; soil extract, 200 ml.; water, 800 ml. Soil extract was made by boiling 1 kg. of a calcareous clay soil for half an hour in 2 litres water. After filtration the volume of this extract was restored to 2 litres.

## *THE WIERINGERMEER POLDER*

### *Numbers of bacteria*

Shortly after the water of the Wieringermeer polder had receded in August 1930, fixed sampling sites were chosen on the soil types recorded in Table 1. The numbers of bacteria were initially very small. It is of interest to note that the highest numbers were found in the fine sand overgrown with seaweed that formerly became dry at low tide. The other data show that high numbers of bacteria were found in the heavier and younger soils. Generally the numbers of bacteria were about 1,000-fold less than the numbers of bacteria present in corresponding normal soils of old land (Table 2).

The first period after the water had receded was characterized by an increase in the numbers of soil bacteria (Table 3). The increase was approximately proportional to the decrease in moisture and salt content and the improved aeration of the soils (Fig. 2). The increase in salt content during periods of drought always resulted in a temporary decrease in the numbers of bacteria.

In September 1932 the total numbers of bacteria had increased to about half the number in corresponding old soils. The same applied to the protein and starch decomposers. In uncultivated areas, however, microbial numbers showed only a slow increase over a period of years, even after the salt had been washed out of the soil. Not until after a crop had been grown, and in particular a leguminous crop had been ploughed under, did the numbers rise fairly steeply. Then, within a relatively short time, figures were recorded which differed little from those of older soils

TABLE 1

*Average number of bacteria in the layer 0–15 cm. in the Wieringermeer polder immediately after water had receded in 1930 (in thousands per g. of soil)*

| Soil type | Total numbers of bacteria | Numbers of protein decomposers | Numbers of starch decomposers | g. NaCl per litre of soil solution |
|---|---|---|---|---|
| 1. Old calcareous marine clay loam (southern part of the polder) | 65 | 35 | 30 | 29 |
| 2. Calcareous loam (central part of the polder) | 40 | 30 | 30 | 26 |
| 3. Coarse bare sand | 15 | 8 | 8 | 30 |
| 4. Fine sand overgrown with seaweed, formerly becoming dry during low tide | 350 | 250 | 200 | 31 |
| 5. Young marine deposits (mud) | 115 | 100 | 65 | 23 |

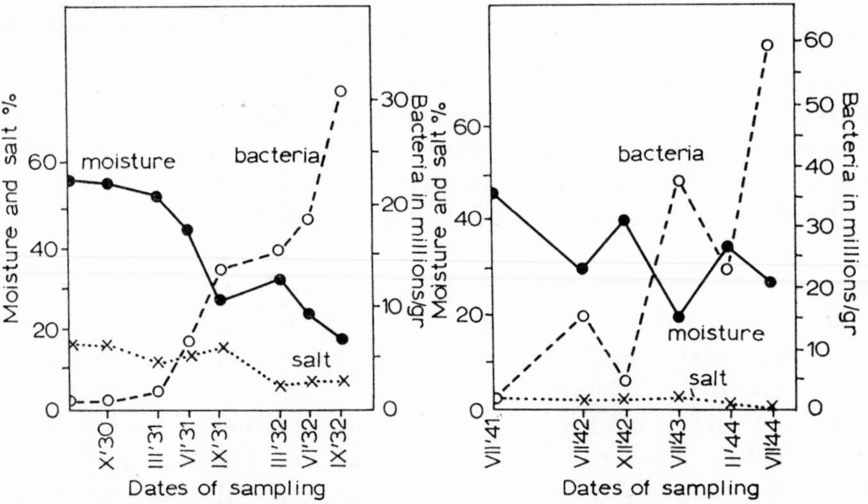


Fig. 2. Increase in the number of bacteria in an old sea clay in the southern part of the Wieringermeer polder in the first period after the sea water had receded, in relation to the decrease of moisture and salt contents of the soil. This soil was provided with a drainage system in June, 1931.

Fig. 3. Numbers of bacteria in a silt loam of the North East polder in the first years after the water had receded, in relation to the moisture and salt contents of the soil. This soil was provided with a drainage system in the spring of 1944.

TABLE 2

*Mean number of bacteria in the 0–20 cm. layer, for some representative soil types in the Netherlands (in thousands per g. of soil)*

| Soil type | Total numbers of bacteria | Protein decomposers | Starch decomposers | Cellulose decomposers | Nitrifying bacteria | *Azotobacter* |
|---|---|---|---|---|---|---|
| Excellent calcareous, heavy soil of normal composition (young sea clay), arable land | 80,000 | 50,000 | 30,000 | 9,000 | 100 | 10 |
| Do., permanent grassland | 130,000 | 70,000 | 40,000 | 20,000 | 75 | 8 |
| Calcareous, light loam, arable land | 45,000 | 30,000 | 20,000 | 4,000 | 90 | 2·5 |
| Slightly acid, diluvial sand lacking $CaCO_3$ | 8,000 | 5,000 | 3,000 | 1,000 | 0·5 | 0.0 |
| Mature Dollard-saltings (*Festuca-rubra* phase) | 18,000 | 12,000 | 7,500 | 2,500 | 0·75 | 0·3 |

TABLE 3

*Total numbers of bacteria in thousands per g. of soil at 4 sampling sites in the Wieringermeerpolder*

| Soil type** | At the start | Oct. 1930 | March 1931 | June 1931 | Sept. 1931 | March 1932 | June 1932 | Sept. 1932 |
|---|---|---|---|---|---|---|---|---|
| 1 | 65 | 175 | 1,200 | 6,000* | 13,000* | 15,000* | 18,500* | 30,000* |
| 2 | 40 | 100 | 300 | 1,500 | 8,500 | 9,000 | 15,500* | 19,000* |
| 3 | 15 | 800 | 850 | 2,500* | 5,500* | 4,000* | 6,000* | 6,000* |
| 4 | 350 | 2,000 | 4,000 | 5,500* | 15,000* | 13,000* | 15,000* | 16,000* |

* Cultivated soils.
** Compare Table 1.

TABLE 4

*Total numbers of bacteria in thousands per g. of soil in the experimental field D 48 of the Wieringermeer polder (soil type 1) in the summers of 1932 to 1935 inclusive*

| Year of sampling | Untilled fallow | Tilled but not cropped since 1932, fallow | Tilled fallow in 1932 sugar beet in 1933 barley in 1934 wheat in 1935 | Cultivated green manure in 1932 beet in 1933 barley with stubble clover in 1934 wheat in 1935 |
|---|---|---|---|---|
| 1932 | 12,000 | 18,000 | 28,000 | 33,000* |
| 1933 | 19,000 | 27,000 | 36,000 | 56,000 |
| 1934 | 21,000 | 29,000 | 45,000 | 64,000 |
| 1935 | 23,000 | 29,000 | 51,000 | 75,000 |

* Determined before the green manure had been ploughed under.

TABLE 5

*Numbers of nitrifying bacteria in thousands per g. of soil in three soils of the Wieringermeer polder*

| Soil type** | Initially 1930 | | Sept. 1932 | | Jan. 1933 | | Sept. 1933 | | Aug. 1934 | | Sept. 1935 | | Sept. 1938 | | Old soils | |
|---|---|---|---|---|---|---|---|---|---|---|---|---|---|---|---|---|
| | Nm | Nb | Nm | Nb | Nm | Nb | Nm | Nb | Nm | Nb | Nm | Nb | Nm | Nb | Nm | Nb |
| 1 | 0·01 | sp | 1·5 | 0·6 | 2·2 | 0·9 | 8 | 3·5 | 58 | 52 | 68 | 60 | 71 | 68 | 50 | 60 |
| 2 | 0·03 | sp | 2·0 | 1·3 | 3·1 | 1·2 | 69 | 54 | 125 | 76 | 135 | 90 | 130 | 103 | 45 | 50 |
| 3 | sp | sp | 1·0 | 0·7 | 0·9 | 0·7 | 31 | 19 | 37 | 23 | 40 | 25 | 42 | 38 | — | — |

Nm = *Nitrosomonas;* Nb = *Nitrobacter;* sp = sporadic.
** Compare Table 1.

(Table 4). It was concluded that the humus originally present in the soil was not easily decomposed by the bacteria. This was also indicated by the fact that little nitrogen was mineralized, notwithstanding the fact that the humus content was often as high as that found in old soils. This explained the necessity for applying large amounts of nitrogenous fertilizers to the soils in this polder. The fact that normal populations of bacteria appeared quickly in most of the cultivated soils in this polder was due to the supplies of fresh organic matter which were introduced in the early years by growing leguminous crops on a big scale.

*Nitrifying bacteria*

The development of the nitrifying bacteria, *Nitrosomonas* and *Nitrobacter*, is shown in Table 5. Initially the numbers were very small. These bacteria proved to be very dependent on the maturation processes of the soil. The numbers rose greatly only after good drainage had been established. Then higher numbers than in old soils were often recorded, probably due to the fact that most soils in this polder had a high lime content.

*Azotobacter chroococcum*

The numbers of *Azotobacter chroococcum* also remained very small for several years and even in 1935 the soils on the sampling sites did not contain more than 100 to 250 cells per g. In 1938 the same soils contained 2,000 to 3,500 *Azotobacter* cells per g. The numbers also increased after the introduction of green manure.

*Rhizobia*

Investigations revealed that the various leguminous crops differed fairly widely in their need for inoculation with rhizobia. The crops could be classified in ascending order of inoculation requirement as follows:

(1) *Pisum*, *Vicia faba* and other *Vicia* spp;
(2) *Trifolium repens* and *Trifolium pratense*;
(3) *Phaseolus*;
(4) *Medicago sativa* and *Medicago lupulinus*;
(5) *Lupinus* and *Serradella*.

For *Pisum* and all *Vicia* spp, inoculation was not, as a rule, imperative. Further, *Trifolium repens* and *Trifolium pratense* could, if necessary, be sown without having been inoculated, although inoculation yielded better results in the first years; on the other hand, crops of *Phaseolus*, *Medicago sativa* and *M. lupulinus*, *Lupinus* and *Serradella* failed completely for several years if non-inoculated seed was used. Some 17,000 hectares had to be inoculated, often more than once, since the treatment had to be repeated if a different leguminous crop was raised on a field previously inoculated for another crop.

## *THE NORTH-EAST POLDER*

### *Numbers of bacteria*

The first bacterial counts in soils of the future North-east polder were made in October 1938, when the soil was still covered with water. These data are recorded in Table 6. In the samples a distinction was made between the upper aerated layer and the unaerated underlayer. The numbers of organisms were always higher in the aerated layer than in the unaerated layer. In the unaerated layer the numbers of bacteria were generally 5 to 10 times higher than in the corresponding soils of the Wieringermeer polder after the recession of the water in 1930, probably because most of the salt had disappeared from the upper soil layer by the transformation of the Zuider Zee into a fresh-water lake. It is also of interest to note that, while in the new soils of the Wieringermeer polder the azotobacters and nitrifying bacteria could be detected only very rarely, these organisms were found in 50 to 70 per cent of the samples of the future North-east polder.

After most of the water had been pumped out in 1941 some fixed sampling sites were laid out in the eastern and southern part of this polder. In the spring of 1942 some further sites were laid out in the central and western part of the polder.

The soil types and some data on the total numbers of bacteria found in successive years at these sites are recorded in Table 7. From these data it is clear that the numbers of bacteria increased in the first year, but remained at a rather low level as long as the soils had not been drained and cultivated. As may be seen from Fig. 3, the numbers of bacteria were dependent upon the moisture content of the soil, especially in soil not yet brought into cultivation. Normal populations of bacteria were attained only after good drainage and cultivation had been established. It was found that the numbers of protein, cellulose and starch decomposing bacteria ran parallel with the numbers of total bacteria. The number of nitrifying bacteria rose very rapidly when the fields were drained.

## TABLE 6

*Numbers of bacteria in thousands per g. of fresh soil in the future North-east polder and the presence or absence of* Azotobacter *and nitrifying bacteria (1938)*

| Soil type | Layer in cm. | Number of bacteria | Protein decomposers | Cellulose decomposers | Azoto-bacters[1] | Nitrifying bacteria[1] | g. NaCl per 1. | Moisture % |
|---|---|---|---|---|---|---|---|---|
| Medium coarse sand | 0–3* | 2,250 | 1,620 | 0·4 | −−−−− | −−−−− | 0·70 | 17·3 |
| | 3–15† | 170 | 107 | 2·8 | −−−−− | −−−−− | 0·50 | 15·7 |
| Medium fine sand[2] | 0–2* | 900 | 822 | 4·4 | ++−−− | −−−−− | 0·81 | 24·7 |
| | 2–15† | 87 | 57 | 4·8 | +−−−− | ++−−− | 0·50 | 22·5 |
| Fine sand[3] | 0–2* | 1,560 | 1,920 | 360 | −−−−− | − | 0·70 | 24·2 |
| | 2–15† | 740 | 420 | 86 | −−−−− | − | 0·40 | 26·1 |
| Fine sand | 0–4* | 500 | 470 | 18 | −−−−− | −−−−− | 0·46 | 34·5 |
| | 4–15† | 118 | 49 | 8 | −−−−− | −−−−− | 0·41 | 24·5 |
| Sandy loam A | 0–4* | 3,202 | 1,710 | 80 | ++++− | +++++ | 0·25 | 32·5 |
| | 4–15† | 300 | 720 | 21 | ++−−− | +++++ | 0·27 | 33·5 |
| Sandy loam A | 0–1* | 1,470 | 319 | 17 | −−−−− | +++++ | 0·64 | 37·1 |
| | 1–15† | 107 | 45 | 12 | −−−−− | ++−−− | 0·70 | 27·7 |
| Sandy loam B | 0–3* | 2,670 | 504 | 31 | +−−−− | +++++ | 0·32 | 37·1 |
| | 3–15† | 515 | 194 | 80 | +++−− | +++−− | 0·26 | 42·1 |
| Clay loam A | 0–2* | 769 | 384 | 32 | +−−−− | +++−− | 0·26 | 42·1 |
| | 2–15† | 218 | 104 | 38 | +−−−− | +++++ | 0·34 | 43·8 |
| Clay loam B | 0–1* | 1,880 | 672 | 57 | −−−−− | +−−−− | 0·50 | 48·5 |
| | 1–15† | 432 | 157 | 19 | −−−−− | −−−−− | 0·50 | 45·9 |
| Clay loam B | 0–1* | 8,700 | 2,200 | 28 | −−−−− | ++−−− | 0·60 | 45·9 |
| | 1–15† | 338 | 220 | 22 | ++−−− | +−−−− | 0·50 | 45·7 |

[1] Determined from five replicates in flasks, as shown.
[2] Covered with *Scirpus maritimus* in places.
[3] Covered with *Potamogeton L.* in places.
* Aerated layer. † Unaerated layer.

TABLE 7

*Numbers of bacteria in thousands per g. of soil in fixed sampling sites in the North-east polder in the layer 0–15 cm.*

| Soil type | Oct. 1941 | July 1942 | Dec. 1942 | July 1943 | Oct. 1943 | June 1944 | Sept. 1946 | June 1948 | June 1950 |
|---|---|---|---|---|---|---|---|---|---|
| Fine sand | 669 | 6,560 | 7,300 | 10,830 | 8,420 | 72,040[4] | 37,680[1] | 37,760[1] | 50,950[1] |
| Medium fine sand | 4,740 | 4,580 | 11,860 | 28,040 | 10,560 | 32,840[1] | 21,920[1] | 18,840[3] | 59,900[1] |
| Clay loam B | — | 16,200 | 4,680 | 38,260 | 7,120 | 63,440[2] | 67,360[1] | 53,600[1] | 64,800[1] |
| Clay loam A | — | 9,360 | 2,400 | 8,645 | 1,555 | 10,392 | 8,900 | 78,520[1] | 83,700[4] |
| Sandy loam B | — | — | — | 4,040 | 3,865 | 7,990 | 9,040 | 12,360 | 46,600[1] |

[1] Cultivated.
[2] Recently ploughed for combating weeds.
[3] Fallow.
[4] Leguminous crop ploughed under.

TABLE 8

*Development of* Azotobacter chroococcum *at fixed sampling sites in the North-east polder (numbers per g. of fresh soil)*

| Soil type | Oct. 1941 | July 1942 | Sept. 1942 | Dec. 1942 | July 1943 | Oct. 1943 | Feb. 1944 | Oct. 1948 | Aug. 1949 | Nov. 1957 |
|---|---|---|---|---|---|---|---|---|---|---|
| Fine sand | 0 | 0 | 0 | 0 | 0 | 1 | 1[1] | 2[1] | 218[1] | 140[1] |
| Medium fine sand | 0 | 0 | 75 | 150 | 224 | 268 | 212[1] | 78[1] | 294[1] | 182[1] |
| Clay loam B | — | 0 | 2 | 2 | 38 | 2 | 60[2] | 201[1] | 575[1] | 526[1] |
| Clay loam A | — | — | 2 | 2 | 0 | 2 | 5 | 12 | 128[1] | 1,316[1] |
| Sandy loam B | — | — | — | — | 1 | 2 | 1 | 20 | 175[1] | 1,214[1] |

[1] Cultivated. [2] Weeds had recently been ploughed under.

*Azotobacters*

*A. chroococcum* generally developed at a slow rate. Table 8 gives some results for the fixed sampling sites. In the fine sand *Azotobacter* was absent for several years and the numbers also remained very small for several years after the soil had been cultivated. In the medium fine sand their numbers rose markedly during 1942. In this soil, however, the numbers were not greatly stimulated by cultivation. By contrast, cultivation clearly influenced the numbers in the heavier soils. However, the numbers of *Azotobacter* found in 1949 at the fixed sampling sites give no clear idea of the numbers present elsewhere in the polder soils. As may be seen from the data in Table 9, much higher numbers were

TABLE 9

*Total number of bacteria in millions per g. of soil and numbers of* A. chroococcum *in a number of allotments in the North-east polder in the summer of 1949, in addition to $CO_2$ production and pH*

| Allot- ment | Soil type | Crop in 1949 | Total number of bacteria | Azoto- bacters | $CO_2$* | pH |
|---|---|---|---|---|---|---|
| P 99 | Medium fine sand | Rye + grass | 41·0 | 1,320 | 1·24 | 7·8 |
| P 98 | ,, ,, ,, | Winter wheat + grass | 47·1 | 3,380 | 1·48 | 8·0 |
| P 55 | ,, ,, ,, | Grass | 51·6 | 2,580 | 1·28 | 8·0 |
| S 31 | Coarse sand | Grass | 25·3 | 256 | 1·43 | 7·4 |
| D 80 | ,, ,, | Not cultivated | 9·8 | 25 | 0·68 | 7·6 |
| R 20 | Fine sand | Grass | 41·2 | 0 | 1·59 | 7·6 |
| K 7 | ,, ,, | Oats + grass | 20·2 | 15 | 1·41 | 7·5 |
| L 36 | Diluvial sand | Grass | 45·6 | 0 | 1·34 | 7·8 |
| T 110 | Sandy loam B | Spring barley | 50·9 | 1,460 | 0·88 | 7·8 |
| B 90 | ,, ,, ,, | Wheat + *Medicago lupulinus* | 57·5 | 5,400 | 1·81 | 7·6 |
| C 15 | ,, ,, ,, | Not cultivated | 14·8 | 86 | 1·62 | 7·3 |
| E 23 | ,, ,, ,, | Not cultivated (reed) | 31·5 | 2,960 | 2·56 | 7·2 |
| M 86 | Clay loam B | Barley + *Trifolium pratense* | 41·4 | 5,860 | 2·40 | 7·5 |
| E 3 | Clay | Grass | 147·3 | 64,700 | 4·73 | 6·9 |
| M 87 | ,, | *Medicago sativa* | 39·4 | 2,720 | 1·76 | 7·5 |
| M 85 | Clay loam B | Grass | 138·8 | 5,200 | 2·34 | 7·5 |
| E 140 | ,, ,, ,, | Not cultivated (reed) | 49·7 | 240 | 3·08 | 7·2 |
| D 4 | ,, ,, ,, | ,, ,, ,, | 34·8 | 33,240 | 1·97 | 7·1 |

* ml. 0·1 N $CO_2$ per kg. of soil per hr. (determined in the laboratory).

found at some sites at that time. Great variations in the numbers of *Azotobacter* were noted. In some sandy soils (fine sand and diluvial sand), *Azotobacter* was entirely absent. This could be due neither to a lack of organic materials, since these soils had been under grass for several years, nor to an unfavourable reaction. The only explanation seems to be that these soils were entirely lacking in *Azotobacter* from the start. It is very striking that on some uncultivated, heavy soils very large numbers of *Azotobacter* were present on sites overgrown with reed (*Phragmites communis*). The most common species proved to be *A. chroococcum*; *A. beijerinckii*, which is adapted to a more acid reaction, has never been found in the polder soils.

No clear correlation was found between the total numbers of bacteria in the field and the $CO_2$ production of the soil determined in the laboratory.

*Rhizobia*

Just as in the Wieringermeer polder, the rhizobia of *Pisum*, *Vicia*, *Trifolium repens* and *T. pratense* were initially much more strongly represented than those of *Phaseolus*, while the rhizobia of *Medicago sativa*, *M. lupulinus* and *Lupinus* were practically absent. After the soil conditions had been improved by drainage and cultivation, the numbers of *R. leguminosarum*, *R. trifolii* and *R. phaseoli* increased spontaneously and, for this reason, inoculation of *Pisum*, *Vicia* and *Trifolium* and *Vicia faba* was not urgent after a few years. Inoculation of *Phaseolus* was necessary for a longer period, while inoculation of lucerne and black medic was essential, even in 1951, for all the soils in which these crops were grown for the first time. The results obtained for 12 experimental fields are presented in Table 10. They show the occurrence of the various species of *Rhizobium* in 1949 on fields that had been cultivated for several years and fields which had not yet been cultivated. Although peas had never been grown in these fields, the plants produced nodules in all the soils, with only one exception. Further, inoculated clover had been grown previously on two fields only but clover formed nodules in all the soils, with just two exceptions on non-cultivated soils. *Phaseolus* produced nodules in only 50 per cent of the soils. *Medicago lupulinus* (black medic) formed nodules only when previously inoculated *M. sativa* or *M. lupulinus* had been grown. No nodules were found on the roots of *Lupinus*.

It has been shown by Bosma (1962) that at quite an early stage of soil maturation, leguminous crops have a great need for readily assimilable phosphates. This was found to be the case also in the East Flevoland polder (Fig. 4).

TABLE 10

*Formation of nodules by a number of leguminous crops in 12 experimental fields in 1949 in the North-east polder*

| Allot-ment | Soil type | Succession of crops | | | | | | | Formation of nodules in 1949 | | | | |
|---|---|---|---|---|---|---|---|---|---|---|---|---|---|
| | | 1942 | 1943 | 1944 | 1945 | 1946 | 1947 | 1948 | *Pisum* | *Trifolium repens* | *Phaseolus* | *Medicago lupulinus* | *Lupinus* |
| E 16 | Fine sand | | | | | | | V | — | — | — | — | — |
| K 16 | Fine sand | R<br>V | R+Cl<br>V | Cl<br>V | Be<br>V | W+Gr<br>V | Gr<br>V | Gr<br>V | + | + | — | — | — |
| C 89 | Sandy loam A | | | | | | | 0 | + | + | — | — | — |
| L 8 | Sandy loam A | | | Ba+L<br>V | Oa<br>V | W+L<br>V | Be<br>V | W+Bm<br>V | + | + | + | + | — |
| R 6 | Sandy loam A | Bm<br>V | W<br>V | Oa<br>V | W+Cl<br>V | Cl<br>V | W+Gr<br>V | Gr<br>V | + | + | — | + | — |
| H 20 | Sandy loam B | | | | | | | | + | — | — | — | — |

| | | | | | | | | | | | | | |
|---|---|---|---|---|---|---|---|---|---|---|---|---|---|
| Q 41 | Sandy loam B | | L<br>V | L<br>V | W<br>V | Ba+Bm<br>V | Oa<br>V | W+Bm<br>V | + | + | + | + | — |
| P 17 | Clay loam A | | | Ba<br>V | V | Ba+Bm<br>V | Oa<br>V | Fl<br>V | + | + | + | + | — |
| T 10 | Clay loam A | | L<br>V | L<br>V | W<br>V | Ba+Bm<br>V | L<br>V | Fl+Bm<br>V | + | + | + | + | — |
| E 136 | Clay loam B | | | | | V | V | Ba<br>V | + | + | — | — | — |
| T 84 | Clay loam B | | | | | | V | W<br>V | + | + | + | — | — |
| M 96 | Clay loam B | | | | | V | Bm<br>V | Ba<br>V | + | + | + | + | — |

V = Drained by trenches
O = Drained by tile drains

R = Rye
Cl = Red Clover
Be = Beets

Gr = Grass
Ba = Barley
L = Lucerne

W = Wheat
Oa = Oats
Bm = Black medic

Fl = Flax

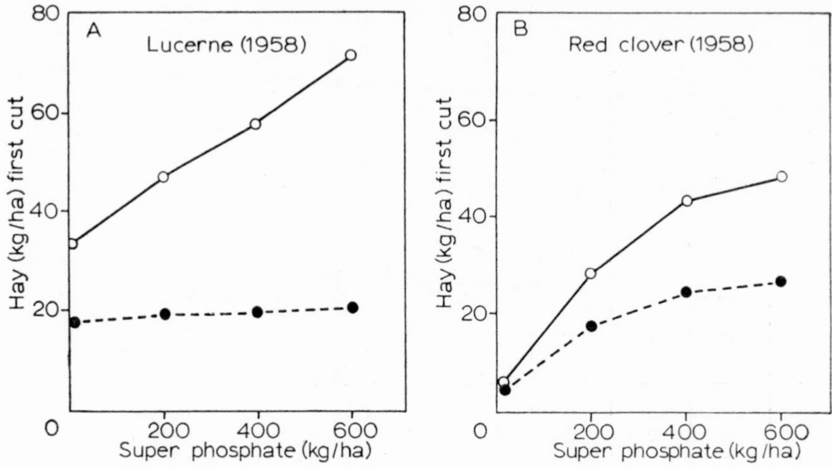


Fig. 4. Influence of increasing amounts of superphosphate in the yields of *Medicago sativa* (A) and *Trifolium pratense* (B) on a loam soil of the East Flevoland polder in the second year after the water had receded.
o———o inoculated. ●- - - -● not inoculated.

## *THE EAST FLEVOLAND POLDER*

The same general trend of bacterial development that has just been described for the North-east polder occurred in the East Flevoland polder. Here the water was pumped out in June 1957.

In 1965 some characteristics of micro-organisms, isolated from submerged soils (calcareous clays), of the future South Flevoland polder and from uncultivated and cultivated soils of the East Flevoland polder, were studied using colonies selected at random from the plates. For this purpose 30–35 isolates from each sampling site, obtained over a period of 2 months, were used. Results are given in Table 11, which shows, for each test, the percentage of isolates which gave a positive reaction. Evidently much variation may be present in soils of submerged areas with regard to the percentages of actinomycetes, cocci, sporeformers (*Bacillus spp*.) and pigmented forms. Fungi were practically absent in these fresh-water muds. Although relatively more Gram-negative rods were present than Gram-positive rods, Gram-positive forms could be dominant at both sites. Other workers, such as Zobell (1941) and Turner and Gray (1962), have found up to 89–95 per cent of the bacteria of marine muds to be Gram-negative. Taylor (1942) reported similar findings for fresh-water muds. In the uncultivated immature soil, overgrown with reeds since 1958, relatively more Gram-negative organisms

TABLE 11

*Characteristics of micro-organisms in submerged, immature and cultivated polder soils (1965)*

| | Percentage of isolates from 0–20 cm. layer showing character | | | |
|---|---|---|---|---|
| | South Flevoland | | East Flevoland polder | |
| | Submerged area | | Immature soil (reed since 1958) | Cultivated since 1959 |
| | Site 4 | Site 106 | Site 238 | Site 233 |
| Bacteria | 100 | 78·7 | 88·2 | 45·9 |
| Actinomycetes | 0 | 31·3 | 11·1 | 53·6 |
| Fungi | 0·01 | 0·02 | 0·7 | 0·5 |
| Casein hydrolysed | 66·5 | 69·9 | 50·5 | 54·4 |
| Starch hydrolysed | 19·1 | 14·8 | 17·8 | 12·7 |
| Gram-positive reaction | 70·6 | 62·5 | 19·4 | 64·3 |
| (*a*) Rods | 11·8 | 21·9 | 5·6 | 7·1 |
| (*b*) Actinomycetes | 0 | 31·3 | 11·1 | 53·6 |
| (*c*) Cocci | 58·8 | 9·4 | 2·8 | 3·6 |
| Gram-negative rods | 29·4 | 37·5 | 80·6 | 35·7 |
| Spore-formers (*Bacillus spp.*) | 0 | 6·3 | 0 | 4·5 |
| Pigmented forms | 0 | 50·0 | 16·7 | 39·3 |
| Number of micro-organisms (in thousands) | 3,160 | 492 | 16,780 | 96,960 |

were present than in the other soils. Gram-positive forms predominated in the cultivated soil; this was largely due to the presence of a large number of Gram-positive actinomycetes.

Bacterial counts were made in the East Flevoland polder during the growth of different crops. Some results obtained in 1964 on experimental fields are presented in Figs. 5 and 6. In Fig. 5a are shown the total numbers of bacteria, determined on 4 sampling dates, in a fallow clay soil and in an adjacent soil cropped with potatoes as the first crop after reed. A decidedly higher number of bacteria was noted in the soil cropped with potatoes. However, in the last month before harvest the number of bacteria decreased to the same level as that found for the

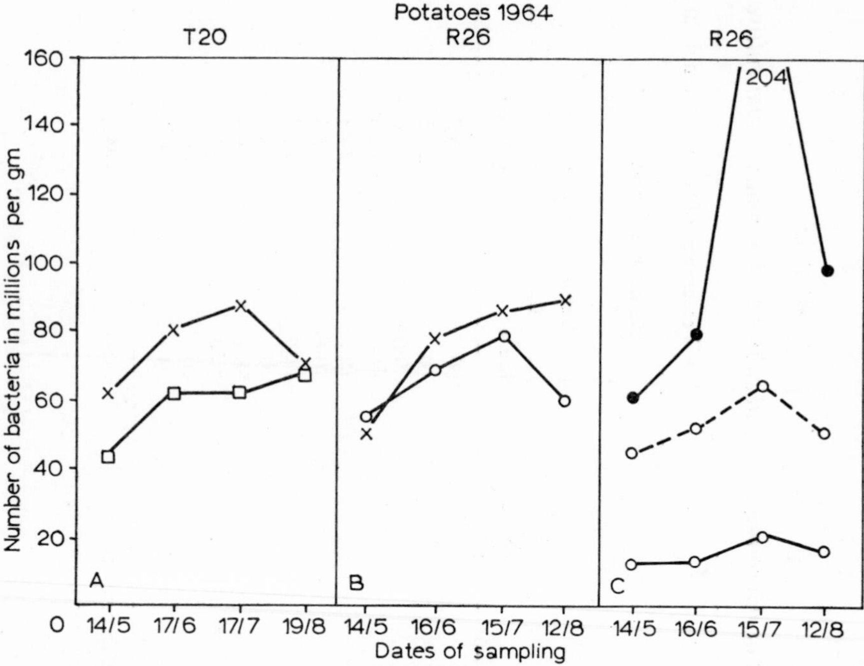


Fig. 5. Numbers of bacteria in clay soils of the East Flevoland polder cropped with potatoes in 1964.

(A) ×——× total number of bacteria under potatoes as the first crop after reeds.
□——□ total number of bacteria in a fallow soil after reeds.

(B) ×——× total number of bacteria in a plot cropped with potatoes in two successive years.
o——o total number of bacteria under potatoes preceded by oats.

(C) Potatoes preceded by 3 crops of *Medicago sativa*.
●——● total number of bacteria.
o- - - -o number of protein decomposers.
o——o number of starch decomposers.

fallow soils. Fig. 5b shows the total numbers of bacteria in a clay soil in another experimental field (allotment R 26). One curve applies to a plot cropped with potatoes in 2 successive years, preceded by oats in 1962 and by sugar beet in 1961; the other one refers to a plot grown with potatoes in 1964, sugar beet in 1963, barley in 1962 and rape seed in 1961. The first curve indicates that the number of bacteria did not decrease during the last month before harvest; the other curve does fall during the last month before harvest and has the same shape as that shown in Fig. 5a for the soil cropped with potatoes.

Fig. 5c shows the changes in the total numbers of bacteria, the protein decomposers and starch decomposers for a plot in the same experimental field (allotment R 26), cropped with potatoes in 1964 and with *Medicago*

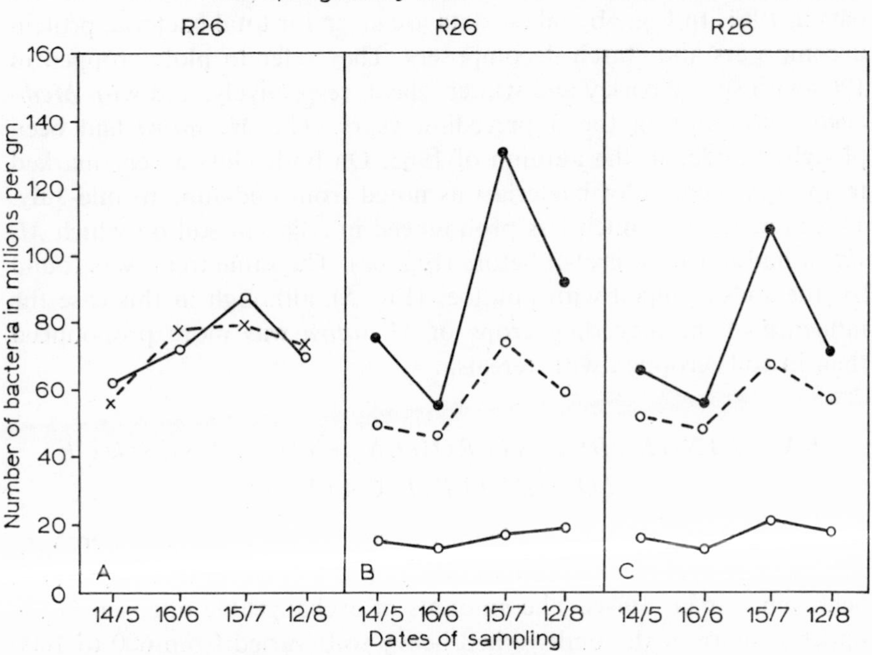


Fig. 6. Numbers of bacteria in clay soils of the East Flevoland polder cropped with spring barley or winter wheat in 1964.

(A) ×----× 2 × spring barley — total number of bacteria.
o——o 1 × spring barley — total number of bacteria.

(B) Spring barley preceded by 3 × *Medicago sativa.*
●——● total number of bacteria.
o----o number of protein decomposers.
o——o number of starch decomposers.

(C) Winter wheat preceded by 3 × *Medicago sativa.*
●——● total number of bacteria.
o----o number of protein decomposers.
o——o number of starch decomposers.

*sativa* during the 3 preceding years. In this plot, the total number of bacteria rose very steeply during the period mid-June to mid-July and then decreased very markedly during maturation of the crop. Undoubtedly the counts were connected with the numbers of bacteria in the rhizosphere of the potato plant which, apparently, were stimulated greatly by the preceding crops of *Medicago sativa*. The marked increase in numbers of bacteria from mid-June to mid-July must have been due mainly to bacteria other than the protein and starch decomposers.

The data in Fig. 6 refers to the same experimental field of allotment R 26. Fig. 6a shows the total numbers of bacteria in 2 plots cropped with spring barley in 1964. One curve applies to a plot cropped with oats in 1963, potatoes in 1962 and spring wheat in 1961, and the other to a plot cropped with barley in 1964 and 1963, sugar beet in 1962 and oats in 1961. In Fig. 6b and 6c, data are given for total bacteria, protein decomposers and starch decomposers. They refer to plots cropped in 1964 with spring barley and winter wheat, respectively, and with *Medicago sativa* during the 3 preceding years. The *M. sativa* had been ploughed under in the autumn of 1963. On both plots a very marked temporary increase of bacteria was noted from mid-June to mid-July. This increase was much less pronounced in adjacent soil on which *M. sativa* had not been grown before (Fig. 6a). The same trend was found for the soils cropped with potatoes (Fig. 5), although in this case the influence of the preceding crops of *M. sativa* was more pronounced than in soils cropped with cereals.

## *EXCHANGEABLE NITROGEN AND LOSSES DUE TO DENITRIFICATION*

It was found that the heavy subaqueous soils of the IJssel-lake were very rich in exchangeable ammonium nitrogen to a considerable depth (van Schreven, 1963*a*; 1964). The amounts of exchangeable nitrogen in the upper 1 metre of the undisturbed heavy soils varied from 600 to 1000 kg. per hectare. A considerable proportion of the ammonium ions could be extracted by shaking with water. This fraction increased with depth in the profile. Large amounts of ammonium nitrogen were undoubtedly lost by diffusion into the water during the course of time. It has been shown that very large losses of nitrogen, due to denitrification, may take place when such soils rich in ammonium nitrogen are allowed to dry out slowly (van Schreven, 1963*a*, *b*; 1965). These losses take place after nitrates have been formed in the upper layers and while the soil is still in a semi-anaerobic condition. It was shown that large losses, due to denitrification, also take place in soils cropped with perennial reeds. Reeds are able to take up practically all the available exchangeable ammonium in the soil down to a depth of 80 cm. within two years and 1 metre within three years; important amounts of nitrogen may even be absorbed down to a depth of 1·50 metres (van Schreven, 1963*c*, 1965).

## *TOXIC SUBSTANCES*

Recently it was found that the unaerated subaqueous soils of Lake IJssel contain substances which are toxic to bacteria. This was demonstrated as follows. A soil, solution, obtained by applying hydraulic pressure to a fresh soil was sterilized by filtration (filter, 11G5f). This soil solution, at half strength, was incorporated in an agar medium used for the determination of the total numbers of bacteria. Much smaller numbers of bacteria were found than with the normal medium (Table 12). If the soil solution was aerated for three days with an air

TABLE 12

*Effect of adding a sterile soil solution (obtained from a subaqueous soil in Lake Ijssel) to an agar medium used for the determination of the total number of bacteria, on the numbers found in 3 old arable soils.*

| Treatment of the agar medium | Total number of bacteria per g. of soil | | |
|---|---|---|---|
| | Loam soil | River clay | Sandy soil |
| Normal medium (sodium albuminate) | 81,120,000 | 55,960,000 | 35,820,000 |
| Medium with addition of soil solution sterilized by filtration | 1,220,000 | 1,200,000 | 920,000 |
| Medium with addition of soil solution sterilized by autoclaving | 82,860,000 | 58,640,000 | 34,860,000 |
| Medium with addition of soil solution aerated for 3 days | 9,200,000 | 8,400,000 | 5,780,000 |

stream and then sterilized by filtration the inhibiting effect of the solution was reduced a little. The inhibitory effect was removed entirely by autoclaving the solution for half an hour. It was also found that the inhibitory effect of the soil solution was greatly reduced by keeping the subaqueous soils dry for 4 weeks. The inhibitory effect was removed entirely by keeping the soils for 4 weeks at a moisture content of 65 per cent of the water-holding capacity.

Bactericidal substances were also found in solutions obtained by shaking unaerated polder soils with water for 2 hours, although the inhibitory effect of such solutions was less marked than when the soil moisture was pressed out from the soil. At least part of the toxic substances present in such soils may thus be washed out by rain water. Indeed, bactericidal substances were found in the drainage water collected from the drain pipes of some fields used since 1962 (Table 13).

TABLE 13

*Effect of the addition of sterile drainage water* to an agar medium used for the determination of the total number of bacteria, on the number of bacteria found in a loam soil (Dec. 1964)*

| Treatment of the medium | Total number of bacteria per g. of soil |
|---|---|
| Normal medium | 67,860,000 |
| Medium + drainage water from field A used since 1962 | 36,480,000 |
| Medium + drainage water from field B used since 1962 | 43,620,000 |
| Medium + drainage water from field C used since 1959 | 65,520,000 |

* Sterilized by filtration.

TABLE 14

*Effect of the maturation of the soil on the presence of toxic substances in the upper 20 cm. of the soil*

| Treatment of the medium | Total number of bacteria per g. old loam soil |
|---|---|
| Normal medium | 89,040,000 |
| Medium + soil solution from an uncultivated soil cropped with reeds | 49,920,000 |
| Medium + soil solution from an uncultivated bare soil not yet drained | 42,540,000 |
| Medium + soil solution from a field cultivated for the first time in 1964 | 59,460,000 |
| Medium + soil solution from a field cultivated since 1959 | 82,680,000 |

The drainage water from a field that had been used since 1959, which was collected on the same day, was practically free from toxic substances.

Evidently as the soil matured the bactericidal substances gradually disappeared (Table 14).

It seems very likely that the general development of aerobic bacteria during the first period of reclamation of the polder soils may be hampered by the presence of toxic substances in the soil moisture, although probably most of these substances are present in an adsorbed state. It seems very likely also that in the course of time other toxic substances are produced in the well-aerated polder soils, since substances having a toxic effect towards micro-organisms have been found by other workers in many old soils (Krasilnikov, 1958; McCalla and Haskins, 1964). Dobbs and Hinson (1953, 1956) even concluded that a widespread fungistasis occurs in soils. Their findings have been supported by the work of Chinn (1953), Park (1955), Chinn and Ledingham (1957), Jackson (1957), Dobbs, Hinson and Bywater (1957, 1960), Caldwell (1958) and Dobbs and Carter (1962).

Soil solutions obtained by pressing out well-aerated, old soils and then sterilizing by filtration, always proved to contain bactericidal substances when tested on a medium used for the determination of the total number of bacteria (Table 15). Evidently the inhibitory effect was not always entirely removed by autoclaving, proving that there are different types of inhibitory substances. The conclusion may be drawn, however, that the presence of bactericidal substances in older soils is a widespread

TABLE 15

*Effect of the addition of sterile soil solutions obtained by pressing out three well-aerated soils from the old land to an agar medium used for the determination of the total number of bacteria, on the number of bacteria found in a loam soil*

| Treatment of the medium | Total number of bacteria per g. of soil |
|---|---|
| Normal medium | 67,780,000 |
| Medium + soil solution from an old arable land (A) sterilized by filtration | 4,500,000 |
| Medium + soil solution from an old arable land (A) sterilized by autoclaving | 66,420,000 |
| Medium + soil solution from an old arable land (B) sterilized by filtration | 840,000 |
| Medium + soil solution from an old arable land (B) sterilized by autoclaving | 68,940,000 |
| Medium + soil solution from an old meadow (C) sterilized by filtration | 15,020,000 |
| Medium + soil solution from an old meadow (C) sterilized by autoclaving | 33,240,000 |

phenomenon. It is very likely that most of these substances are products of microbial metabolism, although some may be derived from crop residues.

The nature of the inhibitory substances in the unaerated polder soils has not yet been investigated. Since the toxicity may be reduced or removed by aeration, it is possible that rather simple substances may be responsible for at least part of the toxicity of these soils. Carbon dioxide, sulphides, or other toxic agents have been proposed by Mitchell and Alexander (1962) as fungicidal principles generated during flooding.

The draining of the polder soils round the IJssel-lake has provided a unique opportunity for studying the development of soil bacteria in relation to crop cultivation. Thanks to the enlightened policy of the Government full advantage has been taken of this opportunity. The investigations are still continuing in the laboratories at Kampen.

## *REFERENCES*

Bosma, W. A. (1962). Het verband tussen de rijping der gronden in de IJsselmeerpolders en de verbouw van landbouwgewassen (The relationship between the ripening process and the cultivation of arable crops). *Van Zee Ld.*, **32**, 71.

Caldwell, R. (1958). Fate of spores of *Trichoderma viride* Pers. ex Fr. introduced into soil. *Nature, Lond.*, **172**, 197.

Chinn, S. H. F. (1953). A slide technique for the study of fungi and actinomycetes in soil, with special reference to *Helminthosporium sativum*. *Can. J. Bot.*, **31**, 718.

Chinn, S. H. F. & Ledingham, R. J. (1957). Studies on the influence of various substances on the germination of *Helminthosporium sativum* spores in soil. *Can. J. Bot.*, **35**, 697.

Dobbs, C. G. & Hinson, W. H. (1953). A widespread fungistasis in soils. *Nature, Lond.*, **172**, 197.

Dobbs, C. G. & Hinson, W. H. (1960). Some observations on fungal spores in soil. *The ecology of soil fungi*, Ed. Parkinson, D. & Waid, J. S. Liverpool. Liverpool University Press.

Dobbs, C. G., Hinson, W. H. & Bywater, J. (1957). Mycostasis in soil. *J. gen. microbiol.*, **17**, 11.

Dobbs, C. G., Hinson, W. H. & Bywater, J. (1960). Inhibition of fungal growth in soil. *The ecology of soil fungi*, Ed. Parkinson, D. & Waid, J. S. Liverpool. Liverpool University Press.

Dobbs, C. G. & Carter, N. G. C. (1962). Studies in soil Mycology. VI. Mycostasis in soils. *Rep. Forest Res., Lond.*, 103.

Harmsen, G. W. (1932). Het microbiologisch grondonderzoek van deze proefpolder te Andijk in de jaren 1927-1931. *Rapporten m.b.t. de onderzoekingen in de Andijker proefpolder gedurende de eerste vier cultuurjaren*, **2**, 277.

Harmsen, G. W. (1934). Microbiologische problemen bijhet in cultuur brengen der Zuiderzeegronden. *Chem. weekbl.*, 61.

Harmsen, G. W. (1935). De microbiologie der Zuider zeegronden. *Landbouwk. Tijdschr., 's-Grav.*, **47**, 852.

Harmsen, G. W. (1940). The influence of the method of sampling on the accuracy of the determination of bacterial numbers in soil. *Ant. van Leeuwenhoek*, **6**, 178.

HARMSEN, G. W. (1944). Rijping der Zuiderzeegronden. *Versl. van de op 20 juni 1944 te Marknesse gehouden ontwikkelingsdag voor de landbouwkundige opzichters, Zwolle*, **2**, 19.

HARMSEN, G. W. (1946). *Onderzoekingen over de aërobe cellulose-ontleding in den grond.* Thesis. Wageningen.

JACKSON, R. M. (1957). Fungistasis as a factor in the rhizosphere phenomenon. *Nature, Lond.*, **180**, 96.

KRASILNIKOV, N. A. (1958). *Soil Microorganisms and Higher Plants.* Moscow. Academy of Sciences. USSR.

MCCALLA, T. M. & HASKINS, F. A. (1964). Phytotoxic substances from soil microorganisms and crop residues. *Bact. Rev.*, **28**, 181.

MITCHELL, R. & ALEXANDER, M. (1962). Microbial changes in flooded soils. *Soil Sci.*, **93**, 413.

PARK, D. (1955). Experimental studies on the ecology of fungi in soil. *Trans. Br. mycol. Soc.*, **38**, 130.

QUISPEL, A., HARMSEN, G. W. & OTZEN, D. (1952). Contribution to the chemical and bacteriological oxidation of pyrite in soil. *Pl. Soil*, **4**, 43.

SCHREVEN, D. A. VAN (1951). De microbiologie van de Noordoostpolderbodem (The microbiology of the North-Eastern polder soil). *Van Zee Ld.*, **5**, 1.

SCHREVEN, D. A. VAN. (1962). De microbiologische rijping der gronden in de IJsselmeerpolders (The microbiological ripening of the soils in the IJssel-lake polders). *Van. Zee Ld.*, **32**, 34.

SCHREVEN, D. A. VAN (1963). Nitrogen transformations in the former subaqueous soils of polders recently reclaimed from Lake IJssel. I. Water-extractable, exchangeable and fixed ammonium. *Pl. Soil*, **18**, 143.

SCHREVEN, D. A. VAN (1963). Nitrogen transformations in the former subaqueous soils of polders recently reclaimed from Lake IJssel. II. Losses of nitrogen due to denitrification and leaching. *Pl. Soil*, **18**, 163.

SCHREVEN, D. A. VAN (1963). Nitrogen transformations in the former subaqueous soils of polders recently reclaimed from Lake IJssel. III. The uptake of mineral nitrogen by the pioneer vegetation and the influence of the organic material of the pioneer vegetation on nitrogen mineralization in recently drained polder soils. *Pl. Soil*, **28**, 277.

SCHREVEN, D. A. VAN (1965). Stikstofomzettingen in jonge IJsselmeerpoldergronden (Nitrogen transformations in the former subaqueous soils of polders recently reclaimed from Lake IJssel). *Van Zee Ld.*, **41**, 1.

SMITS, H. (1962). De fysische rijping der gronden in der IJsselmeerpolders (The physical ripening of the soils in the IJssel-lake polders). *Van Zee Ld.*, **32**, 7.

TAYLOR, C. B. (1942). Bacteriology of fresh water. III. The types of bacteria present in lakes and streams and their relationship to the bacterial flora of soil. *J. Hyg. Camb.*, **42**, 284.

TURNER, M. & GRAY, T. R. G. (1962). Bacteria of a developing salt marsh. *Nature, Lond.*, **194**, 559.

WAKSMAN, S. A. (1932). *Principles of Soil Microbiology.* Baltimore. Williams and Wilkins.

ZOBELL, C. E. (1941). Studies on marine bacteria. I. The cultural requirements of heterotrophic aerobes. *J. Mar. Res.*, **4**, 42.

ZUUR, A. J. (1962). De chemische rijping der gronden in de IJsselmeerpolders (The chemical ripening of the soils in the IJssel-lake polders). *Van Zee Ld.*, **32**, 24.

# BACTERIA IN A PINE FOREST SOIL

M. GOODFELLOW, I. R. HILL and T. R. G. GRAY

*Hartley Botanical Laboratories, The University of Liverpool*

## *INTRODUCTION*

Studies concerning the ecology of soil bacteria and the biochemical processes which occur in soil must be based upon a knowledge of the main types of bacteria which live and grow in this habitat. Because of the enormous spatial and temporal variations in the numbers and types of organisms present in a soil, a complete characterization of the bacterial flora is not yet feasible. Indeed, it may never become feasible. It is possible, however, to characterize the population at one or a few points in space and time and to study factors affecting the distribution of the bacteria which have been shown to be present under such restricted conditions.

To carry out such work it is essential to use techniques which permit the isolation of either a large random sample of the total microflora or of a segment of it in which one is interested. Secondly it is necessary to characterize as many of these organisms as possible on the basis of a varied and comprehensive range of properties (Gray and Goodfellow, 1966). Such work has been started on the microflora of a developing podzol soil which has formed under a cover of *Pinus nigra laricio*. This investigation has been concerned initially with determining the principal types of both fungi (Indraratne, 1964) and bacteria present. This paper reports the preliminary results concerning the bacteria.

The soil being studied occurs in a small area of pine forest planted on sand dunes at a distance of 800 metres from the coast at Freshfield, Lancashire (National Grid Reference: SD289096. The formation of dunes in this area began in the 17th century when sand was deposited over a layer of peat. The mineralogy of the sand suggests that it originated from the Millstone grits of the Pennines (and the boulder clays derived from these grits) and was carried to the coast by the River Mersey and the River Dee (Ashton, 1920).

Before afforestation, the dunes bore a whole complex of higher plant communities, the plant cover ranging from nil in freshly eroded areas to dense in areas colonized by *Ammophila arenaria*, *Carex arenaria*,

*Dicranum* spp. and *Polytrichum* spp. The more stable areas were colonized by *Hippophae rhamnoides*, *Festuca rubra*, *Carex arenaria*, *Lotus corniculatus*, *Viola canina*, *Hieracium pilosella* and *Fragaria vesca*. In the moister parts, the vegetation was dominated by *Salix repens*. Afforestation of the sampling area occurred about 1924. As a result, herbaceous plants have been almost completely eliminated; now only *Epipactis dunensis* and *Epipactis pendula* occur sporadically. At the present time the circumference of the pine trees, measured 1 metre above ground level, varies from 15 to 70 cm. The distance between individual trees is from 1·2 to 5·0 m.

The development of a dense carpet of pine needles has caused the formation of a distinct soil profile in an otherwise little stratified dune soil. The pine needles form a well marked $A_0$ horizon which overlies the mineral soil. L, $F_1$, $F_2$ and H layers are all present, though the H layer is usually only a few millimetres thick. As the pine litter has been broken down, the decomposition products have been washed into the mineral soil and have caused the formation of an undifferentiated *acidic* $A_1$ horizon. This can be distinguished visually from the alkaline C horizon (parent dune sand), by its grey colour. This colour decreases in intensity and at a depth of 6 cm. it has usually disappeared, although

TABLE 1

*Physical and chemical properties of the Freshfield pine forest soil*

| | $A_1$ horizon | C horizon |
|---|---|---|
| pH (glass electrode)* | 3·7–4·9 | 7·6–8·8 |
| Total Nitrogen (Kjeldahl method)** | 210 ppm. | 75 ppm. |
| % organic carbon*** | 0·67 | 0·17 |
| % organic matter (loss on ignition, corrected for losses from carbonates)* | 1·6 | 0·54 |
| C/N ratio* | 32·0 | 23·0 |
| Chloride concentration (%)**** | 0·007 | 0·002 |
| % free carbonate | 0·0 | 2·1 |
| Field capacity (%)* | 30·0 | 24·2 |
| Mechanical analysis* | | |
| % coarse sand | 46·3 | 41·9 |
| % fine sand | 50·5 | 55·4 |
| % silt | 0·18 | 0·19 |
| % clay | 0·22 | 0·58 |

* Piper (1944).
** Jackson (1958).
*** Shaw (1959).
**** Hall (pers. comm.)

it may extend to a depth of 14 cm. in a few places. In some places, a narrow but distinct B horizon is present, as judged by the deposition of iron at the $A_1$/C boundary. The C horizon consists of light yellow, *alkaline* sand, having a free calcuim carbonate content of about 2 per cent. In contrast to the organic matter in the A horizons, which consists mainly of the products of decomposition and humification of leaf material, the organic matter in the C horizon originates chiefly from the roots of *Pinus*. An analysis of some of the physical and chemical properties of the soil is given in Table 1.

## *METHODS*

### *Dilution plate technique*

Soil was taken from the profile in sterile 3 in. × 1 in. glass tubes. Normally the soil that was sampled was taken from the middle of the $A_1$ horizon and from about 8 cm. below the $A_1$/C borderline in the C horizon. The initial dilution of the soil was prepared within 2 to 3 hrs. of sampling by adding 5·0 g. soil to 500 ml. $\frac{1}{4}$ strength Ringer's solution. The $10^{-2}$ dilution obtained was agitated, using a magnetic stirring bar revolving at 2,800 ± 40 revs. per min. After agitating the suspension for 30 mins., 1·0 ml. was pipetted into 9·0 ml. of $\frac{1}{4}$ strength Ringer's solution containing 1,111 μg. nystatin per ml. Using a fresh pipette, 1·0 ml. samples of this $10^{-3}$ dilution were transferred to each of 8 sterile Petri dishes containing a basal layer of 10 ml. sterile demineralized water agar (Orcutt, 1940). Twenty ml. peptone yeast extract actidione agar [0·5 per cent peptone; 0·1 per cent yeast extract (Oxoid); 0·001 per cent ferric phosphate; 0·005 per cent actidione; pH 7·0] were poured into each dish. The dishes were then rotated to ensure thorough mixing of the inoculum with the agar which was allowed to set. A further 1·0 ml. of the $10^{-3}$ dilution was then pipetted into another 9·0 ml. $\frac{1}{4}$ strength Ringer's solution containing 1,000 μg. nystatin per ml. to obtain a $10^{-4}$ dilution. Agar plates wer prepared from this dilution and further $10^{-5}$ and $10^{-6}$ dilutions prepared and plated when necessary. The plates were incubated at 25° for 14 days. They were placed upside down in vertical piles of 6 (Wilson, 1935). After rejecting plates with fungal and spreading bacterial colonies, colony counts were made to determine the numbers of bacteria present in the soil; alternatively bacteria were isolated for purification and identification. The results were expressed as 'bacteria per g. of oven dried soil, estimated on peptone yeast extract agar'. Only plates with between 30 and 300 colonies per plate were used in calculating the results (Breed and Dotterer, 1916; Wilson, 1935). In some experiments soil extract agar was used, made from fertile garden soil (James, 1958).

In addition to the 50 μg. actidione per ml., the medium used also contained 50 μg. nystatin per ml., which originated from the dilution fluid. Nystatin was added in this way as it was thermolabile. Together these two antibiotics suppressed the growth of most of the fungi that would otherwise have interfered with the development of bacterial colonies (Williams and Davies, 1965).

All pipetting operations were preceded by sucking in and blowing out the suspensions 12 times in order to counteract the effects of adsorption of bacteria on the walls of the pipette (Wieringa, 1958).

*Purification of isolates*

All the bacteria growing on plates with 60 or fewer colonies were subcultured into tubes of peptone yeast broth (pH, 7·2) and grown for 7 days at 25°. These isolates were purified using the poured plate method. Discrete colonies were removed from the poured plates and purified further using the same technique once or twice more. The cultures obtained were maintained on peptone yeast extract agar at 5° under oil (Rhodes, 1957).

*Morphological characters*

These were recorded from bacteria that had been grown on nutrient agar slopes for 24 to 48 hrs. at 25°. Hucker's modification of Gram's method was used to stain the bacteria (Hucker and Conn, 1923). Motility was determined using the hanging drop method and the flagella were stained using Leifson's method (Leifson, 1951). Spore production was examined on 3 different media, peptone yeast extract agar, glucose nutrient agar and soil extract agar (Gordon and Rynearson, 1964).

*Colony characters*

The characteristics of the bacterial colonies, e.g. shape, pigmentation, etc., were recorded on peptone yeast extract agar after 7 days incubation at 25°.

*Growth and biochemical tests*

These tests were performed mainly by using the multipoint inoculation method described by Goodfellow and Gray (1966) and Gray and Goodfellow (1966). All inoculations were made with bacteria from 18 to 24 hr. cultures in nutrient broth that had been growing at 25°. The inoculated test media were incubated for 3 days at 25° except where specified otherwise. The tests used were as follows: growth in nutrient broth at different temperatures; growth in nutrient broth at different sodium chloride concentrations; acid production from sugars, sugar alcohols, alcohols and glycosides (Hugh and Leifson, 1953), using Seitz filtered or diethyl ether sterilized carbohydrates, etc.; catalase production on peptone yeast agar; casein and gelatin hydrolysis after 4 days (Smith, 1946); aesculin hydrolysis after 4 days, (Sneath, 1956); starch hydrolysis (Conn, Jennison and Weeks, 1957); tributyrin hydrolysis after 7 days, using Oxoid tributyrin agar; urease production (Christensen, 1946) (N.B. precautions were taken to ensure that the ammonia liberated from the medium in this test did not affect the medium in adjacent compartments in the dish by removing cultures from the dish as soon as they became positive); nitrate reduction to nitrite (Conn, Jennison and Weeks, 1957).

Other tests, especially those involving the production of gas or the clearing of insoluble compounds, were performed by more conventional methods for the reasons reported by Goodfellow and Gray (1966). The tests performed in this way were as follows: utilization of glucose by the oxidative or fermentative pathways after 7 and 14 days (Hugh and Leifson, 1953); hydrogen sulphide production from tryptophan using lead acetate papers (Conn, Jennison and Weeks, 1957); indole production from tryptophan (Kovács, 1928) after 2, 7 and 14 days; pectinase production after 7 days (Paton, 1959*a*); oxidase production (Steel, 1961); xylanase production (Sørensen, 1957); cellulose hydrolysis

TABLE 2

*The occurrence of bacteria of different morphological types in the $A_1$ and C horizons*

| | Total | Morphological groups | | | | | |
|---|---|---|---|---|---|---|---|
| | | 1 | 2 | 3 | 4 | 5 | 6 |
| Number of isolates—$A_1$ horizon | 259 | 11 | 24 | 154 | 7 | 36 | 27 |
| Number of isolates—C horizon | 268 | 24 | 74 | 63 | 34 | 26 | 47 |
| % of isolates—$A_1$ horizon | 100 | 4 | 9 | 60 | 3 | 14 | 10 |
| % of isolates—C horizon | 100 | 9 | 27 | 24 | 13 | 10 | 17 |

1—Gram negative, pigmented rods.
2—Gram negative, non-pigmented rods.
3—Gram positive and Gram variable, spore-forming rods.
4—Gram positive streptomycetes.
5—Gram positive, pleomorphic rods.
6—Gram positive cocci and coccoid rods.

TABLE 5

*Selected biochemical characteristics of the morphological groups of bacteria (percentage of strains positive) from the C horizon*

| | Group 1 24 strains | Group 2 74 strains | Group 3 63 strains | Group 4 34 strains | Group 5 26 strains | Group 6 47 strains | Total 268 strains |
|---|---|---|---|---|---|---|---|
| Hydrolysis of starch | 25 | 19 | 39 | 29 | 19 | 13 | 28 |
| Liquefaction of pectin | — | 7 | 19 | — | 12 | 4 | 8 |
| Breakdown of xylan | 4 | 5 | 25 | 14 | — | 4 | 9 |
| Breakdown of cellulose | — | — | — | 3 | — | — | 0·5 |
| Hydrolysis of aesculin | 42 | 42 | 73 | 56 | 16 | 34 | 43 |
| Clearing of humic acid | — | — | 5 | 53 | 4 | — | 9 |
| Reduction of $NO_3$ to $NO_2$ | 12 | 15 | 57 | 38 | 46 | 47 | 32 |
| Hydrolysis of gelatin | 25 | 23 | 71 | 18 | 4 | 11 | 26 |
| Hydrolysis of casein | 17 | 5 | 71 | 12 | 31 | 30 | 30 |
| Peptonization of purple milk | 8 | 11 | 44 | — | 16 | 17 | 15 |
| Urease production | 4 | 7 | 2 | — | 23 | 4 | 6 |
| Production of indole | — | — | — | — | — | — | — |
| Production of $H_2S$ from peptone (7 days) | 4 | 23 | 27 | 12 | 27 | 17 | 18 |
| Production of $H_2S$ from peptone (14 days) | 12 | 31 | 29 | 18 | 35 | 30 | 29 |
| Hydrolysis of tributyrin | 12 | 39 | 60 | 18 | 42 | 40 | 40 |
| Oxidase production | 25 | 67 | 29 | — | 8 | — | 29 |
| Catalase production (weak) | 54 | 53 | 41 | 65 | 35 | 21 | 43 |
| Catalase production (strong) | 46 | 47 | 59 | 35 | 65 | 79 | 57 |
| Growth in 3% NaCl | 62 | 62 | 88 | 56 | 92 | 83 | 76 |
| 5% NaCl | 42 | 59 | 85 | 41 | 81 | 81 | 69 |
| 7% NaCl | 12 | 34 | 66 | 14 | 12 | 66 | 45 |
| 10% NaCl | 8 | 23 | 47 | 6 | 8 | 58 | 31 |
| 15% NaCl | — | — | — | — | — | 4 | 1 |
| Growth at 30° | 58 | 47 | 100 | 62 | 89 | 85 | 74 |
| 35° | 42 | 32 | 100 | 32 | 38 | 66 | 57 |
| 40° | 8 | 13 | 100 | 14 | 27 | 30 | 38 |
| 45° | 8 | 4 | 79 | 9 | 8 | 19 | 25 |

TABLE 4

*The fermentation patterns of the different morphological groups of bacteria (percentage of strains positive) from the C horizon*

| | Group 1 24 strains | Group 2 74 strains | Group 3 63 strains | Group 4 34 strains | Group 5 26 strains | Group 6 47 strains | Total 268 strains |
|---|---|---|---|---|---|---|---|
| Acid from glucose (Oxidative) 7 days | 12 | 21 | 9 | 44 | 42 | 32 | 26 |
| Acid from glucose (Oxidative) 14 days | 33 | 34 | 17 | 68 | 50 | 47 | 41 |
| Acid from glucose (Fermentative) 7 days | — | — | 63 | — | — | 30 | 21 |
| Acid from D-arabinose | — | 18 | 8 | 9 | 12 | 13 | 12 |
| L-arabinose | 8 | 43 | 60 | 12 | 19 | 36 | 37 |
| xylose | 12 | 28 | 44 | 6 | 27 | 55 | 33 |
| rhamnose | 4 | 35 | 21 | 9 | 23 | 32 | 24 |
| fructose | 12 | 40 | 63 | 14 | 46 | 60 | 45 |
| galactose | 4 | 40 | 33 | 9 | 31 | 32 | 30 |
| mannose | 17 | 36 | 58 | 6 | 27 | 51 | 38 |
| cellobiose | 12 | 39 | 63 | 26 | 35 | 47 | 42 |
| lactose | — | 13 | 6 | 9 | 4 | 13 | 9 |

| | | | | | | | |
|---|---|---|---|---|---|---|---|
| maltose | 21 | 42 | 63 | 14 | 35 | 68 | 36 |
| sucrose | 12 | 38 | 65 | 9 | 38 | 60 | 43 |
| trehalose | 8 | 32 | 60 | 14 | 31 | 47 | 38 |
| melizitose | 4 | 32 | 15 | 9 | 19 | 45 | 24 |
| raffinose | 4 | 30 | 66 | 9 | 19 | 32 | 30 |
| glycogen | — | — | 27 | 3 | — | 9 | 9 |
| inulin | 12 | 28 | 68 | — | 27 | 40 | 31 |
| amygdalin | 12 | 32 | 55 | 12 | 27 | 47 | 36 |
| salicin | 8 | 24 | 66 | 6 | 27 | 36 | 27 |
| dulcitol | 4 | 11 | 2 | 3 | 12 | 26 | 10 |
| glycerol | — | 40 | 66 | 14 | 46 | 58 | 38 |
| inositol | 4 | 30 | 66 | 3 | 38 | 26 | 30 |
| mannitol | 8 | 38 | 76 | 14 | 27 | 50 | 40 |
| sorbitol | 4 | 36 | 47 | 6 | 42 | 49 | 36 |
| glucosamine | 4 | 16 | 65 | 3 | 23 | 43 | 30 |
| dextrin | 8 | 11 | 27 | — | 8 | 6 | 12 |
| ethanol | — | 24 | 13 | 12 | 27 | 29 | 16 |

N.B. Group 2 strains often appeared to attack many sugars and yet could not attack glucose. This is due to the fact that the attack of glucose was tested for by the original Hugh and Leifson (1953) technique, whilst the other tests were carried out using multipoint inoculation micro-techniques which are more sensitive.

(Eggins and Pugh, 1962), but in a medium at pH 7·2 and with 0·5 per cent cellulose read after 6 weeks; clearing of humic acid at pH 7·0 (Hurst, Burges and Latter, 1962), using humic acid supplied by L. Light and Co. Ltd. and reading the results during a 6 week period; action on purple milk after 7, 14 and 21 days; production of a fluorescent pigment (Paton, 1959*b*).

## *RESULTS*

### *Characteristics possessed by the isolates*

Using the tests described, 268 isolates from the C horizon soil were examined. Currently, a similar number of isolates from the $A_1$ horizon are being studied. The organisms could be divided into 6 morphological groups: (1) Gram-negative pigmented rods; (2) Gram-negative non-pigmented rods; (3) Gram-positive or Gram-variable spore-forming rods; (4) streptomycetes; (5) Gram-variable pleomorphic forms; (6) Gram-positive cocci and coccoid rods. Strains possessing diffusible fluorescent pigments were included in Group 2. The number and percentage of isolates in each group are shown in Table 2, whilst the results of the biochemical and growth tests are shown in Tables 3 and 4.

TABLE 5

*The genera of bacteria present in the C horizon soil*

| Genus | Number of isolates | % of isolates |
|---|---|---|
| *Achromobacter* | 32 | 12 |
| *Arthrobacter* | 21 | 8 |
| *Bacillus* | 63 | 24 |
| *Flavobacterium* | 24 | 9 |
| *Micrococcus* | 18 | 6 |
| *Nocardia* | 5 | 2 |
| *Pseudomonas* (Group 1)* | 5 | 2 |
| (Group 2)* | 11 | 4 |
| (Group 3)* | 24 | 9 |
| *Staphylococcus* | 17 | 6 |
| *Streptomyces* | 34 | 13 |
| Unidentified | 14 | 5 |

* *Pseudomonas*, Group 1: Fluorescent pigment; oxidative glucose dissimilation; gelatin hydrolysed; starch not hydrolysed.
Group 2: No pigment; oxidative glucose dissimilation; gelatin not hydrolysed; starch sometimes hydrolysed.
Group 3: No pigment; glucose not attacked; gelatin hydrolysed; starch not hydrolysed.

*Generic composition of the bacterial flora*

The Gram-negative rods were identified using a scheme based on that described by Shewan, Hobbs and Hodgkiss (1960). Spore-forming bacteria were determined using the key of Smith, Gordon and Clark (1952). Other forms were identified using Skerman's key (Skerman, 1959). The number and percentage of the isolates in each genus are shown in Table 5. In addition the species composition of the *Bacillus* populations in

TABLE 6

*The species of* Bacillus *in the* $A_1$ *and C horizon soils*

| Species | % of isolates | |
|---|---|---|
| | $A_1$ (pasteurized) | C (unpasteurized) |
| B. lichenformis | 2·0 | — |
| B. subtilis | 13·0 | 59·0 |
| B. pumilus | 1·0 | 5·0 |
| B. firmus | — | 9·0 |
| B. lentus | 1·0 | — |
| B. alvei | 1·0 | — |
| B. circulans | 27·5 | — |
| B. circulans-laterosporus-brevis intermediates (do not hydrolyse starch) | — | 24·0 |
| B. brevis | 6·0 | — |
| Bacillus (Group 1)* | — | 3·0 |
| Rods with spore-like swellings | 32·5 | — |
| Rods with no swellings and no spores | 16·0 | — |

* Smith, Gordon and Clark (1953).

TABLE 7

*The ability of* Bacillus *spp. to utilize ammonium nitrogen without growth factors*

| Species | No. of strains tested | No. of strains growing |
|---|---|---|
| B. subtilis | 56 | 50 |
| B. licheniformis | 3 | 3 |
| B. pumilus | 3 | 1 |
| B. firmus | 5 | 0 |
| B. lentus | 3 | 1 |
| B. brevis | 9 | 0 |
| B. alvei | 2 | 0 |
| B. laterosporus | 1 | 0 |
| B. circulans | 56 | 3 |

TABLE 8

*Variations in the numbers of bacteria and certain environmental factors in soil from the $A_1$ horizon*

| | Date of sampling | | | | | | | | | | |
|---|---|---|---|---|---|---|---|---|---|---|---|
| | 1963 | | | | | 1964 | | | | | |
| | 7/11 | 13/11 | 19/11 | 27/11 | 29/11 | 14/1 | 21/1 | 24/1 | 11/2 | 14/2 | 27/2 |
| No. of bacteria/g. soil in millions | 0·213 | 0·814 | 0·691 | 2·308 | 0·463 | 0·253 | 1·343 | 0·862 | 0·371 | 0·883 | 0·289 |
| pH | 3·8 | 4·4 | 3·7 | 4·0 | 3·9 | 4·3 | 3·9 | 4·2 | 4·0 | 4·0 | 3·8 |
| Soil temperature | 10·5 | 8·5 | 9·0 | 8·0 | 7·5 | 3·5 | 5·0 | 6·0 | 6·0 | 7·0 | 7·5 |
| % moisture content | 6·3 | 5·3 | 5·4 | 4·5 | 5·9 | 2·8 | 3·5 | 3·8 | 3·9 | 3·9 | 4·4 |
| % organic carbon | 0·6 | 0·6 | 0·6 | 0·4 | 0·6 | 0·5 | 0·6 | 0·7 | 0·6 | 0·5 | 0·6 |

both the $A_1$ and the C horizons are compared in Table 6. The bacilli from the $A_1$ horizon were isolated from dilution plates prepared from a soil suspension heated at 80° for 10 minutes. Table 7 shows the number of bacilli capable of utilizing ammonium nitrogen without added growth factors.

*Numbers of bacteria in the soil*

The results of a series of dilution plate counts of bacteria in the $A_1$ horizon soil, made over a 5 month period, are recorded in Table 8 together with variations in pH, soil temperature, percentage moisture content and organic carbon content. Table 9 compares counts of bacteria in samples taken from the $A_1$ and the C horizons. No correlations between any one factor and the numbers of bacteria in the soil are evident. This may mean that the counting methods employed are not sufficiently sensitive to detect correlations or that the variations in the

TABLE 9

*Numbers of bacteria developing from $A_1$ and C horizon soils on different media*

| | Numbers of bacteria in millions/g. of soil | | | |
|---|---|---|---|---|
| | November, 1963 | | December, 1963 | |
| | $A_1$ | C | $A_1$ | C |
| Peptone yeast extract agar pH 7·0 | 8·0 | 1·1 | 135·6 | 187·6 |
| | | | 141·6 | 338·6 |
| | | | 264·0 | 398·8 |
| Peptone yeast extract agar pH 5·5 | 7·7 | 1·2 | 155·0 | 191·1 |
| | | | 157·0 | 393·8 |
| Garden soil extract agar pH 7·0 | 7·9 | 0·7 | 137·5 | 228·8 |
| | | | 159·1 | 342·3 |

soil environment cause changes in the populations, other than quantitative ones. As a result, the figures are quoted merely to show the approximate size and variation of the population. Figures obtained by direct methods of counting give similar results and are referred to elsewhere in this symposium (pp. 173 and 185).

A feature of the counts worth noting is that a heated soil extract medium permitted the growth of smaller numbers of bacteria.

## *DISCUSSION*

Different soil types have been shown to support characteristic bacterial floras. In cultivated soils, corynebacteria have been shown to be one of the dominant groups (Topping, 1937; Lochhead, 1939; Rouatt and Katznelson, 1961), although Gram-negative rods, e.g. *Pseudomonas* predominate in the rhizospheres of cultivated plants (Holding, 1960; Rouatt and Katznelson, 1961). In contrast, acidic, peaty soils are characterized by *Bacillus* species (Holding, Franklin and Watling, 1965). In this respect they resemble the acidic $A_1$ horizon soil of the present investigation, where bacilli constitute about 59·5 per cent of the isolates (cf. 67 per cent, Holding *et al.*, 1965).

In the alkaline C horizon soil the percentage of spore-forming bacteria is much reduced and the incidence of Gram-negative rods increased; cocci, streptomycetes and Gram-negative, pigmented rods are also more important. In some ways, this type of flora is similar to that reported by Jensen (1963) for a beech forest soil, where no one group of bacteria was clearly dominant. The increase in the number of streptomycetes in the alkaline soil agrees with the results of Jensen (1930); further, Taber (1960) found that streptomycetes from alkaline soils were partly suppressed by slight acidity. Evidently *Bacillus* species are much more tolerant of acid conditions, possibly because they are better fitted to survive in such environments as a result of their ability to produce endospores.

The commonest species of *Bacillus* in this soil are *B. subtilis*, *B. circulans* and forms closely related to, though not identical with, *B. circulans*. In addition there are a large number of forms isolated from the pasteurized samples which produce only spore-like swellings or no spores at all. Mishustin and Mirsoeva (p. 459) have suggested that the distribution of bacilli in the soil is related to their ability to use either organic or inorganic nitrogen. Thus in soils where mineralization is slow and there is little inorganic nitrogen, species with complex nutritional requirements will predominate. Examination of the bacilli isolated from the Freshfield soil for their ability to utilize ammonium nitrogen has shown that one of the common species does utilize inorganic nitrogen (*B. subtilis*), whilst the other does not (*B. circulans*). Though Mishustin and Mirsoeva do not deal with the distribution of *B. circulans*, it seems to us that their view may be an over-simplification. It does not account for the fact that organisms utilizing inorganic nitrogen can usually utilize organic nitrogen as well and yet are absent from soils abundant in organic nitrogen. Furthermore, as Proom and

Knight (1955) have shown, the ability of bacilli to utilize ammonium nitrogen is complicated by the fact that many strains will use ammonium nitrogen if growth factors are present.

An interesting feature of the results is the number of cocci isolated. These have been reported from other acid soils (Beck and Poschenrieder, 1958; Holding, Franklin and Watling, 1965). Generally, however, they are regarded as being insignificant (Conn, 1948; Stout, 1958; Jensen, 1963). The chloride concentration of the Freshfield soil is low, but is greater than that of a similar inland soil at Cannock Chase (Hall, personal communication). Possibly localized drying of the dune soils might lead to the occurrence of high salinities which would favour cocci.

Many workers have reported the occurrence of the genera *Achromobacter* and *Pseudomonas* in soil (Holding, 1960; Jensen, 1963; Stout, 1958). However, *Flavobacterium*, which is abundant in the dune soil, has previously been reported to be rare, although it is apparently common on plant leaves, including *Pinus* leaves (Stout, 1960*b*, 1961).

Most of the isolates proved to be inactive as far as their ability to attack complex carbohydrates was concerned, a feature also noted by Holding *et al.* (1965). Lignin was not attacked at all. Decomposition of xylan was restricted to a few strains of *Bacillus subtilis* and some streptomycetes. Cellulose was attacked only by 1 streptomycete isolate. Pectin was liquefied by a few strains from a wide range of types. In contrast, over half the streptomycetes caused decolourization of humic acid. Possibly these strains are not breaking the molecule down but are accumulating it on the cell surface (Flaig and Schmidt, 1957; Burges and Latter, 1960).

Some organisms seemed to be inactive in respect of almost all the biochemical reactions tested. These included the *Flavobacterium* spp. (Group 1, Table 2), the *Bacillus circulans-laterosporus-brevis* group, the *Arthrobacter* group and the *Achromobacter* group.

The schemes of identification used in this work are based on essentially monothetic classifications. We are attempting to classify the isolates we have obtained using polythetic methods. It will be interesting to see if these enable us to construct more satisfactory keys for the identification of the common forms of bacteria present in this soil.

## *ACKNOWLEDGMENTS*

The authors wish to thank Mr. B. Hall of the Soil Survey for permission to quote some of his data and Mr. K Winterhalder for determining the physical and chemical properties of the soil. One of us (I.R.H.) is indebted to the Agricultural Research Council for financial support. We wish to thank Mr. R. Grierson and Miss A. P. Kerrigan for valuable technical assistance.

## REFERENCES

ASHTON, W. (1920). *The evolution of a coastline*. Southport. Ashton & Sons.

BECK, T. & POSCHENRIEDER, H. (1958). Über die artenmässige Zusammensetzung der Mikroflora eines sehr sauren Waldsmoorprofiles. *Zentbl. Bakt. ParasitKde., Abt. II*, **111**, 672.

BREED, R. S. & DOTTERER, W. D. (1916). The numbers of colonies allowable on a satisfactory agar plate. *J. Bact.*, **1**, 321.

BURGES, N. A. & LATTER, P. M. (1960). Microbiological problems associated with the decomposition of Humic acid. In *The ecology of soil fungi*. Ed. Parkinson, D. & Waid, J. S. Liverpool. Liverpool University Press.

CHRISTENSEN, W. B. (1946). Urea decomposition as a means of differentiating *Proteus* and para-colon cultures from each other and from *Salmonella* and *Shigella* types. *J. Bact.*, **52**, 461.

CONN, H. J. (1948). The most abundant groups of bacteria in soil. *Bact. Rev.*, **12**, 257.

CONN, H. J., JENNISON, M. W. & WEEKS, O. B. (1957). Routine tests for the identification of bacteria. In *Manual of microbiological methods*. Ed. Pelczar, M. J. *et al.* New York. McGraw-Hill.

EGGINS, H. O. W. & PUGH, G. J. F. (1962). Isolation of cellulose decomposing fungi from the soil. *Nature, Lond.*, **193**, 94.

FLAIG, W. & SCHMIDT, H. L. (1957). Über die einwirkung von Huminsäuren auf das Wachstum einiger Penicilliumarten. *Arch, Mikrobiol.,* **27**, 1.

GOODFELLOW, M. & GRAY, T. R. G. (1966). A multipoint inoculation method for performing biochemical tests on bacteria. In *Methods for the Identification of Bacteria*. Ed. Skinner, F. & Gibbs, B. E. London. Academic Press.

GORDON, R. E. & RYNEARSON, T. R. (1964). Maintenance of strains of *Bacillus* species. In *Culture collections: Perspectives and problems*. Ed. Martin, S. M. Toronto. University of Toronto Press.

GRAY, T. R. G. & GOODFELLOW, M. (1966). Rapid methods for making routine physiological tests on soil bacteria. *Proc. 8th Int. Congr. Soil Sci.*, **3**. Bucharest.

HOLDING, A. J. (1960). The properties and classifications of the predominant Gram-negative bacteria occurring in soil. *J. appl. Bact.*, **23**, 515.

HOLDING, A. J., FRANKLIN, D. A. & WATLING, R. (1965). The microflora of peat-podsol transitions. *J. Soil Sci.*, **16**, 44.

HUCKER, G. J. & CONN, H. J. (1923). Methods of Gram-staining. *Tech. Bull. N. Y. St. agric. exp. stn.*, **93**.

HUGH, R. & LEIFSON, E. (1953). The taxonomic significance of fermentative versus oxidative metabolism of carbohydrates by various Gram-negative bacteria. *J. Bact.*, **66**, 24.

HURST, H. M., BURGES, N. A. & LATTER, P. (1962). Some aspects of the biochemistry of humic acid decomposition by fungi. *Phytochemistry*, **1**, 227.

INDRARATNE, B. A. (1964). *Fungi in a pinewood soil*. Thesis. Liverpool. University of Liverpool.

JACKSON, M. L. (1958). *Soil chemical analysis*. Englewood Cliffs, N.J. Prentice-Hall.

JAMES, N. (1958). Soil extract in soil microbiology. *Can. J. Microbiol.*, **4**, 363.

JENSEN, H. L. (1930). Actinomycetes in Danish soils. *Soil Sci.*, **30**, 59.

JENSEN, V. (1963). Studies on the microflora of Danish beech forest soils. III.

Properties and composition of the bacterial flora. *Zentbl. Bakt. ParasitKde., Abt. II*, **116**, 594.

KOVÁCS, N. (1928). Eine vereinfachte Methode zum Nachweis der Indolbildung durch Bakterien. *Immunforschung*, **55**, 311.

LEIFSON, E. (1951). Staining, shape and arrangement of bacterial flagella. *J. Bact.*, **62**, 377.

LOCHHEAD, A. G. (1939). The qualitative nature of the bacterial soil flora with special relation to productivity and the rhizosphere. *Proc. Soil Sci. Soc. Am.*, **4**, 241.

ORCUTT, F. S. (1940). Methods for more accurately comparing plate counts of soil bacteria. *J. Bact.*, **39**, 100.

PATON, A. M. (1959*a*). An improved method for preparing pectate gels. *Nature, Lond.*, **183**, 1812.

PATON, A. M. (1959*b*). Enhancement of pigment production by *Pseudomonas. Nature, Lond.*, **184**, 1250.

PIPER, C. S. (1944). *Soil and plant analysis*. Adelaide. University of Adelaide Press.

PROOM, H. & KNIGHT, B. C. G. J. (1955). The minimal nutritional requirements of some species in the genus *Bacillus*. *J. gen. Microbiol.*, **13**, 474.

RHODES, M. (1957). The preservation of *Pseudomonas* under mineral oil. *J. appl. Bact.*, **20**, 108.

ROUATT, J. & KATZNELSON, H. (1961). A study of the bacteria on the root surface and in the rhizosphere soil of crop plants. *J. appl. Bact.*, **24**, 164.

SHAW, K. (1959). Determinations of organic carbon in soil and plant material. *J. Soil Sci.*, **10**, 316.

SHEWAN, J. M., HOBBS, G. & HODGKISS, W. (1960). A determinative scheme for the identification of certain genera of Gram-negative bacteria, with special reference to the Pseudomonadaceae. *J. appl. Bact.*, **23**, 379.

SKERMAN, V. B. D. (1959). *A guide to the identification of certain genera of bacteria*. Baltimore. Williams & Wilkins.

SMITH, N. R. (1946). Aerobic mesophilic spore-forming bacteria. *U.S. Dept. Agric. Misc. Publ.*, **559**.

SMITH, N. R., GORDON, R. E. & CLARK, F. E. (1952). Aerobic spore-forming bacteria. *U.S. Dept. Agric. Monograph*, **16**.

SNEATH, P. H. A. (1956). Cultural and biochemical characteristics of the genus *Chromobacterium*. *J. gen. Microbiol.*, **15**, 70.

SØRENSEN, H. (1957). Microbial decomposition of xylan. *Acta. agric. Scand. Suppl.*, **1**.

STEEL, K. J. (1961). The oxidase reaction as a taxonomic tool. *J. gen. Microbiol.*, **25**, 297.

STOUT, J. D. (1958). Biological studies of some tussock grassland soils: bacteria of two cultivated soils. *N.Z. Jl agric. Res.*, **1**, 943.

STOUT, J. D. (1960). Bacteria of soil and pasture leaves at Claudelands showgrounds. *N.Z. Jl agric. Res.*, **3**, 413.

STOUT, J. D. (1961). A bacterial survey of some New Zealand forest lands, grasslands and peats. *N.Z. Jl agric. Res.*, **4**, 1.

TABER, W. A. (1960). Evidence for the existence of acid-sensitive actinomycetes in soil. *Can. J. microbiol.*, **6**, 503.

TOPPING, L. E. (1937). The predominant micro-organisms in soils. I. Description and classification of the organisms. *Zentbl. Bakt. ParasitKde., Abt. II*, **97**, 284.

WIERINGA, K. T. (1958). The problems of standardization of methods in use in microbiological soil research. *Neth. J. agric. Sci.*, **6**, 61.

WILLIAMS, S. T. & DAVIES, F. L. (1965). Use of antibiotics for selection, isolation and enumeration of actinomycetes in soil. *J. gen. Microbiol.*, **38**, 251.

WILSON, G. S. (1935). The dilution plate count. *Spec. Rep. Ser. med. Res. Coun.*, **201**.

# EFFECTS OF METALLIC IONS ON SOIL BACTERIA

A. J. HOLDING and D. C. JEFFREY

*The Edinburgh School of Agriculture*

## *INTRODUCTION*

Although considerable attention has been given to the influence of metallic micro-nutrients in soil on plant growth, very little information is available on their effect on the soil microbial population. For example, information is lacking which shows how an excess or deficiency of one or more metallic ions in soil influences the composition or biochemical activities of the microbial population, particularly in the root region.

In the experiments detailed in this paper an attempt has been made to investigate a few of the complex interactions between micro-organisms and metals and to a lesser extent plants. The 3 compounds used to alter the availability of metallic ions, were (*a*) 8-hydroxyquinoline (oxine), a chelating agent usually exhibiting marked antimicrobial properties, (*b*) the iron salt of ethylenediaminetetra-acetic acid (Fe-EDTA) which was expected to increase the availability of iron, and (*c*) $MnSO_4.4H_2O$, since under certain circumstances microbial activity has been shown to influence the uptake of manganese by plants. An arable loam soil and an uncultivated brown earth were used for the main experiments. The 3 compounds were added individually to the medium which was being used for making plate counts to show their effect on the growth of the various components of the microbial population. Also, the effect of the compounds on the microflora in the soil itself was investigated by adding them, with and without fertilizer treatments, to soils in which perennial ryegrass was growing.

## *METHODS*

The methods have been detailed by Holding, Franklin and Watling (1965) and only a brief summary will be given here. The fresh aseptically sampled soil was mixed with sterile tap water and macerated for 3–4 mins. Decimal dilutions were then prepared in sterile tap water. To obtain the total count of micro-organisms, the dilutions were plated onto a soil extract yeast extract agar (prepared from a fertile garden soil) (SEYE) and the plates were incubated at 22° for 14 days. Fungal counts, when required, were obtained by plating the dilutions onto the same medium adjusted to pH 3·5 with citric acid solution.

The bacteria were classified into the four main groups of *Bacillus* spp; *Arthrobacter* spp; actinomycetes (mainly *Streptomyces* spp. but occasionally, where stated, *Nocardia* spp.) and Gram-negative bacteria with regular morphology. Occasionally a very small proportion of the isolates, which were not clearly related to the above groups, were encountered. These were disregarded. No attempt was made to identify the fungi.

## *EXPERIMENTAL RESULTS*

### *The effect of adding the compounds to SEYE*

This experiment was devised in order to obtain some indication of the effect of the changes in the availability of certain metallic ions on the various groups of soil micro-organisms.

Two soils were used: a fallow arable loam (pH 6·8), which had not received fertilizer treatment for about 12 months and a brown earth (pH 4·2) covered with *Festuca ovina*, *Deschampsia flexuosa*, and *Nardus stricta*. Soil dilutions were plated in triplicate onto SEYE to which had been added individually immediately prior to pouring 0·01, 0·1 and 1 mM oxine, 2, 20 and 200 ppm. iron as Fe-EDTA solution and 70, 700 and 1,400 ppm. manganese as $MnSO_4$ solution.

The results for the concentrations showing the most interesting effects are given in Table 1. With oxine the lowest concentration showed that *Bacillus* spp. and actinomycetes were more sensitive than either the *Arthrobacter* spp. or Gram-negative bacteria, in both soils. Previous work demonstrating that Gram-positive bacteria are more susceptible to oxine than Gram-negative types has been reviewed by Weinberg (1957). At the higher oxine concentrations the growth of the *Arthrobacter* strains was inhibited to a greater extent than the Gram-negative group, the numbers of which were, however, reduced considerably at the 1mM concentration. Amongst the Gram-negative bacteria the proteolytic pseudomonads appear to be the least affected by oxine.

The considerable increase in the number of organisms developing on the plates with the two lower concentrations of Fe-EDTA is mainly due, in both soils, to increased growth of strains of *Bacillus* and *Arthrobacter*. The pink-pigmented organisms which made up a large proportion of the Gram-negative group in both the iron and manganese treatments in

TABLE 1

*Growth of soil organisms in relation to the availability of metals in the SEYE agar*

| Microbial group | Loam | | | | Brown earth | | | |
|---|---|---|---|---|---|---|---|---|
| | Addition to SEYE | | | | Addition to SEYE | | | |
| | None | Oxine (0·01 mM) | Fe (20 ppm) | Mn (70 ppm) | None | Oxine (0·01 mM) | Fe (20 ppm) | Mn (70 ppm) |
| Total bacteria | 16·0* | 5·7 | 53·3 | 80·0 | 9·1 | 0·6 | 17·4 | 12·3 |
| *Bacillus* spp. | 7·0 | 1·8 | 20·5 | 12·0 | 6·6 | 0·2 | 14·9 | 10·7 |
| Actinomycetes | 3·5 | 0·4 | — | 12·0 | 0·4 | — | — | 0·8 |
| *Arthrobacter* spp. | 2·0 | 0·8 | 16·4 | 4·0 | 0·4 | 0·03 | 2·5 | 0·8 |
| Gram-negative types | | | | | | | | |
| (*a*) Pink-pigmented | — | — | 12·0 | 28·0 | — | — | — | — |
| (*b*) Other types | 3·5 | 2·7 | 4·4 | 24·0 | 1·7 | 0·4 | — | — |
| Fungi | 0·4** | 0·4 | 0·2 | 0·2 | 0·03 | 0·04 | 0·03 | 0·04 |

* All figures refer to count SEYE × $10^6$/g. oven dried soil.
** As above on SEYE adjusted to pH 3·5.

the loam were not encountered in the brown earth. Further studies are required to show their relationship to the metal treatments. At the 200 ppm. iron level, general inhibition became evident, all the groups being affected to the same extent.

With the lowest manganese treatment an increase in the number of organisms developing was again encountered. The growth of all groups seemed to be promoted, except the Gram-negative types, in the brown earth. At the higher manganese concentrations overall inhibition was observed but the *Bacillus* spp. were the most resistant group from the brown earth and actinomycetes and *Arthrobacter* spp. from the loam. There is very little information available on the iron and manganese requirements of the different types of soil organisms or of their ability to tolerate high concentrations of the metals. Casida and Santoro (1961) observed that manganese was the component of a NaCl solution extract of soil which stimulated the growth of certain strains of *Bacillus* and other soil bacteria growing on the surface of agar media normally assumed to contain adequate nutrients for bacterial growth. In studies on the manganese requirements of *Bacillus megaterium* Weinberg (1964) has shown that the organism requires a higher concentration for the production of endospores and certain secondary metabolites than for normal vegetative growth. However the effect of manganese on the physiology of *Bacillus* spp. has not been investigated in this study.

None of the treatments appeared to affect the fungal populations as indicated by numbers or the visual appearance of the colonies on the plates.

(a) *The inhibitory action of oxine*. The antimicrobial effect of oxine has been investigated in a limited range of organisms. Weinberg (1957) has reviewed the conditions under which various micro-organisms are inhibited by the compound and the metals that reversed its toxic effect. The work of Albert (1958) has shown that with *Staphylococcus aureus* the antibacterial effect of oxine is associated with an increase in the activity of iron rather than making an essential metal available. However, the literature does not clearly indicate whether this type of inhibition is common to other types of bacteria.

A series of experiments were conducted to investigate the inhibitory action of oxine on pure cultures of the soil bacteria which grew on the untreated SEYE. Ordinary nutrient agar was used for the experiments, the various compounds investigated being added to the agar immediately prior to pouring plates and inoculating with an actively growing culture. Preliminary experiments showed that 0·02, 0·1, 0·2 and 0·5 mM oxine were useful concentrations for showing the inhibitory action on the various bacterial groups. Ordinary nutrient broth and soil extract yeast extract broth or agar gave the same results. The 7 salts used to investigate a reversion of the oxine inhibition were $MgSO_4.7H_2O$, $CuSO_4.5H_2O$, $ZnSO_4.7H_2O$. $CaSO_42H_2O$, $FeCl_3.6H_2O$, $MnSO_44H_2O$ and $Co(NO_3)_2.6H_2O$. These salts were added to the agar together with the oxine at 1, 5, 10, 15 and 20 equivalents of the oxine concentrations used. After inoculation the plates were incubated at 22°. The salt concentration of 10 equivalents gave satisfactory reversion in all cases and the results are given in Table 2.

TABLE 2

*Reversal of oxine inhibition by metallic ions*

| Microbial group | No. of strains tested | Lowest oxine conc. inhibiting (mM) | Metals reversing inhibition |
|---|---|---|---|
| *Bacillus* spp. | 18 | 0·02 | Co* |
| *Streptomyces* ,, | 8 | 0·02 | Co |
| *Arthrobacter* ,, | 4 | 0·1 | } Cu Fe |
| ,, ,, | 2 | 0·2 | } or Mn |
| Gram-negative organisms | 12 | 0·5 | Fe or Mn |
| Gram-negative organisms | 8 | 0·5 | Fe |

* At a concentration of 10 equivalents of inhibitory oxine concentration.

It is clear that the inhibition of *Bacillus* spp. and *Streptomyces* spp. which are the most sensitive groups can be eliminated by cobalt. Albert (1958) observed this effect in his studies with *Staphylococcus aureus* but here, unlike his observations, trace amounts of the cobalt were not active in the soil organisms under the conditions of the test. An interesting point is the tolerance to oxine of the *Arthrobacter* strains, some of which are Gram-variable. Whilst having greater tolerance than the more definitely Gram-positive organisms, they are less tolerant than the Gram-negative types but share with them the reversion effect of iron and manganese. The inhibition of 5 of the Gram-negative strains tested was not reversed by any of the salts added singly. A mixture containing equi-equivalent quantities of all 7 salts (total 10 equivalents) did however reverse the inhibition. This reversion requires further examination. Differences between the various *Arthrobacter* and Gram-negative strains did not appear to be related to the soil from which the organisms were isolated.

(b) *Further studies on the effect of $MnSO_4.4H_2O$ on the bacteria developing on SEYE.* In the experiment described earlier using a loam and brown earth soil, it was apparent that the higher concentrations of manganese had an inhibiting effect on all groups especially the *Bacillus* spp. in the loam and actinomycetes and *Arthrobacter* strains in the brown earth. Further information on the effect of manganese was therefore sought using 2 other soils. These were the $A_0H$ horizon (pH 4·5) of a *Juncus squarrosus* moor and a sandy-loam (pH 5·7). The latter had remained fallow for many years. The procedure was the same as that adopted previously, but higher concentrations of the manganese sulphate were included. The results are given in Table 3.

The most interesting feature of the results was the survival, even with the highest manganese concentrations, of representatives of the predominant group of organisms in each soil. As in the first experiment, *Arthrobacter* spp. were the most resistant organisms in the loam soil and the *Bacillus* group in the acid soil. A preliminary taxonomic investigation of the organisms developing above the 1,120 ppm. manganese level indicated that they are variants or mutations of the predominant types on the untreated plates.

*The effect of manganese sulphide*

Woiwod (1954) observed that certain heavy metallic sulphides are more toxic than the free metallic ion to Gram-positive bacteria. The sulphides appeared to have little effect on Gram-negative bacteria. Experiments were therefore devised to investigate the response of the organisms isolated from the *Juncus* moor and sandy-loam to sulphide, particularly manganese sulphide.

In the first experiment sodium sulphide solution was added to ordinary nutrient agar to give final concentrations of 0·0001, 0·001, 0·01 and 0·1 per cent sodium sulphide. Actively growing cultures were immediately inoculated and incubated at 22°. The *Streptomyces* strains and the *Bacillus* isolates from the sandy-loam were inhibited at the 0·0001 per cent level. The *Nocardia* strains and a large proportion of the *Arthrobacter* strains were inhibited at the 0·001 per cent level. The remaining *Arthrobacter* isolates, the *Bacillus* strains in the moor and a selection of Gram-negative bacteria from other soils were unaffected at the highest concentration tested. These observations are likely to reflect the effect of the small amounts of heavy metallic sulphides produced in the agar together with excess sodium sulphide particularly at the higher concentrations. The persistence of the sulphide in the medium was not investigated.

In order to show more specifically the effect of manganese sulphide, 10 ml. of the nutrient agar containing 140 ppm. manganese was added

TABLE 3

*Effect of adding $MnSO_4 . 4H_2O$ to SEYE on bacterial growth*

| Mn concentration added (ppm) | Moor ($A_0H$ horizon) | | | Sandy-loam | | | | |
|---|---|---|---|---|---|---|---|---|
| | Total count* | Bacterial group** | | Total count* | Bacterial group** | | | |
| | | *Bacillus* | *Arthrobacter* | | *Arthrobacter* | *Nocardia* | *Streptomyces* | *Bacillus* |
| 0 | 150 | 70 | 30 | 164 | 58 | 22 | — | 20 |
| 140 | 133 | 88 | 12 | 110 | 82 | 14 | 4 | — |
| 280 | 120 | 100 | — | 82 | 74 | 20 | 6 | — |
| 560 | 38 | 100 | — | 65 | 96 | 4 | — | — |
| 1120 | 33 | 100 | — | 38 | 100 | — | — | — |
| 2240 | 10 | 100 | — | 36 | 100 | — | — | — |
| 2800 | 8 | 100 | — | 38 | 100 | — | — | — |
| 4200 | 6 | 100 | — | 34 | 100 | — | — | — |
| 5600 | 2 | 100 | — | 33 | 100 | — | — | — |

* Count × $10^5$/g. oven dried soil.
** Per cent of population growing on plates.

to a Petri dish tilted so that the agar only covered two-thirds of the base of the dish. The plate was then tilted in the opposite direction and 10 ml. of the agar containing 0·1 per cent sodium sulphide added to the other part of the dish so that the agars overlapped. Cultures tolerating these compounds independently were then streak inoculated across the two agars. In general the organisms grew on the sodium sulphide side of the plate, but were inhibited on the manganese sulphate side where a blackish precipitate often accompanied by a metallic sheen on the agar surface indicated the production of manganese sulphide. There does not appear to be any clear relationship between the tolerance of sodium sulphide and tolerance of manganese in the isolation medium.

*The effect of adding the 3 compounds to soil*

In the foregoing experiments the effects of the 3 compounds on bacteria growing in artificial media were examined. An attempt was therefore made to examine their effects on the bacteria in soil under several different conditions.

The loam soil and brown earth, the latter brought to pH 6·5 with calcium hydroxide, were used. In addition to control pots (approximately 2·25 kg. fresh soil) not receiving fertilizer, a series of pots received 3·6 g. of $CaHPO_4.2H_2O$ and a second series 1 g. $KNO_3$ in addition to the phosphate. The fertilizer was intimately mixed before perennial ryegrass seed was thinly sown in the appropriate pots. The pots were placed in the glasshouse and the seedlings were reduced to 25 per pot after germination. Unplanted control pots were also prepared except for the treatments in which the fertilizers and a compound added to affect metallic ion availability were applied together.

In the loam the plants were allowed to grow for 6 weeks from early July, during which time 9 applications each of 40 ppm. (of total fresh weight of soil) of Fe as Fe-EDTA solution, 110 ppm. manganese as $MnSO_4.4H_2O$ solution or 0·002 mM oxine were applied at intervals of about 4 days in addition to routine watering. The brown earth experiment was continued for a further 10 weeks during which time 2 more applications of the compounds were made.

At the end of the experiment the plants were carefully separated from the soil and loose soil was shaken off the roots. A 10 g. sample of the roots and attached soil was made up to 100 ml. with sterile water, macerated, diluted and plated out to obtain the count of organisms in the rhizosphere soil. With the remainder of the fresh material previously weighed, the soil was washed off the roots into a sterile flask and the volume made up to 1 litre. To obtain dry weights, samples of this suspension and of the washed root material were dried at 100° for 24 hours. Counts of the non-rhizosphere control soil sample were obtained as described previously.

The total number of organisms per g. dry control soil and rhizosphere soil, together with the R/S values, are detailed in Table 4. An estimation of fungal populations was not made in this experiment.

The addition of the calcium phosphate clearly increased the microbial count more in the loam than in the brown earth. However, it is not obvious whether this is related to the age of the plants, the difference in soil type or the requirement for calcium being satisfied with the calcium hydroxide application. A higher content of nitrogenous materials in the arable soil may also be associated with the smaller response to nitrate in that soil.

As would be expected the oxine treatment generally reduced the counts and no obvious trend in relation to soil type or fertilizer application was evident. The results obtained with the iron treatment were of considerable interest, because there was in all samples a considerable reduction in root growth, but not shoot yield, compared with the control treatment. In the loam the average root yield in the iron treatment was approximately 10 per cent of that of the control. In the brown earth the figure was about 40 per cent. However, this reduction in root growth did not produce a decided trend common to both soils in the number of organisms per g. of rhizosphere soil, although there was clearly a much smaller population in the total rhizosphere. It is possible that under these conditions smaller amounts of nutrients are being released by the roots. The small R/S values associated with the iron treatments largely resulted from the increased population in the control soils, and in the brown earth a reduction, though sometimes small, in the rhizosphere population.

The manganese treatment had no significant effect on the root yield in the loam but reduced the root in the brown earth by 40 per cent. As with the iron treatment, numbers increased in the control soil and loam rhizosphere, but decreased in the brown earth rhizosphere. It is possible that in a brown earth, in which there is usually a high content of heavy metals, the additional metallic ions are in some way reducing the release of microbial nutrients by the root. Stotzky and Norman (1961) clearly showed that in their sandy soil, the increased rate of oxidation of glucose brought about by the addition of magnesium sulphate was due to a shortage of available sulphur compounds in the soil. However, in this experiment, since comparable increases in count were obtained with the Fe-EDTA and manganese sulphate, it would appear that sulphate is not a limiting factor for microbial activity under these conditions.

TABLE 4

*The effect of the various treatments on the total numbers of micro-organisms*

| Soil | Fertilizer application | Bacterial count with different treatments** | | | | | | | | | | | |
|---|---|---|---|---|---|---|---|---|---|---|---|---|---|
| | | None | | | Oxine | | | Fe-EDTA | | | $MnSO_4 4H_2O$ | | |
| | | S | R | R/S ratio | S | R | R/S ratio | S | R | R/S ratio | S | R | R/S ratio |
| Loam | None | 35·3 | 69·4 | 2·0 | 29·9 | 76·7 | 2·7 | 71·5 | 128 | 1·8 | 37·8 | 185 | 4·9 |
| | $CaHPO_4$ | 61·0 | 250·0 | 4·1 | * | 144·0 | — | * | 247 | — | * | 383 | — |
| | $CaHPO_4 + KNO_3$ | 90·0 | 225·0 | 2·5 | * | 193·0 | — | * | 490 | — | * | 309 | — |
| Brown earth | None | 90·0 | 425·0 | 4·7 | 74·6 | 286·0 | 3·8 | 204·0 | 329 | 1·6 | 145·0 | 344 | 2·4 |
| | $CaHPO_4$ | 133·0 | 454·0 | 3·4 | * | 299·0 | — | * | 377 | — | * | 542 | — |
| | $CaHPO_4 + KNO_3$ | 162·0 | 592·0 | 3·7 | * | 480·0 | — | * | 579 | — | * | 305 | — |

S = Control soil  R = Rhizosphere soil

** Count $\times 10^6$/g. oven dried soil.
* Not investigated.

The occurrence of the four major bacterial groups in the total populations of the treatments not receiving the various fertilizer treatments are given in Table 5. The predominant trends resulting from the fertilizer treatments are also presented. The data indicate that the effect on the various groups of adding the 3 compounds to soil may be different from their effect in SEYE. In soil, interactions between metals and competition between micro-organisms for nutrients may be amongst the factors associated with this observation. At the oxine concentration used, *Bacillus* spp. were less affected than would be expected, but Albert (1958) pointed out that the ratio of iron to oxine influences the antimicrobial activity of the complex and in addition the availability of cobalt would be expected to influence the inhibitory action. However, as expected, the metal additions increased the number and proportion of *Bacillus* spp. in the control soils, reflecting better competitive power for nutrients or possibly more suitable conditions for the germination of endospores. With the metal treatments, the addition of the fertilizers or the presence of plant roots usually makes conditions less suitable for the spore-forming bacilli.

As in the SEYE, the actinomycetes were amongst the organisms most sensitive to the oxine additions, but no investigation has been carried out to show whether conidia and vegetative forms differ in their tolerance. The group did not preferentially respond in any way to the addition of the metals to the SEYE. The influence of metals in this experiment was noteworthy because of their different effects on the 2 soils. In the loam the increased proportion developed in the control soils and in some of the samples receiving the fertilizer, whereas in the brown earth the fertilizers tended to reduce the proportional representation and an increase was only observed in the unfertilized rhizosphere samples. The type of *Streptomyces* developing in the different samples has not been investigated, but large variation in the mineral requirements of *Streptomyces* strains has been observed by Heim and Lechevalier (1956).

With the *Arthrobacter* spp. a salient feature was their sensitivity to the metal additions in the unfertilized brown earth samples. Metallic ion inter-relationships within this group might be used to investigate further the reasons why *Arthrobacter* spp. only occur infrequently as predominant organisms in acidic soils (Jensen, 1963; Holding *et al.*, 1965). In the unfertilized loam the reasons for the marked reduction with the oxine treatment in the rhizosphere but not in the control soil are not clear. Comparing the results obtained with the SEYE, the metal treatments might have been expected to promote a larger increase of

TABLE 5

*The effect of changes in metallic ion availability and fertilizer treatments on the bacterial flora occurring in soil and the rhizosphere of perennial ryegrass*

| Soil | Microbial group | Fertilizer application | Treatment | | | | | | | | |
|---|---|---|---|---|---|---|---|---|---|---|---|
| | | | None | | | Oxine | | Fe-EDTA | | $MnSO_44H_2O$ | |
| | | | Fresh Soil | S | R | S | R | S | R | S | R |
| Loam | *Bacillus* spp. | None | 7·0* | 7·1 | — | 7·5 | 25·5 | 35·5 | 16·1 | 19·0 | — |
| | Actinomycetes | | 3·5 | — | 21·4 | — | 12·8 | 12·0 | — | 9·4 | 62·0 |
| | *Arthrobacter* spp. | | 2·0 | 14·1 | 21·3 | 22·4 | — | 24·0 | 48·2 | 9·4 | 62·0 |
| | Gram-negative | | 3·5 | 14·1 | 26·7 | — | 38·4 | — | 63·7 | — | 61·0 |
| | | $CaHPO_4$ | | A+,B− | ** | | A+,C+,N− | | A+,B− | | B+,N− |
| | | $CaHPO_4$ $+KNO_3$ | | A+,B− | ** | | ** | | A+,B−,C+ | | C+,N− |
| Brown earth | *Bacillus* spp. | None | 6·6 | 10·0 | 106·0 | 16·6 | 71·5 | 122·0 | 36·6 | 36·0 | 137·0 |
| | Actinomycetes | | 0·4 | 30·0 | 35·0 | 16·6 | — | 41·0 | 73·4 | — | 137·0 |
| | *Arthrobacter* spp. | | 0·4 | 10·0 | 70·0 | — | 71·5 | — | — | — | — |
| | Gram-negative | | 1·7 | 40·0 | 214·0 | 41·4 | 143·0 | 41·0 | 219·0 | 109·0 | 70·0 |
| | | $CaHPO_4$ | | A− | A−,C−,N+ | | C− | | B− | | A−,B−,N+ |
| | | $CaHPO_4$ $+KNO_3$ | | A− | C− | | C+ | | B−,C+,N− | | A−,B−,C+ |

* Total count × $10^6$/g. oven dried soil. ** No change in proportional representation.
+ and − Large increase and decrease in proportion in relation to non-fertilized treatment.
A = Actinomycetes B = *Bacillus* spp. C = *Arthrobacter* spp. N = Gram-negative bacteria
S = Control soil R = Rhizosphere soil

*Arthrobacter* strains than that observed. It is not obvious why fluctuations in the proportion of *Arthrobacter* strains occurred in the large microbial populations associated with the fertilizer treatments.

The results relating to the occurrence of the Gram-negative organisms bear little relationship to those obtained in the SEYE studies. In the non-rhizosphere soils the addition of the 3 compounds to the loam made conditions less suitable for the proliferation of the group than in the brown earth. Noteworthy, however, is their regular occurrence in the rhizosphere soils, although the proportion appears to be unrelated to the treatments. The fertilizers appear to have little general effect on the proportional representation of the Gram-negative group.

## *DISCUSSION*

Because of the great complexity of the interactions between micro-organisms, plant roots and metals in soil, the results obtained in this study only reflect the final outcome of these interactions. No attempt has been made to conduct a detailed study of the individual reactions under carefully defined conditions. The results draw attention to the general influence metals may have on the soil microflora and emphasize that this aspect of soil microbiology merits investigation.

The additions of oxine, Fe-EDTA and manganese sulphate to an undefined medium (SEYE) and the subsequent growth of the organisms has shown a variation in the response of the different soil groups to metallic ion availability. Oxine was selected as a chelating agent with marked antimicrobial activities and whilst its activity against some groups of organisms may be due to producing metal deficiency conditions, Albert's work showed that this was not the inhibitory mechanism with some Gram-positive cocci. Because very little attention has been given to the activities of natural chelating agents in soil, the significance of the oxine inhibition and its reversion, other than demonstrating the varying response of the organisms to this type of chelating agent, cannot be assessed.

The addition of the iron and manganese compounds to SEYE also emphasized the differing requirements for metals of the various groups of bacteria. Attention has been drawn to the high requirement for iron shown by some of the *Bacillus* and *Arthrobacter* strains, whilst the increased number of organisms growing with the manganese sulphate addition was not restricted to any particular groups. Apart from the extensive studies on the manganese requirement of a few *Bacillus* strains very little information is available on the requirements of these metals by micro-organisms. Consequently it is not known whether the differences between micro-organisms reflect the absolute requirement or the ability of the organisms to assimilate metals combined in a not readily available form. The metallic ion content of isolation media merits further attention.

The absence of any marked change in the fungal count indicates that fungi are far less sensitive than bacteria to changes in metal availability.

The differences between the response of the various bacterial groups in the SEYE and in the soil experiments require further investigation. Such experiments, conducted under carefully controlled conditions, may yield much interesting information on the availability and influence of metals on the different types of micro-organisms. Further investigations of variations in the response in different soils, as exemplified by the effects of oxine on the *Arthrobacter* and Gram-negative groups or the effect of iron treatment on the numbers of organisms in the rhizosphere, might yield interesting data on the ecological distribution of the different groups, and populations. Further rhizosphere studies involving metallic ions should undoubtedly include more investigations of the effect of the organisms on the uptake by the plant of the nutrients under consideration. Some of the interesting results obtained so far have been reviewed by Hodgson (1963).

## *CONCLUSIONS*

In soil extract yeast extract agar, *Bacillus* spp., actinomycetes, *Arthrobacter* spp. and Gram-negative bacteria from a loam (pH 6·8) and brown earth soil (pH 4·2) vary in their sensitivity to the addition of 8-hydroxyquinoline (oxine) and in their growth response to the addition of Fe-EDTA and $MnSO_4.4H_2O$. The addition of the 3 compounds individually to the 2 soils, sown with perennial ryegrass, shows that their response in soil sometimes differs from that in the SEYE and in some cases can be affected by soil type, plant growth and the addition of fertilizers.

## *REFERENCES*

ALBERT, A. (1958). Metal-binding agents in chemotherapy: the activation of metals by chelation. *The strategy of chemotherapy*. Ed. Cowan, S. T. & Rowatt, E. *8th Symp. Soc. gen. Microbiol.* Cambridge. Cambridge University Press.

CASIDA, L. E., Jr. & SANTORO, T. (1961). Growth response of some soil micro-organisms to manganese. *Soil. Sci.*, **92**, 287.

HEIM, A. H. & LECHEVALIER, H. (1956). Effect of iron, zinc, manganese and calcium on the growth of various strains of *Streptomyces*. *Mycologia*, **48**, 628.

Hodgson, J. F. (1963). Chemistry of micronutrient elements in soils. *Adv. Agron.*, **15**, 119.

Holding, A. J., Franklin, D. A. & Watling, R. (1965). The microflora of peat-podzol transitions. *J. Soil Sci.*, **16**, 44.

Jensen, V. (1963). Studies on the microflora of Danish beech forest soils. III. Properties and composition of the bacterial flora. *Zbl. Bakt. ParasitKde., Abt. II*, **116**, 593.

Stotzky, G. & Norman, A. G. (1961). Factors limiting microbial activities in soil. II. The effect of sulphur. *Arch. Mikrobiol.*, **40**, 370.

Weinberg, E. D. (1957). The mutual effects of antimicrobial compounds and metallic cations. *Bact. Rev.*, **21**, 46.

Weinberg, E. D. (1964). Manganese requirement for sporulation and other secondary biosynthetic processes in *Bacillus. Appl. Microbiol.*, **12**, 436.

Woiwod, A. J. (1954). The inhibition of bacterial growth by colloidal heavy-metal sulphides and by colloidal sulphur. *J. gen. Microbiol.*, **10**, 509.

# GROWTH AND EFFECTS OF BACTERIA INTRODUCED INTO SOIL

MARGARET E. BROWN, R. M. JACKSON
and S. K. BURLINGHAM

*Rothamsted Experimental Station, Harpenden, Hertfordshire*

## *INTRODUCTION*

There are many reports of plant growth being increased by introducing micro-organisms into soil, but consistent increases in yield are found only by inoculating leguminous plants with *Rhizobium*, an agricultural practice that has been common since the beginning of the century. Inoculating seed of legumes increases the yield by improving nodulation and nitrogen fixation. Other bacteria have also been used as seed inoculants for other crops and have sometimes improved yield but the mechanisms by which they affect growth are mostly obscure and have been attributed to such various causes as disease control, nitrogen fixation and stimulation of growth by hormones.

A few notable early successes in control of plant diseases by modifying the soil microflora (Millard and Taylor, 1927; Sanford and Broadfoot, 1931) led to many experiments on this subject, but disappointing results caused biological control of soil-borne pathogens to fall into disfavour. However, with better understanding of how micro-organisms interact the subject is again attracting interest, as shown by the contributions to a symposium held in California (Baker and Snyder, 1965). Hence the time is appropriate to review the problems connected with establishing potentially useful organisms in soil and the ways in which they may affect plant growth, as increasing use of chemical sterilants to control soil-borne pests and diseases, and the development of methods for heating soil to specified temperatures (Baker and Olsen, 1960) offer increased opportunities for introducing organisms into soil.

Establishing a large population of alien organisms in soil, previously free from or containing few such organisms, seems, from general ecological principles, to depend on modifying the soil environment so that the alien is given a competitive advantage over the indigenous microflora.

Many common agricultural practices, such as ploughing in organic manures or crop residues, applying fertilizers or soil sterilants, modify the soil and stimulate specific micro-organisms and microbial processes which in turn affect soil nutrients. Effects from such treatments occur throughout the soil, but in addition to such general changes, important local ones are brought about by root exudates and the decomposition of root cells.

The infection of leguminous plants from *Rhizobium* applied to the seed provides a striking example of how a specific organism can be established in soil without needing to add large quantities of organic materials or use any drastic physical or chemical treatments. All that is needed is to bring together the appropriate species of plant and bacterium for the plant will create the environment that favours the bacterium.

## *GROWTH OF* RHIZOBIUM *IN SOIL*

*Rhizobium* is a specialized symbiotic organism that also multiplies abundantly in the rhizosphere phase but is poorly adapted to life as a soil inhabitant away from its appropriate host plant. Its natural distribution corresponds with its host's and when a leguminous crop is newly introduced into a region free from related plant genera, it usually requires inoculation with rhizobia to succeed. Nutman (pers. comm.) did not find *Rhizobium meliloti* in plots of the Park Grass experiment at Rothamsted where *Medicago* spp. have never been recorded whereas strains that infect *Trifolium pratense*, *T. repens*, *Lathyrus pratensis* and *Lotus corniculatus* occur on the plots carrying these plants. The rate at which populations of rhizobia decline in soil in the absence of host plants depends both on soil conditions, particularly pH and the strain of bacteria. For example, *Rhizobium meliloti* is less tolerant of acid conditions than *R. trifolii* (Jensen, 1942).

Strains of nodule bacteria are peculiar among rhizosphere organisms in being stimulated more by legumes than by other plants, and most strongly by plants they can infect. The stimulation occurs as far as 10 – 20 mm. from the root surface (Rovira, 1961). Thus with continuous cropping, all the soil in the root zone becomes effectively a rhizosphere so that large populations of *Rhizobium* can develop; for example, an acre under pasture may often contain as many as $10^{14}$ free-living rhizobia in the top 6 in. of soil. The nature of the specific host effect is unknown. Root exudates of legumes differ quantitatively and qualitatively from those of other families, but if any component of the legume root exudates is a specific stimulant it remains to be identified. It seems unlikely that any substance will be a specific source of energy or nutrient for *Rhizobium*. An alternative explanation could be that the legume root supplies a substance that confers a competitive advantage on *Rhizobium*, possibly by acting as a precursor for antibiotic production. Although there is no evidence that this kind of mechanism influences bacterial development in the rhizosphere, Buxton (1960) found that fungi that are not otherwise antagonistic towards other organisms become so in the presence of the root. *Rhizobium* strains secrete abundant gum and induce legume roots to secrete certain enzymes (Fåhraeus and Ljunggren, 1959) and these factors may also help to explain the unique status enjoyed by *Rhizobium* in the rhizosphere. *Rhizobium* can sometimes be stimulated by non-legumes. Krasilnikov (1958) reported strong stimulation by cotton, and at Rothamsted Nutman (pers. comm.), noted that *Rhizobium* populations increased when non-legume weeds grew on land previously maintained under fallow for several years. Experiments with plants in pots showed that clover and pea *rhizobia* were stimulated in the rhizosphere of *Urtica urens* and *Gnaphalium* sp.

The reason for large populations of rhizobia in the soil to establish symbiosis is not clear, because a nodule can arise from a single infection (Hughes and Vincent, 1963). Most work on the influence of bacterial numbers on nodulation has been done in pure culture, where distinction can be made between the effects of bacterial numbers on hair infection and on nodule formation. Lim (1963) showed that fewer than 100 bacteria are needed to initiate root hair infection of plants of *Trifolium glomeratum*, *T. parviflorum* and *T. pratense* grown on agar. Before nodulation began, numbers of bacteria and infections were simply related, and doubling the bacterial density doubled the infections, but after the first nodule formed more bacteria were required for each additional infection. Purchase and Nutman (1957) showed that the number of nodules on *T. pratense* was related to the numbers of bacteria in the rhizosphere in a modified Mitscherlich fashion; few bacteria were needed to occupy one or two nodule sites, but as the proportion of occupied sites increased, more and more bacteria were needed to fill the remainder.

Lim (1963) found that the pattern of root hair infection in soil resembled that in pure culture in consisting of two phases, the first rapid and ending when nodules form. Root hairs of clover plants, growing in soil with a natural population of *Rhizobium*, became infected earlier when the seed was inoculated with *Rhizobium* than when it was uninoculated, ultimately both series of plants had equal numbers of nodules.

Soil often contains more than one strain of *Rhizobium* capable of infecting the same legume species. These strains may differ in their ability to infect the plant and fix nitrogen. Clover establishes poorly in many hill pastures even when inoculated with rhizobia that fix nitrogen well, because the inocula cannot compete with the ineffective natural population. However, Read (1953) showed that strains of *Rhizobium* selected for increased competitive ability could become established. Factors other than competition may also limit nodulation. Thornton, Alencar and Smith (1948) demonstrated antagonism towards *Rhizobium* in sterilized soil by two species of *Penicillium* and *Streptomyces albus*. Using Harley and Waid's method (1955), Lim (1961) isolated several root-surface fungi from inoculated and control clover seedlings and found much the same kind of fungal flora on both. Some of these fungi were examined for their effects on root-hair infection of *Trifolium glomeratum* grown in agar on Fåhraeus slides (Fåhraeus, 1957). *Verticillium* and *Pullularia* decreased and *Gliocladium*, *Paecilomyces* and *Humicola* increased infection; but all the fungi hastened nodulation by 2 days. The rhizosphere populations of *Rhizobium* were unaffected by the fungi; the interactions were unexplained, nor was it known whether they occurred in soil. Hely, Bergersen and Brockwell (1957) showed that subterranean clover nodulated poorly in a yellow podzolic soil because the seed inoculum of *Rhizobium* failed to establish in the rhizosphere due to the activities of other micro-organisms. The inhibitory factor slowly disappeared from the soil as the pasture improved under cultivation.

The effects on numbers of rhizobia by such factors as synergism or antagonism by other organisms, or lysis by bacteriophage have received little attention (Vincent, 1954). Kleczkowska (1957) suggested that where bacteriophage is common in soil it causes selection of phage-resistant variants of *Rhizobium* that differ from the parent type in other properties, such as differences in nitrogen fixation.

The large populations of rhizobia produced in the rhizosphere of legumes may affect the host plant in other ways than by forming nodules. For example, they may provide growth factors or increase the availability to the host plant of nutrients in soil. Webley (pers. comm.) showed that strains of *Rhizobium* from 3 cross-inoculation groups release small amounts of soluble phosphate from Gafsa rock phosphate.

Ecological work on *Rhizobium* in soil has been hampered by the lack of a convenient counting technique, and the present method depends on using host seedlings. A better understanding of the selective stimulation of *Rhizobium* in the legume rhizosphere could lead to developing satisfactory selective media for counting this organism in a mixed soil population.

## *INOCULATION OF PLANTS WITH BACTERIA OTHER THAN* RHIZOBIUM

Work on plant inoculation with bacteria other than *Rhizobium* has demonstrated the possible importance of introducing other species into the rhizosphere. Russian scientists have been most active in this work and have applied different bacterial species to either seeds or roots. *Azotobacter chroococcum*, originally chosen because it fixed nitrogen, and *Bacillus megaterium* var. *phosphatium*, because it releases phosphate from bound organic forms, are the two most widely used 'bacterial fertilizers', but *Pseudomonas*, *Clostridium*, *Lactobacillus*, *Achromobacter* and *Bacillus* species are also used. Mishustin and Naumova (1962), in a critical review of this work, consider that many reported increases in yield of crops are within the range of experimental error to be expected in field trials. More reliable and significant effects are obtained with market-garden crops than with agricultural crops.

Workers in other countries than Russia have also sometimes improved plant growth and yield by seed inoculation, but results are inconsistent. In America, Smith, Allison and Soulides (1961) obtained a significant 7·5 per cent increase in tomato yields using a Soviet 'phosphobacterin' preparation. In Germany, Jessen (1949) reported an 11 per cent increase in carrot yield. Stapp (1951) found increases of 6 – 25 per cent with potatoes and Wichtmann (1952) found a 13 per cent increase in green matter of mustard; these effects all came from inoculation with *Azotobacter*.

We have recently studied the effects of inoculation with *Azotobacter chroococcum* on plant growth and yield using 3 methods to intrcduce the bacterium into the soil and rhizosphere. Cultures grown in a liquid medium, deficient in nitrogen and with sucrose as the carbon source, were applied either to seeds, roots or to the soil (Brown, Burlingham and Jackson, 1962*b*). The seeds and roots received only a small volume of inoculum, for example, tomato seeds imbibed 0·001 ml. and roots received 0·25 ml. of the culture. A wide range of crops was treated; spring and winter wheat, barley, lettuce, radish, cabbage, cress, carrot, spinach, sugar beet and tomatoes. The crop plants gave very variable responses to inoculation, and tomato was the only one that showed consistent effects; it was therefore selected for most experiments to study effects on growth. However, other crops sometimes showed significant responses, most often when treated seed was sown in soil where plants from untreated seed developed poorly, either because of disease or other causes. Inoculating wheat seed sown in soil infested with *Ophiobolus graminis* increased the weight of ears by 34 per cent. The reason for this increase was not clear because *Azotobacter* did not decrease the apparent damage of the roots by *Ophiobolus*. In an experiment with barley, which grew poorly and was infected with *Erysiphe graminis*, *Azotobacter* inoculation more than doubled ear weight. In another experiment, inoculating barley, sown in soil known to be unsuitable, increased ear weight by 41 per cent, although the uninoculated plants were not obviously damaged by pathogens (Brown, Burlingham and Jackson, 1964).

In addition to effects on crop yield there are many reports, mostly from the Soviet Union, of *Azotobacter* inoculation affecting germination rates, root growth and general rate of plant development. Rubenchik (1960) reviews this work fully, but some examples given here will indicate how much the results have varied. Samtsevich (1940) reported that germination of oat and flax seeds was stimulated by inoculation with *Azotobacter*, whereas Brantsevich (1954) found that some strains of *Azotobacter* had no effect on germination of lupin, barley, flax and oats, and others inhibited germination of flax. Rubenchik investigated the effect of *Azotobacter* on the germination of wheat grain stored for long periods. Allowing grain to imbibe an *Azotobacter* culture for 6 hrs. greatly increased germination but longer or shorter periods were less effective. Effects of inoculation, therefore, seem to depend on the type of seed, the duration of treatment and the bacterial strains used.

Changes in root morphology by inoculation have been described. Zolotov (1954) found that after treatment of maize seed with *Azotobacter*, radicles were longer and more numerous, but Gebgardt (1958) found that inoculation stunted and thickened roots of cabbage.

Changes in rates of plant development were found by Gubanov (1953). *Azotobacter* inoculation increased ear length, ear number and absolute grain weight of both spring and winter wheat. Ponomareva (1953) found that bacterization increased the weight of white acacia, spruce and pine seedlings. Increases of leaf area have also been found (Zinov'eva, 1954).

Outside the USSR, Sundara Rao, Mann, Paul and Mathur (1963) and Rovira (1963) found that *Azotobacter* inoculation accelerated the emergence of wheat ears. Rovira also reported that *Azotobacter*, *Clostridium* and a *Bacillus* species increased the yield of wheat. We have also observed that, after seed inoculation, wheat flowered about a week earlier than control plants.

TABLE 1

*% Increase of stem and petiole length of tomatoes inoculated with* Azotobacter

| Leaf No. | Root Treatment | | | | Seed Treatment | |
|---|---|---|---|---|---|---|
| | Stem length | | Petiole length | | Stem length | Petiole length |
| | Money Maker | Potentate | Money Maker | Potentate | Money Maker | Money Maker |
| 2 | — | — | 15·7* | — | — | 8·1* |
| 4 | — | 25·1* | — | 14·8* | 38·7* | 20·0* |
| 6 | 20·8* | 24·8* | 2·6 | 13·4* | 13·5 | 6·7 |
| 8 | 8·6 | 24·8* | 6·2 | 14·4* | — | — |
| 9 | — | 7·4* | — | 14·2* | 9·4 | 11·9 |
| 10 | 4·4 | — | 2·6 | — | — | — |

* Denotes significance at P = 0·05.

TABLE 2

*Nos. of* Azotobacter × $10^3$*/g. dry rhizosphere soil on different parts of wheat roots*

| Time weeks | Part of root | | | | | | Soil count |
|---|---|---|---|---|---|---|---|
| | 0–5 cm. | 5–10 cm. | 10–15 cm. | 15–20 cm. | 20 cm.–end | Adventitious | |
| 2 | 58 | 13 | 16 | 15 | — | — | 2 |
| 4 | 20 | 10 | 5 | 98 | 18 | — | — |
| 6 | 276 | 37 | 17 | 16 | 12 | 31 | 5 |

Our experiments (Jackson, Brown and Burlingham, 1964) with two varieties of tomato, Money Maker and Potentate, have given consistent results. Table 1 shows that internodal growth and petiole development were accelerated by *Azotobacter* inoculation during the first weeks of growth, but effects became less as the first flowering truss appeared.

Treated and control plants produced the same number of leaves before the flower buds appeared. Flowers and fruits formed on the first truss up to a week earlier than on control plants but the fruits neither ripened faster nor did final yields differ from those of control plants. Later truss development was advanced by 2 – 4 days (Fig. 1). Addi-

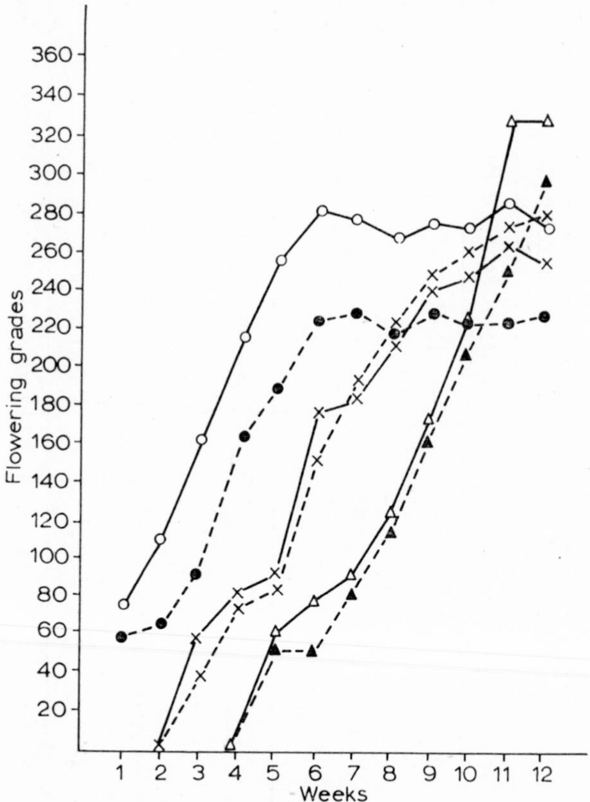


Fig. 1. Development of flower trusses of tomato plants. (a) ——— inoculated plants; (b) - - - - control plants. ○ or ● 1st truss. × 2nd truss. △ or ▲ 3rd truss.

tional weekly applications of *Azotobacter* culture to plants grown from treated seed had no further effect.

These effects on the early development of plants by a small initial inoculum suggested, like other growth effects already mentioned, that

*Azotobacter* alters development either directly or indirectly by producing growth-regulating substances. However, these results cannot exclude the possibility that changes in the rhizosphere microflora may be involved. Work in the Soviet Union indicates that *Azotobacter* increases the total number of micro-organisms in the rhizosphere (Zinov'eva, 1954; Afanas'eva and Voronova, 1950), especially some physiological groups, such as ammonifiers, nitrifiers and cellulose decomposers (Geller and Khariton, 1953). However, Clark (1948) and Macura (1957) found no such increases and seed-inoculation by Patel, at Rothamsted, did not affect total rhizosphere populations of wheat and tomato, or change numbers of glucose fermenters, cellulose and chitin decomposers, spore-formers, anaerobes and actinomycetes. Patel sampled plants at 3, 7 and 12 weeks after sowing, so he would have missed any changes that might have occurred during the first few days after germination.

Claims of disease control after *Azotobacter* inoculation include smaller incidence of flax wilt (Berezova, Naumova and Raznitsyna, 1938), lodging of spring cereals (Trizno, 1954), decrease in potato scab and potato blight (Sidarov, 1954) and bacterial rot of potato tubers (Petrenko, 1958); also inoculated cabbages were reported to be less susceptible to club root (Naumova, 1958). It is difficult to assess the value of these reports and unlikely that all the effects are explicable by *Azotobacter* being antagonistic towards all the pathogens, although *Azotobacter* has been shown to antagonize some bacteria and fungi. Indirect effects again cannot be excluded. Novak and Dvorzhakova (1955) reported that *Pseudomonas* species, which inhibit the growth of phytopathogenic fungi such as species of *Alternaria*, *Venturia*, *Sclerotinia*, *Rhizoctonia* and *Pythium*, were stimulated by *Azotobacter*. It has also been proposed that *Azotobacter* acts by synthesizing biologically active substances that stimulate plant development so enabling seedlings to grow away from the disease.

Some workers have concluded that introducing *Azotobacter* into soil increased soil nitrogen by nitrogen fixation. Their experiments were reviewed by Rubenchik (1960), who pointed out that such effects need not be caused only by *Azotobacter*, but that other nitrogen-fixing organisms may also be stimulated. However, evidence has accumulated against nitrogen fixation being of any significance, for energy-rich materials in the rhizosphere are probably not abundant enough to support active fixation (Jensen, 1942*b*; Mishustin and Naumova, 1962) and our work with $^{15}N$ showed no greater fixation in inoculated wheat rhizosphere soil containing $10^6$ *Azotobacter* per g. than in uninoculated rhizosphere soil. Wheat plants and root-free soil showed no enrichment of $^{15}N$ (Brown and Cooper, 1962).

## *STUDIES ON POPULATIONS OF* AZOTOBACTER *IN SOIL*

The effects described from inoculation with *Azotobacter* could have 2 explanations: either the inoculum may not only survive, but multiply and *Azotobacter* become established in the rhizosphere, where it produces substances that affect plant growth; or the initial inoculum may contain enough specific substance to affect seedling growth. Because the inoculum applied either to seeds or to roots is very small, the first hypothesis is the more likely, but to gain information on the 2 possibilities populations of naturally occurring and introduced *Azotobacter* were studied.

We found that natural populations of *Azotobacter* in rhizosphere and soil samples are small, from 20 – 8,000 per g. dry weight of soil. Whether there are more in the rhizosphere than elsewhere depends on plant species, age of plant at sampling and soil type. The rhizosphere stimulation, when it occurs, is small with only 2 – 3 times as many *Azotobacter* present as in the soil (Brown, Burlingham and Jackson, 1962*b*).

Gainey (1930) and Katznelson (1940) showed that soil pH is the chief factor governing the survival of *Azotobacter chroococcum* when inoculated directly into soil free from a natural population; *Azotobacter* will not survive below pH 6·5. Liming led to its survival and adding a suitable carbon source allowed it to multiply. *Azotobacter* inoculated into a Rothamsted soil (clay-loam pH 7·2) with a natural population survived at the original inoculum level for 20 weeks, the period of the experiment, but it did not multiply.

Clark (1948) inoculated with *Azotobacter* the roots of seedling tomatoes growing in soils at pH 6·2 and 5·9, with and without a natural *Azotobacter* flora respectively. The introduced bacteria decreased steadily in number in both soils. However, Timonin (1948) found that tobacco roots, inoculated at transplanting, supported *Azotobacter* which were recovered from nearly all samples of the root system profile down to a depth of 15 in. They were also present in the upper 5 in. of the soil but did not spread to root systems of adjacent uninoculated plants.

Fedorov and Nepomiluev (1954) found *Azotobacter*, inoculated into soil before sowing perennial herbage (timothy grass and clover mixture), persisted well in the soil and herbage rhizosphere. Organic manures or potassium and phosphorus stimulated multiplication of the inoculum and helped to maintain nitrogen-fixing activity; ploughing in the sod increased multiplication still more. Vančura, Macura, Fischer and Vondraček (1959) showed that inoculating barley seed with *Azotobacter* increased populations in the rhizosphere and that strains adapted to the rhizosphere developed more than unadapted isolates. *Azotobacter* was not found in the rhizosphere of uninoculated barley in the soil they used.

After inoculation by any of the methods we used, numbers of *Azotobacter* in soil and rhizosphere samples were determined by the plate-dilution technique (Brown, Burlingham and Jackson, 1962*a*). Bacteria introduced by all methods became established and survived in rhizospheres of a wide range of test plants, but they were not found in adjacent root-free soil. Numbers of *Azotobacter* in rhizospheres at harvest were of the same order as those counted in seedling rhizospheres. Fig. 2 shows the results of an experiment with wheat in fen soil supporting a natural population of *Azotobacter*. Similar results were obtained in a soil free from natural *Azotobacter*, provided the soil pH was above 6·7.

A minimum inoculum of $10^4$ bacteria per seed was needed for establishment in the rhizosphere to be detected by our counting method,

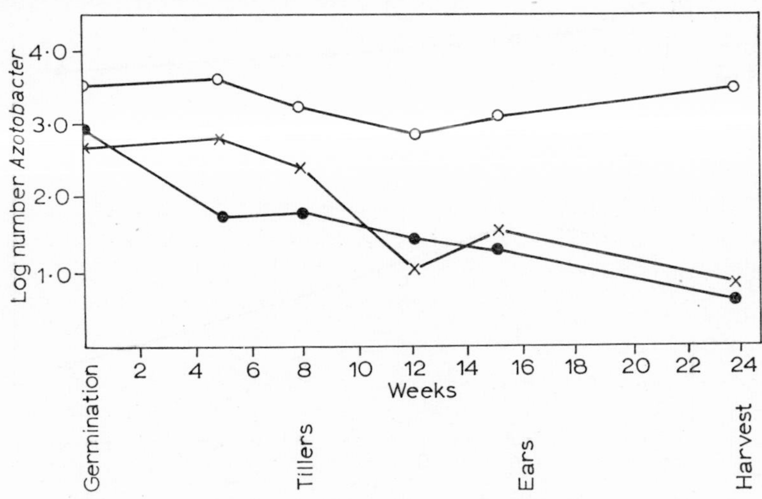


Fig. 2. Counts of natural and inoculated populations of *Azotobacter* in fen soil. o——o inoculated rhizosphere; ×——× control rhizosphere; ●——● control soil.

which is not sensitive to fewer than 10 per g. rhizosphere soil or $10^2$ per whole seedling root system; the number in the rhizosphere was directly correlated with inoculum size. Inoculum age was also important when seed was to be stored even for a short time before sowing. Fig. 3 shows that, at 18° and 50 per cent relative humidity, the viability of a 2 day culture of vegetative cells on the surface of wheat seed declined to less than a thousandth in 24 hrs., whereas that of an encysted 14 day culture did not decline to a tenth.

Root or soil inoculation would be expected to establish *Azotobacter* in the rhizosphere, provided the soil is suitable, but such establishment by seed treatment requires migration from seed to the developing roots. An inoculum introduced into root-free soil does not spread appreciably away from the site of application. Table 2 shows that all parts of the root system became colonized when seeds were inoculated, but bacteria were most abundant near the seed.

The distribution of colonies of *Azotobacter* developing from roots of wheat was mapped, using the following method. Inoculated seed was sown in soil without a natural *Azotobacter* population and the pots watered from below. At regular intervals the plants were lifted, excess

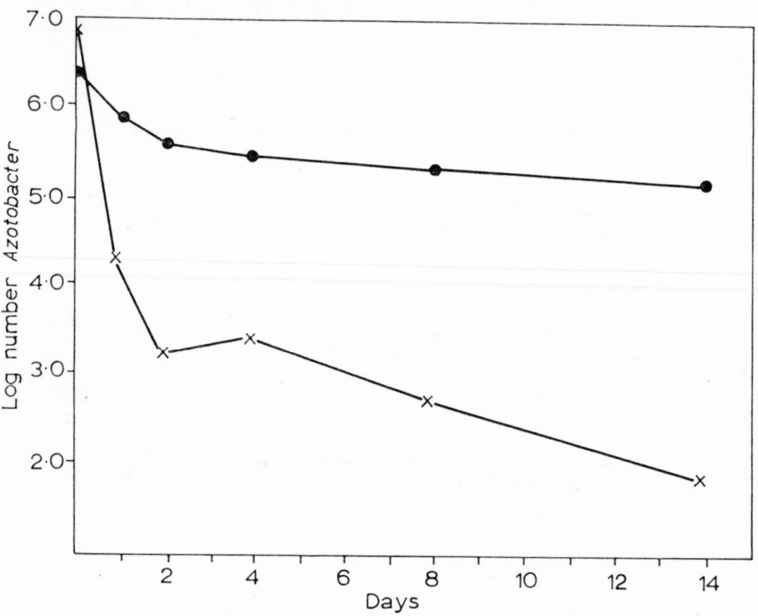


Fig. 3. Numbers of *Azotobacter* on wheat seed incubated at 18° and 50 per cent relative humidity. ●——● 14 day culture; ×——× 2 day culture.

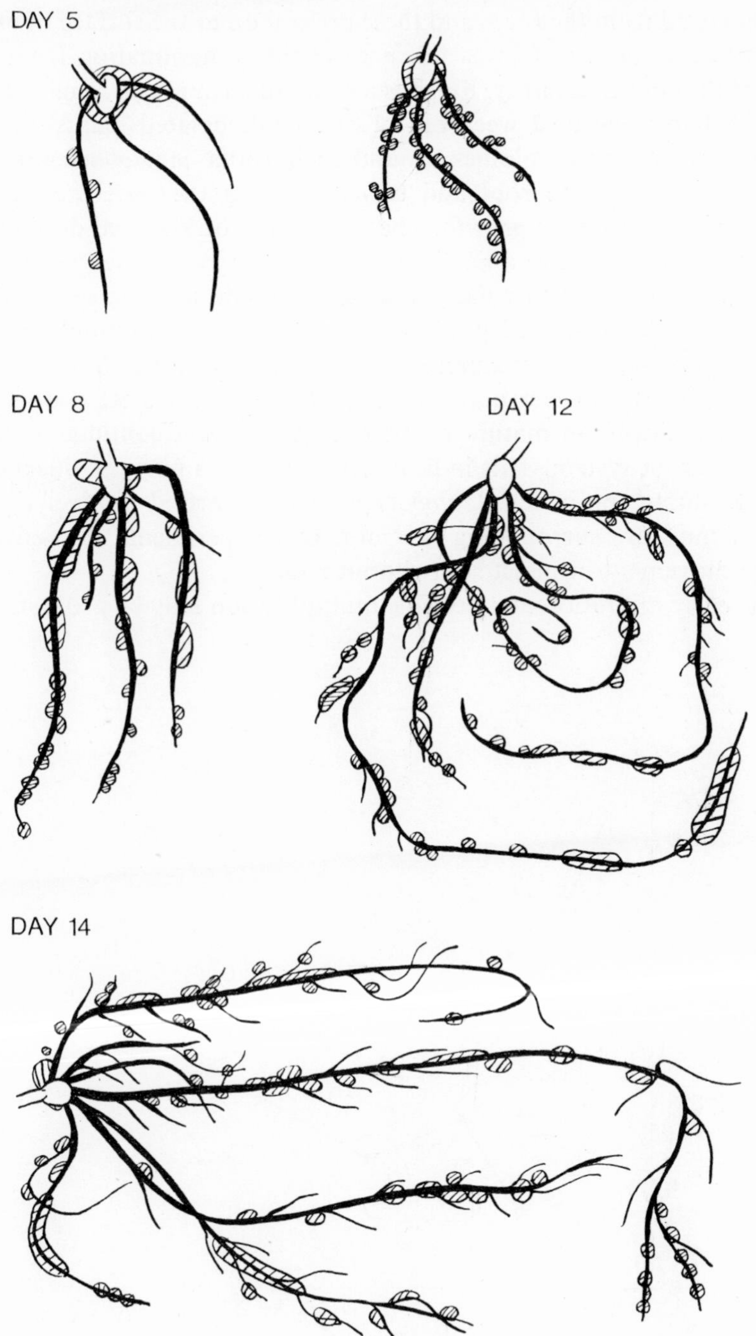


Fig. 4. Growth of *Azotobacter* colonies on wheat roots of seedlings at different times after germination.

soil removed from the roots and these pressed on to the surface of nitrogen-deficient agar. Care was taken to avoid contamination from one part of the root to another. Fig. 4 is a series of such maps, ranging from the seedling stage to 2 week old plants. Uninoculated plants did not develop *Azotobacter* colonies around their roots. *Azotobacter* moved from the seed to the root and travelled along the root presumably keeping pace with root growth. The population on the seed declined as that on the root rose to a maximum, which was maintained until plant maturity (Fig. 5). At this stage *Azotobacter* could be isolated from any point within a root-bound pot (virtually a rhizosphere sample), but in a field crop *Azotobacter* was present only in rhizosphere soil.

Once the *Azotobacter* population reaches a steady state it does not seem to multiply on mature roots, but the bacteria continue to move along the root system. This indicates that the roots may provide a continuous surface on which *Azotobacter* cells are carried passively in the film of moisture surrounding the root. Our experiments showed negligible movement in moist soil without roots.

The early migration and possible multiplication may be promoted by

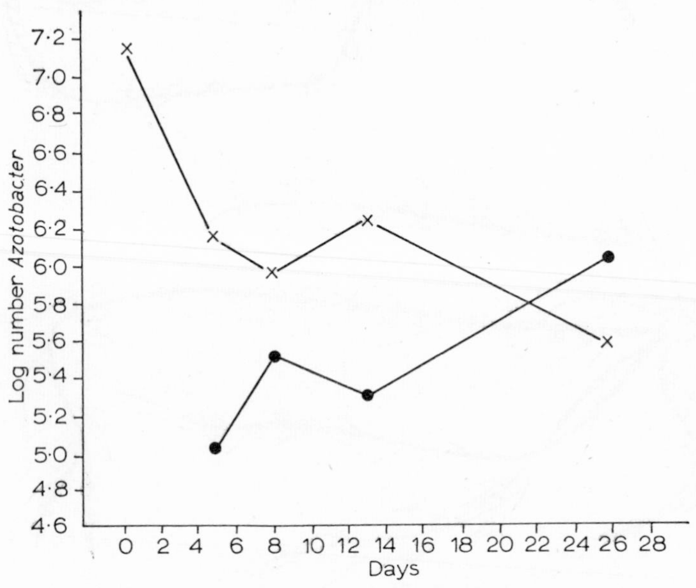


Fig. 5. Numbers of inoculated *Azotobacter* on seed and roots of wheat. ●——● root count; ×——× seed count.

the nature of the exudates from the young root. Rovira (1956) showed that during the first 3 weeks of growth of oats and peas, root excretions rather than cell debris supply the bulk of the material coming from the roots and are important in stimulating micro-organisms on and around roots. Sugars, mostly glucose and fructose, are released in greatest quantity during the first 10 days but, as the roots mature, sugars disappear from the exudates and cell debris has more influence on the rhizosphere flora, possibly changing it from one predominantly requiring amino acids to one requiring more complex substances derived from root debris. Jackson (1958) showed that glucose, sucrose and traces of fructose are excreted from peas during the first 24 hrs. of germination and the amount of fructose increases in 48 hrs. Vančura and Macura (1961) found that the lag phase of *Azotobacter chroococcum* was shorter in Burk's medium containing exudates from barley and wheat than in the medium with glucose. The sugar and organic fractions of the exudates stimulated *Azotobacter* growth, and of the amino acids, cysteic acid, methionine and cystine were most stimulatory. Vančura (1964) recently made a very thorough study of the root exudates from barley and wheat, produced during the first 10 days growth. Both plants produce a wide range of sugars, carboxylic and amino acids, and other compounds, many of which can be readily used by *Azotobacter*.

We did some experiments in which peas were germinated in soil so that their emerging radicles grew over a slide coated with a dilute suspension of *Azotobacter* cysts in distilled water agar. Cyst germination was stimulated in the seed and root regions and micro-colonies developed. *Azotobacter* did not multiply away from germinating seeds, but cysts in distilled water agar germinated when the slides were incubated in a soil-free environment. Peas were chosen for this test because they produce greater amounts of root exudates than wheat or barley, although qualitatively the exudates are very similar. The observed effects suggest that a phenomenon similar to fungistasis operated in soil, preventing *Azotobacter* cysts from germinating, and that pea root exudate can overcome this bacteriostasis. Jackson (1960) found that fungal spores, unable to germinate in root-free soil, do so in the root region, and that sugars in the root exudates are probably the cause of this stimulation.

Evidence has now accumulated that *Azotobacter* is established and multiplies in the rhizosphere. The activity in this zone, therefore, may considerably influence plant growth, particularly if it produces growth-regulating substances. There are several reports that it does produce them in culture media.

## *PRODUCTION OF PLANT GROWTH REGULATORS BY* AZOTOBACTER

Raznitsina (1938) first detected auxin-like substances in *Azotobacter* cultures and Bukatsch, Burger and Schlütter (1956) identified β-indole acetic acid. Vančura and Macura (1960) found that 1 ml. of *Azotobacter* culture produced an effect on oat roots and shoots that was equivalent to applying 6 μg. β-indole acetic acid, but they could not detect this amount in the culture by biological assay. We detected β-indole acetic acid in our cultures by paper chromatography and confirmed its presence by tests with *Avena* coleoptile sections. Amounts increased from 0·05 μg./ml. in cultures 2 days old to 1 μg./ml. in cultures 30 days old. There was no evidence that IAA was degraded in old cultures, as was reported by Vančura and Macura (1960). Vančura (1961) later identified gibberellic acid in *Azotobacter* cultures, the amount increasing to 20 μg./ml. in 17 days.

To produce the effects observed with tomato large amounts of gibberellins must either be in the small volume of imbibed *Azotobacter* inoculum or be produced later in the rhizosphere, perhaps during the short period when *Azotobacter* is multiplying rapidly on the seedling roots. We examined cultures of the strain of *Azotobacter* that produces considerable effects on plants for gibberellin-like substances, by chromatography and bioassay. Extracts were made by Katznelson, Sirois and Cole's (1962) method, of whole cultures, of supernatant fluids and cells separated by centrifugation, and of cell-free filtrates. Barley endosperm bioassays (Cohen and Coombe, pers. comm.) detected gibberellic acid in whole cultures; approximately $4 \times 10^{-5}$ μg./ml. were detected in 7 day cultures, the amount increasing to $2{\cdot}7 \times 10^{-2}$ μg./ml. in 21 days. Chromatograms of extracts of supernatant fluids, cells, and cell-free filtrates were run in isopropanol/ammonia/water (10:1:1) and eluates from different Rf values tested on dwarf peas, barley endosperms and lettuce and cucumber hypocotyls. The supernatant fluids and filtrates from 7, 14 and 21 day old cultures contain active materials with an Rf of 0·5 – 0·6 (the value for gibberellic acid) and eluates increased internodal length of dwarf peas by 25 per cent. The more sensitive barley endosperm test indicated that 1 ml. of 14 day old supernatant fluid contained at least $10^{-3}$ μg. of gibberellic acid, a conclusion confirmed by lettuce and cucumber bioassays. Eluates with an Rf of 0·5 – 0·6 obtained in chromatograms of 14 day old bacterial cells did not affect dwarf peas, indicating that gibberellic acid was excreted into the medium rather than stored in the cells.

Supernatant fluids from cultures of all ages also contained a substance that ran at an Rf of 0·8-0·9; eluates of this greatly extended the internode length of dwarf peas, but were inactive in the barley endosperm, lettuce or cucumber assays. Pea internodes were also occasionally extended by eluates with an Rf of 0-0·1, 0·3-0·5, and 0·7-0·8. Fig. 6 shows histograms obtained from assay systems with 14 day old supernatant fluids.

These assays showed that the gibberellic acid content of the *Azotobacter* culture was not enough to account for the morphological effects on tomatoes. Further experiments in which *Azotobacter* culture and gibberellic acid were applied to seeds or roots showed that 5 μg. of $GA_3$ was needed to produce effects on tomato similar to those produced by *Azotobacter*. Less $GA_3$ (0·05 or 0·005 μg. per plant) had no significant

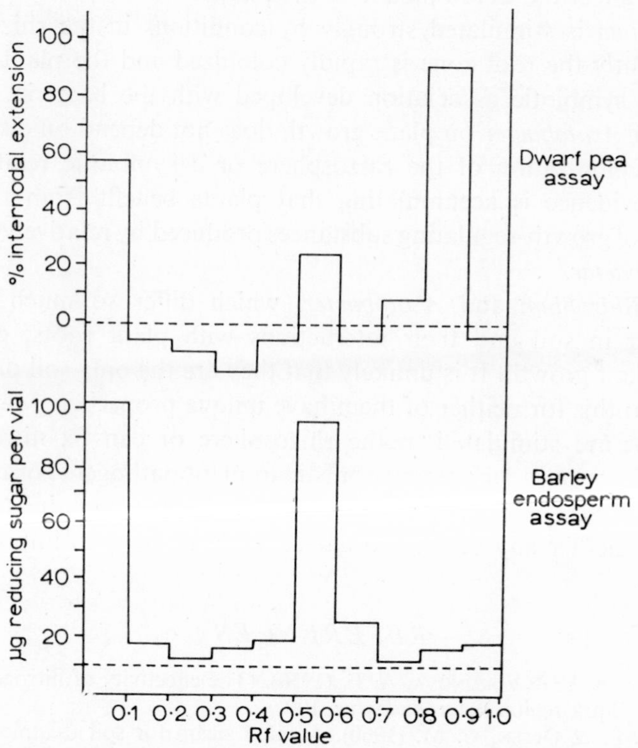


Fig. 6. Bioassay of fractions eluted from chromatograms of *Azotobacter* cultures.

effects. Gray (1957) found that treating seed with $GA_3$ less concentrated than 5·0 per cent did not affect tomato growth; the 5 μg. per seed used in our experiments was equivalent to 0·3 per cent. The *Azoto-*

*bacter* inoculum may contain growth substances other than $GA_3$ that cause the effects, or other substances may be produced after inoculation. Our observation of *Azotobacter* growth during early seedling development shows that there is a period when such substances could be produced in the rhizosphere, coinciding with a critical stage in plant development.

## *CONCLUSIONS*

In summary, there is abundant evidence that introduced bacteria can grow in a soil environment such as the rhizosphere, provided the nutritional status there suits the bacteria and that the inoculum is large enough to give the bacteria an initial competitive advantage over the normal rhizosphere population. In such conditions the introduced bacteria can affect the development of the plant.

*Rhizobium* is stimulated strongly by conditions in the rhizosphere, consequently the root zone is rapidly colonized and the plant benefits from the symbiotic association developed with the bacteria. The influence of *Azotobacter* on plant growth does not depend on either such massive colonization of the rhizosphere or a symbiotic relationship. Instead evidence is accumulating that plants benefit from the small amounts of growth-regulating substances produced by relatively few cells of *Azotobacter*.

Thus *Rhizobium* and *Azotobacter*, which differ so much in their behaviour in soil and their interactions with plant roots, can each benefit plant growth. It is unlikely that they are the only soil organisms able to do this for neither of them have unique properties. Many other organisms are stimulated in the rhizosphere or can fix nitrogen, or produce hormones, or are antagonistic to plant pathogens, or can enter into symbiotic relationship with plants. However, it remains to be discovered whether any of these organisms can be used to improve crop yield.

## *REFERENCES*

AFANAS'EVA, A. L. & VORONOVA, A. F. (1950). (The effectivity of nitrogen in soils of the Omsk region.) *Agrobiologiya*, 100.

BAKER, K. F. & OLSEN, C. M. (1960). Aerated steam for soil treatment. *Phytopathology*, **50**, 82.

BAKER, K. F. & SNYDER, W. C. (1965). *Ecology of soil-borne plant pathogens.* Berkeley. University of California Press.

BEREZOVA, E. F., NAUMOVA, A. N. & RAZNITSYNA, E. A. (1938). Mode of action of azotogen. *Dokl. Akad. Nauk. SSSR.*, **18**, 357.

BRANTSEVICH, L. G. (1954). Survival of *Azotobacter* in soil under some plants and its effect on seed germination. *Zbirn. Prats' dniprov. biol. Sta.*, 14.

BROWN, M. E., BURLINGHAM, S. K. & JACKSON, R. M. (1962*a*). Studies on *Azotobacter* species in soil. I. Comparison of media and techniques for counting *Azotobacter* in soil. *Pl. Soil*, **17**, 309.

BROWN, M. E., BURLINGHAM, S. K. & JACKSON, R. M. (1962*b*). Studies on *Azotobacter* species in soil. II. Populations of *Azotobacter* in the rhizosphere and effects of artificial inoculation. *Pl. Soil*, **17**, 320.

BROWN, M. E., BURLINGHAM, S. K. & JACKSON, R. M. (1964). Studies on *Azotobacter* species in soil. III. Effects of artificial inoculation on crop yields. *Pl. Soil*, **20**, 194.

BROWN, M. E. & COOPER, R. (1962). Pot experiments on *Azotobacter* inoculation. *A. Rep. Rothamsted Experimental Station.*

BUKATSCH, F., BURGER, K. & SCHLÜTTER, M. (1956). Investigation into protein metabolism by *Azotobacter* with particular reference to indole derivatives. *Zentbl. Bakt. ParasitKde., Abt. II*, **11**, 226.

BUXTON, E. W. (1960). Effect of pea root exudate on the antagonism of some rhizosphere micro-organisms towards *Fusarium oxysporum f. pisi. J. gen. Microbiol.*, **22**, 678.

CLARK, F. E. (1948). *Azotobacter* inoculation of crops. III. Recovery of *Azotobacter* from the rhizosphere. *Soil Sci.*, **65**, 193.

FÅHRAEUS, G. (1957). The infection of clover root hairs by nodule bacteria, studied by a simple glass slide technique. *J. gen. Microbiol.*, **16**, 374.

FÅHRAEUS, G. & LJUNGGREN, H. (1959). The possible significance of pectic enzymes in root-hair infection by nodule bacteria. *Physiol. Plant.*, **12**, 145.

FEDOROV, M. V. & NEPOMILUEV, V. F. (1954). Distribution and nitrogen-fixing activity of *Azotobacter* in the rhizosphere of perennial grasses. *Mikrobiologiya*, **23**, 166.

GAINEY, P. L. (1930). A study of factors influencing inoculation experiments with *Azotobacter*. *Tech. Bull. Kans. agric. Exp. St.*, **26**, 3.

GEBGARDT, A. G. (1958). Some data on the mode of action of *Azotobacter* on plants. In *'Poluchenie i Primenenie bacterial'n Udorenii.' Kiev. Akad. Nauk. Ukrain. SSR.*

GELLER, I. A. & KHARITON, E. G. (1953). The effect of *Azotobacter* and phosphobacterin on the nutrition of sugar beet. *Mӯkrobiol. Zh.*, **15**, 43.

GRAY, R. A. (1957). Alteration of leaf size and shape and other changes caused by gibberellins in plants. *Am. J. Bot.*, **44**, 674.

GUBANOV, Y. V. (1953). The effect of Azotobacterin on the growth, development and yield of wheat in the Krasnodar territory. *Author's summary of thesis.* Krasnodar.

HARLEY, J. L. & WAID, J. S. (1955). A method of studying active mycelia on living roots and other surfaces in the soil. *Trans. Br. mycol. Soc.*, **38**, 104.

HELY, F. W., BERGERSEN, F. J. & BROCKWELL, J. (1957). Microbial antagonism in the rhizosphere as a factor in the failure of inoculation of subterranean clover. *Aust. J. agric. Res.*, **8**, 24.

HUGHES, D. Q. & VINCENT, J. M. (1942). Serological studies of the root nodule bacteria. III. Tests of neighbouring strains of the same species. *Proc. Linn. Soc. N.S.W.*, **67**, 142.

JACKSON, R. M. (1958). Soil fungistasis. *A. Rep. Rothamsted Experimental Station.*

JACKSON, R. M. (1960). Soil fungistasis and the rhizosphere. In *The Ecology of Soil Fungi*. Ed. Parkinson, D. & Waid, J. S. Liverpool. Liverpool University Press.

JACKSON, R. M., BROWN, M. E. & BURLINGHAM, S. K. (1964). Similar effects on tomato plants of *Azotobacter* inoculation and application of gibberellins. *Nature, Lond.*, **203**, 851.

JENSEN, H. L. (1942*a*). Nitrogen fixation in leguminous plants. I. General characters of root-nodule bacteria isolated from species of *Medicago* and *Trifolium* in Australia. *Proc. Linn. Soc. N.S.W.*, **67**, 98.

JENSEN, H. L. (1942*b*). Bacterial treatment of non-leguminous seeds as an agricultural practice. *Aust. J. Sci.*, **4**, 117.

JESSEN, W. (1949). Effect of inoculants on non-leguminous plants. *Z. Pflanzenernähr. Düng Bodenk.*, **44**, 206.

KATZNELSON, H. (1940). Survival of *Azotobacter* in soil. *Soil Sci.*, **49**, 21.

KATZNELSON, H., SIROIS, J. C. & COLE, S. (1962). Production of a gibberellin-like substance by *Arthrobacter globiformis. Nature, Lond.*, **196**, 1012.

KLECZKOWSKA, J. (1957). A study of distribution and effects of bacteriophage of root nodule bacteria in the soil. *Can. J. Microbiol.*, **3**, 171.

KRASILNIKOV, N. A. (1958). *Soil Microorganisms and Higher Plants.* Moscow. Academy of Sciences, USSR.

LIM, G. (1961). Microbiological factors influencing infection of clover by nodule bacteria. Thesis. London. University of London.

LIM, G. (1963). Studies on the physiology of nodule formation. VIII. The influence of the size of the rhizosphere population of nodule bacteria on root hair infection in clover. *Ann. Bot.*, **27**, 55.

MACURA, J. (1957). Experiments with inoculation of sugar beet seeds with *Azotobacter. Sb. čsl. Akad. Zeměd. Věd. Rostlinná Výroba*, **30**, 1223.

MILLARD, W. A. & TAYLOR, C. B. (1927). Antagonism of micro-organisms as the controlling factor in the inhibition of scab by green manuring. *Ann. appl. Biol.*, **14**, 202.

MISHUSTIN, E. N. & NAUMOVA, A. H. (1962). Bacterial fertilizers, their effectiveness and mechanism of action. *Microbiology*, **31**, 442.

NAUMOVA, A. N. (1958). Survival of *Azotobacter* in podsol soils. *Kiev. Akad. Nauk. Ukrain. SSR.*

NOVAK, P. & DVORZHAKOVA, H. (1955). The destruction of some phytopathogenic fungi by *Azotobacter. Sb. čsl. Akad. Zeměd. Věd. Rostlinná Výroba.*, **28**, 304.

PETRENKO, M. B. (1958). Microbiological investigations on potato rhizosphere. *Author's summary of thesis.* Kharkov.

PONOMAREVA, A. V. (1953). The effect of *Azotobacter* on the growth of seedlings of some woody plants and on the accumulation of chlorophyll in their leaves. *Izv. Akad. Nauk. beloruss. SSR*, 5.

PURCHASE, H. F. & NUTMAN, P. S. (1957). Studies on the physiology of nodule formation. VI. The influence of bacterial numbers in the rhizosphere on nodule initiation. *Ann. Bot.*, **21**, 439.

RAZNITSINA, E. A. (1938). Formation of auxin-type growth factors by bacteria. *Dokl. Akad. Nauk. SSSR.*, **18**, 353.

READ, M. (1953). The establishment of serologically identifiable strains of *Rhizobium trifolii* in field soils in competition with the native microflora. *J. gen. Microbiol.*, **9**, 1.

ROVIRA, A. D. (1956). Plant root excretions in relation to the rhizosphere effect. I. The nature of root exudates from oats and peas. *Pl. Soil*, **7**, 178.

ROVIRA, A. D. (1961). *Rhizobium* numbers in the rhizospheres of red clover and paspalum in relation to soil treatment and numbers of bacteria and fungi. *Aust. J. agric. Res.*, **12**, 77.

ROVIRA, A. D. (1963). Microbial inoculation of plants. I. Establishment of free-living nitrogen-fixing bacteria in the rhizosphere and their effects on maize, tomato and wheat. *Pl. Soil*, **19**, 304.

RUBENCHIK, L. I. (1963). *Azotobacter and its use in agriculture*. Academy of Sciences of the Ukrainian SSR. English edn. Jerusalem. Israel Programme for Scientific translations.

SAMTSEVICH, S. A. (1940). On the problem of the mode of action of seed bacterization. *Dokl. Akad. Nauk. SSSR*, **20**.

SANFORD, G. B. & BROADFOOT, W. C. (1931). Studies of the effects of other soil-inhabiting micro-organisms on the virulence of *Ophiobolus graminis*. *Sci. Agric.*, **11**, 512.

SIDOROV, F. E. (1954). The effect of Azotobacterin on potato yields. *Dokl. vses. Akad. sel.'-khoz Nauk.*, **25**.

SMITH, J. H., ALLISON, F. E. & SOULIDES, D. A. (1961). Evaluation of phosphobacterin as a soil inoculant. *Proc. Soil Sci. Soc. Am.*, **25**, 109.

STAPP, C. (1951). The value of *Azotobacter* inoculating preparations for German agriculture. *Landwirtsch. Forsch.*, **3**, 176.

SUNDARA RAO, W. V. B., MANN, H. S., PAUL, N. B. & MATHUR, S. P. (1963). Bacterial inoculation experiments with special reference to *Azotobacter*. *Ind. J. agric. Sci.*, **33**, 279.

THORNTON, G. D., ALENCAR, J. & SMITH, F. B. (1949). Some effects of *Streptomyces albus* and *Penicillium* spp. on *Rhizobium meliloti*. *Proc. Soil Sci. Soc. Am.*, **14**, 188.

TIMONIN, M. I. (1948). *Azotobacter* preparation (azotogen) as a fertilizer for cultivated plants. *Proc. Soil Sci. Soc. Am.*, **13**, 246.

TRIZNO, S. I. (1954). Inoculation of seeds with *Azotobacter* as a method of preventing lodging of spring cereals on peat bogs. *Trudȳ Inst. Melior. vod. bolot. Khoz., Minsk*, **4**, 36.

VANČURA, V. (1961). Detection of gibberellic acid in *Azotobacter* cultures. *Nature, Lond.*, **192**, 88.

VANČURA, V. (1964). Root exudates of plants. I. Analysis of root exudates of barley and wheat in their initial phases of growth. *Pl. Soil*, **21**, 231.

VANČURA, V. & MACURA, J. (1960). Indole derivatives in *Azotobacter* cultures. *Folia Microbiol., Praha*, **5**, 293.

VANČURA, V. & MACURA, J. (1961). The effect of root excretions on *Azotobacter*. *Folia Microbiol., Praha*, **6**, 250.

VANČURA, V., MACURA, J., FISCHER, O. & VONDRAČEK, J. (1959). The relation of *Azotobacter* to the root system of barley. *Folia Microbiol., Praha*, **4**, 119.

VINCENT, J. M. (1954). The root-nodule bacteria of pasture legumes. *Proc. Linn. Soc. N.S.W.*, **79**, iv.

WICHTMANN, H. (1952). Studies on the relationship between *Azotobacter* content and soil fertility. *Arch. Mikrobiol.*, **17**, 54.

ZINOV'EVA, K. G. (1954). The effect of the rhizosphere of some agricultural plants on *Azotobacter*. IV. The effect of sugar beet root system on *Azotobacter*. *Mȳkrobiol. Zh.*, **16**, 3.

ZOLOTOV, V. I. (1954). Effective use of mineral and bacterial fertilizers under corn in chernozems of the Ukrainian steppes. *Author's summary of thesis.* Dneiperpetrovsk.

# PLANT PATHOGENIC BACTERIA IN SOIL

J. E. CROSSE

*East Malling Research Station, Kent*

## *INTRODUCTION*

About two hundred 'species' of plant pathogenic bacteria have been described in the genera *Corynebacterium*, *Agrobacterium*, *Pseudomonas*, *Xanthomonas* and *Erwinia*. They are widely distributed throughout the world causing hypertrophic growth, wilts, rots and blights in a variety of crop plants. No genus is associated exclusively with any particular type of disease syndrome, except *Agrobacterium* with hypertrophic growths. The largest and most versatile genus, *Pseudomonas*, includes organisms causing hypertrophy (*P. savastanoi*), wilts (*P. solanacearum*), leaf spots (*P. tabaci*), soft rots (*P. marginalis*), blights (*P. syringae*) and cankers (*P. mors-prunorum*). The *Corynebacterium* spp. are predominantly vascular pathogens and the *Xanthomonas* spp. leaf infecting organisms. The genus *Erwinia* contains blight organisms (*E. amylovora*), vascular pathogens (*E. salicis*), and a group of strongly pectolytic soft rot pathogens which Waldee (1946) has proposed should be separated and put into the germs *Pectobacterium*.

Most studies on the plant pathogenic bacteria in the soil have been prompted by the desire to control disease rather than to elucidate the ecology of the causal organisms. The resulting information inevitably has a strong epidemiological bias. It also has a fragmentary and inconclusive quality which further adds to the difficulty of interpretation in ecological terms. Plant pathogenic bacteria are dispersed and maintained in many different ways (Crosse, 1957), and their behaviour in soils is only one aspect of their varied and complex biological relationships. Before discussing the role of the soil in bacterial diseases it will be as well to consider briefly the nature of the bacteria as plant pathogens.

Host relationships in plant diseases are dominated by three fundamental attributes of the plant, (1) its stationary nature, (2) its growth periodicity, and (3) its protective surfaces. These impose on plant pathogens requirements for (1) autonomous dispersal, (2) some form of resting stage to survive the temporary absence of a host or susceptible host organs and, preferably, (3) some mechanism for active penetration of protective surfaces. In these respects the fungi are well adapted. They possess elaborate airborne spore forms and the apparatus for launching them. They commonly produce special resting structures, e.g. spores, sclerotia, rhizomorphs or fructifications which enable them readily to survive any barren period, and many are capable of mechanical penetration into the host. In all these characters the bacteria are deficient. A few have developed special relationships with insects, e.g. *E. amylovora* (Waite, 1902) and *E. tracheiphila* (Rand and Cash, 1920), but the majority of bacteria causing the numerous leaf spot and similar diseases in plants are dispersed within the crop only by rain splash. Rain plays a vital role in these diseases, providing simultaneously for mobilization and dispersal, and for the penetration of inoculum through wounds and natural openings (Crosse, 1957). Splash dispersal may be extremely effective in a monoculture (Faulwetter, 1917) but in natural vegetation, where pathogenic forms probably first evolved, its limitations are obvious. None of the pathogenic bacteria have special resting structures and in common with many pathogenic fungi most have lost, or failed to acquire, the ability to compete as saprophytes. These deficiencies are to some extent offset by the extraordinary capacity of the plant pathogenic bacteria to survive in intimate association with the host in all stages of its life history. Many persist, and are transmitted from generation to generation of the host in cyclical infection. Most appear to be capable of surviving as dormant epiphytes in seed and other organs where they are remarkably resistant to desiccation (Burkholder, 1945). This latter feature has been attributed to the protective effects of the polysaccharide slime which many of them exude (Leach, Lilly, Wilson and Purvis, 1957).

## *THE ROLE OF THE SOIL IN BACTERIAL PLANT DISEASES*

In his valuable survey, Buddenhagen (1965) has classified bacterial diseases according to the ecology of the causal organism. Group A is characterized by pathogens which develop almost exclusively in the plant. Group B is characterized by pathogens that build up populations in the plant which only gradually decline when returned to the soil; such pathogens are ultimately host dependent, their populations in the soil increasing or decreasing according to cropping practice. Group C consists of diseases where the pathogenic populations are largely produced in the soil. The alternative scheme, below, emphasizes the role of the soil in the epidemiology of disease. Groups I and II correspond closely to Buddenhagen's Group A, and Groups III and IV to his Groups B and C respectively.

I. *Diseases with no soil phase*

In these diseases a soil phase has no conceivable relevance since the host is permanently and cyclically infected and infection is transmitted through the air by insects or rain splashing. The best examples are the diseases of deciduous fruit trees such as fireblight (*E. amylovora*) and bacterial canker of *Prunus* spp. (*Pseudomonas mors-prunorum* and *Pseudomonas syringae*). The fireblight pathogen overwinters quiescently in dormant 'holdover' cankers on the stems and branches of the host. It becomes active again in the spring and is carried from the surface of cankers by rain or insects to the blossoms. Here the pathogen initiates the primary infections. Under suitable climatic conditions secondary spread from blossom to blossom by pollinating insects rapidly expands the disease to epidemic proportions. From the flowers, the infection spreads to the branches and stems of the trees forming cankers. The further development of these is arrested in the autumn and they are transformed into holdover cankers. Holdover cankers are the only certain source of overwintered inoculum in fireblight disease and their elimination from orchards and from alternative hosts in the vicinity are a major factor in the control of this disease.

In bacterial canker of stone fruits (*P. mors-prunorum*) the pathogen is adapted to a continuous pathogenic cycle. It invades the stems and branches through leaf or wound scars in the autumn and cankers develop during the winter and spring. These are eventually sealed off in early summer and the pathogen dies out. Meanwhile, the bacteria enter the leaves through the stomata forming leaf spots. The leaf phase persists until the autumn when the cycle is completed by the re-establishment of the canker phase. Other predominant foliar diseases of trees, e.g. walnut blight (*X. juglandis*) and leaf spot of stone fruits (*X. pruni*) have similar host relationships. Many herbaceous plants may also be permanently infected, the pathogens invading the resting organs, e.g. tubers, rhizomes and bulbs. *C. sepedonicum*, the cause of ring rot of potato, finally migrates into tubers and these, when slightly infected, may give rise to diseased plants the following year. Cyclical infection is occasionally a feature of certain diseases of annual legumes, the pathogens *P. pisi* and *P. phaseolicola* invading the testa of the seed and even, in the case of the latter organism, the embryo itself (Pugsley, 1936).

II. *Diseases with a transitory or ephemeral soil phase*

Most bacterial plant diseases are seed borne or potentially so (Orton, 1931). In these diseases, transfer of the pathogen from the seed to the emergent seedling occurs within the soil environment, and in some cases the soil may act as the vehicle for transmission. Bacteria may be carried on the seed as a surface contaminant or in the micropyle, e.g. *X. malvacearum* (Wickens, 1953), in an infected funiculus, e.g. *P. lachrymans* (Wiles and Walker, 1952), or as an infection of the seed itself, e.g. *X. stewarti.* (Ivanoff, 1933). In halo blight of beans (*P. phaseolicola*), the pathogen may be carried as a commensal in the micropyle or within the infected testas or cotyledons (Pugsley, 1936). In the former case the hypocotyl becomes infected externally from the micropyle as it emerges from the soil. Where the cotyledons are infected the pathogen migrates internally through the tissue to the vascular system of the seedling giving rise directly to the systemic infections characteristic of the disease. In this case no external soil transference is involved and the disease behaves cyclically. In bacterial blight of cotton (*X. malvacearum*), external infections of the cotyledonary margins occur during germination of the seed and this process has been shown to be considerably influenced by soil temperature, moisture and type (Stoughton, 1930, 1933).

In the majority of seed borne diseases the existence of an independent reservoir of infection in the soil is not obligatory for the perpetuation of the disease. Nevertheless, a few of the seed borne pathogens do persist in the soil in residues from diseased plants long enough to be a source of infection for succeeding crops. Examples of this are *C. michiganense* (bacterial canker of tomato) and *X. campestris* (black rot of crucifers).

III. *Diseases with a protracted soil phase*

These are the true soil borne diseases caused by *P. solanacearum* and species of *Agrobacterium*. *P. solanacearum* is widespread throughout the tropical and warm temperate regions of the world as the cause of a lethal disease in a wide range of dicotyledonous crop plants, including many of the Solanaceae, e.g. tobacco, tomato and potato. It is also responsible for the serious Moko disease of banana. It enters the plant from the soil through wounds in the root system and invades the xylem tracheal elements causing wilt and death of the plant. *P. solanacearum* exists in several distinct pathological forms. Thus on the basis of their own work and that of Okabe and Goto (1961) and Hayward (1964), Buddenhagen and Kelman (1964) have distinguished 3 races of this organism: on solanaceous and other plants (race 1);

on banana and *Heliconia* spp. (race 2); and on potato (race 3). *P. solanacearum* can be disseminated independently of the soil in diseased plant material, and one strain of the banana race, designated SFR, has been shown to be insect transmitted (Buddenhagen and Elsasser, 1962). The principal source of infection in this disease is nevertheless the soil. At one time it was believed, from its long persistence in the soil, that *P. solanacearum* was an indigenous component of the soil microflora but in the light of recent work this appears less certain.

The hypertrophic diseases caused by *A. tumefaciens* and related organisms are predominantly soil borne and survive for long periods in the soil independently of plants. Some authors have claimed that they are capable of a completely independent saprophytic existence in the soil. The soft rot *Erwinia* (*Pectobacterium*) spp. may also belong to this group, but their soil relationships are too ill-defined to be certain of this.

IV. *Diseases with a permanent phase in the soil*

These are the diseases caused by the oxidase positive, pectolytic, green fluorescent *Pseudomonas* spp. which cause soft rots in plant organs in or near the soil (Dowson, 1941; Paton, 1958). These organisms are abundant in the soil and rhizosphere as saprophytes. Their pathogenicity is incidental and their disease relationships erratic and transitory. *P. marginalis*, the cause of a marginal leaf spot in lettuce, endives and chicory probably belongs to this group.

## *LONGEVITY OF PLANT PATHOGENIC BACTERIA IN THE SOIL*

There has been no systematic study of this problem. Most of the information has been acquired through the investigation of control measures for specific diseases, and much of it is based on inferences from crop rotations. Direct methods have also been employed, however, and selective media developed specifically for this purpose (Patel, 1926; Ark, 1932; Ivanoff, 1933; Peterson, 1963). The occurrence of symptoms in susceptible plant tissues after infiltration with soil suspensions has been another method commonly used to detect pathogenic bacteria in soils (Fulton, 1920; Bryan, 1930; North, 1935; Valleau, Johnson and Diachun, 1944; Boosalis, 1952).

It is never clear in any of these investigations how far the results obtained reflect the sensitivity of the methods employed. Crop rotation studies are open to the objection that they detect pathogens in soil only at concentrations above the threshold necessary for the establishment of disease. Nevertheless the accumulated evidence from the large number oι investigations carried out leaves little doubt that the majority of the bacterial pathogens do not persist for very long in the soil in the absence of suitable hosts.

*C. michiganense* does not survive for long in the free state, but may overwinter in the soil in diseased plant residues (Bryan, 1930; Grogan and Kendrick, 1953). Poor survival is also a characteristic of the potato ring rot organism, *C. sepedonicum* (Bonde, 1939; Dykstra, 1942; Tyner, 1947; Sniesko and Bonde, 1943). By plating techniques, confirmed by inoculation of alfalfa seedlings with soil suspensions, Nelson and Semenuik (1963) found that *C. insidiosum* disappeared from moist non-sterile soils in a matter of days at average temperatures. It has been suggested that *C. fascians*, a hyperplastic organism sharply separated from all the other *Corynebacterium* species in its pathological effects, is common in the soil (Jacobs and Mohanty, 1951). There is other evidence that it may persist on plants as an epiphyte rather than in the soil (Pitcher and Crosse, 1958).

In the free state, none of the *Xanthomonas* species investigated survived for long in unsterile soils. Thus under experimental conditions, *X. vasculorum* (North, 1935), *X. citri* (Fulton, 1920; Lee, 1920) and *X. vesicatoria* (Peterson, 1963) declined rapidly, reaching extinction within a period of days or weeks. Certain species, e.g. *X. campestris* (Clayton, 1924), *X. malvacearum* (Hare and King, 1940), *X. translucens* (Boosalis, 1952) and *X. phaseoli* (Graham, 1953) may in some circumstances survive in or on the soil long enough to infect a succeeding crop, but probably only in the debris of diseased plants. *X. pelargonii*, for example, rapidly becomes extinct as soon as infected debris is fully decomposed (Munnecke, 1956).

The few observations made on the green fluorescent seed borne *Pseudomonas* species suggest that these also are incapable of persisting in the soil for long periods, e.g. *P. pisi* (Skoric, 1927), *P. syringae* (Hedges, 1946) and *P. phaseolicola* (Hedges, 1946; Wilson, 1946). Two pathogens of soybean, *P. tabaci* and *P. glycinea*, remained viable in warm moist soils for only a few months (Graham, 1953). The soil relations of *P. tabaci* have been more extensively investigated in relation to wildfire and angular leaf spot disease of tobacco. It survives for extended periods in plant debris (Clinton and McCormick, 1922) but not, according to Anderson (1924), in the soil. Reid, Naghski, Farrell and Haley (1942) have claimed that *P. tabaci* is always present in soil and is identical with the common soil form, *P. fluorescens*. This view is difficult to reconcile with the epidemiological characteristics of wildfire disease and has proved unacceptable to some plant pathologists (Burkholder, 1948).

Using direct plating and a fairly sensitive fruit-inoculation technique to detect *E. amylovora* in sterile and unsterile soils, Ark (1932) found that it rapidly declined to undetectable levels in 38 days. Thomas and Parker (1933) also reported that *E. amylovora* failed to overwinter in unsterile soils exposed outdoors between December and April. The vascular pathogen *E. tracheiphila* does not persist for long in the soil (Rand and Enlows, 1916), but overwinters within the body of hibernating adult beetles which carry and inoculate it into succeeding crops (Rand and Cash, 1920).

The evidence on the soil relations of the soft rot *Erwinia* species is conflicting. Earlier workers considered that they were not soil inhabitants and that the widespread distribution of these organisms was due to recurrent introduction with infected or contaminated planting material. Leach (1930), however, using potato tissues for the selective isolation of *E. atroseptica*, concluded that it was possibly of widespread occurrence in soils. He suggested that the absence of proper conditions for infection rather than the incidence of the pathogen was the main limiting factor in the disease. With a similar technique Kerr (1953) isolated soft rot bacteria from a wide range of Scottish soils. These were not specifically identified but there was an implication in the work that they were *Erwinia* species. In a similar survey, Graham (1958*a*) identified all the Gram-negative soft rot organisms isolated by Kerr's technique as fluorescent *Pseudomonas* species. These were also the only soft rot organisms recovered from soils which he had irrigated a few months previously with heavy suspensions of *E. atroseptica*. Vorokevich (1960) concluded that soft rot *Erwinia* species were unable to survive for long in soil; they persist in killed plant tissues, but die quickly when they are decomposed.

Many of these short lived species remained viable indefinitely in sterile soils and some even increased (Lee, 1920). Several which suffered prompt extinction in warm, moist unsterile soils persisted for longer periods when the soil moisture was reduced or the soil held at low temperatures (Fulton, 1920; Graham, 1953; Nelson and Semenuik, 1963). For these reasons, their decline in soils has been attributed to the activities of antagonistic micro-organisms. Patrick (1954) isolated a great number of antagonists from virgin soils, mostly actinomycetes and bacteria, and claimed that there was some correlation between the sensitivity of the plant pathogenic bacteria to these organisms and their ability to survive in the soil. There were, however, anomalous results.

Thus *A. tumefaciens*, an organism with a protracted soil phase, was one of the most susceptible organisms tested. There was some evidence to suggest, however, that under certain conditions the concentration of antibiotics in soils might be such as to cause stimulation rather than inhibition of this organism.

Bacteriophages active against plant pathogenic bacteria are present in soils (Stolp, 1961; Crosse and Hingorani, 1958) and these have been held responsible by some authors for the disappearance of pathogens (Coons and Kotila, 1925; Massey, 1931). This is highly improbable. The ideal requirements for elimination of a bacterium by a phage are a very high concentration of phage and a very low concentration of sensitive cells. Anderson (1957) found, for example, that under favourable *in vitro* conditions the minimum initial concentration of a virulent phage necessary to eliminate a single cell of *Salmonella typhi* was of the order of $10^7$ particles/ml. He concluded that, in the natural environment, changes in bacterial populations due to mass elimination of sensitive bacteria by phage were unlikely. In the author's experience the yield of phages from soils enriched with concentrated suspensions of the plant pathogens *P. mors-prunorum* and *P. syringae* has rarely exceeded $10^2$ particles/ml. of soil suspension. Since this yield is equivalent to the lysis of only two or three cells, it is clear that the initial concentration of phage is very low and the chances of absorption onto sensitive cells occuring, therefore, extremely remote.

Of the true soil borne pathogens, *A. tumefaciens* and *P. solanacearum*, the latter has been the most extensively investigated in the field. Since it was first tentatively described at the turn of the century there has been a constant stream of reports describing the persistence of *P. solanacearum* in soils under a wide variety of crop and cultural conditions (Kelman, 1953). There are several instances of it causing severe epidemics in susceptible crops planted for the first time on virgin land, sometimes in circumstances excluding any possibility of outside introduction (Schwartz, 1926; Eddins, 1936; Wager, 1945). It has also been known to survive for periods of up to 10 years in soils cropped continuously with non-susceptible hosts (Roque, 1933) and there are reports of the tobacco strain surviving for 4 years or more in bare fallow (Wiehe, 1939; Smith, 1944). Sequeira (1962) concluded, however, that in many of these cases the absence of alternative weed hosts had not been established with certainty. He found that the banana race of *P. solanacearum* tended to disappear fairly rapidly from soils kept in dry fallow or under continuous cultivation with a non-susceptible host (Sequeira, 1958, 1962). The effect of continuous cultivation in reducing the incidence of banana wilt was earlier reported by Wardlaw and McGuire (1933).

*P. solanacearum* attacks a wider range of plants than any of the other bacterial pathogens. Kelman (1953) has compiled a list of about 200 plant species in several different families which are natural hosts of this organism or are susceptible to it under experimental conditions. Earlier workers (e.g. Briant, 1932) have attributed the occurrence of *P. solanacearum* in virgin soils to its presence on wild weed hosts in the natural flora. Recently Buddenhagen (1960) reported the isolation of the banana race from the musaceous weed, *Heliconia latispatha*, growing in abandoned banana plantations. Sequeira and Averre (1961) surveyed large tracts of virgin woodland in Costa Rica and found extensive infection by the banana race of 3 native species of *Heliconia*, many plants of which were showing no external symptoms of disease. They also isolated the solanaceous race from wilted *Eupatorium odoratum* plants present in virgin woodland.

In the absence of any substantial experimental evidence the ecological status of *P. solanacearum* remains an enigma. Its wide host range, however, its occurrence as an apparently indigenous pathogen in native vegetation, and its capacity for parasitic adaptation are probably more consistent with an organism specialized as a root inhabitant (Garrett, 1950) rather than as a soil inhabitant. The distribution of *P. solanacearum* is known almost exclusively from crop diseases, and it is a distribution of races and 'pathotypes' rather than a species. The pathogen may lie undetected in many areas because the particular races present do not react with the indigenous vegetation to produce a visible disease syndrome. Crop diseases, in other words, may be only a manifestation of an abnormal host relationship with an organism more widely distributed as a relatively harmless inhabitant of plant roots.

Field observations of *A. tumefaciens* indicate protracted survival in the soil, although interpretation of these observations is similarly complicated by the wide host range of the organism (Elliott, 1951) and by the existance of specialized races (Wormald, 1945) capable of independent dissemination in planting material (Banfield, 1934). There is in this case, however, supporting experimental evidence. Patel (1928, 1929*b*), for example, successfully re-isolated *A. tumefaciens* from artificially infested unsterile soils devoid of plant cover after 669 days on one occasion and after 420 days on another. Banfield (1934) recorded survival of between 14 and 18 months in neutral peat. Dickey (1961) devised a sensitive plating technique to enumerate *A. tumefaciens* in soils and then studied the effect of various edaphic factors on the fate of soil populations. He found that the pathogen only gradually decreased and was generally favoured by low temperatures, moist and alkaline soil conditions and by fine soil textures. In an unsterile clay loam populations declined asymptotically with time from approximately $10^8$ to $10^3$ per g. of dry soil over a period of 250 days. The resultant curve suggests the possibility of indefinite survival at the lower concentrations, although Dickey himself did not regard his results as conclusive evidence that *A. tumefaciens* is able to maintain itself in the soil as a saprophyte.

## *THE OCCURRENCE OF PLANT PATHOGENS ON PLANT ROOTS*

There is evidence that some plant pathogens which do not survive in the soil may be able to colonize the surface of plant roots. Valleau *et al.* (1944), who were unable to detect *P. tabaci* in soils, isolated pathogenic bacteria readily from the rhizoplane of tobacco and other crop plants. They concluded that *P. tabaci* was not primarily a tobacco pathogen, but an organism adapted to a life on the surface of plant roots. The tomato leaf spot pathogen, *X. vesicatoria*, may overwinter on wheat roots, but not, apparently, *X. phaseoli* and *P. phaseolicola* (Diachun and Valleau, 1946). All three pathogens, however, grew on roots of host and non-host plants under aseptic conditions. The plea of Valleau *et al.* (1944) for more investigations of this kind has evoked little response, and it is difficult at this stage therefore to assess the significance of their observations in terms of the soil and epidemiological relations of the plant pathogenic bacteria in general. Smith (1962), who isolated *X. malvacearum* from the roots of 14 different weed plants growing in cotton fields, concluded that weed roots were not a significant factor in the overwintering of the cotton pathogen. Many plant pathogens survive as epiphytes in seed and there are some known to be capable of epiphytic growth on the surface of plants (Crosse, 1959; Leben, 1963). Is it possible, perhaps, that the growth of pathogens on roots represents a partial and perhaps temporary extension of an epiphytic phase?

## *RELATIONSHIPS OF PLANT PATHOGENS WITH SOIL BACTERIA*

Although the plant pathogens have obvious affinities with the soil bacteria, the detailed relationships of the 2 groups are obscured by our inadequate knowledge of soil bacteria at the species level. *Xantho-*

*monas*, a genus consisting at the moment entirely of plant pathogens, presents a particular problem. Yellow saprophytes are commonly found on plants, but those examined by Burkholder (1948) were stated to be distinctly unlike xanthomonads in other characters. *X. trifoliorum*, a non-pathogenic organism described from wheat seed by James (1955), was frequently multiflagellate and also differed from the plant pathogens in utilizing asparagine as a sole source of carbon and nitrogen. It was also shown by Starr and Stephens (1964) to possess a pigment distinct from the unique carotenoid found in the true *Xanthomonas* species. Holding (1960) referred yellow, polar flagellate aerobic bacteria isolated from the soil and rhizosphere to the genus *Xanthomonas*, but none of these produced the copious slime on sugar media characteristic of the genus. Similar organisms have been reported from the surfaces of leaves (Stout, 1960*b*).

Recent taxonomic studies have confirmed *Pseudomonas* as one of the predominant genera in the rhizosphere (Holding, 1960; Rouatt and Katznelson, 1961). More definitive studies will be necessary, however, before their relationships with the plant pathogens can be established. The latter are not themselves homogeneous, at least 3 groups now being recognized.

The first consists of the pathologically specialized fluorescent *Pseudomonas* species, typically found causing leaf spots and similar diseases in the aerial organs of plants, e.g. *P. phaseolicola*, *P. mors-prunorum*, *P. syringae* and *P. lachrymans*. These organisms produce distinctive, radially striated, levan colonies on sucrose media and in contrast to the majority of other *Pseudomonas* species (Shewan, Hobbs and Hodgkiss, 1960), they are oxidase negative (Billing, 1963). They are also less active biochemically than fluorescent soil and water types (Rhodes, 1959, 1961). They nevertheless have affinities with the soil and water forms, with which they share common antigens (St. John-Brooks, Nain and Rhodes, 1925; Friedman, 1953) and common phage sensitivities (Stolp, 1961; Billing, 1963; Crosse and Garrett, 1963).

The second group are the non-fluorescent, oxidase positive pathogens with the capacity to produce massive refractile sudanophilic cell inclusions on peptone media containing glucose or sucrose (Hayward, 1964). This group is comprised of *P. solanacearum*, *P. rubrilineans*, *P. stizolobii* and *P. caryophylli*. These may possibly be related to the oxidative non-fluorescent pseudomonads isolated from the rhizosphere of plants by Holding (1960).

The third group are the fluorescent, oxidase positive, pectolytic bacteria causing soft rots of plant tissues. Pathogenicity in these organisms is probably only incidental to a normal saprophytic existence. They are common in soils (Graham, 1958*a*; Paton, 1958), and in the rhizosphere (Barclay, pers. comm.) where they may be involved in the initial degradation of sloughed-off root tissues.

Saprophytic representatives of *Erwinia* are not known for certain in the soil. *E. lathyri*, a yellow chromogenic organism once credited with causing plant diseases, is now considered to be a common saprophyte in soil and plant debris (Graham, 1958*b*), but the taxonomic position of *E. lathyri* and its relations with the plant pathogens are still uncertain. It resembles *E. amylovora* in some characters, including phage sensitivity (Billing, Baker, Crosse and Garrett, 1961), and Billing and Baker (1963) have suggested that it might be considered with similar organisms as a member of an ill-defined group within the genus *Erwinia*. Waldee (1945), on the other hand, concluded that *E. lathyri* was quite unlike the plant pathogens in its biochemical activities and had closer affinity with *Serratia marcescens*.

The relations of the soft rot *Erwinia* species with the *coli-aerogenes* bacteria are fairly clear. The *Erwinia* species are chiefly distinguished from these bacteria by their capacity to macerate plant tissues. Biochemically they appear to be closest to *Escherichia freundii* and *Aerobacter* spp. (Elrod, 1942; Waldee, 1945; Taylor, 1951*b*). The latter are widely distributed in a variety of habitats including plant surfaces (Thomas and Hobson, 1955; Frazer, Reid and Malcolm, 1956). They are also common in the soil (Koser, 1926; Medrek and Litsky, 1960; Holding, 1960), although it is not always clear how far this reflects contamination of soils with materials of faecal origin. Under experimental conditions they tended to die out in soils (Bardsley, 1948) and Taylor (1951*a*) considered this and other evidence sufficient to discredit statements that the soil is their natural habitat.

The close morphological and cultural similarities between the plant pathogenic *Agrobacterium* species and the common soil and rhizosphere organism *A. radiobacter* have been known for years (Patel, 1929*a*; Sagen, Riker and Baldwin, 1934; Brown and Leonard, 1932). Some minor physiological differences have been reported but the main distinguishing character of these organisms appears to be virulence to plants (Hendrickson, Baldwin and Riker, 1934). Coleman and Reid (1945) showed that *A. radiobacter* and *A. tumefaciens* differed antigenically in the 'M' phase but were identical in the decapsulated 'S' phase. They described the interconversion of these two organisms and produced evidence suggesting that lack of virulence was primarily associated with the presence of a capsule of the *A. radiobacter* type (Coleman and Reid, 1949). Klein and Klein (1953, 1956) transmitted virulence to *A. radiobacter* with extracts from virulent cultures of *A. tumefaciens* and identified the transforming principle as DNA. This work confirmed the close genetic relations between the two organisms, and supported the claim of Coleman and Reid (1945), namely, that they are different forms of the same species.

The small group of Gram-positive pleomorphic plant pathogens is at present classified with the animal diphtheroids in *Corynebacterium*. This practice originated with the transfer of *Aplanobacter michiganense* to the genus by Jensen (1934). Following this precedent, Dowson (1942) transferred other species to the genus and all new Gram-positive pathogens since discovered have been automatically assigned to it. It is doubtful whether this indicates their true affinities. The original transfer (Jensen, 1934) was based on similarities with soil rather than animal diphtheroids. Conn and Dimmick (1947), however, objected to the inclusion of soil diphtheroids in *Corynebacterium* and suggested the generic name *Arthrobacter* for members of the soil group which they found to be morphologically and physiologically distinct from the animal forms. Motility is another character which distinguishes a large number of soil diphtheroids from the true *Corynebacterium* species (Topping, 1937; Clark and Carr, 1951). Many of the plant pathogens are also motile and two of the four species examined by Conn and Dimmick (1947), i.e. *C. flaccumfaciens* and *C. poinsettiae* were considered to be wrongly placed in *Corynebacterium* for this reason. These authors regarded the plant pathogens as physiologically intermediate between the soil and animal diphtheroids, but showed such differences among themselves, particularly in morphological characteristics, as to raise doubts about their inclusion in the same genus. Clark (1952) was also of the opinion that the plant pathogens should be segregated from *Corynebacterium*, but was unable to suggest any alternative genus to accommodate them. He pointed out that they cannot be included in *Arthrobacter* as at present defined, and that they differ from other genera of soil diphtheroids in their plant pathogenicity and lack of cellulase activity. Nevertheless he felt that they would be better allocated to *Cellulomonas* than to *Corynebacterium*, since in general they showed greater similarity to *Cellulomonas biazotea*, the type species, than to *Corynebacterium diphtheriae*.

Recent studies on the chemical composition and antigenic structure of cell walls of *Corynebacterium*, *Mycobacterium*, *Nocardia* and *Arthrobacter* have thrown fresh light on the affinities of these organisms and of the plant pathogenic forms (Cummins and Harris, 1956, 1959;

Cummins, 1962). Thus the cell walls of *C. diphtheriae* and similar animal pathogens, and of many *Nocardia* and *Mycobacterium* species, were shown to be antigenically related and to have a very similar pattern of major cell wall components, consisting of arabinose, galactose, alanine, glutamic acid and diaminopimelic acid. The plant pathogen *C. fascians* showed the same cell wall components and antigenic relationships, and since this organism has a tendency towards acid fastness and filamentous growth on certain media (Lacey, 1955), its true affinities may lie with *Nocardia*. Its growth on agar media also resembles *Nocardia* (Conn and Dimmick, 1947). The remaining plant pathogens examined by Cummins and his collaborator, e.g. *C. triciti*, *C. betae*, *C. poinsettiae*, *C. insidiosum* and *C. flaccumfaciens* were heterogeneous in respect of their cell wall constituents and may be of diverse origin. Their immuno-chemical reactions and those of *Arthrobacter* species were distinct from the animal diphtheroids. The cell wall components of these plant pathogens also suggested that they are not very closely related to *Arthrobacter*.

## *ORIGIN OF PLANT PATHOGENIC BACTERIA*

It is commonly assumed that the plant pathogenic bacteria have evolved from related forms in the soil. Buddenhagen (1965) has discussed an hypothetical evolutionary process in terms of population dynamics, and suggested ways in which the competitive saprophytic ability of pathogens may have been lost or retained according to its relevance in the perpetuation of the infection chain. The ultimate stage is reached in organisms like *E. amylovora*, *P. mors-prunorum* and the *Xanthomonas* species, which, through the acquisition of efficient methods of airborne transmission and by continuous association with the host through its dormant stages, have been essentially liberated from the requirements of a soil phase The assumption of a soil origin for foliar pathogens of this type may not be justified. It has been known for years that the aerial structures of plants support a characteristic epiphytic flora (Burri, 1903; Düggelli, 1904), independent of that in the soil, and there is evidence that this is transmitted from generation to generation of plants in seed (Wallace and Lochhead, 1951; James, Wilson and Stark, 1946; Leben, 1961). Recent work indicates the presence in the epiphytic flora of organisms having affinities with the plant pathogens (Gibson, Stirling, Keddie and Rosenberger, 1958; Stout, 1960*a*, *b*; Ruinen, 1961). It seems probable that many foliar infecting bacteria may have evolved from these forms. Since epiphytes are almost certainly driven into leaves through the stomata during rain, the process of evolution is not difficult to envisage. Plant pathogens share other characters with epiphytes. Thus they have a high capacity for survival in seed, while certain pathogens, e.g. *P. mors-prunorum* (Crosse, 1959) and *X. vesicatoria* (Leben 1963), have been shown to be capable of multiplying on the surface of leaves. In bacterial canker of stone-fruits, the epiphytic growth of *P. mors-prunorum* is a major factor in maintaining the supply of inoculum for infection of branches in the autumn (Crosse, 1963).

Our notions as to *how* the plant pathogens are derived are equally speculative. It has been suggested that they are being frequently and continuously generated or regenerated as relatively simple variants of the saprophytic microflora (Reid *et al.*, 1942; Starr, 1959; Stolp, 1961). Buddenhagen and Kelman (1964), however, considered strains of *P. solanacearum* to be the product of long evolution and they dismissed as most improbable the idea that soil pseudomonads were readily converted to *P. solanacearum*. The remarkable homogeneity of character found in isolates of *E. amylovora* (Elrod, 1941; Billing, Baker, Crosse and Garrett, 1961) and *P. mors-prunorum* (Crosse and Garrett, 1963) is also consistent with the view that these are species or ecotypes stabilized through a long period of gene interaction with their hosts. The history of some now widely distributed bacterial diseases (Crosse, 1957) further points to a localized origin of the pathogens at some distant point in time. Evidence of this kind suggests that the evolution of an epidemiologically competent pathogen, i.e. one capable of sustaining a continuous infection chain *in the field*, may be a comparatively rare event.

## *REFERENCES*

ANDERSON, E. S. (1957). The relations of bacteriophages to bacterial ecology. In *Microbial Ecology*. Ed. Williams, R. E. O. & Spicer, C. C. *7th Symp. Soc. gen. Microbiol.* Cambridge. Cambridge University Press.

ANDERSON, P. J. (1924). Overwintering of tobacco wildfire bacteria in New England. *Phytopathology*, **14**, 132.

ARK, P. A. (1932). The behaviour of *Bacillus amylovorus* in the soil. *Phytopathology*, **22**, 657.

BANFIELD, W. M. (1934). Life history of the Crown gall organism in relation to its pathogenesis on the red raspberry. *J. agric. Res.*, **48**, 761.

BARDSLEY, D. A. (1948). A study of the coliform organisms in the Melbourne water supply and in animal faeces, with observations on their longevity in faeces and in soil. *J. Hyg., Camb.*, **46**, 269.

BILLING, E. (1963). The value of phage sensitivity tests for the identification of the phytopathogenic *Pseudomonas* spp. *J. appl. Bact.*, **26**, 193.

BILLING, E. & BAKER, L. A. E. (1963). Characteristics of *Erwinia*-like organisms found in plant material. *J. appl. Bact.*, **26**, 58.

BILLING, E. BAKER, L. A. E., CROSSE, J. E. & GARRETT, C. M. E. (1961). Characteristics of English isolates of *Erwinia amylovora* (Burrill) Winslow *et al. J. appl. Bact.*, **24**, 195.

BONDE, R. (1939). Bacterial wilt and soft rot of the potato in Maine. *Bull. Me agric. Exp. Stn*, **396**, 675.

BOOSALIS, M. G. (1952). The epidemiology of *Xanthomonas translucens* on cereals and grasses. *Phytopathology*, **42**, 387.

BRIANT, A. K. (1932). Tomato diseases in Trinidad. *Trop. Agric., Trin.*, **9**, 63 & 101.

BROWN, N. A. & LEONARD, L. T. (1932). Is *Bacterium tumefaciens* a mutant or one of the pleomorphic forms of *Bacillus radiobacter*? *Phytopathology*, **22**, 5.

BRYAN, M. K. (1930). Studies on bacterial canker of tomato. *J. agric. Res.*, **41**, 825.

BUDDENHAGEN, I. W. (1960). Strains of *Pseudomonas solanacearum* in indigenous hosts in banana plantations of Costa Rica, and their relationship to bacterial wilt of bananas. *Phytopathology*, **50**, 660.

BUDDENHAGEN, I. W. (1965). The relation of plant-pathogenic bacteria in the soil. In *Ecology of soil-borne plant pathogens*. Ed. Baker, K. F. & Snyder, W. C. Berkeley. University of California Press.

BUDDENHAGEN, I. W. & ELSASSER, T. A. (1962). An insect spread bacterial wilt epiphytotic of Bluggoe banana. *Nature, Lond.*, **194**, 164.

BUDDENHAGEN, I. W. & KELMAN, A. (1964). Biological and physiological aspects of bacterial wilt caused by *Pseudomonas solanacearum. A. Rev. Phytopath.*, **2**, 203.

BURKHOLDER, W. H. (1945). The longevity of the pathogen causing wilt of the common bean. *Phytopathology*, **35**, 743.

BURKHOLDER, W. H. (1948). Bacteria as plant pathogens. *A. Rev. Microbiol.*, **2**, 389.

BURRI, R. (1903). Die Bakterienvegetation auf der Oberfläche normal entwickelter Pflanzen. *Zentbl. Bakt. ParasitKde., Abt. II*, **10**, 756.

CLARK, F. E. (1952). The generic classification of the soil corynebacteria. *Int. Bull. bact. Nomencl. Taxon.*, **2**, 45.

CLARK, F. E. & CARR, P. H. (1951). Motility and flagellation of the soil corynebacteria. *J. Bact.*, **62**, 1.

CLAYTON, E. E. (1924). A progress report on black rot investigations with special reference to cauliflower on Long Island. *Phytopathology*, **14**, 24.

CLINTON, G. P. & MCCORMICK, F. A. (1922). Wildfire of tobacco in Connecticut. *Bull. Conn. agric. Exp. Stn*, **239**.

COLEMAN, M. F. & REID, J. J. (1945). A serological study of *Alcaligenes radiobacter* and *Phy. tumefaciens* in the 'M' and 'S' phases. *J. Bact.*, **49**, 187.

COLEMAN, M. F. & REID, J. J. (1949). The conversion of strains of *Alcaligenes radiobacter* and *Phytomonas tumefaciens* in the 'S' phase to the 'M' phase of the heterologous species. *Phytopathology*, **39**, 182.

CONN, H. J. & DIMMICK, I. (1947). Soil bacteria similar in morphology to *Mycobacterium* and *Corynebacterium. J. Bact.*, **54**, 291.

COONS, G. H. & KOTILA, J. E. (1925). The transmissible lytic principle (bacteriophage) in relation to plant pathogens. *Phytopathology*, **15**, 357.

CROSSE, J. E. (1957). The dispersal of bacterial plant pathogens. In *Biological aspects of the transmission of disease*. Ed. Horton-Smith, C. Edinburgh. Oliver and Boyd.

CROSSE, J. E. (1959). Bacterial canker of stone-fruits. IV. Investigation of a method for measuring the inoculum potential of cherry trees. *Ann. appl. Biol.*, **47**, 306.

CROSSE, J. E. (1963). Bacterial canker of stone-fruits. V. A comparison of leaf-surface populations of *Pseudomonas mors-prunorum* in autumn on two cherry varieties. *Ann. appl. Biol.*, **52**, 97.

CROSSE, J. E. & GARRETT, C. M. E. (1963). Studies on the bacteriophagy of *Pseu-*

*domonas mors-prunorum*, *Ps. syringae* and related organisms. *J. appl. Bact.*, **26**, 159.

CROSSE, J. E. & HINGORANI, M. K. (1958). A method for isolating *Pseudomonas mors-prunorum* phages from the soil. *Nature, Lond.*, **181**, 60.

CUMMINS, C. S. (1962). Chemical composition and antigenic structure of cell walls of *Corynebacterium*, *Mycobacterium*, *Nocardia*, *Actinomyces* and *Arthrobacter*. *J. gen. Microbiol.*, **28**, 35.

CUMMINS, C. S. & HARRIS, H. (1956). The chemical composition of the cell wall in some Gram positive bacteria and its possible value as a taxonomic character. *J. gen. Microbiol.*, **14**, 583.

CUMMINS, C. S. & HARRIS, H. (1959). Taxonomic position of *Arthrobacter*. *Nature, Lond.*, **184**, 831.

DIACHUN, S. & VALLEAU, W. D. (1946). Growth and overwintering of *Xanthomonas vesicatoria* in association with wheat roots. *Phytopathology*, **36**, 277.

DICKEY, R. S. (1961). Relation of some edaphic factors to *Agrobacterium tumefaciens*. *Phytopathology*, **51**, 605.

DOWSON, W. J. (1941). Soft rots due to green fluorescent bacteria. *Trans. Br. mycol. Soc.*, **25**, 311.

DOWSON, W. J. (1942). On the generic name of the Gram-positive bacterial plant pathogens. *Trans. Br. mycol. Soc.*, **25**, 311.

DÜGELLI, M. (1904). Die Bakterienflora gesunder Samen und darans gezogener keim pflanzchen. *Zentbl. Bakt. ParasitKde., Abt. II*, **12**, 602.

DYKSTRA, T. P. (1942). Compilation of results in control of potato ring rot in 1941. *Am. Potato J.*, **19**, 175.

EDDINS, A. H. (1936). Brown rot of Irish potatoes and its control. *Bull. Fla agric. Exp. Stn*, **299**, 44.

ELLIOT, C. (1951). *Manual of bacterial plant pathogens*. Massachusetts. Chronica Botanica Co.

ELROD, R. P. (1941). Serological studies of the Erwineae. I. *Erwinia amylovora*. *Bot. Gaz.*, **103**, 123.

ELROD, R. P. (1942). The *Erwinia*—coliform relationship. *J. Bact.*, **44**, 433.

FAULWETTER, R. C. (1917). Wind blown rain, a factor in disease dissemination. *J. agric. Res.*, **10**, 639.

FRAZER, M. H., REID, W. B. & MALCOLM, J. F. (1956). The occurrence of coli-aerogenes organisms on plants. *J. appl. Bact.*, **19**, 301.

FRIEDMAN, B. A. (1953). Serological tests with some phytopathogenic species of *Pseudomonas*. *Phytopathology*, **43**, 412.

FULTON, H. R. (1920). Decline of *Pseudomonas citri* in the soil. *J. agric. Res.*, **19**, 207.

GARRETT, S. D. (1950). Ecology of root inhabiting fungi. *Biol. Rev.*, **25**, 220.

GIBSON, T., STIRLING, A. C., KEDDIE, R. M. & ROSENBERGER, R. F. (1958). Bacteriological changes in silage made at controlled temperatures. *J. gen. Microbiol.*, **19**, 112.

GRAHAM, D. C. (1958*a*). Occurrence of soft rot bacteria in Scottish soils. *Nature, Lond.*, **181**, 61.

GRAHAM, D. C. (1958*b*). The status of *Erwinia lathyri* and related bacteria. *Commonw. phytopath. News*, **4**, 49.

GRAHAM, J. H. (1953). Overwintering of three bacterial pathogens of soybean. *Phytopathology*, **43**, 189.

GROGAN, R. G. & KENDRICK, J. B. (1953). Seed transmission mode of overwintering and spread of bacterial canker of tomato caused by *Corynebacterium michiganense*. *Phytopathology*, **43**, 473.

HARE, J. F. & KING, C. J. (1940). The winter carry over of angular leaf spot infection in Arizona cotton fields. *Phytopathology*, **30**, 679.

HAYWARD, A. C. (1964). Characteristics of *Pseudomonas solanacearum*. *J. appl. Bact.*, **27**, 265.

HEDGES, F. (1946). Experiments on the overwintering in the soil of bacteria causing leaf and pod spots of Snap and Lima bean. *Phytopathology*, **36**, 677.

HENDRICKSON, A. A., BALDWIN, I. L. & RIKER, A. J. (1934). Studies on certain physiological characters of *Phytomonas tumefaciens*, *Phytomonas rhizogenes* and *Bacillus radiobacter*. *J. Bact.*, **28**, 597.

HOLDING, A. J. (1960). The properties and classification of the predominant Gram-negative bacteria occurring in soil. *J. appl. Bact.*, **23**, 515.

IVANOFF, S. S. (1933). Stewart's wilt disease of corn, with emphasis on the life history of *Phytomonas stewarti* in relation to pathogenesis. *J. agric. Res.*, **47**, 749.

JACOBS, S. E. & MOHANTY, U. (1951). Studies in bacteriosis. XXVII. Factors influencing infection by *Corynebacterium fascians* (Tilford) Dowson. *Ann. appl. Biol.*, **38**, 237.

JAMES, N. (1955). Yellow chromogenic bacteria on wheat. II. Determinative studies. *Can. J. Microbiol.*, **1**, 479.

JAMES, N. WILSON, J. & STARK, E. (1946). The microflora of stored wheat. *Can. J. Res.*, **24**, 224.

JENSEN, H. L. (1934). Studies on saprophytic mycobacteria and corynebacteria. *Proc. Linn. Soc. N.S.W.*, **59**, 19.

KELMAN, A. (1953). The bacterial wilt caused by *Pseudomonas solanacearum*. *Tech. Bull. N. Carol. agric. Exp. Stn*, **99**, 194.

KERR, A. (1953). A method of isolating soft rotting bacteria from soils. *Nature, Lond.*, **172**, 1155.

KLEIN, D. T. & KLEIN, R. M. (1953). Transmittance of tumor inducing ability to avirulent Crown-gall and related bacteria. *J. Bact.*, **66**, 220.

KLEIN, D. T. & KLEIN, R. M. (1956). Quantitative aspects of transformation of virulence in *Agrobacterium tumefaciens*. *J. Bact.*, **72**, 308.

KOSER, S. A. (1926). The *coli-aerogenes* group in soil. *J. Am. Wat. Wks Ass.*, **15**, 641.

LACEY, M. S. (1955). The cytology and relationships of *Corynebacterium fascians*. *Trans. Br. mycol. Soc.*, **38**, 49.

LEACH, J. G. (1930). Potato blackleg: the survival of the pathogen in the soil and some factors influencing infection. *Phytopathology*, **20**, 215.

LEACH, J. G., LILLY, V. G., WILSON, H. A. & PURVIS, M. R. (1957). Bacterial polysaccharides: the nature and function of the exudates produced by *Xanthomonas phaseoli*. *Phytopathology*, **47**, 113.

LEBEN, C. (1961). Microorganisms on cucumber seed. *Phytopathology*, **51**, 553.

LEBEN, G. (1963). Multiplication of *Xanthomonas vesicatoria* on tomato seedlings. *Phytopathology*, **53**, 778.

LEE, H. A. (1920). Behaviour of the citrus canker organism in the soil. *J. agric. Res.*, **19**, 189.

MASSEY, R. E. (1931). Studies on blackarm disease of cotton. *Emp. Cott. Grow. Rev.*, **8**, 187.

MEDREK, T. F. & LITSKY, W. (1960). Comparative incidence of coliform bacteria and enterococci in undisturbed soils. *Appl. Microbiol.*, **8**, 60.

MUNNECKE, D. E. (1956). Survival of *Xanthomonas pelargonii* in soil. *Phytopathology*, **46**, 297.

NELSON, G. A. & SEMENUIK, G. (1963). Persistence of *Corynebacterium insidiosum* in the soil. *Phytopathology*, **53**, 1167.

NORTH, D. S. (1935). The gumming disease of sugar cane, its dissemination and control. *Agric. Rep. colon. Sug. Refg. Co.*, **10**, 149.

OKABE, N. & GOTO, M. (1961). Studies on *Pseudomonas solanacearum*. XI. Pathotypes in Japan. *Rep. Fac. Agric. Shizuoka Univ.*, **11**, 25.

ORTON, C. R. (1931). Seed borne parasites—a bibliography. *W. Va Agric. Stn Bull.*, **245**, 47.

PATEL, M. K. (1926). An improved method of isolating *Pseudomonas tumefaciens*, Sm. and Town. *Phytopathology*, **16**, 577.

PATEL, M. K. (1928). A study of pathogenic and non-pathogenic strains of *Pseudomonas tumefaciens*. *Phytopathology*, **18**, 331.

PATEL, M. K. (1929*a*). Biological studies of *Phytomonas tumefaciens* Sm. and Town. and fifteen related non-pathogenic organisms. *Iowa St. Coll. J. Sci.*, **3**, 271.

PATEL, M. K. (1929*b*). Viability of certain plant pathogens in soils. *Phytopathology*, **19**, 295.

PATON, A. M. (1958). Pectin decomposing strains of *Pseudomonas*. *Nature, Lond.*, **181**, 61.

PATRICK, Z. A. (1954). The antibiotic activity of soil micro-organisms as related to bacterial plant pathogens. *Can. J. Bot.*, **32**, 705.

PETERSON, G. H. (1963). Survival of *Xanthomonas vesicatoria* in soil and diseased tomato plants. *Phytopathology*, **53**, 765.

PITCHER, R. S. & CROSSE, J. E. (1958). Studies on the relationship of eelworms and bacteria to certain plant diseases. II. Further analysis of the strawberry cauliflower disease complex. *Nematologica*, **3**, 244.

PUGSLEY, A. T. (1936). Halo blight of beans. Varietal resistance tests. *J. Dep. Agric. Vict.*, **34**, 311.

RAND, F. V. & CASH, E. C. (1920). Some insect relations of *Bacillus tracheiphilus* Erw. Sm., *Phytopathology*, **10**, 133.

RAND, F. V. & ENLOWS, E. M. A. (1916). Transmission and control of bacterial wilt of cucurbits. *J. agric. Res.*, **6**, 417.

REID, J. J., NAGHSKI, J., FARRELL, M. A. & HALEY, D. E. (1942). Bacterial leaf spots of Pennsylvania tobacco. I. Occurrence and nature of the micro-organisms associated with wildfire. *Bull. Pa agric. Exp. Stn*, **422**, 36.

RHODES, M. E. (1959). The characterisation of *Pseudomonas fluorescens*. *J. gen. Microbiol.*, **21**, 221.

RHODES, M. E. (1961). The characterisation of *Pseudomonas flourescens* with the aid of an electronic computer. *J. gen. Microbiol.*, **25**, 331.

ROQUE, A. (1933). Bacterial wilt of tobacco in Puerto Rico and its inter-transmisssion to other solanaceous hosts. *J. Dep. Agric. P. Rico*, **17**, 145.

ROUATT, J. W. & KATZNELSON, H. (1961). A study of the bacteria on the root surface and in the rhizosphere of crop plants. *J. appl. Bact.*, **24**, 164.

RUINEN, J. (1961). The phyllosphere. I. An ecologically neglected milieu. *Pl. Soil*, **15**, 81.

SAGEN, H. E., RIKER, A. J. & BALDWIN, I. L. (1934). Studies on certain physiological characters of *Phytomonas tumefaciens*, *Phytomonas rhizogenes* and *Bacillus radiobacter*. *J. Bact.*, **28**, 571.

ST. JOHN-BROOKS, R., NAIN, K. & RHODES, M. (1925). The investigation of phytopathogenic bacteria by serological and biochemical methods. *J. Path. Bact.*, **28**, 203.

SCHWARZ, M. B. (1926). De invloed van de voorvrucht op het optreden van slijmziekte (*Bacterium solanacearum*) in *Arachis hypogaea* en eenige andere gewassen. *Meded. Inst. PlZiekt.*, **71**, 37.

SEQUEIRA, L. (1958). Bacterial wilt of bananas: dissemination of the pathogen and control of the disease. *Phytopathology*, **48**, 64.

SEQUEIRA, L. (1962). Control of bacterial wilt of bananas by crop rotation and fallowing. *Trop. Agric., Trin.*, **39**, 211.

SEQUEIRA, L. & AVERRE, C. W. (1961). Distribution and pathogenicity of strains of

*Pseudomonas solanacearum* from virgin soils in Costa Rica. *Pl. Dis. Reptr*, **45**, 435.

SHEWAN, J. M., HOBBS, G. & HODGKISS, W. (1960). A determinative scheme for the identification of certain genera of Gram-negative bacteria with special reference to the Pseudomonadaceae. *J. appl. Bact.*, **23**, 379.

SKORIC, V. (1927). Bacterial blight of pea: overwintering, dissemination and pathological histology. *Phytopathology*, **17**, 611.

SMITH, T. E. (1944). Control of bacterial wilt (*Bacterium solanacearum*) of tobacco as influenced by crop rotation and chemical treatment of the soil. *Circ. U.S. Dep. Agric.*, **692**, 16.

SMITH, T. E. (1962). A variant culture of *Xanthomonas malvacearum* obtained from weed roots. *Phytopathology*, **52**, 1313.

SNIESZKO, S. F. & BONDE, R. (1943). Studies on the morphology, physiology, serology, longevity and pathogenicity of *Corynebacterium sepedonicum*. *Phytopathology*, **33**, 1032.

STARR, M. P. (1959). Bacteria as plant pathogens. *A. Rev. Microbiol.*, **13**, 211.

STARR, M. P. & STEPHENS, W. L. (1964). Pigmentation and taxonomy of the genus *Xanthomonas*. *J. Bact.*, **87**, 293.

STOLP, H. (1961). Neue Erkenntinisse über phytopathogene Bakterien und die von ihnen verursachten Krankheiten. I. Verwandtschaftsbeziehungen zwischen phytopathogenen *Pseudomonas*—'Arten' und saprophytischen Fluoreszenten auf der Grundlage von Phagenreaktionen. *Phytopath. Z.*, **42**, 197.

STOUGHTON, R. H. (1930). The influence of environmental conditions on the development of angular leaf-spot disease of cotton. II. The influence of soil temperature on primary and secondary infection of seedlings. *Ann. appl. Biol.*, **17**, 493.

STOUGHTON, R. H. (1933). The influence of environmental conditions on the development of angular leaf-spot disease of cotton. V. The influence of alternating and varying conditions on infection. *Ann. appl. Biol.*, **20**, 590.

STOUT, J. D. (1960*a*). Biological studies of some tussock-grassland soils. XV. Bacteria of two cultivated soils. *N.Z. J. agric. Res.*, **3**, 214.

STOUT, J. D. (1960*b*). Bacteria of soil and pasture leaves at Claudelands Showgrounds. *N.Z. J. agric. Res.*, **3**, 413.

TAYLOR, C. B. (1951*a*). *Coli-aerogenes* bacteria in soils. *J. Hyg., Camb.*, **49**, 162.

TAYLOR, C. B. (1951*b*). The soft-rot bacteria of the *coli-aerogenes* group. *Proc. Soc. appl. Bact.*, **14**, 95.

THOMAS, H. E. & PARKER, K. G. (1933). Fireblight of pear and apple. *Bull. Cornell Univ. agric. Exp. Stn*, **557**, 24.

THOMAS, S. B. & HOBSON, P. M. (1955). Coli-aerogenes bacteria isolated from ears and panicles of cereal crops. *Proc. Soc. appl. Bact.*, **18**, 1.

TOPPING, L. E. (1937). The predominant micro-organisms in soils. I. Description and classification of the organisms. *Zentbl. Bakt. ParasitKde., Abt. II*, **97**, 289.

TYNER, L. E. (1947). Studies on ring rot of potato caused by *Corynebacterium sepedonicum*. *Scient. Agric.*, **27**, 81.

VALLEAU, W. D., JOHNSON, E. M. & DIACHUN, S. (1944). Root infection of crop plants and weeds by tobacco leaf spot bacteria. *Phytopathology*, **34**, 163.

VOROKEVICH, I. V. (1960). On the survival in the soil of bacteria of the genus *Erwinia*, causal agent of soft rots in plants. *Byull. mosk. Obshch. Ispyt. Prir. Ser. biol.*, **65**, 95.

WAGER, V. A. (1945). Bacterial wilt in potatoes. *Fmg S. Afr.*, **20**, 501.

WAITE, M. B. (1902). The relation of bees to the orchard. *Calif. Cultiv.*, **18**, 390.

WALDEE, E. L. (1945). Comparative studies of some peritrichous phytopathogenic bacteria. *Iowa St. Coll. J. Sci.*, **19**, 435.

WALLACE, R. H. & LOCHHEAD, A. G. (1951). Bacteria associated with seeds of various crop plants. *Soil Sci.*, **71**, 159.

WARDLAW, C. W. & MCGUIRE, L. P. (1933). Cultivation and diseases of bananas in Brazil. *Trop. Agric., Trin.*, **10**, 211.

WICKENS, G. M. (1953). Bacterial blight of cotton. *Res. Mem. Emp. Cott. Grow. Corp.*, **15**, 23.

WIEHE, P. O. (1939). Division of plant pathology. *A. Rep. Mauritius Dept. Agr. for 1938*, 34.

WILES, A. B. & WALKER, J. C. (1952). Epidemiology and control of angular leaf spot of cucumber. *Phytopathology*, **42**, 105.

WILSON, R. D. (1946). Soil carry-over of the bean halo blight disease. *J. Aust. Inst. agric. Sci.*, **12**, 103.

WORMALD, H. (1945). Physiologic races of the crown gall organism in Britain. *Trans. Br. mycol. Soc.*, **28**, 134.

# THE ANAEROBIC BACTERIA OF SOIL

F. A. SKINNER

*Soil Microbiology Department, Rothamsted Experimental Station, Harpenden, Hertfordshire*

## *INTRODUCTION*

Well-drained soils are usually aerobic, especially in the upper layers, though those rich in organic matter can become deficient in oxygen even near the surface. In soils with impeded drainage, waterlogging can cause widespread anaerobiosis. These anaerobic conditions favour the biological production of characteristic reduced compounds which may be organic such as methane, or inorganic such as gaseous nitrogen or hydrogen sulphide. Some such compounds are formed by obligate anaerobes that have specialized nutritional requirements. Other reductions are mediated by facultative anaerobes most of which are less specialized.

Facultative anaerobes are numerous and occur in all the major taxonomic groups of bacteria Estimates based upon *Bergey's Manual of Determinative Bacteriology* (Breed, Murray and Smith, 1957) for numbers of facultative species in the Pseudomonadales and Eubac teriales are 36 per cent and 38 per cent respectively; the Actinomycetales, a predominantly aerobic order, has only 3 per cent of facultative anaerobes. These figures are under-estimates because many bacteria referred to as aerobic are probably facultatively so, and because for many species there is no information. It is impracticable to discuss the many reactions by which facultative anaerobes obtain energy for cell synthesis, so attention is directed to one activity, nitrate reduction, which is shared by many.

## *THE REDUCTION OF NITRATE*

Many bacteria, including some usually regarded as typical aerobes, can derive energy by using nitrate instead of molecular oxygen to oxidize substrates. Of the soil species in the orders mentioned above, the proportions able to reduce nitrate are 39 per cent, 49 per cent and 57 per cent respectively. Almost all of the species reduce nitrate to nitrite, a process that has been termed 'nitrate respiration' by Sato (1950), to distinguish it from processes by which bacteria utilize nitrate as a nitrogen source.

Taniguchi, Sato and Egami (1956) noted that, in *E. coli*, the same electron transport chain involving cytochrome $b_1$ seemed to serve in both aerobic and anaerobic respiration, though the terminal steps differed. Anaerobically, the enzyme nitrate reductase transfers electrons to nitrate and thus takes the place of molecular oxygen and the terminal oxidase that function in aerobic conditions. Sadana and McElroy (1957) separated a nitrate-reducing system from *Achromobacter fischeri* into 2 soluble portions: one, the electron donor system, contained a component similar to mammalian cytochrome c; the other contained the terminal system, including nitrate reductase.

Though there is now much evidence to implicate cytochromes in nitrate-reducing systems (Granick and Gilder, 1946), there are some bacteria, e.g. *Bacillus subtilis*, in which the reduced state of the cytochromes is not affected by the nitrate reduction process and is therefore probably not concerned in it. There are, too, certain obligate anaerobes such as *Clostridium welchii* that lack cytochromes, but can still reduce nitrates (Sato, 1956). Many facultative anaerobes possess a nitrate-reducing system in which cytochrome pigments undoubtedly play an essential part.

Some steps in nitrate respiration can be expected to yield energy, probably by forming high-energy phosphate bonds. Evidence for this is inconclusive but the work of Takahashi, Taniguchi and Egami (1956) and Ohnishi and Mori (1960) with intact cells indicated the coupling of phosphorylation to nitrate respiration.

Nitrite itself can be reduced further by some bacteria, even to the extent of yielding gaseous nitrogen or nitrous oxide. This phenomenon was first studied by Gayon and Dupetit (1886) who called it 'denitrification'. Bacteria able to denitrify have since been found almost universally in soil and water though the well-characterized species are few and occur mainly in the genera *Pseudomonas*, *Micrococcus*, and *Bacillus*. The autotroph, *Thiobacillus denitrificans*, can oxidize thiosulphate to sulphate anaerobically, using nitrate as the hydrogen acceptor, which is thereby reduced to molecular nitrogen.

The importance of cytochromes to the denitrifiers has been established. Sacks (1948) found cytochrome c to be implicated in the reduction of nitrate and nitrite in *Pseudomonas denitrificans*, and Kamen and Vernon (1955) confirmed the presence of cytochromes of the c type in this species and in *Micrococcus denitrificans*.

The importance of maintaining strictly anaerobic conditions for denitrification is still controversial but the general view is that oxygen inhibits denitrification because it competes with nitrate as an acceptor of electrons (Delwiche, 1956). Skerman and MacRae, (1957*a*, *b*) failed to observe nitrate reduction by *Pseudomonas denitrificans* even when only a little oxygen was present in the medium. They concluded that when nitrate reduction occurred in aerated suspensions it was brought about by cells deprived of oxygen. Collins (1955) came to a similar conclusion for *P. aeruginosa*, and Fedorov and Sergeeva (1957) for this same organism and for *P. fluorescens*. However, Verhoeven (1952), working with *Denitrobacillus* (*Bacillus*) *licheniformis*, found that though vigorous aeration largely prevented nitrate reduction, small amounts of oxygen did not stop the reduction of a large proportion of the nitrate to ammonia.

Kefauver and Allison (1957) found that *Bacterium denitrificans* could use both molecular oxygen and nitrite simultaneously, but oxygen was used preferentially. Meiklejohn (1940) found that two strains of denitrifying *Pseudomonas* reduced nitrate to nitrite, then to nitrogen in a shallow layer of liquid medium in a vessel supplied with air. She concluded that there were two nitrate-reducing systems, an oxygen-sensitive nitrate reductase system and a reducing enzyme system in some denitrifying bacteria which is not sensitive to oxygen.

Further details on the biochemistry of nitrate reduction and denitrification are given in the extensive review by Nason and Takahashi (1958).

Bacterial denitrification is probably mainly responsible for the losses of gaseous nitrogen and nitrous oxide from soils. These losses are considerable, a mean figure for the rate of reduction of organic nitrogen compounds to gaseous nitrogen products is about 20 lb. of nitrogen/acre/year for the whole of the earth's surface (Russell, 1961). Denitrification occurs typically in waterlogged soils that have been supplied with nitrate fertilizer, or in soils that become waterlogged after aerobic nitrification has increased the nitrate content. Soils with much readily decomposable organic matter, such as farmyard manure, will denitrify easily even when well-aerated, probably because many small pockets of soil are rendered anaerobic by aerobes rapidly removing oxygen. Skerman and MacRae (1957*b*) consider that soil water held in capillary spaces between soil particles is likely to become deficient in oxygen and so permit nitrate reduction even in relatively dry soil. In moderately well-aerated soils, ammonium ions can first be oxidized to nitrate in the more aerobic parts of the soil, and then be denitrified in the anaerobic regions. Both processes can sometimes proceed simultaneously in the same soil (Loewenstein, Englebert, Attoe and Allen, 1957).

Though waterlogging is avoided in temperate agriculture, it is a normal feature of rice cultivation. Flooded paddy soil is anaerobic but nitrate reduction is rare unless nitrate is added in fertilizer: nitrites can then accumulate sufficiently to poison the crop. For this reason ammonium salts or green manures are used instead of nitrate fertilizers. Organic amendments that are rich in protein typically yield ammonia by deamination of amino acids when decomposed anaerobically.

Decomposing organic matter rich in carbohydrates produces organic acids such as lactic, acetic and butyric, which serve as substrates for methane bacteria. According to Harrison and Aiyer (1913, 1914), the principal gas in waterlogged paddy soils is methane with only small amounts of $CO_2$, $H_2$ and $N_2$, but the gases in the water above the soil are almost entirely oxygen and nitrogen. The surface layers of the submerged soil contain methane oxidizing bacteria and algae; the bacteria produce carbon dioxide which is then converted by the algae to oxygen. Drainage of this water through the flooded soil provides oxygen for the rice plant roots.

## *THE REDUCTION OF SULPHATE*

Unlike the reduction of nitrate, which can be brought about by many different facultative bacteria, sulphate is reduced by only a few specialized obligate anaerobes. Two or three mesophilic species have been described of which *Desulphovibrio desulphuricans* is the most studied; a thermophilic spore-former, *Clostridium nigrificans*, seems not to be closely related to the other species. These organisms are widely distributed in soils and water and grow best near neutrality although they have a pH range of 5·5–9·0, and in strongly reducing conditions (Eh of about − 200 mv.). Development is promoted by reducing agents or by the presence of decomposable organic matter that encourages the proliferation of micro-organisms and thereby lowers the redox potential. The end-product, sulphide, is itself a powerful reducing agent so once the organisms start to grow they tend to spread rapidly, provided the appropriate nutrients and sulphate are present and air is excluded.

Sulphate serves as oxidizing agent for a wide range of organic compounds acting as hydrogen donors. Sulphate reducing bacteria cannot attack cellulose but are commonly encountered where cellulose is decomposing anaerobically, probably because the organic acids produced become substrates for the sulphate reducers. Sulphate reducers can also utilize sulphite, thiosulphate and tetrathionate.

*D. desulphuricans* possesses a c type cytochrome; an unusual feature because cytochromes are typically absent from obligate anaerobes

(Postgate, 1954*a*). This cytochrome becomes oxidized when sulphate or sulphite is added to a cell suspension (Postgate, 1954*b*), so probably sulphate works in conjunction with a cytochrome-mediated electron transfer chain, electrons being finally transferred to sulphate by an appropriate reductase. This system is perhaps comparable with the nitrate-reducing system of facultative anaerobes, except that the terminal oxidase system is missing.

Sulphate-reducing bacteria are important in soils because they can cause serious corrosion of buried iron pipes and other structures. Many topsoils and sub-soils contain sulphate-reducing bacteria, and enough sulphate and organic matter to support their growth once conditions become sufficiently reducing. Iron then starts to corrode and strongly reducing areas form on the metal surface where the bacteria are actively producing sulphide. These areas become anodic to other parts which are free from sulphide or in contact with water containing dissolved oxygen. During the electrolytic corrosion process, which is accelerated by decomposable organic matter, hydrogen accumulates at the cathodic areas and must be removed if corrosion is to continue. The cathodic areas are thought to be continually depolarized by bacteria removing the hydrogen; many strains of *D. desulphuricans* can oxidize molecular hydrogen. Evidence generally supports this explanation of corrosion but there is still some doubt about the fate of the hydrogen from the depolarized cathode (Starkey, 1961; Booth, 1964).

Certain disorders of rice such as stunted growth and damaged root systems have been attributed to the toxic effects of sulphide accumulating in the anaerobic soil zone but De and Mandal (1957) found no evidence to support this view. Rodriguez-Kabana, Jordan and Hollis (1965) described an example of biological control of nematode populations in Louisiana rice soils in which hydrogen sulphide seems to play a key role. They observed that the populations of total and plant parasitic nematodes increased greatly in rice fields drained 2 weeks before harvest. This increase took place from August to November and was stimulated by fresh plant growth. The first traces of $H_2S$ (0·1 to 1 ppm.) appeared 5-7 days after flooding and increased to c. 35 ppm. in the soil water after 120 days; after 40 days nematode numbers declined markedly. The authors isolated what appeared to be a strain of *D. desulphuricans* from these soils. Rodriguez-Kabana and Jordan (1964) suggested that the $H_2S$ could also arise from a reaction between hydrogen ions of organic acids and sulphide ions from ferrous sulphide. This reaction would depend upon a supply of organic acids from organic matter, such as cellulose decomposing anaerobically.

## *THE REDUCTION OF PHOSPHATE*

The existence of obligate anaerobic bacteria able to reduce organic phosphorus compounds to hydrogen phosphide was recorded by Barrenscheen and Beckh-Widmanstetter (1923) who also reviewed the earlier literature on this subject. Rudakov (1927, 1929) claimed to have isolated bacteria able to reduce inorganic phosphate anaerobically first to phosphite, then to hypophospite, and finally to phosphine. However, Rudakov's results were adversely criticized by Liebert (1927) who maintained, on thermodynamic grounds, that microbiological reduction of phosphate was impossible.

More recently, Tsubota (1959) reported that some paddy soils reduced phosphate to gaseous phosphine and suggested that this was a mechanism by which phosphorus could be lost from soils: this process was called 'dephosphorification', by analogy with denitrification. Loss of soil phosphorus in this way was favoured by abundance of organic matter and warmth. However, Woolfolk and Whiteley (1962) found that extracts of the obligate anaerobe *Veillonella alcalescens* reduced some compounds of nitrogen, arsenic and bismuth using molecular hydrogen but not various inorganic compounds of phosphorus. They also considered that the reduction of phosphate was unlikely for thermodynamic reasons.

I have tried to detect phosphate-reducing bacteria in several soils but have failed to find any. Rudakov's medium (Rudakov, 1927), which was used, is not selective, because phosphate is required by all micro-organisms but tests with media containing phosphite as hydrogen acceptor were also unsuccessful. Evidence for the bacterial reduction of phosphate or organically bound phosphorus is still inconclusive.

## *THE BACTERIAL FORMATION OF METHANE*

The production of methane in flooded paddy soils has already been noted; it is also commonly produced from the mud at the bottom of ponds and lakes where organic debris accumulates. However, production in waterlogged arable or pasture soils in any but trace quantities seems so rare that it is perhaps of some interest to describe the formation of methane in considerable quantities from some unusual garden soil that was investigated at Eckington in Derbyshire in 1960 (Skinner, 1962).

Inflammable gas was observed coming from holes and small fissures in the topsoil of several gardens but a deep borehole did not yield any evidence of gas originating from underlying coal measures; the gas was evidently produced in the top layers of soil. Three bores were made with a $1\frac{1}{4}$ in. auger to a depth of c. 75 cm. After removing each core section (c. 25 cm. long) a match was applied to the hole; each time the gas within ignited and burned with a hot and almost colourless flame for 2 or 3 seconds. Other holes 25 cm. deep were bored in many parts of the affected area, about 0·2 acre, and showed widespread occurrence of the gas.

The topsoil extending to c. 38 cm. in depth was black, moist and friable with a sweetish foetid odour, and a slightly alkaline reaction (pH 7·5). Below this was a layer of silty clay, which between 58 and 75 cm. became sandy. Analysis of soil from the top 25 cm. gave 9·9 per cent organic carbon and 0·76 per cent combined nitrogen, both unusually high. A 220 g. sample of this soil was enclosed in a 6 oz. bottle connected to a reservoir to collect gas and incubated at 35°. Between the 7th and 34th days, c. 1,200 ml. gas were produced: this burned readily and an analysis on the 32nd day gave $CH_4$, 70·7 per cent; $CO_2$, 27·3 per cent; $N_2$, 2·0 per cent. Such a gas is typical of those produced by the anaerobic fermentation of organic matter under neutral or slightly alkaline conditions. Samples of soil from 25-38 cm. and 38-50 cm. did not yield methane on incubation.

Partial waterlogging resulting from impeded drainage and the unusually large content of organic matter was adequate to explain the evolution of methane. This soil originated by the dumping of topsoil from piggeries, containing much pig manure, on to an already badly drained soil.

When classified by cell morphology the methane bacteria do not appear as a homogeneous group; however, they have unusual physiological features in common so perhaps it is justifiable to include them in a single family, the Methanobacteriaceae, as suggested by Barker (1956). The commonest substrates for these bacteria are fatty acids (formic to n-caproic), alcohols (methanol to n-pentanol), CO, and $CO_2$ and $H_2$. Knowledge of the physiology of these organisms has progressed slowly because of the great difficulty in obtaining them in pure culture. Barker (1936*b*) isolated several pure cultures using specially developed techniques, the key features of which were the use of simple mineral media with the required substrate (e.g. formate), a suitable reducing agent (e.g. sulphide) in the medium, and the strict exclusion of oxygen at every stage of cultivation or transfer of inoculum.

Successive transfer into tubes of molten agar medium is probably still the most satisfactory method for isolating separate colonies of methane bacteria (Barker, 1936*b*). Various modifications of Barker's original method have been used, mostly changing the reducing agent employed. The same basic method has been used in my work on an acetate-decomposing methane bacterium. The culture tube preferred is a Burri tube modified by including a black glass rod supported vertically in the lower stopper to facilitate counting of colonies, a technique similar to that recommended for test tubes by Ingram and Barnes (1956). Removing the lower stopper withdraws the whole agar culture, thus making it easy to pick the colonies without having to break open the tube or break up the agar. Care must be taken not to expose the colonies unduly to the air, but it seems unnecessary to resort to complicated apparatus such as that depicted by Buraczewski (1964).

To maintain methane cultures, Barker devised a tube with an inner fermentation compartment closed with a glass ball which allows fermentation gases to escape but not air to enter. Attempts to use small screw-capped bottles with more reliable valves than glass balls showed that it was not necessary to allow fermentation gases to escape continuously; slight occasional loosening of the cap was all that was necessary. The strain of acetate-decomposer mentioned above grows well in such bottles when permanently sealed. Gas pressures greater than 35 psi, with gas still rising from the bottom deposit, are common in such cultures after a few days' incubation. The 1 oz. bottles used for these cultures have never burst but, for handling, use of a protective metal container is advised before the pressure is released by hypodermic needle through the rubber cap liner.

No general explanation of the methane-forming process was formulated until Van Niel advanced the carbon dioxide reduction theory (Barker, 1936*a*). This postulates that organic compounds are oxidized completely to $CO_2$, some or all of which is subsequently reduced to methane. However, Stadtman and Barker (1949, 1951) showed by tracer experiments that methane is produced from acetate entirely from the methyl carbon, and carbon dioxide entirely from the carbonyl carbon of acetate. Pine and Barker (1956) confirmed these results for acetate and also established that one hydrogen atom per molecule of methane derives from the solvent water. Some organisms, e.g. a species of *Methanosarcina* that ferments acetate and methanol, can also reduce $CO_2$ to methane in the presence of hydrogen. It seems improbable that one organism possesses two mechanisms for making methane from different substrates. Barker (1956) has suggested a scheme to reconcile these concepts by postulating the linkage of $CO_2$ to a carbon dioxide acceptor (XH) to yield X.COOH, which is reduced step by step to

X.$CH_3$ and finally to XH + $CH_4$. The compound X.$CH_3$ might be formed directly from an organic methyl group donor such as acetate. The nature of XH is still unknown but the ability of methane bacteria to form cyanocobalamin and other closely related compounds has led some to suspect their implication in this reductive pathway (Knivett, 1960).

There is no doubt that $H_2$ and $CO_2$ are often the major nutrients for methane bacteria (Smith and Hungate, 1958), and they have been used successfully for the enrichment and isolation of formate decomposers (Mylroie and Hungate, 1954). Carroll and Hungate (1955) in tracer experiments with $H^{14}COONa$ and rumen contents showed that the carbon was converted quantitatively to $^{14}CO_2$, so that methane production from formate includes an initial split to $CO_2$ and $H_2$. The $CO_2$ is then reduced and the methane is not formed directly from the formate. Brill, Wolin and Wolfe (1964) showed that, in cell-free extracts of *Methanobacillus omelianskii*, the electron carrier pigment ferredoxin liberates $CO_2$ from formate, the reduced ferredoxin being subsequently re-oxidized by pyridine nucleotides. The naturally occurring ferredoxin was removed and could be replaced by partially purified ferredoxin from the same organism or from *Clostridium pasteurianum* and *C. acidi-urici*.

It is interesting to note that the inflammable gas produced in the soil at Eckington (see above) did not contain hydrogen although hydrogen is produced in many types of fermentation by both facultative and obligate anaerobes. It is probable that any hydrogen produced was utilized by methane bacteria to reduce $CO_2$. The ability of a suspension of this soil to ferment formate rapidly showed that it contained many bacteria likely to be able to reduce $CO_2$ with molecular hydrogen.

## *THE CLOSTRIDIA*

The soil is the principal habitat of the spore-forming obligate anaerobes, the clostridia. The genus *Clostridium* divides fairly neatly into two sections, comprising the saccharolytic and proteolytic types; as a group they can decompose anaerobically a wide range of carbohydrate and nitrogenous substrates. The clostridia have been most studied by food and medical bacteriologists because *Clostridium* contains several species that are pathogens and others that spoil food and make it toxic.

Gibbs and Freame (1965) using a most probable number (MPN) method found the number of clostridia (as spores) in 6 Midland soils to range from $35 \times 10^3$ to $13 \times 10^5$/g.: one of the commonest species was *C. welchii*, present in at least several thousands per g. in these soils. These *C. welchii* strains are usually highly pathogenic (for mice) when freshly isolated but quickly lose the ability to form toxin when cultured on laboratory media (Gibbs, personal communication).

Although counting clostridia poses special problems, because of the requirement for strict anaerobic conditions, and because the gas which forms disrupts solid media, there are reasonably satisfactory methods. The reinforced clostridial medium (RCM, Oxoid) designed by Hirsch and Grinsted (1954) grows clostridia well, though it is not completely selective as some lactobacilli and streptococci grow in it, and when solidified with agar (RCA) it can be used for deep agar cultures. For counting, serial dilutions of inoculum are made in RCA contained either in Miller-Prickett tubes (Mossel *et al.*, 1956) or in narrow test tubes with black glass rods to facilitate colony observation (Ingram and Barnes, 1956). A more selective medium based on the ability of most clostridia to blacken media containing sulphite and iron was devised by Gibbs and Freame (1965), who also reviewed other media and methods in common use.

Two anaerobic processes largely caused by specialized groups of clostridia are of particular interest to soil bacteriologists; these are cellulose decomposition and nitrogen fixation.

*Anaerobic cellulose decomposition*

The spore-forming cellulose decomposers are widely distributed in soils but not often numerous, though in some more constantly anaerobic habitats, such as pond muds, they are plentiful and active. Enrichment cultures of soil cellulose decomposers can be readily prepared by adding cellulose and maintaining anaerobic conditions. The method commonly employed is to use a small bottle completely filled with a mineral salt solution, such as that of Omelianski (1902), together with chopped filter paper, the whole being autoclaved to sterilize and remove air. The bottle is then inoculated with soil and the stopper replaced to leave no air space. Attack on the cellulose is usually detectable after a few days at 35°. Oxygen need not be excluded from a primary enrichment culture because the many contaminants present will quickly grow on other substrates in the soil inoculum and bring about reducing conditions favouring cellulolytic anaerobes. In subsequent enrichments, containing almost no substrates but cellulose, reducing agents must be provided and oxygen excluded completely.

As a technique for isolating species, enrichment has the disadvantage that when more than one species is present they are unlikely all to grow at the same rates and one may quickly predominate. Hungate (1950) has pointed out that when a population of cellulolytic anaerobes contains both spore-forming and non spore-forming species, enrichment rapidly eliminates the latter; probably the spore formers are more resistant to the highly acid conditions that develop in such cultures. Thus, though enrichment may help to isolate a pure strain, it may diminish the chance of finding new and more delicate types.

For many years attempts to isolate these bacteria met with little success though some isolations were made from human faeces (Khouvine, 1923), soil (Clausen, 1931), horse faeces (Cowles and Rettger, 1931) and the bovine rumen (Hungate, 1944). Rumen studies by Hungate (1944, 1950) demonstrated the importance of maintaining strictly anaerobic conditions throughout all the isolation procedures, especially when dealing with non spore-forming types. Spore formers seem to be more characteristic of soils and are more robust, but even these can be isolated with the least trouble by using these methods. Hungate (1950) stressed the need to grow these organisms in solid media containing finely-divided cellulose. Only thus can individual colonies of obviously cellulolytic bacteria be secured. It is also important to provide growth factors (e.g. soil extract), a buffering system (e.g. carbonate-bicarbonate or phosphate) and reducing agents (e.g. cysteine). The preparation of such cultures has been described in detail by Hungate (1950).

Using different though related techniques, Skinner (1960) made isolations from soil with and without enrichment. Agar medium containing finely-divided cellulose was sterilized in 85 ml. flat screw-capped bottles so as to exclude oxygen. After inoculating the molten cooled medium, each bottle was flushed with oxygen-free nitrogen and the medium allowed to set as a thin layer on one of the larger sides. Growth in such cultures is slow and 2-3 weeks at 35° are needed before cellulose-digesting colonies appear. Growth is also slow even when the cellulose particles are prevented from flocculating by traces of carboxymethyl cellulose in the medium so it seems therefore not to be caused by inability of the bacteria to make contact with the cellulose; it is perhaps a feature of the bacterial breakdown of native cellulose in pure form (Halliwell, 1963). Colonies are usually punctiform and surrounded by well-defined clear digestion zones, though thin spreading colonies also appear on the agar surface or at the agar-glass interface. Punctiform colonies often yield pure cultures but the thin spreading growth is almost always contaminated by having mingled with other colonies on the agar surface.

A special relationship is generally considered to exist between the cellulolytic anaerobes and the methane bacteria. Typical end-products of the cellulolytic clostridia are formic and acetic acids, $CO_2$ and hydrogen; all of these act as substrates for methane-producing bacteria. Thus, when both kinds of bacteria are present insoluble cellulose is converted entirely to gaseous products. This conversion of cellulose to methane was studied with mixed cultures containing a strain of *Clostridium cellobioparum* (Skinner, 1960) and two strains of methane bacteria able to use formate and acetate respectively.

The methane cultures were first established in a liquid medium containing cellulose and some of the appropriate fatty acids and 5 days later the cellulolytic bacteria were introduced. Cellulose was digested with a steady evolution of methane for 10 weeks. By this time about $\frac{3}{4}$ of the cellulose had disappeared; the pH remained at c. 7·0, and the culture had a 'tarry' odour characteristic of digesting sewage sludge. Control cultures without methane bacteria quickly became acid (pH 5·2) but the cellulose disappeared in less than 10 weeks. Cellulose was not digested faster when the end-products were removed but rather seemed to be slowed (Skinner, 1961). Attempts to make composite cultures by inoculating both types of bacteria together failed because the cellulose decomposers always made the medium too acid before the methane bacteria could begin to convert the end-products.

*Nitrogen-fixing clostridia*

The nitrogen content of soils can increase even when they are not carrying any leguminous plants, and the increase largely reflects the activities of soil micro-organisms (Russell, 1961). Several types of organism can fix atmospheric nitrogen of which the most intensively studied are aerobic bacteria of the genera *Azotobacter* and *Beijerinckia*, and anaerobes of the genus *Clostridium*. Representatives of all these genera fix nitrogen actively in culture but whether they contribute much to soil nitrogen is uncertain. Greater attention now centres on the clostridia because they occur more widely in soils and are more abundant than *Azotobacter* and *Beijerinckia*.

Meiklejohn (1956), using the potato tube method of Jensen (1951), found that nitrogen-fixing clostridia numbered $10^3$ to $10^5$/g. in soils of 4 plots from Broadbalk field (Rothamsted) whereas *Azotobacter* cells numbered only 0–800/g. similar results were found for soils from Ghana (Meiklejohn, 1962). How much nitrogen clostridia fix in soil is almost impossible to determine at the present time because: (*a*) it is not known how actively the clostridia fix nitrogen in soil, (*b*) there is doubt about the reliability of the counting methods used, and (*c*) there is uncertainty (though less often recognized) about which are the relevant organisms to count.

The soil bacterium observed by Winogradsky (1893) to grow in a liquid medium free from combined nitrogen was a saccharolytic clostridium. This organism, named *C. pasteurianum* (Winogradsky, 1895), forms gas and butyric acid from carbohydrates and is similar in many ways to *C. butyricum*, the type species of the genus. *C. pasteurianum* was described as a sub-species of *C. butyricum* in *Bergey's Manual of Determinative Bacteriology*, 6th edn. (Breed, Murray and Hitchens, 1948), but in the 7th edition it was raised to specific rank (Breed, Murray and Smith, 1957). Nitrogen fixation is now recognized as a property of several butyric acid clostridia though *C. pasteurianum* is a more efficient fixer than the others.

Batchelor and Curie (1929) counted nitrogen-fixing *C. butyricum* by a modification of the Winogradsky method for *Azotobacter*. Minute soil particles were distributed over a layer of N-free glucose-salts agar and then covered with a second layer to render them anaerobic. Typical *C. butyricum* colonies were recognized by adjacent gas splits in the agar; colonies of typical clostridial forms also stained deep blue with iodine. Swaby (1939) further modified this method for studies on the soils of Victoria. Soil particles and soil suspensions were each used as inocula and the plates were incubated in an oxygen-free atmosphere. *C. butyricum* was scarce in these soils: the highest count in 57 soils was 1,640/g.

Parker (1954) criticized Swaby's technique on the grounds that (*a*), many clostridia need growth factors not provided in the classical N-free media (based on that of Winogradsky), (*b*) essential $CO_2$ is absorbed by alkaline pyrogallol used to provide an oxygen-free atmosphere, and (*c*) pyrogallol evolves carbon monoxide which inhibits N-fixation. He regarded completely nitrogen-free media as unsatisfactory because all strains tested required growth factors contained in potato or yeast extracts. Unfortunately, the inclusion of more than trace quantities of nitrogenous compounds destroy the selectivity of media and so permit growth of other anaerobes.

These ideas have been further developed by Emtsev (1962) who showed that adding yeast extract and peptone to N-free Winogradsky-type medium increased the count of a reputedly pure strain of *C. pasteurianum* considerably. Five g./litre of peptone were used with trace elements and an unspecified amount of yeast extract. Colonies developing in deep tubes of this agar medium inoculated with soil suspensions were transferred to tubes of semi-solid N-free medium; the colonies that yielded gas and contained clostridia were identified as N-fixers. Of 152 colonies growing in the medium containing peptone and yeast extract only 3 failed to grow in the N-free medium. The use of an

N-free medium gave extremely low estimates of the numbers of N-fixing clostridia in the soil, whereas the numbers given by the supplemented medium were only a little too high. Emtsev concludes that the results for the richer non-selective medium reflect more accurately the number of N-fixing anaerobes present in soils.

The results of Emtsev have not been confirmed at Rothamsted. Soil solutions were used to inoculate series of Burri tubes containing RCA, and both of Emtsev's media (8 ml./tube). These Burri tubes were equipped with central black glass rods to facilitate counting, as described previously. Tubes of RCA, when set, were capped with RCA containing methylene blue (Ingram and Barnes, 1956). Some RCA tubes were incubated in air in the usual way (anaerobiosis being ensured by reducing substances in the medium and agar cap), others were incubated in McIntosh and Fildes jars with the tubes of inoculated Emtsev media. Inoculated plates of Emtsev media were also incubated in the jars. Jars were filled with nitrogen containing c. 10 per cent $CO_2$ and traces of oxygen were removed by pads of activated iron wool (Parker, 1955). Incubation was at 25° C. for 6 days; further incubation did not affect the counts. The results for duplicate cultures show almost identical total counts for RCA and the Emtsev medium (Table 1).

The use of an Emtsev medium with less agar, recommended to avoid the appearance of gas splits in the medium, was not satisfactory. Colonies appeared as faint diffuse spheres several mm. in diameter by outward spread of the organisms or as small pockets of sediment in the cavities of collapsed gas bubbles. Low counts suggested that minute colonies were undetectable in this medium.

The interesting point about these results is that the supplemented Emtsev medium gave almost the same counts as the RCA medium, specially designed to grow as many different species of *Clostridium* as possible. A nitrogen-free medium without growth factors gave very much smaller counts. Almost all the isolates from the rich media failed to grow well on N-free medium, but a few isolates grew outstandingly well even without growth factors. These results show that rich non-selective media have not given satisfactory indications of the number of nitrogen-fixing clostridia.

A further point of interest concerns the activity of these N-fixing clostridia in soils. Hart (1955) found that spore-forming bacteria able to grow on N-free glucose medium could be isolated from soil under aerobic conditions on a potato extract medium. Isolations on synthetic N-free media succeeded only in conditions of limited aeration or anaerobiosis. His results suggested that these organisms might be able to

TABLE 1

*Numbers of colonies of anaerobic bacteria growing in different media at 25°*

*(1 ml. of a $10^{-4}$ soil dilution to 8 ml. medium)*

| Medium | | No. colonies/tube or plate (means of duplicate counts) | | |
|---|---|---|---|---|
| | | Smooth colonies | Filamentous colonies | Total colonies |
| RCA (Oxoid) (incubated in air) | tube | 9·5 | 4·5 | 14·0* |
| RCA (Oxoid) (incubated in anaerobic jar) | tube | 10·0 | 3·0 | 13·0 |
| Emtsev N-free base + peptone and yeast extract | tube | 8·3 | 4·0 | 12·3 |
| | plate | 7·0 | 5·5 | 12·5 |
| Emtsev N-free base | tube | 0 | 1·0 | 1·0 |
| | plate | 1·5 | 0 | 1·5 |

* A count of 14 colonies/tube gives an estimate of 166,000 viable units/g. dry wt. of soil. (Water content of soil was 15·8 per cent.)

grow in a natural medium, such as soil, containing enough combined nitrogen. A high proportion of vegetative cells in the upper layer of garden soils suggested that the site of maximum growth was near the surface, though it was not certain that they were actively fixing nitrogen there. Hart suggested that the clostridia compete with aerobic bacteria for the sources of combined nitrogen in the upper soil layers. As the combined nitrogen is used, the clostridia may become increasingly active because of their ability to fix nitrogen when oxygen is lacking.

There seems no doubt that nitrogen fixers are stimulated by growth factors in potato. The indications are that growth factors, from potato or other sources such as yeast, should be included in media for the nitrogen-fixing clostridia, so as not to prejudice the chance of growth, but that the amounts should be kept to a minimum to preserve the selective quality of the media.

For many years *C. pasteurianum* and *C. butyricum* were regarded either as the sole or the principal nitrogen-fixing anaerobes for the good reason that the amount of nitrogen fixed could be clearly demonstrated by Kjeldahl analysis. However, more refined techniques using $^{15}N_2$ (Rosenblum and Wilson, 1949) have shown that some other *Clostridium* species also fix nitrogen but with varying efficiency.

Cells of almost all nitrogen-fixing species listed by Rosenblum and

Wilson (1949) stain blue with iodine (granulose reaction), a reaction long held to be diagnostic for N-fixing clostridia. However, there is no information about this reaction with species supposed not to fix N; moreover, there is some evidence that non-granulose storing anaerobes may also fix nitrogen (Tchan and Pochon, 1950).

This uncertainty about the nature of the bacteria that should be counted as nitrogen fixers makes it even more difficult to assess the role of the N-fixers in nature: a reasonable hypothesis would be to assign the major role to those able to fix nitrogen well, to grow vigorously in culture and to be plentiful in soil.

## *CONCLUSIONS*

The soil bacteria discussed in this paper are of many different kinds and have been grouped together solely because they can grow anaerobically. However, some of them have other features in common. For example, the cytochromes and associated enzymes important in nitrate reduction and denitrification may also be concerned in an analogous way in the reduction of sulphate. The pigment ferredoxin, which occurs in some clostridia, and is implicated in nitrogen fixation, also occurs in methane bacteria where it plays a part in the splitting of formate to $CO_2$ and $H_2$. That some methane bacteria also fix nitrogen suggests that ferredoxin may sometimes have a dual role. The spore-forming cellulose-decomposing bacteria resemble other saccharolytic clostridia in that they can utilize many different carbohydrates, but they have also a specialized enzyme system for digesting cellulose.

Much progress has been made recently in elucidating the mechanism of anaerobic nitrogen fixation and it may not be long before the way in which atmospheric nitrogen is activated and reduced becomes known (Mortenson, 1963). Other unusual biochemical reactions, such as the pathway of $CO_2$ reduction to methane and the nature of the primary enzymic attack on native cellulose by the cellulolytic anaerobes, are fascinating subjects for study, but progress may well depend upon greater facility in isolating undoubted pure cultures of these strictly anaerobic micro-organisms.

Soils that are not waterlogged for long periods or over-supplied with organic matter are unlikely to favour the considerable development of the more specialized obligate anaerobes. Only quickly growing facultative anaerobes, such as those that can change from aerobic to nitrate respiration at a high redox potential, and the butyric acid clostridia, are likely to respond to the occasional and temporary anaerobic conditions that obtain in many soils. The presence of many facultative anaerobes does not, of course, indicate the degree of anaerobiosis in the soil at that time. The proliferation of the more rapidly growing clostridia may be a better guide to the soil condition. Even so, the effect of such intermittent anaerobic activity cannot yet be assessed.

It is interesting to note that Casida (1965) has reported the presence of very large numbers of microaerophilic coccoid micro-organisms in several soils. He suggests that organisms of this type, which grow only on very rich media, make up a large part of the soil microflora.

Clearly, much remains unknown about the anaerobes themselves and about their significance in soil processes.

## *REFERENCES*


Barker, H. A. (1936*a*). On the biochemistry of the methane fermentation. *Arch. Mikrobiol.*, **7**, 404.

Barker, H. A. (1936*b*). Studies upon the methane-producing bacteria. *Arch. Mikrobiol.*, **7**, 420.

Barker, H. A. (1956). *Bacterial fermentations.* New York. John Wiley & Sons Inc.

Barrenscheen, H. K. & Beckh-Widmanstetter, H. A. (1923). Über bakterielle Reduktion organisch gebundener Phosphorsäure. *Biochem. Z.*, **140**, 279.

Batchelor, H. W. & Curie, I. H. (1929). A practical method for determining the number of *Clostridium butyricum* colonies in acid soil. *I. Bact.*, **17**, 25.

Booth, G. H. (1964). Sulphur bacteria in relation to corrosion. *J. appl. Bact.*, **27**, 174.

Breed, R. S., Murray, E. G. D. & Hitchens, A. P. (1948). *Bergey's manual of determinative bacteriology, 6th Edn.* London. Baillière, Tindall & Cox.

Breed, R. S., Murray, E. G. D. & Smith, N. R. (1957). *Bergey's manual of determinative bacteriology, 7th Edn.* London. Baillière, Tindall & Cox.

Brill, W. J., Wolin, E. A. & Wolfe, R. S. (1964). Anaerobic formate oxidation: a ferredoxin-dependent reaction. *Science*, **144**, 297.

Buraczewski, G. (1964). Methane fermentation of sewage sludge. I. The influence of physical and chemical factors on the development of methane bacteria and the course of fermentation. *Acta microbiol. pol.*, **13**, 321.

Carroll, E. J. & Hungate, R. E. (1955). Formate dissimilation and methane production in bovine rumen contents. *Arch. Biochem. Biophys.*, **56**, 525.

Casida, L. E. Jr. (1965). Abundant microorganism in soil. *Appl. Microbiol.*, **13**, 327.

Clausen, P. (1931). Studien über anaerobe Zellulosebazillen unter besonderer Berücksichtigung der Züchtungstechnik. *Zentbl. Bakt. ParasitKde., Abt. II*, **84**, 20.

Collins, F. M. (1955). Effect of aeration on the formation of nitrate-reducing enzymes by *Ps. aeruginosa. Nature, Lond.*, **175**, 173.

Cowles, P. B. & Rettger, L. F. (1931). Isolation and study of an apparently widespread cellulose-fermenting anaerobe, *Cl. cellulosolvens* (n. sp.?). *J. Bact.*, **21**, 167.

De, P. K. & Mandal, L. N. (1957). Physiological diseases of rice. *Soil Sci.*, **84**, 367.

Delwiche, C. C. (1956). Denitrification. In *Inorganic Nitrogen Metabolism.* Baltimore. The Johns Hopkins Press.

Emtsev, V. T. (1962). Quantitative estimation of anaerobic nitrogen-fixing butyric acid bacteria belonging to the genus *Clostridium* in soil. *Mikrobiologiya*, **31**, 288.

Fedorov, M. V. & Sergeeva, R. V. (1957). The effect of oxidation-reduction conditions of the medium on the rate of reduction of nitrates by denitrifying bacteria. *Mikrobiologiya*, **26**, 137.

Gayon, V. & Dupetit, G. (1886). Recherches sur la réduction des nitrates par les infiniment petits. *Mém. soc. sci. phys. nat. Bordeaux*, **2**, 201.

Gibbs, B. M. & Freame, B. (1965). Methods for the recovery of clostridia from foods. *J. appl. Bact.*, **28**, 95.

Granick, S. & Gilder, H. (1946). The porphyrin requirements of *Haemophilus influenzae* and some functions of the vinyl and propionic acid side chains of heme. *J. gen. Physiol.*, **30**, 1.

Halliwell, G. (1963). The biochemical breakdown of cellulose. In *Progress in Nutrition and Allied Sciences*. Ed. Cuthbertson, D. P. Edinburgh & London. Oliver & Boyd.

Harrison, W. H. & Aiyer, P. A. S. (1913). The gases of swamp rice soils: their composition and relationship to the crop. *Mem. Dep. Agric. India chem. Ser.*, **3**, 65.

Harrison, W. H. & Aiyer, P. A. S. (1914). The gases of swamp rice soils. Part II. Their utilization for the aeration of the roots of the crop. *Mem. Dep. Agric. India chem. Ser.*, **4**, 1.

Hart, M. G. R. (1955). *A study of sporeforming bacteria from soil.* Thesis. London. University of London.

Hirsch, A. & Grinsted, E. (1954). Methods for the growth and enumeration of anaerobic sporeformers from cheese, with observations on the effect of nisin. *J. Dairy Res.*, **21**, 101.

Hungate, R. E. (1944). Studies on cellulose fermentation. I. The culture and physiology of an anaerobic cellulose-digesting bacterium. *J. Bact.*, **48**, 499.

Hungate, R. E. (1950). The anaerobic mesophilic cellulolytic bacteria. *Bact. Rev.*, **14**, 1.

Ingram, M. & Barnes, E. M. (1956). A simple modification of the deep shake tube for counting anaerobic bacteria. *Lab. Pract.*, **5**, 145.

Jensen, H. L. (1951). Notes on the microbiology of soil from Northern Greenland. *Meddr Grønland*, **142**, 23.

Kamen, M. D. & Vernon, L. P. (1955). Comparative studies on bacterial cytochromes. *Biochem. Biophys. Acta.*, **17**, 10.

Kefauver, M. & Allison, F. E. (1957). Nitrite reduction by *Bacterium denitrificans* in relation to oxidation-reduction potential and oxygen tension. *J. Bact.*, **73**, 8.

Khouvine, Y. (1923). Digestion de la cellulose par la flore intestinale de l'homme. *B. cellulosae dissolvens*, n. sp. *Annls Inst. Pasteur, Paris*, **37**, 711.

Knivett, V. A. (1960). The microbiological production of vitamin $B_{12}$ and sulphide from sewage. *Prog. ind. Microbiol.*, **2**, 29.

Liebert, F. (1927). Reduzieren Mikroben Phosphate? *Zentbl. Bakt. ParasitKde., Abt. II*, **72**, 369.

Loewenstein, H., Engelbert, L. E., Attoe, O. J. & Allen, O. N. (1957). Nitrogen loss in gaseous form from soils as influenced by fertilizers and management. *Proc. Soil Sci. Soc. Am.*, **21**, 397.

Meiklejohn, J. (1940). Preliminary notes on numbers of nitrogen fixers on Broadbalk field. *Proc. 6th Int. Congr. Soil Sci., Paris, C*, 243.

Meiklejohn, J. (1962). Microbiology of the nitrogen cycle in some Ghana soils. *Emp. J. exp. Agric.*, **30**, 115.

Mortenson, L. E. (1963). Nitrogen fixation: role of ferredoxin in anaerobic metabolism. *A. Rev. Microbiol.*, **17**, 115.

Mossel, D. A. A., DeBruin, A. S., Van Diepen, H. M. J., Vendrig, C. M. A. & Zoutewelle, G. (1956). The enumeration of anaerobic bacteria, and of *Clostridium* species in particular, in foods. *J. appl. Bact.*, **19**, 142.

MYLROIE, R. L. & HUNGATE, R. E. (1954). Experiments on the methane bacteria in sludge. *Can. J. Microbiol.*, **1**, 55.

NASON, A. & TAKAHASHI, H. (1958). Inorganic nitrogen metabolism. *A. Rev. Microbiol.*, **12**, 203.

OHNISHI, T. & MORI, T. (1960). Oxidative phosphorylation coupled with denitrification in intact cell systems. *J. Biochem., Tokyo*, **48**, 406.

OMELIANSKI, W. (1902). Über die Gärung der Cellulose. *Zentbl. Bakt. ParasitKde., Abt. II*, **8**, 225.

PARKER, C. A. (1954). Non-symbiotic nitrogen-fixing bacteria in soil. I. Studies on *Clostridium butyricum. Aust. J. agric. Res.*, **5**, 90.

PARKER, C. A. (1955). Anaerobiosis with iron wool. *Aust. J. exp. Biol. med. Sci.*, **33**, 33.

PINE, M. J. & BARKER, H. A. (1956). Studies on the methane fermentation. XII. The pathway of hydrogen in the acetate fermentation. *J. Bact.*, **71**, 644.

POSTGATE, J. R. (1954*a*). Presence of cytochrome in an obligate anaerobe. *Biochem. J.*, **56**, xi.

POSTGATE, J. R. (1954*b*). Dependence of sulphate reduction and oxygen utilization on a cytochrome in *Desulphovibrio. Biochem. J.*, **58**, xi.

RODRIGUEZ-KABANA, R. & JORDAN, J. W. (1964). A mechanism for continuous production of hydrogen sulphide in soils submerged in water. *Phytopathology*, **54**, 897.

RODRIGUEZ-KABANA, R., JORDAN, J. W. & HOLLIS, J. P. (1965). Nematodes: Biological control in rice fields: Role of hydrogen sulphide. *Science, N.Y.*, **148**, 524.

ROSENBLUM, E. D. & WILSON, P. W. (1949). Fixation of isotopic nitrogen by clostridium. *J. Bact.*, **57**, 413.

RUDAKOV, K. I. (1927). Die Reduktion der mineralischen Phosphate auf biologischem Wege. *Zentbl. Bakt. ParasitKde., Abt. II*, **70**, 202.

RUDAKOW, K. J. (RUDAKOV, K. I.) (1929). Die Reduktion der mineralischen Phosphate auf biologischem Wege. *Zentbl. Bakt. ParasitKde., Abt. II*, **79**, 229.

RUSSELL, E. W. (1961). *Soil conditions and plant growth. 9th Edn.* London. Longmans.

SACKS, L. E. (1948). *Metabolic studies on denitrification by* Pseudomonas denitrificans. Thesis. Berkeley. University of California.

SADANA, J. C. & MCELROY, W. D. (1957). Nitrate reductase from *Achromobacter fischeri*. Purification and properties: function of flavines and cytochrome. *Arch. Biochem. Biophys.*, **67**, 16.

SATO, R. (1950). Fiziologia oksidado per nitrato. *Scienca Revuo*, **2**, 122.

SATO, R. (1956). The cytochrome system and microbial reduction of nitrate. In *Inorganic Nitrogen Metabolism.* Baltimore. The Johns Hopkins Press.

SKERMAN, V. B. D. & MACRAE, I. E. (1957*a*). The influence of oxygen on the reduction of nitrate by adapted cells of *Pseudomonas denitrificans. Can. J. Microbiol.*, **3**, 215.

SKERMAN, V. B. D. & MACRAE, I. C. (1957*b*). The influence of oxygen availability on the degree of nitrate reduction by *Pseudomonas denitrificans. Can. J. Microbiol.*, **3**, 505.

SKINNER, F. A. (1960). The isolation of anaerobic cellulose-decomposing bacteria from soil. *J. gen. Microbiol.*, **22**, 539.

SKINNER, F. A. (1961). Cellulose decomposition and methane formation. *A. Rep. Rothamsted Exp. Sta., 1960*, 89.

SMITH, P. H. & HUNGATE, R. E. (1958). Isolation and characterization of *Methanobacterium ruminantium*, n. sp. *J. Bact.*, **75**, 713.

STADTMAN, T. C. & BARKER, H. A. (1949). Studies on the methane fermentation.

VII. Tracer experiments on the mechanism of methane formation. *Arch. Biochem.*, **21**, 256.

STADTMAN, T. C. & BARKER, H. A. (1951). Studies on the methane fermentation. IX. The origin of methane in the acetate and methanol fermentations by *Methanosarcina*. *J. Bact.*, **61**, 81.

STARKEY, R. L. (1961). Sulfate-reducing bacteria, their production of sulfide and their economic importance. *TAPPI*, **44**, 493.

SWABY, R. J. (1939). The occurrence and activities of *Azotobacter* and *Clostridium butyricum* in Victorian soils. *Aust. J. exp. Biol. med. Sci.*, **17**, 401.

TAKAHASHI, H., TANIGUCHI, S. & EGAMI, F. (1956). Nitrate reduction in aerobic bacteria and that in *Escherichia coli* coupled to phosphorylation. *J. Biochem., Tokyo*, **43**, 223.

TANIGUCHI, S., SATO, R. & EGAMI, F. (1956). The enzymatic mechanisms of nitrate and nitrite metabolism in bacteria. In *Inorganic Nitrogen Metabolism*. Baltimore. The Johns Hopkins Press.

TCHAN, Y. T. & POCHON, J. (1950). Une espèce nouvelle de bactérie fixatrice d'azote moléculaire isolée du sol: *Endosporus azotophagus* n. sp. *C. r. hebd. Séanc. Acad. Sci., Paris*, **230**, 417.

TSUBOTA, G. (1959). Phosphate reduction in the paddy field, I. *Soil Pl. Fd, Tokyo*, **5**, 10.

VERHOEVEN, W. (1952). *Aerobic sporeforming nitrate reducing bacteria*. Thesis. Delft. The Netherlands.

WINOGRADSKY, S. (1893). Sur l'assimilation de l'azote gazeux de l'atmosphere par les microbes. *C. r. hebd. Séanc. Acad. Sci., Paris*, **116**, 1385.

WINOGRADSKY, S. (1895). Recherches sur l'assimilation de l'azote libre de l'atmosphere par les microbes. *Archs Sci. biol., St. Pétersb.* (*Arkh. biol. Nauk*), **3**, 297.

WOOLFOLK, C. A. & WHITELEY, H. R. (1962). Reduction of inorganic compounds with molecular hydrogen by *Micrococcus lactilyticus*. I. Stoichiometry with compounds of arsenic, selenium, tellurium, transition and other elements. *J. Bact.*, **84**, 647.

# NITRIFYING BACTERIA IN SOIL

F. E. CHASE, C. T. CORKE and J. B. ROBINSON

*Department of Microbiology, Ontario Agricultural College, University of Guelph, Canada*

## *INTRODUCTION*

In agronomic literature 'nitrification' is sometimes improperly used to designate the conversion of organic nitrogen to nitrate nitrogen; but soil microbiologists prefer to keep its meaning more restricted, reserving it for the conversion of ammonium to nitrite or nitrate nitrogen. Nitrification has been stated to occur in three ways: (*a*) photonitrification, (*b*) heterotrophic and (*c*) autotrophic nitrification.

Photonitrification, reported first in India (Dhar and Rao, 1933), apparently has little if any significance (Joshi and Biswas, 1948). Heterotrophic nitrification seems to be mainly a laboratory phenomenon occurring in the presence of a plentiful supply of organic energy material. A number of fungi and bacteria are capable of this form of nitrification, but its significance in soil appears to be small (Alexander, 1961), at least in relation to that brought about by the autotrophs.

The autotrophic reaction involves a two stage conversion, $NH_4^+ \rightarrow NO_2^- \rightarrow NO_3^-$. Each oxidative step provides the energy necessary for growth of the organisms capable of bringing it about, hence they can develop in a simple inorganic salts medium containing $NH_4^+$ or $NO_2^-$ as their sole source of energy. These organisms, by being capable of sustained growth upon a simple inorganic medium with $CO_2$ as the sole carbon source, are termed autotrophs.

The oxidation of ammonium to nitrite is brought about by small Gram-negative rod-shaped bacteria belonging to the genus *Nitrosomonas* and the oxidation of nitrite to nitrate involves a second group of bacteria of similar morphology belonging to the genus *Nitrobacter*. Other genera have been named but the concensus of opinion places greatest significance on the two mentioned above (Meiklejohn, 1954). Both groups are obligate aerobes.

Although these organisms have been recognized and grown in crude cultures for many years, few workers have claimed to grow them in pure culture. Despite the limitation of having to work with crude cultures, much of interest has been learned of their peculiar physiology (Lees, 1955).

The principal interest of our research group has been to examine the more practical considerations of the nitrification process in relation to various aspects of soil, climate and plants, and it is mainly with these experiences that this paper deals.

## *METHODS OF STUDY*

There is plenty of information available on the response of nitrification to environmental influence and this literature has recently been summarized by Alexander (1961). Many of the early laboratory studies were made using the so-called 'tumbler' method in which containers of moistened, ammonium-treated soil were incubated and periodically analysed for oxidized forms of nitrogen. While this procedure was useful for environmental studies, the inconvenience of the analyses and the fact that quantities of soil were sacrificed at each analysis, retarded detailed study of the kinetics of the process. In 1946, Lees and Quastel described the soil perfusion apparatus, which they used in studying the kinetics of soil nitrification. Their apparatus, which has since been modified by a number of workers, allows frequent analyses of all soluble products of the oxidation (none of which are appreciably adsorbed to soil) without disturbance of the soil which remains under almost ideal conditions of moisture and aeration.

Lees and Quastel (1946*a*) showed that when soil in the perfusion apparatus was well supplied with ammonium-N, a curve representing nitrate-N accumulation was sigmoid. When nitrite-N was added to the soil, the nitrate-N accumulation curve was similar in shape but the rate of conversion of nitrite was more rapid than the conversion of ammonium. This indicated that the first step in the nitrification of ammonium is the rate limiting one and explained why nitrite does not normally accumulate in soil. However, the accumulation of nitrite can be easily induced by increasing alkalinity (Stojanovic and Alexander, 1957) or by various chemical treatments (Corke and Robinson, 1960). In a second paper Lees and Quastel (1946*b*) reported that the lag in nitrate accumulation apparent on first perfusing soil with a solution of ammonium did not occur if the same soil was washed and re-perfused with a similar solution. On re-perfusion a linear rate of nitrate-N accumulation was observed and this was interpreted to mean that during the first perfusion the nitrifying population had reached a maximum—that is the soil had become 'saturated' with nitrifying bacteria. One of our early experiments, which convinced us of the soundness of these conclusions, involved setting up a replicate series of units perfused with N/50 $(NH_4)_2SO_4$. Every third or fourth day a unit was dismantled and the most probable numbers (MPN) of nitrifying bacteria present in the soil were determined (Cunningham, 1950). Fig. 1 shows that the nitrite-oxidizing bacteria in particular displayed a distinct log phase followed by a stable population level that coincided nicely with the 'logarithmic' and 'linear' phases of the curve of nitrate formation. The ammonium-oxidizing bacteria did not behave as expected, for immediately after reaching peak levels their numbers began to decrease in this and in repeat experiments. Apparently this decrease did not proceed far enough to cause a detectable lag on re-perfusion, for when this was done (within a few days) nitrification began without lag in accordance with the concept of 'saturation'.

Apart from its application in fundamental studies of the nitrification process, the soil perfusion apparatus can readily be applied to problems with field significance and in this way we have studied nitrification in soils under a variety of treatments and conditions. Typical of our results are those in Fig. 2 depicting a series of curves obtained by perfusing an infertile grassland soil under a variety of treatments. As obtained from the field, this soil showed no accumulation of nitrate when perfused 50 days with a solution containing 100 ppm. am-

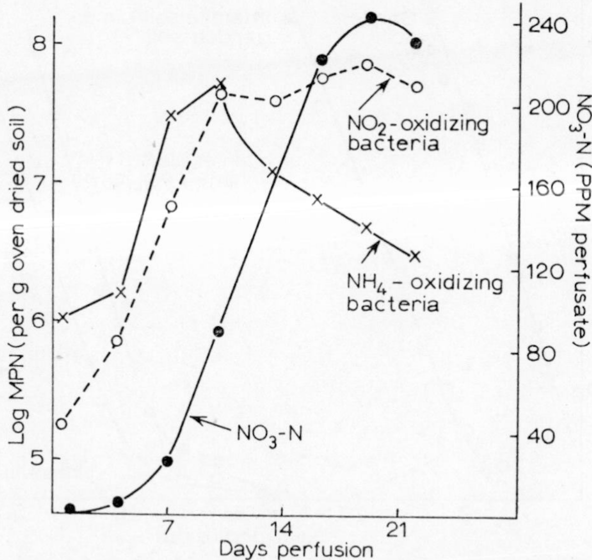


Fig. 1. The numbers of ammonium oxidizing and nitrite oxidizing bacteria in soil perfused with $(NH_4)_2SO_4$ solution in relation to nitrate accumulation in the perfusate.

monium-N. Adjusting the pH to about 7·5 with $CaCO_3$ resulted in a shortening of the lag period from an undetermined length to about 38 days, and adding phosphate to the limed soil further decreased the lag to about 33 days. Inoculation of limed soil with a garden soil shortened the lag to 8 – 9 days. The garden soil was assumed to be saturated with nitrifying bacteria because, when perfused with ammonium solution, it accumulated nitrate at a constant rate from the beginning with no detectable lag period.

From this simple experiment we can conclude that, (*a*) low pH limits the rate at which nitrifying bacteria proliferate; (*b*) phosphate may increase the rate of proliferation of nitrifying bacteria; and (*c*) the grassland soil had but a small part of its potential population of nitrifying bacteria, while the population of the garden soil was not only much larger but already at its maximum at the time the soil sample was collected. Point (*c*) was confirmed by estimating the most probable numbers of nitrifying bacteria in the two soils. It was found that the grassland soil had an ammonium-oxidizing population of about 20 per g. while the garden soil had a population estimated at $2{\cdot}2 \times 10^6$ per g. This gives further evidence of the close relationship between the size of the nitrifying population in a soil and the length of the lag period when the soil is perfused.

Using these methods we have studied soil nitrification under a variety

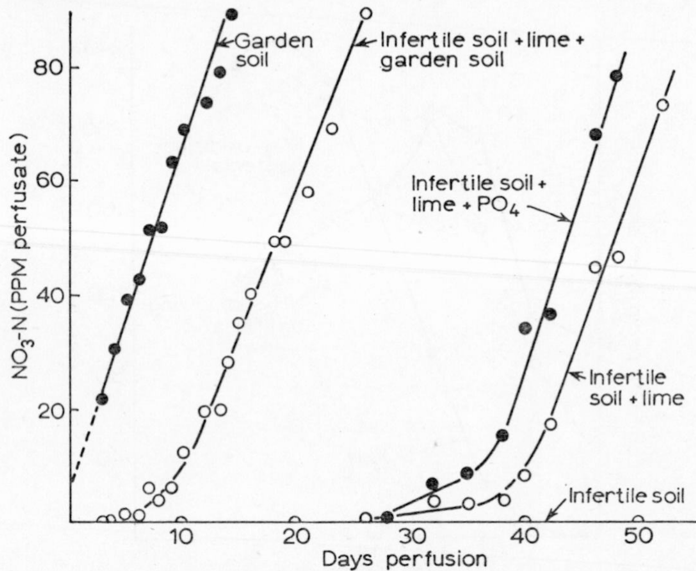


Fig. 2. The effects of lime, phosphate and inoculum on the rate of nitrate production by perfused, acid soil initially having a small nitrifier population (soils perfused with $(NH_4)_2SO_4$ solution).

of cultural and environmental conditions. While these studies are often unrelated they have led us to certain conclusions regarding the role of the process in nature; our conclusions, while not unique, nonetheless differ from those expressed in the older agronomic literature, and suggest the need for a careful and critical re-examination of the significance of nitrification in different soils and for different crops.

## *NITRIFICATION IN THE FOREST ENVIRONMENT*

Since the primary food requirements of mankind have now diverted to agricultural use the more fertile soils on workable terrain, forest soils present difficult ecological situations for the microbiologist since they are increasingly limited to rugged topography where large differences in moisture, types of litter, soil characteristics and pH exist, often even between adjacent trees. In acidic mors and some mulls of Ontario the nitrifiers are found in extremely small numbers (less than several hundred per g.) and these are localized in the organic layer (Corke, 1958). However, their constant presence suggests that nitrification must proceed in spite of the soil acidity (as acid as pH 3·7 to 3·9), though obviously at extremely slow rates; under these specialized environments the nitrifiers are unable to contribute appreciably to the nitrogen cycle.

The biological process of nitrification is stimulated by clear cutting of the forest (Wiedemann, 1928; Frazer, 1929); also controlled burning, particularly of the mor layers, has been shown to induce nitrification (Wiedemann, 1924, 1928; Lutz and Chandler, 1957). Mixing the organic litter with the mineral layers stimulates decomposition and nitrification. The use of lime and green manuring has found limited application in Europe.

The significance of nitrate formation in forest soils is a subject which is not well defined. Wilde (1942) considered that nitrate was only of importance when dealing with deciduous lime-loving trees that require nitrogen in the form of nitrates but not for acidophilous conifers which readily utilize ammonia, or possibly organic nitrogen through mycorrhizal intercession. Lutz and Chandler (1957) state that little is known about the nitrogen nutrition of forest trees, other than that they depend principally on nitrate and ammonium. They further conclude that from present evidence there is little reason to maintain that nitrate is superior to ammonium-nitrogen.

Some years ago we became interested in the significance of nitrification in acid Ontario forest soils developed over the Precambrian shield. In general, regardless of whether the soil came from under deciduous or coniferous cover, lime applications were necessary before any nitrification occurred during perfusion in the laboratory (Chase and Baker, 1954). Fig. 3 indicates the formation of nitrate from forest soils under three covers when perfused with water (nitrate formed from ammonium-nitrogen mineralized from organic-nitrogen) and with N/50 ammonium sulphate. The amounts of nitrate-N produced from the native soil nitrogen indicates that appreciable quantities of nitrogen were made available when the pH was adjusted by lime treatment.

Studies were next carried out in forest experimental plots treated with dolomitic limestone, phosphate, and limestone plus phosphate. Table 1 shows that relatively large populations of nitrifying bacteria developed in all limed plots, and that phosphate showed a further stimulatory effect.

The nitrifying characteristics of these limed plots are shown in Fig. 4. Obviously, although nitrification was functional in these plots, it did not proceed at a maximum rate since the addition of $CaCO_3$ to both limestone and limestone phosphate plots increased the rate of nitrate formation.

Studies currently in progress with neutral mulls of southwestern Ontario indicate that nitrification is active and proceeds similarly in soil samples taken from the forest and adjacent fields.

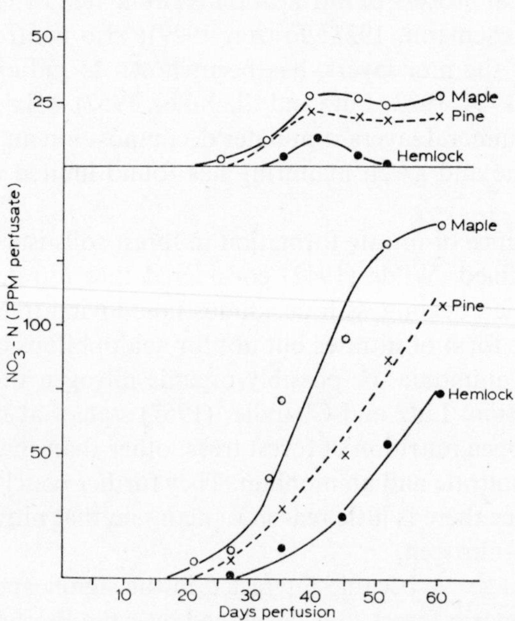


Fig. 3. Nitrate accumulation in perfusates of acid soils from under stands of maple, pine and hemlock respectively. The soils were treated with $CaCO_3$ and perfused with water (top) and $(NH_4)_2SO_4$ solution (bottom).

TABLE 1

*Numbers of nitrifying bacteria in an acid forest soil under maple 8 years after amendment*

| Treatment | *Nitrosomonas** | *Nitrobacter** |
|---|---|---|
| Control $A_0$ | 260 | 240 |
| Super-phosphate (160 lb./acre) | 300 | 250 |
| Limestone (10 tons/acre) | 11,600 | 5,300 |
| Limestone + phosphate | 32,900 | 30,600 |

* Most probable numbers per g. oven-dry $A_0$ horizon.

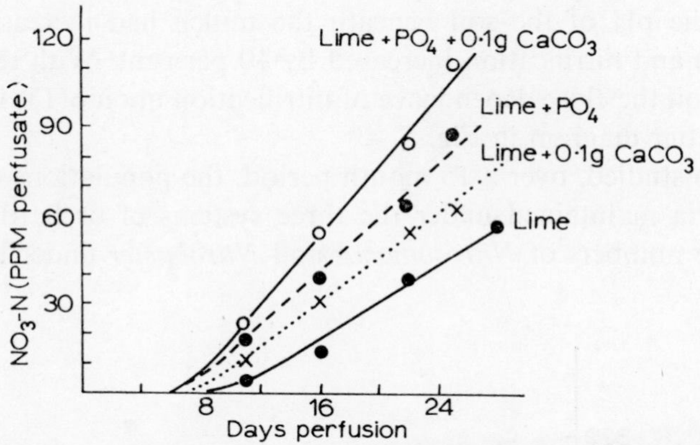


Fig. 4. The effects of field treatments with limestone and phosphate and of laboratory treatment with $CaCO_3$ on nitrate accumulation by acid forest soil perfused with $(NH_4)_2SO_4$ solution.

## *NITRIFICATION IN ORCHARDS*

The orchard environment, particularly when an organic mulch is placed around the trees, represents in some measure a transitional step between forest and cultivated agricultural soils. From time to time during the past 17 years we have studied nitrification in peach and apple orchards at the Vineland Horticultural Experiment Station in the Niagara fruit-growing region of Ontario. The soil was a well-drained light sandy loam containing no free carbonate and having a pH ranging from 4·2 to 6·2; the pH values were lowest in grass sod plots, intermediate in the clean cultivated plots and were highest under a hay-straw mulch that had been maintained within the spread of the branches for several years prior to the beginning of our studies.

Using the perfusion technique, Henderson (1949) found most active nitrification under mulch and the lowest under sod. Suspecting that this might be simply an expression of pH, we obtained confirmatory evidence in the laboratory by artificially exchanging the pH of the sod and mulch samples, which when perfused displayed a reversal of their former nitrifying activity. We later verified our suspicion that pH was the major limiting factor by examining nitrification following the broadcast application of lime to these plots (Stevenson and Chase, 1953). Tests made 4 months later showed that liming elevated the pH of the sod and clean cultivation treated soils and also increased rates of nitrification, but it had not affected the pH or nitrification rates of the mulched plots where it was trapped for a time in the surface layers of the mulch and hence did not reach the soil. However, after another 6 months, the pH of the soil beneath the mulch had increased to 6·3 (from 5·7) and nitrification increased by 10 per cent. With this poorly buffered soil the close dependence of nitrification upon pH is illustrated by the scatter diagram in Fig. 5.

We also studied, over a 15 month period, the populations of nitrifying bacteria maintained under the three systems of orchard management. The numbers of *Nitrosomonas* and *Nitrobacter* under the mulch

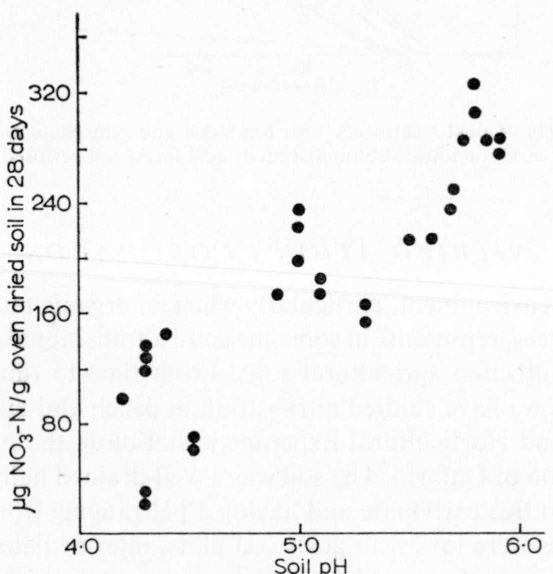


Fig. 5. Correlation of initial soil pH and the extent of nitrate production by soil in 28 days of perfusion with $(NH_4)_2SO_4$ solution. The soil was Vineland sandy loam under a variety of field and laboratory treatments.

were about double those found in the other plots through the winter, spring and early summer. Frost did not penetrate the soil under the mulch until late February, whereas the soil in the other two plots became frozen in December. It seems likely that under mulch somewhat more favourable temperatures prevail for a longer part of the year in our region, and that at the soil surface moisture levels will be higher and more stable, factors that should favour a slow but steady movement of nitrogen from the organic layer into the soil. Whatever the cause, the mulched trees grew more rapidly and outyielded those in the other plots.

## *NITRIFICATION IN GRASSLAND SOILS*

With the publication by Richardson (1938) of his study on Rothamsted soils under grass the idea was established that nitrification is adversely affected in grassland soils. This interpretation of Richardson's data was based on his finding that ammonium-N levels were somewhat higher and nitrate-N levels were much lower in his grassland soils than are usually observed in fallow soils. Other workers made similar observations and, in 1951, Theron made the suggestion that grass roots probably secrete a toxic substance which specifically inhibits the nitrifying bacteria. While Soulides and Clark (1958) obtained indirect evidence in support of this interpretation of low nitrate levels in grassland soils, little direct evidence has accumulated. However, reports by Stiven (1952) and more recently by Boughey *et al.* (1964) of antibiotics found in roots of African grass species have tended to support this concept. In a study of a New Zealand grassland soil using soil perfusion methods, Robinson (1963) advanced the suggestion that the high $NH_4$—N/$NO_3$—N ratio in that soil could be attributed to a low population of nitrifying bacteria resulting from direct competition by grass roots and associated heterotrophs for the scarce ammonium ions. It was found that additions of ammonium (in the form of urea) to the field soil shortened the lag of nitrate appearance when the soil was later perfused in the laboratory, thus indicating a higher nitrifier population in the urea-treated soil (see Fig. 6).

Despite the generally-held view, as expressed by Woldendorp (1963), that 'a suppressed nitrification' is a characteristic of grassland soils, Simpson (1962) found that $NO_3$—N accumulated to very high levels in soils under certain pastures in New South Wales, particularly when such soils were moistened by rainfall after a prolonged dry period. While Simpson drew attention to the minimal N-uptake by the plant association during the dry period, which made his results not strictly comparable to those of Richardson (1938), it appeared that Simpson's soils were quite capable of accumulating nitrate when competition from the grasses was at a minimum.

With these experiences in mind we are presently examining the role of nitrification in the nitrogen cycle of soils under grass in southern Ontario. We established small plot areas on three soils of differing characteristics where grass associations had been established for 8 – 12 years. At each site part of the plot area was kept fallow with sufficient cultivation to control weeds. Urea and ammonium sulphate treatments were applied to both fallow and grass plots and these along with the control plots were analysed regularly for soil ammonium-N, nitrate-N and MPN of nitrifying bacteria; only minor differences in the three soils and in the effects of the two nitrogen treatments were observed, and results typical of these studies are presented in Figs. 7 and 8.

As indicated in Fig. 7, the mineral nitrogen in the untreated soil under grass remained low throughout both seasons, although it was consistently higher in 1964 than in 1963. In contrast to the Rothamsted soils studied by Richardson (1938), however, the mineral N in our grassland soils occurred mainly as nitrate rather than as ammonium. In this respect they did not differ, except quantitatively, from the untreated

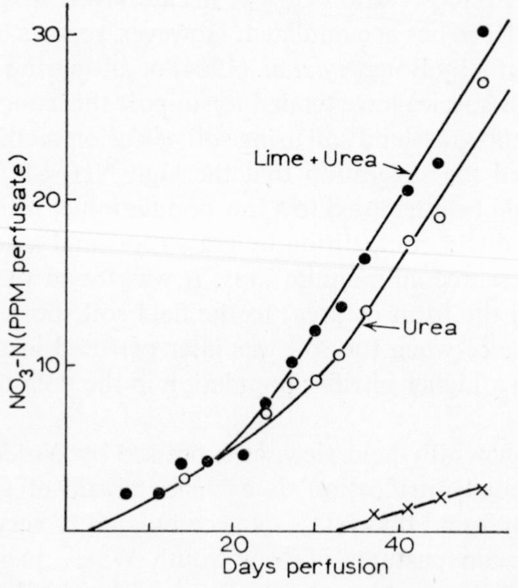


Fig. 6. The effect of field treatments with lime and urea on nitrate production by an acid, infertile grassland soil perfused with $(NH_4)_2SO_4$ solution.

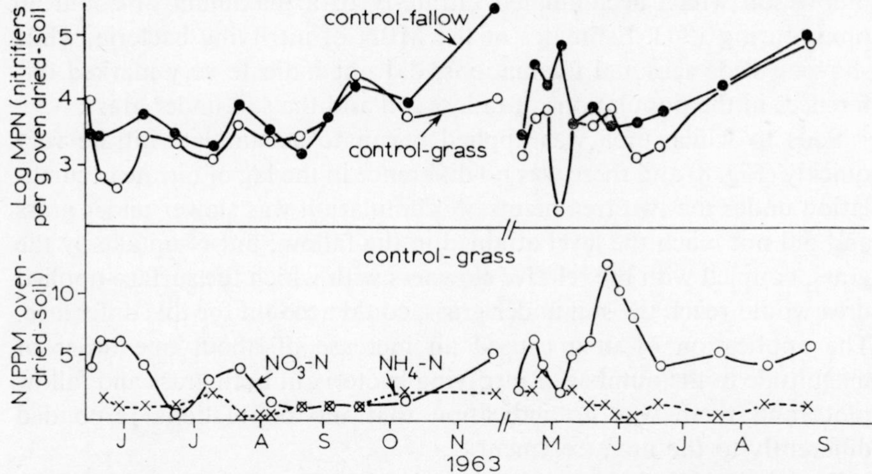


Fig. 7. The levels of ammonium N and nitrate N in a grass plot and numbers of nitrifying bacteria in grass and fallow plots of Guelph loam during 2 growing sessions.

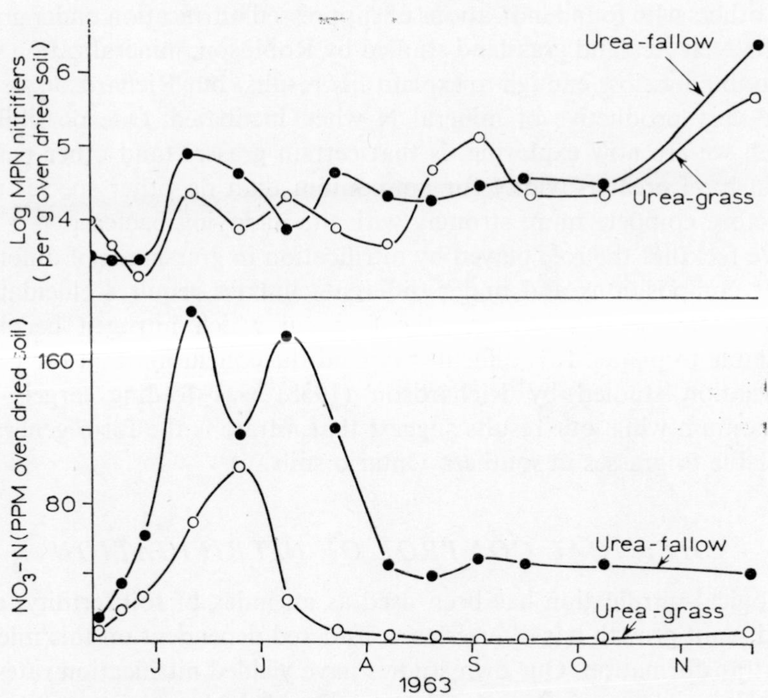


Fig. 8. The levels of nitrate and numbers of nitrifying bacteria in fallow and grass plots on Guelph loam treated with urea (urea applied in mid-May).

fallow soil which accumulated nitrate-N to a maximum of about 30 ppm. during 1963. Estimates of the MPN of nitrifying bacteria, while showing wide seasonal fluctuations, did not indicate very marked differences in the populations of fallow soil and the soil under grass.

Soils to which urea was applied began to accumulate nitrate very quickly (Fig. 8) and there was no difference in the lag of nitrate accumulation under the two treatments. Accumulation was slower under grass and did not reach the level attained in the fallow; but N-uptake by the grass, coupled with the relative slowness with which the surface-applied urea would reach the soil under grass, could account for this difference. The application of urea caused an increase of about one order of magnitude in the number of nitrifying bacteria in both grass and fallow plots and there was no indication that the populations responded differently to the urea treatment.

We have concluded from these results that the grasses growing in our soils do not compete for ammonium to the detriment of the nitrifying population; nor do the grass roots inhibit nitrifiers by other means. This may simply reflect a greater rate of N-mineralization in these soils than in those studied by Richardson (1938), Theron (1951), Robinson (1963) and others who found indications of suppressed nitrification under grass. In the New Zealand grassland studied by Robinson, mineralization was undoubtedly slow enough to explain his results, but Richardson's soils were very productive of mineral N when incubated. One possibility, which we are now exploring, is that certain grasses (and other perennials) have greater avidity for ammonium than do other species and therefore compete more strongly with the nitrifying bacteria.

We feel that the role played by nitrification in grasslands of different plant compositions and under different climates requires elucidation because this process governs the form in which nitrogen becomes available to plants. It is difficult to avoid the conclusion that the plant association studied by Richardson (1938) was feeding largely on ammonium while our results suggest that nitrate is the form generally available to grasses in southern Ontario soils.

## *CHEMICAL CONTROL OF NITRIFICATION*

Biological nitrification has been used as an index of soil fertility, and good plant growth has often been considered dependent on this microbial transformation. Our own studies have yielded nitrification rates in perfusion units equivalent to 2½ tons of added N per acre per week. Field studies of rates of conversion are not widely available but Broadbent, Tyler and Hill (1958) reported that about 40 lb. of nitrate-N per acre per day were formed in a loam treated with ammonium sulphate or aqua ammonia, whereas in Salinas clay a rate of 88 lb. was observed.

If nitrification can proceed normally, it seems that when aqua ammonia, anhydrous ammonia, urea or ammonium sulphate are added to soil, soon most of the nitrogen is presented to the plants as nitrate through the activities of these bacteria. Unlike ammonium which is attached to adsorption sites in soil and is relatively stationary, nitrate is freely mobile in the soil solution. Under certain conditions, particularly in sandy soils, under heavy rainfall, or where excessive irrigation is practised, nitrate may leach away, at least from the zone of root development. Nitrate, moreover, is susceptible to microbial reduction processes and can be denitrified to nitrogen gas or gaseous compounds of nitrogen. On the other hand the cationic form, ammonium, while not susceptible to loss by leaching, may be lost by ammonia volatilization in strongly alkaline soils (Alexander, 1961).

To reduce losses of nitrogen subsequent to biological conversion to nitrate, such approaches as modifying forms, times and rates of nitrogen application have been used; an example of this is the currently expanding use of slow release fertilizers such as urea-formaldehyde formulations. But there is another control mechanism available of particular interest to soil microbiologists, namely, the selective inhibition of nitrifying organisms. Interference with nitrification after field application of certain soil fumigants, including methyl bromide, ethylene dibromide and the dichloropropane-dichloropropenes has been recognized for many years (Koike, 1961) and the increased ammonium that results may be responsible for reduced losses of nitrogen by leaching or cause some changes in the growth of plants, presumably by their forced utilization of ammonium rather than nitrate (Tam and Clark, 1943; Tam, 1945). Lees (1953) suggested that in some instances inhibition of nitrification might be desirable and possibly could be accomplished by a highly active inhibitor like thiourea. In our laboratory Robinson (1952) and Jaques (1954), while pursuing the possibility that ammonia might aid in the control of potato scab, examined several chemical inhibitors of nitrification, including thiourea, ethyl urethane, and several fungicides, e.g. zinc ethylenebisdithiocarbamate and the iron and manganese salts of dimethyldithiocarbamate and others (Jaques, Robinson and Chase, 1959). We found these compounds to be either phytotoxic or too costly to use as inhibitors of nitrification in the field.

Now at least one potentially commercial product, N-Serve (2-chloro-6-(trichloromethyl) pyridine) has been developed by Dow Chemical

Corporation. Goring (1962*a*, 1962*b*) and Corke and Chase (1962) reported field and laboratory studies of this specific inhibitor of ammonium oxidation. This compound is used with nitrogen fertilizers such as urea or ammonium sulphate. In perfusion experiments with these substrates nitrate production follows the pattern shown in Fig. 9, with the length of the lag period being dependent on the concentration of N-Serve used.

Goring (1962*b*) reported that in field trials 0·2 ppm. of N-Serve inhibited nitrification for 4 weeks, 0·5 ppm. for 8 weeks and 1·0 ppm. for 12 weeks. We were interested in this compound both for its agricultural potential and as an experimental tool. We examined the ability of N-Serve to inhibit nitrification in sandy soils at both high and low levels. Fig. 10 shows that the high levels of N-Serve (10 and 20 lb./acre) were capable of maintaining high ammonium levels for periods of at least 4 months. The lowest level (0·4 lb./acre) retarded nitrification for only a few weeks. Thus lower levels could provide for an initial plant utilization of ammonium followed by the utilization of nitrate after redevelopment of the nitrifying population. With the larger amounts, plants were forced to exist mainly on ammonium. As suggested by Goring (1962*a*), N-Serve may play a role in the preservation of ammonium-N applied in the fall. Table 2 shows the results of early spring sampling for mineral

TABLE 2

*Effect in Southwestern Ontario of a field application of a nitrification inhibitor on winter loss of nitrogen*

| Soil treatment Nov. 1964 (per acre) | Mineral nitrogen, April 1965 (lb./acre)* | | |
|---|---|---|---|
| | Ammonium | Nitrate | Total |
| Control | 7 | 8 | 15 |
| N-Serve (10 lb.) | 17 | 11 | 28 |
| Urea (60 lb. N) | 19 | 14 | 33 |
| Urea + N-Serve | 50 | 12 | 62 |

* Average: surface samples (6 in. depth) of three plots per treatment.

nitrogen in corn plots that received 10 lb. of N-Serve and 60 lb. of urea-N the previous fall. In both the control and urea-treated plots, the total inorganic nitrogen was approximately doubled by N-Serve treatment. The ammonium analyses also showed that N-Serve alone retarded nitrification of nitrogen mineralized in the control plots. The similar level of nitrate in all treatments indicates its mobility in this soil.

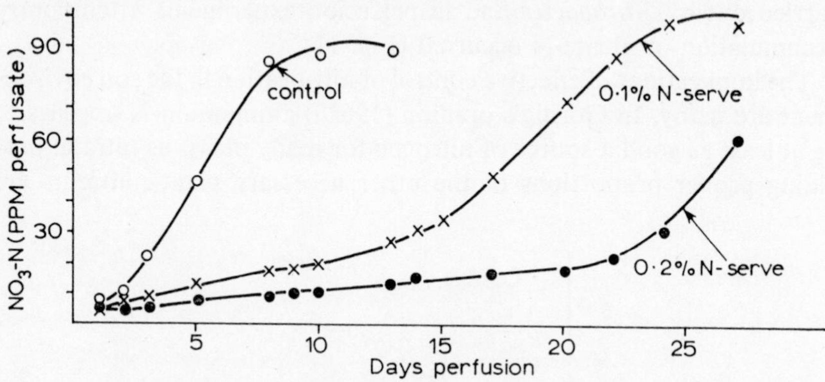


Fig. 9. Nitrate accumulation in perfusates of Guelph loam treated with N-serve and per fused with $(NH_4)_2SO_4$ solution.

While inhibitors are known that specifically block the second step of nitrification, namely the oxidation by *Nitrobacter* of nitrite to nitrate (Quastel and Scholefield, 1951), the resulting accumulation of nitrite, which is phytotoxic, makes this form of inhibition dangerous. This possibility needs to be considered when dealing with pesticides that are incorporated into soil. Corke and Robinson (1960) found that dinitro-o-sec-butyl phenol (DNBP) inhibited the second step of nitrification

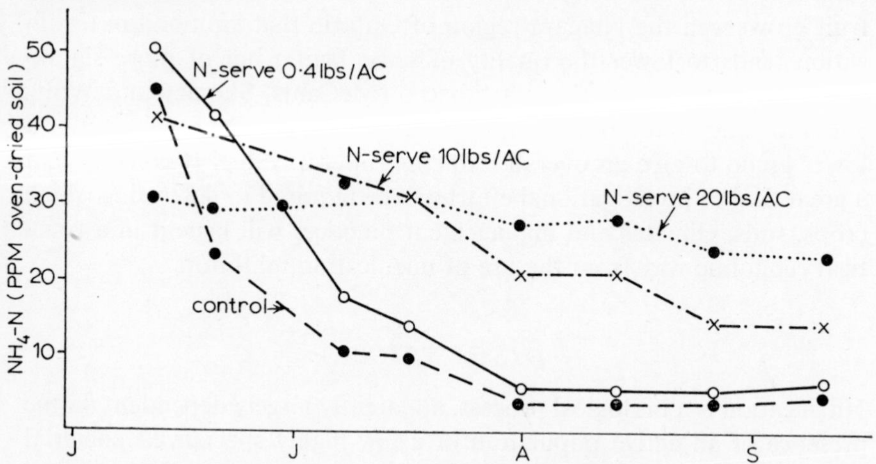


Fig. 10. Seasonal levels of ammonium in plots of Fox sandy loam treated with N-serve at different rates and $(NH_4)_2SO_4$ at 200 lb./acre.

carried out by *Nitrobacter* and in perfusion experiments a temporary accumulation of nitrite-N occurred (Fig. 11).

The implications of effective control of nitrification in the soil environment are many. In Goring's opinion (1962*a*) ammonium-N appears to be at least as good a source of nitrogen for many plants as nitrate, providing proper proportions of the other necessary plant nutrients are

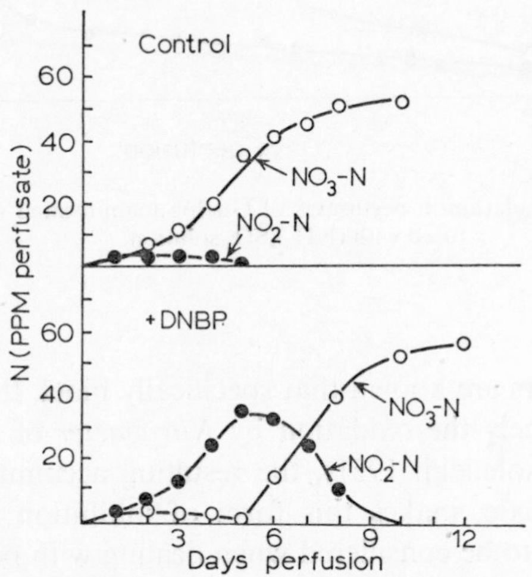


**Fig. 11. The effect of DNBP (equivalent to 16 lb./acre) on nitrite and nitrate accumulation in Fox sandy loam perfused with $(NH_4)_2SO_4$ solution.**

supplied. However, there is an undocumented belief held by many fruit growers in the Niagara region of Ontario that ammonium fertilization tends to lower the quality of some fruits; but of more significance is the careful work with tobacco (McCants, Skogley and Woltz 1959) to show that ammonium-N produced a higher leaf yield but of a lower grade to give an overall reduction in crop value. It is likely that a great deal of investigational effort will be required to determine which crops, soils, climates and management practices will benefit in a practical economic way from the use of nitrification inhibitors.

## *DISCUSSION*

Nitrification is a biological process, apparently largely dependent on the presence of an active population of a few highly specialized bacterial species. It seems to us that too many agronomists think of the process as being not only essential, but fortunately so universally distributed and so rapid that they can consider applications of ammonium-N as being almost equivalent to applications of nitrate-N. Because this was not true of many of the forest, orchard and grassland soils we happened to study, we of necessity became interested in those circumstances where nitrification does not occur. Indeed, there are large areas in which, because of soil or climatic conditions coupled with dense perennial plant cover, nitrate does not occur and plants must subsist on an ammonium diet. Even in areas where nitrification normally goes on, additions of ammonium might be so timed as to allow much uptake of ammonium by plants before a temporarily reduced population of nitrifying bacteria grows sufficiently to nitrify significantly.

These conclusions lead inevitably to speculation on the value of nitrification to plant growth. While early workers often considered nitrate essential to plant nutrition, more recent studies show that ammonium can serve as a nitrogen source for many plants. Nitrate is frequently found to be superior to ammonium in this respect but there is some evidence that adjusting other nutrient levels may improve the efficiency of ammonium as a nitrogen source.

Perhaps equally important considerations lie in the areas of conservation and public health. Nitrate is so mobile an ion that leaching through the profile or in the run-off water can readily occur. Losses of this kind may be of direct economic importance to agriculture and, in addition, can help raise the fertility in ground water, lakes and streams with resultant fouling by water organisms. Well-waters high in nitrate-N are a continuing problem for public health authorities.

Whether the relative immobility of the ammonium ion could outweigh its possible disadvantages as a nitrogen source for plants remains to be seen. The question, of course, remains academic in the absence of an effective, specific, economic inhibitor of nitrification. Nevertheless, it appears that there is a real need for a careful reassessment of the nitrogen nutrition of plants in relation to the environment in which they will be grown. If, as has been suggested by some authors, coniferous trees are generally tolerant of ammonium nutrition while deciduous trees prefer nitrate, perhaps similar differences exist or can be developed among crop and forage plants. Selection for ammonium tolerance is at least a possibility for plants which are to be grown in an environment which favours ammonium nutrition.

Finally, it appears that more information is required on nitrification in specific field environments. Since the presence or absence of an active nitrifying population governs the quality of plant nitrogen nutrition, plant physiologists and those interested in soil management should be more aware of the dynamics of this population. Its response to changes in pH, moisture level, oxygen tension, substrate level and competition from plants and other micro-organisms may have real and so far unrecognized significance to plant growth.

## *REFERENCES*

ALEXANDER, M. (1961). *Introduction to soil microbiology*. New York. J. Wiley & Sons.

BOUGHEY, A. S., MUNRO, P. E., MEIKLEJOHN, J., STRANG, R. M. & SWIFT, J. M. (1964). Antibiotic reactions between African savanna species. *Nature, Lond.*, **203**, 1302.

BROADBENT, F. E., TYLER, K. B. & HILL, G. N. (1958). Nitrification of fertilizers. *Calif. Agric.*, **12**, 9.

CHASE, F. E. & BAKER, G. (1954). A comparison of microbial activity in an Ontario forest soil under pine, hemlock and maple cover. *Can. J. Microbiol.*, **1**, 45.

CORKE, C. T. (1958). Nitrogen transformations in Ontario forest podzols. *N. Am. Forest Soils Conf.*, **1**, 116.

CORKE, C. T. & CHASE, F. E. (1962). Studies on the effects of certain pesticides and of a specific inhibitor on nitrification in agricultural soils. *Abst. 8th Int. Congr. Microbiol.* (*Montreal*), 56.

CORKE, C. T. & ROBINSON, J. B. (1960). Herbicides and the soil population. *Proc. 7th A. Meeting Agricultural Pesticide Technical Society, Guelph*, 67.

CUNNINGHAM, J. D. (1950). *Studies on microfloral changes and developments in soil samples undergoing treatment by the Lees and Quastel percolation technique*. M.S.A. Thesis. Toronto. University of Toronto.

DHAR, N. R. & RAO, G. G. (1933). Nitrification in soil and in atmosphere. A photochemical process. *J. Indian chem. Soc.*, **9**, 81.

FRASER, G. K. (1929). The soil and forest: soil classification and description. *Scott. For. J.*, **43**, 19.

GORING, C. A. I. (1962*a*). Control of nitrification by 2-chloro-6-(trichloromethyl) pyridine. *Soil Sci.*, **93**, 211.

GORING, C. A. I. (1962*b*). Control of nitrification by ammonium fertilizers and urea by 2-chloro-6-(trichloromethyl) pyridine. *Soil Sci.*, **93**, 431.

HENDERSON, R. D. (1949). *The effect of various soil treatments on the rate of nitrification as shown by the perfusion technique*. M.S.A. Thesis. Toronto. University of Toronto.

JAQUES, R. P. (1954). *The effect of carbamates on the soil microflora with reference to actinomycetes and possible application in control of potato scab*. M.S.A. Thesis. Toronto. University of Toronto.

JAQUES, R. P., ROBINSON, J. B. & CHASE, F. E. (1959). Effects of thiourea, ethyl urethane and some dithiocarbamate fungicides on nitrification in Fox sandy loam. *Can. J. Soil Sci.*, **39**, 235.

JOSHI, N. V. & BISWAS, S. C. (1948). Does photonitrification occur in soil? *Indian J. agric. Sci.*, **18**, 115.

KOIKE, H. (1961). The effects of fumigants on nitrate production in soil. *Proc. Soil Sci. Soc. Am.*, **25**, 204.

LEES, H. (1953). Nitrification in soil and culture. *6th Int. Congr. Microbiol.* (*Rome*), **6**, 252.

LEES, H. & QUASTEL, J. H. (1946*a*). Biochemistry of nitrification in soil. 1. Kinetics of, and the effects of poisons on soil nitrification, as studied by a soil perfusion technique. *Biochem. J.*, **40**, 803.

LEES, H. & QUASTEL, J. H. (1946*b*). Biochemistry of nitrification in soil. 2. The site of soil nitrification. *Biochem. J.*, **40**, 815.

LEES, H. (1955). *Biochemistry of autotrophic bacteria*. London. Butterworth.

LUTZ, H. J. & CHANDLER, Jr., R. F. (1957). *Forest soils*. New York. J. Wiley & Sons.

MCCANTS, C. B., SKOGLEY, E. O. & WOLTZ, W. C. (1959). Influence of certain soil fumigation treatments on the response of tobacco to ammonium and nitrate forms of nitrogen. *Proc. Soil. Sci. Soc. Am.*, **23**, 466.

MEIKLEJOHN, J. (1954). Some aspects of the physiology of the nitrifying bacteria. *Autotrophic Micro-organisms*. Ed. Fry, B. A. & Peel, J. L. *4th Symp. Soc. gen. Microbiol.* Cambridge. Cambridge University Press.

QUASTEL, J. H. & SCHOLEFIELD, P. G. (1951). Biochemistry of nitrification in soil. *Bact. Rev.*, **15**, 1.

RICHARDSON, H. L. (1938). The nitrogen cycle in grassland soils: with especial reference to the Rothamsted Park Grass Experiment. *J. Agr. Sci. Camb.*, **28**, 73.

ROBINSON, J. B. (1952). *The effect of ammonia-nitrogen on actinomycetes and its possible application in the control of potato scab*. M.S.A. Thesis. Toronto. University of Toronto.

ROBINSON, J. B. (1963). Nitrification in a New Zealand grassland soil. *Pl. Soil*, **19**, 173.

SIMPSON, J. R. (1962). Mineral nitrogen fluctuations in soils under improved pasture in southern New South Wales. *Aust. J. agric. Res.*, **13**, 1059.

SOULIDES, D. A. & CLARK, F. E. (1958). Nitrification in grassland soils. *Proc. Soil Sci. Soc. Am.*, **22**, 308.

STEVENSON, I. L. & CHASE, F. E. (1953). Nitrification in an orchard soil under three cultural practices. *Soil Sci.*, **76**, 107.

STIVEN, G. (1952). Production of antibiotic substances by the roots of a grass (*Trachypogon phimosus* (H.B.K.) Nees.) and of *Pentanisia variabilis*. (E. Mey.) Harv. (Rubiaceae). *Nature, Lond.*, **170**, 712.

STOJANOVIC, B. J. & ALEXANDER, M. (1958). Effect of inorganic nitrogen on nitrification. *Soil Sci.*, **86**, 208.

TAM, R. K. (1945). The comparative effects of a 50–50 mixture of 1:3 dichloropropene and 1:2 dichloropropane (D-D mixture) and of choropicrin on nitrification in soil and on the growth of the pineapple plant. *Soil Sci.*, **59**, 191.

TAM, R. K. & CLARK, H. E. (1943). Effect of chloropicrin and other soil disinfectants on the nitrogen nutrition of the pineapple plant. *Soil .Sci.*, **56**, 245.

THERON, J. J. (1951). The influence of plants on the mineralization of nitrogen and the maintenance of organic matter in soil. *J. agric. Sci., Camb.*, **41**, 289.

WIEDEMANN, E. (1924). *Fichtenwachstum und Humuszustand. Weitere Untersuchungen über die Wuchsstockungen in Sachsen*. Berlin. Paul Parey.

WILDE, S. A. (1942). *Forest soils*. 2nd Edn. Madison, Wisconsin. Kramer Business Service.

WOLDENDORP, J. W. (1963). The influence of living plants on denitrification. *Meded. LandbHoogesch., Wageningen*, **63**, 1.

# BACTERIA IN RELATION TO MANGANESE METABOLISM

G. A. ZAVARZIN

*Institute of Microbiology, Academy of Sciences, Moscow*

## *INTRODUCTION*

The existence of filamentous aquatic micro-organisms, precipitating manganese oxides has been known since the end of the nineteenth century and the pioneering work of Molisch (1910) and Lieske (1919) lead to the conviction that iron and manganese were metabolically interchangeable in the group of iron bacteria. *Leptothrix discophora* is a well-studied representative of this group (Mulder and van Veen, 1963; Rouf and Stokes, 1964). However, there is still no agreement as to the real role of these filamentous bacteria in the cycle of manganese in water (Wolfe, 1964).

The role of bacteria in the metabolism of manganese compounds in soil was first shown by Gerretsen (1937) and Leeper and Swaby (1940), and by Ukranian scientists whose data are summarized in the monograph of Vlasjuk (1962). The quantitative aspect of manganese metabolism in soil was studied at Rothamsted; it was established that manganese transformations in soil were governed by the microflora, abiogenic processes being of little importance (Quastel and Mann 1946). However, the bacterial species responsible for these transformations remain uncertain.

## *DIRECT OBSERVATION OF MANGANESE OXIDIZING MICRO-ORGANISMS IN SOIL*

In spite of the fact that the formation of manganese oxides in soil is easily seen, there have been no direct observations of soil manganese oxidizing bacteria. The micro-organisms which accumulate oxides of heavy metals are camouflaged by soil particles. Perhaps this is the reason why these micro-organisms were described only recently by Aristovskaya (1958, 1961, 1963), who used the methods elaborated by Perfiliev (Perfiliev and Gabe, 1961, 1964) for the study of lake sediments. This technique involves direct observation of micro-organisms in rectangular capillary tubes named 'pedoscopes'. Only the soil solution, but not soil particles, penetrate into the capillaries. Soil micro-organisms attach themselves to the inner walls and develop there. The pedoscopes are then removed from the soil, dried, fixed, stained and observed in an undisturbed condition under the microscope. Aristovskaya covered the inner walls of the capillaries with an organo-mineral gel extracted from the soil. The glass walls of the capillaries resemble the surface of soil particles; therefore the microflora developing in the capillaries may be regarded as the same as the microflora living on the surface of soil particles on substances in the soil solution. The experiment should take at least 6 weeks, so that equilibrium is reached (Parinkina, 1963). Details of the method are given by Aristovskaya (Aristovskaya and Parinkina, 1963; Aristovskaya, 1961).

In a study of the podzolic soils of Karelia (Aristovskaya, 1963), it was shown that in certain podzols a marked development of micro-organisms accumulating heavy metal oxides took place. In some localities these micro-organisms predominated. Most of these bacteria were forms recently described by Aristovskaya. She distinguished two groups:

(1) Micro-organisms utilizing organic substances in which the mineral compounds are accumulated as waste products and
(2) Micro-organisms accumulating iron and manganese specifically.

In the second group Aristovskaya included the genera *Pedomicrobium* and *Metallogenium*. The filamentous chlamydobacteria which are typical inhabitants of iron-bearing waters were not found in these podzolic soils.

The distribution of manganese oxidizing micro-organisms in the soil profile was determined by the soil moisture. Early in spring, when the snow thawed and much water was present in the soil, development of bacteria took place in the upper layers whilst in the summer it occured in the lower layers. In autumn the activity of the bacteria was interrupted. Bacteria oxidizing iron and manganese were often spatially separated, though this was expressed to different degrees in different soils. Micro-organisms oxidizing manganese flourished in the upper layers, as compared to the iron oxidizers, described in bottom sediments by Perfiliev and Gabe (1964). In sandy soils, in the presence of surplus moisture manganese oxidation occured in all parts of the profile; in heavy soils it was limited to the upper horizons; in podzols, zones of manganese oxidation occured which were separate under dry conditions.

The data obtained by direct microscopy have been supplemented by viable counts on mineral agar covered with a film of organo-mineral gel.

The distribution of manganese and iron accumulating organisms within the soil profile was the same as that detected by direct observation. Among the organisms forming colonies on the plates was *Pedomicrobium*. The absence of filamentous micro-organisms in soil was shown by Saveljeva (1965), using an elective method for the viable count of the manganese oxidizing *Leptothrix*. These organisms were absent from the soil as well as from the parts of the stream bed not covered with water; however, in the water of the stream the viable count of *Leptothrix discophora* was about $10^4$–$10^5$ colonies per ml.

Aristovskaya suggested that micro-organisms oxidizing iron and manganese play an important role in the genesis of podzolic soils. The formation of different forms of concretions of manganese and iron hydroxides in soils might be explained by their activity. The constancy of the environment in the different horizons of the soil causes the marked development of narrow layers of manganese and iron oxidizing micro-organisms. Such layers occur only in sandy soils whilst in heavy ones with a high water content the development of these bacteria occurs in the upper layers or even at the surface of the soil. The theory of biological formation of manganic and ferric concretions in podzolic soils is based upon the supposition that organic compounds of these elements are the main forms of migrating substances (Aristovskaya, 1963). This theory is supported by the following observations:

(1) there exists a specific microflora oxidizing organo-mineral compounds of iron and/or manganese in soil;
(2) the distribution of this microflora within the soil profile and different soil types corresponds to the conditions where accumulation of manganese and iron oxides occurs;
(3) the chemical composition of concretions corresponds to that predicted from our knowledge of the physiology of iron-manganese bacteria.

## *MICRO-ORGANISMS OXIDIZING MANGANESE*

Beijerinck (1913) isolated a specific manganese oxidizing organism, *Bacillus manganicus*, from the soil; however, Söhngen (1914) claimed that the oxidation of manganese was a non-specific function of micro-organisms producing hydroxy acids.

We started our study of manganese oxidation (Zavarzin, 1962) by performing experiments with soil percolators. Good agreement was obtained with the data of Quastel and Mann (1946); oxidation of manganese proceded exponentially. Treatment of the soil with antiseptics inhibited this oxidation, indicating that it was of biological nature. Inoculation of a sterile percolator with the solution from the working one caused the repetition of the cycle. For the isolation of micro-organisms inciting oxidation, Beijerinck's method was chosen. Spots of manganese oxides were obtained easily on plates of agar containing manganese carbonate but isolation of pure cultures was not achieved for a long time. Eventually, the mixture of bacteria was reduced to two pseudomonads; neither of them oxidized manganese in pure culture but each of 10 strains of one form oxidized manganese if combined with one of 10 strains of the other form. Thus the oxidation of manganese was brought about in the way previously reported by Bromfield and Skerman (1953) and Bromfield (1956), with the difference that they reported that oxidation of manganese was caused by a mixed culture of *Corynebacterium* and *Flavobacterium* which are not closely related to *Pseudomonas*. The media used by Bromfield were unsuitable for our strains; however, organic matter inhibited oxidation in both cases. We also confirmed Bromfield's finding that there was no oxidation of manganese, under the conditions tested, by the collection of strains of heterotrophic micro-organisms used by Söhngen.

It seems that oxidation of manganese is brought about by certain but not all heterotrophic forms. This conclusion is supported by observations of manganese oxidation on the shells of *Macoma baltica*. Among the large number of heterotrophic organisms present on the surface of the shells, the only one oxidizing manganese was *Mycoplana* (Zavarzin, 1964).

The medium originally recommended for *Leptothrix* by Lieske (1919) is not suitable for its cultivation as numerous colonies of fungi usually develop. Some of these oxidize manganese. Under the low power microscope it is sometimes possible to see brown spider-like growths between the hyphae of the fungus which are microcolonies of *Metallogenium*. The existence of this peculiar micro-organism was postulated 40 years ago by Perfiliev (1926) when he studied sedimentary ore formation in lakes. Agar media containing manganese acetate (see below) is quite selective for the detection of *Metallogenium* which is widely distributed in soils and water (Zavarzin, 1964).

Morphologically, *Metallogenium* appears to belong to the Hyphomicrobiales (Zavarzin, 1961*b*). The vegetative body consists of very thin filaments enclosed in an envelope of manganese oxide. The filaments are about 10–20 m$\mu$ in diameter and differ from any other filamentous appendages of bacterial cells, i.e. 'hyphae' of hyphomicrobia, stalks of caulobacters, flagella and fimbriae of the eubacteria. They have been called araia by Zavarzin (1963, 1964). Araia are the cores of long conical filaments consisting mainly of manganese oxides. The strains of *Metallogenium* studied in our laboratory have irregular bent filaments which are usually unbranched. Such filaments radiate from a common centre. After solution of the manganese oxides, even with gentle procedures, araia undergo rapid lysis. In addition to these peculiar filaments, *Metallogenium* produces round motile cells which are formed on the surface of the filaments by a process of budding. After a while the buds break away from the short protrusion to which they are attached and swim away. In liquid culture, mass release of such cells occurs and the medium becomes turbid; many round cells may be seen under the microscope. These cells produce new araia which soon become covered with manganese oxides.

The structure and life cycle of *Metallogenium* resemble those of *Gallionella* (van Iterson, 1958). Much of van Iterson's data were confirmed recently in our laboratory.

The physiology of *Metallogenium* is as peculiar as its structure. In culture *Metallogenium* develops only in symbiosis with a fungus. Without the fungus *Metallogenium* does not develop; all attempts to obtain the fungus free from *Metallogenium* by micromanipulation and other methods have been unsuccessful (Zavarzin and Epikhina, 1963). In culture with *Metallogenium*, the fungus remained sterile and therefore it was impossible to identify it. The fungus grew very well in different organic media but there were no signs of *Metallogenium* under such conditions; nevertheless, cryptic growth of *Metallogenium* took place indefinitely since the organism could be detected by inoculating the fungus in a manganese acetate medium. The form in which *Metallogenium* develops in organic media with the fungus is not known. The development of *Metallogenium*, judged by manganese oxidation, may be suppressed by mutation.

Oxidation of manganese carbonate in laboratory culture proceeds rapidly in media containing soluble starch. It was shown by direct determinations of $Mn^4/Mn$ (total) that manganous manganese is oxidized mainly to manganese dioxide. Oxidation proceeds at first exponentially and then linearly. The second step is presumably an autocatalytic oxidation whilst the linear process is thermostable and continues after heating at 100°.

The beginning of manganese oxidation in the culture is indicated by a rapid change in electrode potential which increases to an $E_h$ of $+0{\cdot}7$ volt whilst the pH changes only a little, dropping to the optimal value for growth of 6·2. Oxidation of manganese is very sensitive to the addition of easily utilizable organic substances, nitrogen and phosphorus. The improved growth of the fungus is not followed by oxidation of manganese compounds, however, The optimal conditions for manganese oxidation appear to be in media containing 2 per cent starch or gum-arabic and manganese carbonate. Incubation on the rotary shaker leads to an increase in the manganese oxidation rate with a concomitant suppression of filament development. Within 1 week a few mg. of manganese per ml. are oxidized.

It seems that *Metallogenium* does not oxidize ferrous iron even if it is in the form of an organic salt like oxalate. The increase in ferric ions may be due either to utilization of the organic part of the molecule or to the indirect action of the high potential produced by manganese oxidation. Thus *Metallogenium* is a representative of the manganese oxidizing micro-organisms *sensu stricto*. We have no evidence to suggest that manganous carbonate oxidation may serve as an energy-yielding process for the micro-organisms, since *Metallogenium* develops even in rich organic media. We state simply that the oxidation of manganese is the only process by which we can detect *Metallogenium*. The obligate symbiosis of *Metallogenium* with a fungus indicates that the nutrition of *Metallogenium* may be quite complex.

We can distinguish now between two species in the genus *Metallogenium*. *M. personatum* was observed in samples of water and mud by Perfiliev and Gabe (1961, 1964). This organism has straight filaments in which minute cells can be recognized, after manganese dioxide has been removed. *M. symbioticum* has irregularly banded filaments in which no cells are recognizable.

*Pedomicrobium*, described by Aristovskaya (1961, 1963), also belongs to this same group of budding bacteria. Species of *Pedomicrobium* closely resemble *Hyphomicrobium* and differ in their ability to precipitate oxides of iron and manganese. These organisms were observed in pedoscopes and their colonies were obtained on agar plus an organo-mineral gel. A stable laboratory culture was obtained in this medium but the isolation of a pure culture has not been reported so far. The cells of *Pedomicrobium* are connected to one another by irregularly banded filaments, on the ends of which the new cells develop by a process of budding. The three species of *Pedomicrobium* differ in their ability to precipitate the higher oxides of metals; *P. ferrugineum* precipitates iron, *P. manganicum* manganese, and *P. podzolicum* both these oxides. Recently a group of aquatic micro-organisms has been described by Perfiliev (Perfiliev and Gabe, 1964), in which micro-organisms oxidizing either manganese (*Caulococcus*, *Kusnezovia*, *Metallogenium*), or iron (*Siderococcus*, *Ochrobium*), could be distinguished.

It may be concluded, therefore, that the oxidation of both iron and manganese by *Leptothrix discophora* is exceptional and that specific manganese oxidizing bacteria do exist. Different groups of micro-organisms are important in water and in soil. It seems that filamentous bacteria and the members of the *Siderocapsaceae* do not occur in soil whilst the hyphomicrobia are common.

## *THE MANGANESE CYCLE*

The geochemistry of the manganese cycle has been discussed by Strachov (1947, 1962). It includes the following steps:

(1) extraction of manganese from soil and swamps;
(2) chemical oxidation and precipitation of manganese when it appears on the surface;
(3) transport and precipitation of manganese oxide suspensions in rivers, carrying them to the sea shore where the process is interrupted and the oxides are stabilized by the high pH of sea water.

Manganese may also be transported in the form of the manganous ion which is oxidized and precipitated in sea water because of the high $E_h$ and pH. Strachov denies the participation of a manganese oxidizing microflora in the formation of manganese ores for the following reasons:

(1) sedimentary iron and manganese ores lack unquestionable remains of bacteria;
(2) since iron and manganese are interchangeable in the metabolism of bacteria the sediments of iron and manganese should be analogous, but the distribution of these sediments corresponds rather to the chemical behaviour of the manganese and iron compounds;
(3) distribution of iron and manganese sediments corresponds with geological but not biological factors.

The biogenic hypotheses were discarded, therefore, in favour of physico-chemical ones (Krauskopf, 1957; Listova, 1962; Ahrrenius, 1963). The main difficulty in applying such abiogenic hypotheses is a kinetic one. In order to allow local precipitation of manganese it is necessary to provide high concentrations of manganese and rapid changes in $E_h$ and pH which probably only occur in volcanogenic processes. Nevertheless, the possibility of micro-organisms participating in manganese precipitation in thermal springs is not excluded (Hairiya and Kikuchi, 1964).

Biological agents do not reverse either chemical or geological processes; they act as catalysts determining the specificity and the rate of the process.

Microbiological data available at present demonstrate the following:

(1) the metabolism of manganese in soil is governed by micro-organisms. Abiogenic processes are of less importance;
(2) certain heterotrophic micro-organisms are capable of precipitating manganese oxides;
(3) there are micro-organisms capable of oxidizing manganese *and* iron. In environments where migration of iron is suppressed by physico-chemical factors, they oxidize only manganese;
(4) some bacteria are able to oxidize manganese but not iron, e.g. *Metallogenium*, *Caulococcus*, *Pedomicrobium* and *Kusnezovia*, representatives of the hyphomicrobia which were described only recently.

A hypothetical scheme of manganese migration including the participation of bacteria in terrestrial environments may be put forward as follows

(1) submergence of soil containing organic matter;
(2) reduction of manganese compounds and the transport of manganous ions into the soil solution and afterwards into large water bodies;
(3) oxidation of manganese by bacteria in soil and water at the aerobic/anaerobic interface or in the water mass;
(4) transport of manganese oxide suspensions in rivers to the sea where they are finally deposited;
(5) diagenesis of the primary manganese oxide sediments.

In this scheme steps 2, 3 and 5 are governed by bacteria. The passage of manganese into solution when soil is submerged is clearly observed when new reservoirs are flooded (Frantzev, 1959). Reduction of manganese is caused by the reducing conditions produced by bacteria decomposing plant remains and by direct action of bacteria on manganese oxides, including those strains of bacteria acting on manganese oxides but not on iron oxides (Troshanov, 1964). However, the data are scattered and it is difficult to estimate the quantitative role of bacteria in this process.

Rapid oxidation of manganese by bacteria in continuous culture conditions causes concentration of the oxides. In contrast, comparatively slow chemical oxidation causes the sediments to be spread over a large area. Such bacteria as *Metallogenium personatum* may flourish in plankton (Guseva, 1956; Řecháčová, 1964), producing concentrated suspensions of manganese oxides. These suspensions of manganese oxides may be concentrated further in the processes of migration, precipitation and diagenesis. The participation of bacteria in diagenesis is evident (Perfiliev and Gabe, 1961; Zavarzin, 1963).

This scheme remains provisional since there are no data on the relative intensity of chemical and biological processes but it has the advantage of being consistent with the participation of micro-organisms in contemporary manganese cycles and with essential features of the geochemical scheme elaborated by Strachov.

## *PRACTICAL RECOMMENDATIONS FOR THE CULTIVATION OF MANGANESE OXIDIZERS*

Many micro-organisms are capable of oxidizing manganese but usually only a few dominant forms are actually observed. Manganese oxidizers are easily isolated on media containing low concentrations of organic matter and c. 20–100 mg./l. of manganese compounds, the best one being freshly prepared manganese carbonate. The optimal range of pH is 6·0–7·2.

The presence of known agents of manganese oxidation may be checked as follows:

*Metallogenium* (Zavarzin, 1961*a*). The material should be cultivated on the following medium: manganese acetate, 0·01 per cent; agar agar, 2 per cent, distilled water.

The symbiotic colonies of the fungus and *Metallogenium* which develop in 7–10 days may be recognized by the peculiar morphology of their microcolonies under the low power microscope. Since the presence of the fungus is obligate the method is not quantitative.

*Leptothrix* (Saveljeva, 1965). The material should be cultivated in a medium made from the following constituents: Hay infusion: 5 g. of hay boiled for 5 minutes in 1 litre of distilled water are left overnight, filtered and then sterilized by autoclaving. Fifty ml. of this infusion are added to 750 ml. of a mineral solution containing $NH_4Cl$, 0·1 g./l.; $MgCl_2$, 0·05 g./l.; $KH_2PO_4$, 0·05 g./l.; Fe-citrate 0·01 g./l. in distilled water plus 1·0 ml. Hoagland's micro-element solution and 3·0 ml. of yeast autolysate. Twenty mg. manganese carbonate are added and the volume of solution made up to a volume of 1 litre. Vitamin $B_{12}$ is added at a concentration of 5 $\mu$g./l. One portion of the medium is solidified with 0·6 per cent agar whilst a second portion is solidified with 0·8 per cent agar. To prepare plates, a layer of 0·8 per cent agar is poured and, after gelation and drying, 5 ml. of inoculated 0·6 per cent agar is poured on top of this layer. The concentration of agar is important for the formation of separate colonies. The colonies are counted after 5 days. *Leptothrix discophora* gives rise to compact brown colonies with a woolly edge; *L. sideropus* gives irregular films. The method is quantitative and may be used to perform viable counts of *Leptothrix* in the natural environment.

*Pedomicrobium* (Aristovskaya, 1961) is grown as follows. One kg. of podzolic soil is extracted with 1 N HCl. The extract is neutralized and the precipitate collected. This precipitate is spread over the surface of agar in a Petri dish. Colonies of *Pedomicrobium* and other organisms develop in a month and may be recognized by their morphology.

## *REFERENCES*


ARISTOVSKAYA, T. V. (1958). O razlozhenii fulvokislot mikroorganizmami. (On the decomposition of fulvic acids by microorganisms.) *Pochvovedenie*, 40.

ARISTOVSKAYA, T. V. (1961). Akkumuliatsija zheleza pri razlozhenii organo-mineralnykh komplekcov gumusovykh veshchestv mikroorganizmami. (Accumulation of iron from the decomposition of organic-mineral complexes of humic substances by microorganisms.) *Doklady A.N., SSSR.*, **136**, 954.

ARISTOVSKAYA, T. V. (1963). O razlozhenii organo-mineralnykh soedinenii v podzolistykh pochvakh. (On the decomposition of organic-mineral compounds in podzolic soils.) *Pochvovedenie*, 30.

ARISTOVSKAYA, T. V. & PARINKINA, O. M. (1963). Novyĭ pochvennyĭ mikroorganizm *Seliberia stellata* nov. gen., n. sp. (A new soil organism *Seliberia stellata* nov. gen., n. sp.) *Izv. A.N., SSSR., ser. Biol.*, 49.

ARRHENIUS, G. (1963). Pelagic sediments. In *The Sea*. Ed. Hills, M.N. New York. Interscience.

BEIJERINCK, M. W. (1913). Oxidation des Mangancarbonates durch Bakterien und Schimmelpilze. *Verzam. Geschr.*, **5**, 141.

BROMFIELD, S. M. (1956). Oxidation of manganese by soil microorganisms. *Austr. J. Biol. Sci.*, **69**, 337.

BROMFIELD, S. M. & SKERMAN, V. B. D. (1950). Biological oxidation of manganese in soils. *Soil. Sci.*, **69**, 337.

EPIKHINA, V. V. & ZAVARZIN, G. A. (1963). Okislitelno-vosstanovitelnyi potentsial pri razvitii *Metallogenium*. (Oxidation-reduction potential during growth of *Metallogenium.*) *Mikrobiologiya*, **32**, 227.

GERRETSEN, F. C. (1937). Manganese deficiency of oats and its relation to soil bacteria. *Ann. Bot. N.S.*, **1**, 207.

GUSEVA, K. A. (1956). O dvukh planktonnykh mikroorganizmakh prinimaiushchikh uchastie v krugovorote zheleza. (Two planktonic microorganisms participating in the iron cycle.) *Trudy Biol. Stantsii 'Borok'*, **2**, 24.

HAIRIYA, Y. & KIKUCHI, T. (1964). Precipitation of manganese by bacteria in mineral springs. *Nature, Lond.*, **202**, 416.

ITERSON, W. VAN. (1958). *Gallionella ferruginea* Ehrenberg in a different light. *Verhandl. d. Koning. Neederl. Akad. Wettensch. Naturkunde*, **52**, 2.

KRAUSKOPF, K. B. (1957). Separation of manganese from iron in sedimentary processes. *Geochim. et Cosmochim. Acta*, **12**, 61.

LEEPER, G. & SWABY, R. (1940). The oxidation of manganous compounds by microorganisms in the soil. *Soil Sci.*, **49**, 413.

LIESKE, R. (1919). Zur Ernährungsphysiologie der Eisenbakterien. *Zentbl. Bakt. ParasitKde.*, *Abt. II*, **49**, 413.

LISTOVA, L. P. (1961). *Fiziko-khimicheskie issledovanija uslovii obrazovanija okisnykh i karbonatnykh rud margantsa.* (*Physico-chemical investigations of conditions for the formation of oxide and carbonate ores of manganese.*) Moscow. Academy of Sciences. USSR.

MOLISCH, H. (1910). *Die Eisenbakterien.* Ed. Fischer, G. Jena.

MULDER, E. G. & VAN VEEN, W. L. (1963). Investigations on the *Sphaerotilus-Leptothrix* group. *Antonie van Leeuwenhoek*, **29**, 121.

PARINKINA, O. M. (1963). Opredelenie neobkhodimykh srokov ekspozitsii pedoskopov v pochve dlia vyiavlenija mikrobnogo peĭzazha. (Determination of the necessary times of exposure of pedoscopes in soil for the demonstration of the microbial community.) *Mikrobiologiya*, **32**, 99.

PERFILIEV, B. V. (1926). Novye dannye o roli mikrobov v rudoobrazovanii. (New data on the role of microbes in the formation of ores.) *Izv. Geol. Komiteta*, **45**, 795.

PERFILIEV, B. V. & GABE, D. R. (1961). *Kapilliarnye metody izuchenija mikroorganizmov.* (*The capillary method of studying microorganisms.*) Moscow & Leningrad, Academy of Sciences, USSR.

PERFILIEV, B. V. & GABE, D. R. (1964). Izuchenie metodom mikrobnogo peĭzazha bakteriĭ nakopliaiushchikh marganets i zhelezo v donnykh otlozhenijakh. V kn; *Rol mikroorganizmov v obrazovanii zhelezo-margantsevykh ozernykh rud.* Red. Gurevich, M. S. Leningrad. (Methods for the study of bacteria accumulating manganese and iron in bottom deposits. In *The role of microorganisms in the formation of iron-manganese lake ores.* Ed. Gurevich, M. S. Leningrad.)

QUASTEL, J. & MANN, P. (1946). Manganese metabolism in soils. *Nature, Lond.*, **158**, 154.

ŘECHÁČOVÁ, V. (1963). Leptothrix echinata Beger in dem Stausee Kličava (Böhmen, Tschechoslowakei). *Zentbl. Bakt. ParasitKde.*, *Abt. II*, **117**, 189.

ROUF, M. A. & STOKES, J. L. (1964). Morphology, nutrition and physiology of *Sphaerotilus discophorus. Arch. Mikrobiol.*, **49**, 132.

SAVELJEVA, N. D. (1965). Metod kolichestvennogo ucheta okisliaiushchikh marganets *Leptothrix*. (A quantitative method for counting manganese-oxidizing *Leptothrix*.) *Mikrobiologiya*, **34**, 895.

SÖHNGEN, N. Z. (1914). Umwandlungen von Manganverbindungen unter dem Einfluss mikrobiologischer Prozesse. *Zentbl. Bakt. ParasitKde.*, *Abt. II*, **40**, 545.

STRAKHOV, N. M. (1947). Zhelezorudnye fatsii i ikh analogi v istorii Zemli. (Iron ore facies and their analogies in the history of the earth.) *Trudy Int. Geol. nauk. A.N., SSSR., Geol. ser.*, 73.

STRAKHOV, N. M. (1962). *Osnovy teorii litogeneza*, 2 izd. (*Essential theory of rock formation*, 2nd ed.). Moscow. Academy of Sciences, USSR.

TROSHANOV, E. P. (1964). Bakterii vosstanavlivaiushchiy marganets i zhelezo v donnykh. V kn; *Rol mikroorganizmov v obrazovanii zhelezo-margantsevykh ozernykh rud.* Red. Gurevich, M. S. Leningrad. (Bacteria reducing manganese and iron in bottom sediments. In *Role of microorganisms in the formation of iron-manganese lake ores.* Ed. Gurevich, M. S. Leningrad.)

VLASJUK, P. A. (1962). *Margantsove zhilennia odobrennia roslin.* (*Manganese for the restoration and promotion of growth.*) Kiev. Vid-vo UASHH.

WOLFE, R. S. (1964). Iron and manganese bacteria. In *Principles and Applications in Aquatic Microbiology.* Ed. Heukelekian, H. & Dondero, N. C. London. Wiley.

ZAVARZIN, G. A. (1961*a*). Simbioticheskaja kultura novogo okisliaiushchego marganets mikroorganizma. (Symbiotic culture of a new organism oxidizing manganese.) *Mikrobiologiya*, **30**, 393.

ZAVARZIN, G. A. (1961*b*). Pochkuiushchiesja bakterii. (Budding bacteria.) *Mikrobiologiya*, **30**, 952.

ZAVARZIN, G. A. (1962). Simbioticheskoe okislenie margantsa dvumia vidami *Pseudomonas*. (Symbiotic oxidation of manganese by two species of *Pseudomonas*.) *Mikrobiologiya*, **31**, 586.

ZAVARZIN, G. A. (1963). Stroenie *Metallogenium*. (The structure of *Metallogenium*.) *Mikrobiologiya*, **32**, 1020.

ZAVARZIN, G. A. (1964). K mekhanizmu osazhdenija margantsa na rakovinakh molliuskov. (The mechanism of precipitation of manganese on mollusc shells.) *Doklady Akad. Sci. USSR.*, **154**, 244.

ZAVARZIN, G. A. (1964). *Metallogenium symbioticum*. *Ztschr. f. allgm. Mikrobiol.*. **4**, 390.

ZAVARZIN, G. A. & EPIKHINA, V. V. (1963). Simbioticheskiĭ rost *Metallogenium*. (The symbiotic status of *Metallogenium*.) *Doklady Akad. Sci. USSR.*, **148**, 933.

# *DISCUSSION*

## THE GROWTH OF BACTERIA IN SOIL

*Chairmen: G. W. Harmsen, Institute for Soil Fertility, Groningen*

*H. L. Jensen, Statens Planteavls-Laboratorium, Lyngby*

*Dr. G. W. Harmsen*. It is difficult to synthesize the divergent material that we have heard in this session. Therefore, I will make only some short comments on the papers.

Dr. Clarke made a most important general observation when he said that whilst many of the determinations that have been made over several years (perhaps as long as soil bacteriology has existed) have been made with media and methods which were considered to give reliable results, there are many unexpected effects (such as the volume of the sample and the relation between the volume and the weight of addition of the substrate) which may invalidate the results. We must, therefore, check these older results carefully before beginning new investigations.

Another important thing that Dr. Clarke mentioned, was the influence of $CO_2$ concentration on metabolism in the soil. Many investigators have now found that $CO_2$ has a much greater influence than was originally expected.

Professor Mishustin raised the question of the importance of *Bacillus* spp. in the soil. The evaluation and the enumeration of the spore-forming bacteria in the soil is a very difficult problem because *Bacillus* spp. can, and often do, change from an active to a resting phase as spores. The numbers which are determined will not always, perhaps never, reflect the metabolic importance of this group of organisms in the soil; the numbers of bacteria determined must be thought of as the numbers of organisms which can become active on culture media.

The problems of polder soils, investigated by Dr. van Schreven and myself are somewhat unusual since they are concerned, not with growth in a more or less stabilized medium such as soil, but with growth during the very rapid change from brackish to arable land.

Mr. Goodfellow, working with Mr. Hill and Dr. Gray on the bacteria in dunes planted only with *Pinus nigra*, told us that they could not correlate the numbers of bacteria in the 2 rather different soil horizons with changes in the environmental conditions, even though the top layer was acid and partly podsolized and the sub soil was alkaline and not podsolized. Perhaps this was due to the use of inappropropriate methods.

I hope that these and other topics will form the basis of the discussion.

*Dr. T. R. G. Gray*. Many criticisms of soil mycological work have hinged on the fact that estimations of fungi in the soil have taken no account of whether the fungus is active or not. Dr. Harmsen has reminded us that it is possible to make similar criticisms concerning the activity of bacteria isolated from dilution plates. I would, therefore, like to pose a general question. If bacteria become inactive in the soil, how long are they likely to survive? My own feeling is that in a soil in the field, they would not survive very long since many other organisms would kill them, e.g. protozoa or fungi. On the other hand, bacteria can survive for very long periods of time in dried soil where their competitors are not active; indeed, dried soil has been used as a medium in which to preserve bacteria.

*Dr. T. Gibson*. One excellent example of survival is that of thermophiles in European soils.

*Dr. A. J. Holding*. Surely the occurrence of predominant soil bacteria in soil, many years after the addition of organic materials, indicates that these organisms can survive for a very long time after they have ceased to be active?

*Dr. T. R. G. Gray*. But are they totally inactive? They might still be active within microhabitats in the soil.

*Dr. A. J. Holding*. Possibly.

*Dr. A. N. Barker*. The question of survival is one which must be considered in the light of the conditions in the soil. Quite obviously, if any organism ceases to grow during summer conditions, it will die fairly quickly since the whole soil population is active. Under winter conditions, there may be a lack of competitors, predators, etc., and so a bacterium might survive for quite a considerable period of time. This is an analogy with bacteria in water.

*Dr. H. T. Tribe*. I wonder whether the bacteria in the C horizon soil described by Mr. Goodfellow, Mr. Hill and Dr. Gray are inactive for much of the time. When you think of the enormous populations and the small amount of nutrients present, the rate of turnover of these organisms must be exceedingly low. If it were possible to calculate the $CO_2$ release or the rate of oxygen uptake that would be needed for 1 or 2 divisions of each of these organisms, I imagine it would be very low.

*Dr. T. R. G. Gray*. The actual measured levels of organic matter in soil may not reflect the total amount and *turnover* of available nutrients. The organic matter in the C horizon probably comes mainly from roots and, presumably, there is a fairly good supply of exudates from the roots which disappear quickly.

*Dr. T. Gibson*. One of the implications of isolation work is that isolated bacteria can grow in the soil. One might think that those organisms isolated from a soil of overall pH 4·0 would be able to grow at pH 4·0. This raises the question of what is the mode of life of these organisms in soil? Are they capable of multiplying actively or are they simply persisting, either in the soil as a whole or in very small pockets in the soil. This is very important. Perhaps we should determine whether the bacteria are active in the soil before we study the organisms in detail in culture.

*Prof. N. A. Burges*. When we talk of a soil having a pH of 4·0, this is a bulk average; it is a laboratory measurement. However, the organism is influenced by the pH of its own micro-environment. In a number of the studies I have made on litter, I have found up to 2 pH units difference between individual needles. If you take a bulk pH of litter, you may get a value of 4·0, although individual needles have a higher pH. We must exercise caution in interpreting this data.

*Prof. E. N. Mishustin.* Similarly, you can isolate micro-organisms from acid, Russian soils which grow at a higher pH. The soil is a heterogeneous medium; in some parts you have organic materials with a high pH and in these microzones, micro-organisms develop whose optimum pH is higher than the average pH of the soil.

*Acad. A. A. Imshenetsky.* If you isolate bacteria from hot springs or acid soils it is usually impossible to grow these organisms under the same conditions as those in the natural habitat. Thus bacteria isolated from a soil of pH 3·5 will not grow below pH 4·4 in the laboratory. When you isolate thermophilic bacteria from hot springs (65–70°), they will not grow at temperatures above 55–60°. It is possible to find nitrifying bacteria on the bottom of the sea where the oxygen concentration is low. These are ecological paradoxes.

*Dr. P. J. Harris.* It has been reported that when *Arthrobacter simplex* is grown in culture, it has an incredible ability to absorb hydrogen ions. It has been suggested that this may help the organism to ameliorate its environment and produce conditions more favourable for its growth.

*Dr. T. R. G. Gray.* May I come back to Dr. Gibson's point that we should determine whether bacteria are active in soil before we study them in detail in culture. Although the isolation of a bacterium in large numbers on a dilution plate does not indicate activity at the time of sampling, it does show that the isolate in question must have been able to grow at some time in the soil. Therefore, I think that we must characterize these bacteria, be quite sure what we are dealing with, and then try to determine which precise conditions will permit the organisms to grow and multiply.

Using these ideas as a basis for projected autecological studies, we have shown that *Bacillus* spp. are very commonly isolated from our dune soil. We want to know where and in what form these bacteria exist in soil and whether the fact that they form a high percentage of the isolates on dilution plates is a reflection of their importance in the soil. In the case of *Bacillus* spp. we hope that it will be possible to show whether the cells are in spore form, vegetative form, or are just not there, by using the fluorescent antibody technique. Mr. Hill has stained soil with fluorescent antisera and found that he can detect cells of *Bacillus subtilis* and *Bacillus circulans* on soil particles. However, before this work can be made meaningful, it is necessary to have detailed information on the nature of the whole range of *Bacillus* spp. and other bacteria that are there, otherwise one will not be able to interpret any possible serological cross reactions which might occur.

*Dr. J. Wolf.* There are 2 things which must be considered when using fluorescent antibody techniques for following bacterial changes in soil. Firstly, the antisera will stain both living and dead cells, so that if one is interested in following the active flora of the soil, some other additional information would be required to prove activity. Secondly, whilst one can use the O-antigen of the vegetative phase when examining *Bacillus subtilis*, it cannot be used for other species because of a lack of specificity. One may have to use a mixture of polyvalent antisera and then it may work.

*Dr. E. Grossbard.* Professor Mishustin, may I ask what medium you use to determine the colony characters of *Bacillus* spp. and whether these characters are always constant within a species?

*Prof. E. N. Mishustin.* The medium we use is a mixture of 1 part beef extract agar with 1 part malt agar (pH 7·0). This medium will not support the growth of all spore forming bacteria. We can distinguish many 'sub species' or groups of strains of *Bacillus cereus mycoides*. The same is true of *Bacillus subtilis* and *Bacillus megatherium*, etc. We tend to use large inclusive groups.

*Mr. I. R. Hill.* Can you suggest which factors are responsible for the absence of *Bacillus megatherium*, *B. mesentericus*, *B. subtilis*, *B. granulosus* and *B. gasificans* from northern soils, since these species can grow on complex organic nitrogen containing compounds equally as well as *B. cereus*, *B. cereus mycoides*, *B. virgulans* and *B. adhaerens* which are present in northern soils? Could temperature be important? In 1957, Mahmoud showed that temperature had different effects on different *Bacillus* spp., especially low temperatures.

*Prof. E. N. Mishustin.* The composition of the soil microflora is closely connected with the soil type. In the grey soils of Southern Russia, *B. cereus mycoides* is practically absent, but if you add organic matter to these soils, this organism will begin to multiply and in 1–2 weeks become quite plentiful. *B. megatherium* is associated with cultivated soils and can be used as an indicator of the degree of fertility of the soil.

In some instances, the optimum and maximum temperatures for growth of different bacteria are dependent upon the climatic conditions of the soil, e.g. non-spore forming bacteria like *Pseudomonas* and spore forming types like *Bacillus agglomeratus*, *B. cereus* and *B. cereus mycoides*. Strains of *B. cereus mycoides* from the Moscow area have an optimum temperature of about 27° and a maximum temperature for growth of 36–37°. However, strains of the same organism isolated from grey soils at Tashkent have an optimum temperature of about 30° and a maximum temperature for growth of 42–43°. They are adapted to the climatic conditions. Contrasting with these organisms are such species as *B. megatherium*, *B. subtilis* and *B. mesentericus* which are not adapted to climatic conditions. I think that this is related to the role of these bacteria in the degradation of organic materials. Bacteria which are active in the early stages of degradation of organic matter are adapted to different climatic conditions; forms which develop during the later stages of mineralization of organic matter are not adapted.

It is also interesting that *Clostridium pasteurianum* (typical form) is widespread only in the middle part of the Soviet Union in soils rich in organic matter; it is almost absent in the Southern areas where it is replaced by *Clostridium acetobutyricum*.

*Dr. J. Wolf.* We have tried to test Professor Mishustin's thesis concerning the significance of certain spore forming organisms and their relation to soil fertility. I am afraid that when the work was finished, we were as wise as at the beginning. A number of difficulties must be considered. One is this. Very frequently, the spore population of a soil need not be an index of recent bacterial activity. One can visualize conditions where spores have been enriched from year to year without indicating that, at the moment of analysis, these are the organisms that are biochemically active.

The germination requirements for spores are totally different and unrelated to the nutritional requirements for growth of the vegetative organisms. Germination requirements vary. Some organisms require glucose e.g. *Bacillus subtilis*, *B. megatherium* and possibly *B. licheniformis*, whilst others, e.g. those in groups 2 and 3 of Smith, Gordon and Clark's scheme, have more complex requirements for such substances as alanine and adenosine. When a culture sporulates, as those who have tried to prepare a pure suspension of spores will know, unless you harvest the spores at the moment of formation, you run into the danger of recycling. For a short period certain factors prevent further bacterial growth. Some of these factors are well known. For example, if you have an excess of d-alanine produced, there is no bacterial activity until the ratio of the d to the l form is reduced to a level of 1/30; then vegetative growth starts again because germination starts again.

I think that the reason that we do not find certain spore forming organisms in certain soils is connected with this fact. The organisms may have been there at one time, but they have died out, either because they could not form spores or because the spores have germinated but could not grow.

*Dr. A. N. Barker.* I would like to add to this. We have shown that spore formers in soil, when held at temperatures at which they could not grow, were in the spore condition. However, under these conditions they started to germinate, and having germinated, they died slowly over the winter period. Consequently, we found a considerable decline in the number of spore forms. This is what Mr. Hill was referring to when he said there was a temperature effect. We feel that this temperature effect could explain the distribution of organisms, demonstrated by Professor Mishustin in Russian soils. The nutritionally simple forms might germinate and, because they could not grow, die off over a period of time. We do not think that any of these bacteria have a special optimum temperature that is different from other bacteria; rather, it is this germination under cold conditions, when they cannot grow, that is responsible for the absence of some of these forms in cold regions like the tundras.

*Miss E. S. Pankhurst.* No mention has been made of L-forms, stable or unstable, in the soil. Is this because there are none there or because nobody has looked for them?

*Prof. E. Küster.* A group of workers in Spain have isolated L-forms from soil and concluded that their formation might lead to the production of physiologically different strains in the soil.

*Dr. P. J. Harris.* It has also been postulated that L-forms occur in Egyptian soils. This was inferred from some plate counts which gave such high results that it did not seem possible to fit all the bacteria into the soil, if they were in a normal condition. The major criticism of this is the fact that it would have needed a more rapid and wholesale transformation from the L-form to a normal form (so that normal colonies would form on the plates), than is normally accepted.

*Acad. A. A. Imshenetsky.* The question of L-forms is very important, but somewhat confused. When *Bacillus cereus mycoides* is denerating, yeast like cells arise, the cell wall disappears and the cell contents liquefy. It is possible to find such degenerating cells in soil, cells which are not part of the life cycle, but which are formed because of the action of toxins.

*Prof. L. E. Casida Jr.* I would like to comment upon Dr. Holding's results. Whilst he looked at the effects of manganese on the numbers of organisms that grew on dilution plates, we have taken previously isolated strains and tried to find out whether manganese has any effect on them. We found that most of the soil bacteria were markedly stimulated by manganese. We showed this by impregnating small filter paper discs with a manganese solution and laying these on seeded agar plates. Zones of growth stimulation appeared, the sizes of which were proportional to the amount of manganese present. By cutting a hole in the agar and placing soil in it, we were able to assay the amount of manganese in the soil that was available to the bacteria.

*Dr. A. J. Holding.* Do you think this effect is specific for manganese? Would added iron have the same effect?

*Prof. L. E. Casida Jr.* Iron will stimulate growth slightly, but not nearly to the same extent as manganese.

*Dr. A. T. Bull.* Dr. Holding, when using chelating agents for studying metal requirements of bacteria, have you considered the direct inhibitory action of these chelators on the bacteria? It is well known that some of these substances, e.g. EDTA, have quite pronounced effects on cell wall metabolism, especially in the Gram positive bacteria.

*Dr. A. J. Holding.* We have no information on this.

Might I add that although 8-hydroxyquinoline seems rather a strange substance to use to study soil micro-organisms, it has been shown recently by Morrison and his co-workers that 8-hydroxyquinoline can replace the terregens factor as a nutrient. Dr. Rouatt pointed out that about 20 per cent of *Arthrobacter* strains are terregens requiring organisms, so that it looks as though there are substances in soil which have a similar action to 8-hydroxyquinoline.

*Dr. P. J. Harris.* We once made a medium for *Rhizobium* with 500–1000 times the normal concentration of EDTA in it. The organisms were not particularly happy, but quite a large proportion of them grew. This concentration of EDTA was infinitely higher than Dr. Holding found causing inhibition on his soil dilution plates. At any rate then, old laboratory cultures are quite resistant to about 1000 ppm. EDTA.

*Dr. G. Fåhraeus.* There is a difference between effective and ineffective strains of rhizobia, the former being more sensitive to manganese poisoning. What is the basis of this difference and that between the *Arthrobacter* group and other organisms? Could the difference be at the cellular level?

*Dr. A. J. Holding.* I don't know. I have been unable to obtain any useful information on this point.

*Dr. H. L. Jensen.* Dr. Chase, I understood that the effect of N-serve on nitrifiers was only temporary and that after some time it began to break down and lose its potency. Do you know whether breakdown occurs more rapidly after a second application of N-serve? Is there any evidence that the process of inactivation of N-serve is a biological process?

*Dr. F. E. Chase.* We have no evidence concerning the repeated introduction of N-serve into soil.

Oddly enough, there is an anomaly which we have come across in connection with DD compounds added to soil. When they were added in the autumn, they inhibited nitrification well into the summer; on the other hand, spring additions were relatively transitory. We are still confused about this.

*Dr. J. D. Menzies.* I think that there is a general principle concerned with soil nitrogen/fertilizer nitrogen relationships that goes further than Dr. Clark indicated. If we have 2 sources of nitrogen available for utilization, the soil and the fertilizer, and there is a limited sink or pool represented by the carbon demands of the soil, and a limitless sink or pool represented by the exhaustive uptake of mineral nitrogen by the plant, I think it follows that the more fertilizer nitrogen that goes into this limited pool, the more soil nitrogen will be available for the limitless pool. Although such systems can be very complex, the end results will be the same. It seems to me that we can envisage the reverse situation where the limited pool is not the soil carbon, but is the plant. There might be a large amount of carbonaceous material requiring nitrogen for decomposition and a plant whose uptake of nitrogen is limited in some way, maybe by the deficiency of another element, so that it is not going to crop exhaustively. The demand will be greater for the soil carbon than the plant uptake and so the reverse could happen. If this is so, theoretically it ought to be possible to balance the system with soil carbon demands and plant uptake so that there would be no effect of increased fertilizer addition on the uptake of soil nitrogen.

*Dr. F. E. Clark.* Yes, there are 2 rather different sources of nitrogen in the soil and these intermingle. The situation can be further complicated by considering the mathematics of some of these transformations.

*Dr. E. Timar.* Dr. van Schreven, when the polder soils have dried out, is there an increase or decrease in the organic matter content, or does it remain the same?

*Dr. D. A. van Schreven.* The nitrogen content of the humus seems to increase. During the time that the soils were flooded, the nitrogen (which was mineralized most easily) had, for the most part, disappeared. Consequently, when the polders were reclaimed, nitrogen deficiencies were common. This was compensated for by the addition of vast dressings of nitrogen. Part of this nitrogen was incorporated in the humus. This was a slow process. In those fields where stable manure was applied regularly, increases also took place.

*Acad. A. A. Imshenetsky.* I wish to stress the value of applying the principles of genetics to soil microbiology.

It is very important to establish the origin of different strains of bacteria when you are studying soil populations. When different species are introduced into the soil, e.g. *Azotobacter*, it is very difficult to differentiate the added strains from the indigenous strains. This could be done if special biochemical mutants were added. If you treated *Azotobacter* with a mutagenic agent, e.g. UV light, chemicals, etc., different mutants could be produced. These might be (a) one not synthesizing indole acetic acid, (b) a strain incapable of nitrogen fixation, (c) a non-slime producing type and (d) one with no antifungal action. By introducing these strains into soil, interesting data could be obtained on the action of *Azotobacter* in the natural environment.

*Prof. E. N. Mishustin.* We have studied the action of *Azotobacter* in my laboratory. We found that nitrogen fixing activity near roots is very low because the excretions from the root system are insufficient. I think that whilst the different biologically active substances, e.g. vitamins, can stimulate the growth of plants, this is not the main action of *Azotobacter*. *Azotobacter chroococcum* produces antibiotic substances, active against different fungi. We have shown that the root systems of different plants containing *Azotobacter* are poorly colonized by fungi.

*Dr. M. Alexander. Azotobacter* was undoubtedly chosen for inoculation studies because it is such an active nitrogen fixer in pure culture. However, this organism is not particularly competitive, not versatile, nor biochemically active. I wonder, in view of the comments that Dr. Brown has made in her presentation, and of some of the published reports of Professors Mishustin and Krasilnikov, if another organism might be more suited for inoculation studies than *Azotobacter*, an organism which is more competitive, more versatile and more biochemically active.

*Dr. W. Gams.* There are contradictory reports about the occurrence of *Azotobacter* on wheat roots. If one compares these critically, one gets the impression that there is a stimulation of *Azotobacter*, at least in the first stage of growth of wheat. Later on, inhibition may occur. This is contradictory to Dr. Brown's report. An interesting experiment was carried out by Daste who introduced root exudates into soil in order to produce an artificial rhizosphere; he got inhibition of *Azotobacter*. This experiment does not prove whether there is a direct antagonistic effect of the root exudates upon *Azotobacter* or whether other micro-organisms are stimulated which inhibit *Azotobacter* because of its low competitive saprophytic ability.

*Dr. M. Brown.* Occasionally, we have found that natural populations of *Azotobacter* are stimulated in the rhizosphere. This depends upon the age of the plant. With wheat, we have found occasionally that the very young plants stimulate *Azotobacter*, but this ability disappears as the plant ages. However, introduced inocula are always found on wheat roots, indicating that roots are not themselves inhibiting their development. Possibly *Azotobacter* is not normally present on wheat roots because there are too few cells present in the soil. They do not have a competitive advantage over other normal rhizosphere organisms which are far more numerous.

If you increase the number of cells in the soil, then, at least in the early stages of the seedling's growth, they are able to compete and can increase in number. We have shown this with peas which provide more exudates and give a bigger effect which can be picked up more easily.

*Prof. H. G. Schlegel.* Dr. Crosse has not mentioned the work of Stolp. He found, whilst phage typing *Pseudomonas* strains (200 from the soil and 100 plant pathogens), that many of the plant pathogenic pseudomonads were identical. What is more, he found that they could be grouped together with soil pseudomonads. As a result of this, he chose a soil isolate which was not pathogenic, but which belonged to the same group as *P. tabaci* and infiltrated leaves by suction with about $10^9$ of these bacteria. He got 3 necrotic spots and from these spots, isolated a pathogenic strain. This indicates that plant pathogenic bacteria may originate from soil saprophytes.

*Dr. J. E. Crosse.* Dr. Stolp and I have discussed this in considerable detail. The fact that an organism can induce a lesion in plant tissue does not necessarily give it the status of a pathogen. We have examined a lot of plant pathogens from the soil and have come to the opposite conclusion. The majority of the soil pseudomonads that we have looked at are pectinolytic forms like *P. marginalis*; they are all oxidase positive, very active biochemically and look quite distinct from the true plant pathogens. The true pathogens are all oxidase negative, much less biochemically active and differ in phage type and many other properties. The induction of a lesion by a bacterium under test conditions is no guarantee that it is what I would call an epidemiologically competent organism, i.e. one capable of maintaining itself in the field. We have found that virulence in these organisms is very complex; it may take 10 or more characters to make the bacterium an efficient pathogen. Some of the isolates from the soil only possess 1 or 2 of these characters, but this does not make them epidemiologically competent and there is no evidence that they are.

*Dr. R. L. Starkey.* With regard to the influence of carbon dioxide on the development of certain organisms, we have some unexpected results concerning the limiting effect of $CO_2$ deficiency on certain transformations, and in particular on the dissimilation of streptomycin. We found that an active streptomycin decomposing bacterium would not cause decomposition when an air stream was passed through the culture. If no stream of gas was passed through the medium, decomposition occurred at a rather rapid rate. This was not pursued to a satisfactory conclusion, but the implication is that $CO_2$, in some form, is required for this decomposition to occur. We encountered a similar sort of thing with the decomposition of cellulose. The addition of $CO_2$ to the system initiated cellulose decomposition which proceeded rapidly.

We must remember that neither of these investigations were made in soil, but in liquid media; there would be no opportunity for $CO_2$ to accumulate locally, hence overcoming this effect.

*Dr. D. J. Greenwood.* Such studies would be very valuable if we had a way of measuring $CO_2$ in water saturated soil systems, perhaps an electrode method similar to that used for measuring oxygen concentrations in soil aggregates.

*Dr. S. T. Williams.* Mr. Goodfellow remarked that *Streptomyces* spp. appear to utilize many of the more recalcitrant compounds, including humic acid, as judged by cultural tests. I think it is time that soil bacteriologists and 'actinomycetologists' took a leaf from the book of the mycologists and asked whether these organisms utilize these substrates in competition with other species of their own groups and also other groups of organisms. It would be interesting to design experiments, both in pure systems and in soil, in which resistant substrates were buried, and the capacity of these organisms to actually fulfil their apparent inherent ability for decomposition in competition with other members of the soil flora estimated.

*Dr. H. B. Gunnar*. We have made one observation which might be of interest here. We have been working with an organo-phosphate consisting of a pyrimidinal group and an ethyl acid phosphate with a sulphur atom hooked onto it. Now the sulphur, phosphorus and ethyl esters were very quickly demolished, leaving the pyrimidinal ring in the soil. We found that the population which predominated in the presence of this pyrimidinal ring consisted of *Streptomyces* spp. This may not have a causal relationship, but it gives some grounds for the belief that the presence of *Streptomyces* spp. is connected with their ability to metabolize this recalcitrant molecule.

*Dr. J. Went*. Mr. Goodfellow, are the forms you describe as cocci really cocci, or are they *Arthrobacter*-like organisms? In my studies of forest soils, I found only 2 or 3 isolates out of 100 that were cocci.

*Mr. M. Goodfellow*. The comparison of the morphological and physiological properties of these cocci with a control culture of *Staphylococcus afermentans* showed that most of them were very similar. Some of the remaining forms might be *Arthrobacter* spp.

# SUMMARY

# THE ECOLOGY OF SOIL BACTERIA: DISCUSSION AND CONCLUDING REMARKS[1]

R. L. STARKEY

*New Jersey Agricultural Experiment Station, Rutgers, The State University, New Brunswick, New Jersey, U.S.A.*

## *INTRODUCTION*

Opportunity to participate in the programme of the symposium is appreciated. It is a privilege to meet with this select and knowledgeable group. Indeed, it is an unusual event for soil bacteriologists to gather for consideration of their discipline; it is my impression that this is one of a few, if not the only, symposium that has been devoted exclusively to soil bacteriology.

It is recognized by all of us that there is lack of concern for, and knowledge of, micro-organisms in the soil and their significance in the soil environment. This is the case with scientists as a whole and even those microbiologists who are not soil microbiologists. This I ascribe to the complexity of the soil environment; the complexity of the microbial population and its activities, and the lack of readily recognized means for controlling micro-organisms for practical soil improvement and for increased crop production.

Some months ago it was suggested that I give consideration to summing up the problems and progress indicated by the speakers of the symposium and give some of my own views on future prospects in soil microbiology. The amount of important scientific information and the wealth of ideas presented was such that, even if I was able to properly evaluate the contributions of the speakers and delineate the most important and significant ideas that should be developed in the near future, sufficient time is not available for such a discourse. Unfortunately, I cannot consider all of the many excellent papers and, even if some are mentioned, I cannot hope to give them due attention. Most of my remarks will be generalizations and those that relate to my personal interests. Furthermore, I am no oracle who can anticipate the future

[1] Paper of the Journal Series, New Jersey Agricultural Experiment Station, Rutgers, The State University, Department of Biochemistry and Microbiology.

nor do I understand the implications of much that has been said here. I do not hope to secure your agreement to what I say, so much as to stimulate your concern for what I believe are subjects that deserve attention. There are so many items to consider that my remarks may justify the criticism of an unabridged dictionary for 'introducing too many characters at the expense of the plot'.

All speakers have presented carefully organized reports, many subjects have been explored, papers have been thought-provoking, and the discussion has been animated and illuminating. All of this has contributed to the success of the symposium. We have learned much, but, probably more important, it has become evident that our information is limited and that there is need for penetrating investigation of the soil bacterial population, its composition, its metabolic potentialities, and its effects on soil and plants.

Our concern, as I interpret it, is to learn as much as possible about soil bacteria and, hopefully, to learn enough to be able to predict the course of events if we know the properties of a soil and the environmental conditions. The accumulated information should enable us to indicate the means whereby the population can be regulated, and enable us to modify soils for increased crop production and crop improvement. As yet we are far from this goal.

Our subject of soil bacteriology includes the identification of the soil bacteria, the effects of the factors influencing their development in soil, their effects on soil, their metabolic activities and the interrelations between bacteria and between them and the other living things in the soil including plant roots.

The great differences in conditions of different soils, and in each of them from time to time, provide conditions for growth of a host of bacteria and other micro-organisms and promote the development of micro-organisms with diverse metabolic capacities. In fact, as mentioned by Pramer (p. 220), these capacities are almost inconceivably diverse. It is a fair working hypothesis that all natural substances can be dissimilated by soil micro-organisms, and some of these can be transformed in many ways by several different micro-organisms. This provides justification for the search in soil, which has been remarkably successful, for commercially important cultures for production of antibiotics, vitamins, enzymes, amino acids and other probiotics, for making assays of some of these compounds, for production of solvents, for synthesis of cortical hormones and for other practical uses.

It may be well to make some brief remarks on more specific items following these general statements.

## *SOIL BACTERIAL POPULATION*

There are several items concerned with the soil population. Probably no recent report on the soil population has impressed me so much as one by Casida, only briefly mentioned in his report here (p. 112), about one of the most abundant elements of the soil bacterial population. He found actinomycete-like organisms that are micro-aerophilic and that do not appear on conventional plating media. Because they were found at dilutions greater than those used for preparing plates, there is the implication that this group of micro-organisms is the group or one of the groups responsible for the great differences in numbers determined by direct and plate counts. It is certainly an important finding if this group of micro-organisms, hitherto unknown, is a dominant one, at least numerically. If this is so, certain questions come to mind. What do they do in the soil? Why are they so abundant? It is surprising to me that a dominant group of organisms should be anaerobic or micro-aerophilic. Why is this? Is the soil deficient in oxygen at regions where these micro-organisms develop? Is much of the soil environment for microbial development anaerobic? The discovery provides a new view of soil micro-organisms and serves as a basis for additional searches for other dominant groups of soil bacteria.

Interesting ideas arise from speculation as to what would have been the result of studies of soil bacteria if all soil bacteria had developed on the plating media commonly used to determine their numbers. Would principal attention have been devoted to predominating micro-organisms that are not even known now, to the exclusion of concern for the others? Indeed there might be advantages in having available for use culture media that favour growth of various kinds of bacteria, those that are most abundant, others that are less numerous, and those present in relatively small numbers. If such media were available, we should be able to make much more rapid progress in establishing the morphological and physiological characteristics of the soil bacteria.

Interest in soil bacteria as such has not been great in recent years which I ascribe to various factors, including the lack of good criteria for classifying them and good techniques for recovering them. Many of the bacteria seem to be poorly suited to classification by the methods used for pathogenic bacteria and those of food and water. Accordingly, they have been called physiologically inactive, but this may actually reflect our ignorance of their physiological properties. Also, there is little evidence that they participate in transformations of organic or inorganic materials that are considered by soil microbiologists to be important.

## *NUMBERS OF BACTERIA IN SOIL*

Little of value has resulted from determination of numbers for the purpose of making a census of the populations of soils. The older literature of soil microbiology is replete with data on numbers that are ignored. Census figures may also convey a false impression that the numbers of the members of the soil population are static or nearly so. There is more concern for numbers related to environmental conditions in soil. Marked differences in numbers have been noted in any one soil with changes in temperature, moisture, pH, and other conditions affected by climate, cultural practices, and plant growth. Indeed it has been observed that numbers vary greatly from one microzone to another nearby, due to lack of uniform distribution of the bacterial food supply and to differences in the heterogeneous physical environment depicted by McLaren and Skujins (p. 3) and by Bacon (p. 25). Furthermore, the associative and sequential development of micro-organisms as well as parasitism and predation of one on another result in rapid changes even in the types of micro-organisms in local areas. This was indicated by both Lockwood (p. 44) and Macfadyen (p. 70). Some of the larger micro-organisms such as the microscopic and near microscopic animals are even migratory, and fungi as well as actinomycetes spread as hyphae considerable distances from their initial food base. The important role of small animals in dispersing micro-organisms in soil was clearly indicated by Macfadyen (p. 71).

Total (!) numbers as determined by the plate method or direct count become relatively insignificant when one has visual evidence of a high degree of localization of the bacteria, even as dense and diffuse colonies (p. 172). The contact slide method has provided evidence that has broadened our concept of microbial development in soil materially.

Consciously or unconsciously one assumes an implicit direct correlation between numbers and activity, although this may be unjustified. It may be recalled that some years ago Jensen presented evidence that, at low temperatures, there was an inverse relation between numbers and activity. Accordingly, there are advantages in determining activity directly in preference to determining numbers where information on activity is actually the information being sought. For this purpose determinations have been made for consumption of oxygen, production of carbon dioxide, nitrification, reducing capacity and other chemical changes. I urge that, where numbers are determined, the investigator give thought to the purpose for which the data are sought and the applicability of the data for this purpose.

## *TAXONOMY AND CLASSIFICATION*

I am not convinced that we have exhausted the potentialities of conventional criteria for classifying bacteria. Gordon (p. 293) and others have provided evidence of this. Nevertheless, it seems to me that there is need for ingenuity in developing other tests than the conventional ones whose use characterize many soil bacteria as physiologically inactive, which I believe is a misconception.

The present state of the taxonomy of soil bacteria is less than perfect, but more can be gained by constructive effort to solve the problems than by condemnation. Let us hope that the development of numerical taxonomy will spark new interest in the taxonomy of soil bacteria and lead to better understanding of, at least, the dominant types. I know little about numerical taxonomy, but it has disturbed me that all characteristics have been given equal weight. In my ignorance I look with favour on weighting certain properties or observing great discrimination in selecting the properties and characteristics to be used as criteria. The 'affinity index' as used by Rovira and Brisbane (p. 337) seems to have promising possibilities. At least we should be willing to try to develop new ideas and use new methods and not be restricted by use only of present practices.

## *MOVEMENT OF BACTERIA IN SOIL*

The extent of migration of bacteria in soil was considered during one of the discussions (p. 93). Some observations made by our staff years ago indicate that migration of certain bacteria in soil is slow. The organisms concerned are legume bacteria, the extent of whose migration was estimated by the degree of volunteer inoculation of soybean plants from artificially inoculated ones in soils which lacked soybean bacteria. One-half of each of many plots of soil that had received various fertilizer treatments for about 40 years, was drilled with inoculated seeds and the other half with uninoculated seed. The plots had received no application of lime during the 40 years.

The plants from the inoculated seed became nodulated whereas all of the plants on the uninoculated parts of the plots remained uninoculated throughout the crop season, even those in the adjacent drill row of inoculated seed. Growth of all uninoculated plants was consistently poor in contrast to good growth of the nodulated plants. The results provided striking evidence of the beneficial effect of inoculation, and of restriction of the legume bacteria to a region close to the roots of the parent plant for several weeks. Possibly conditions are different with other soil bacteria that have greater capacity for saprophytic existence in soil.

## *SOIL ORGANIC MATTER*

During the symposium there has been frequent reference to the prominence of polyphenolic substances in the resistant soil organic matter, with particular reference to lignin as a constituent of the polyphenols. Since the polyphenols are major constituents of the soil organic matter, information about their origin, decomposability, and chemical reactivity is fundamental to understanding of the soil organic matter. The subject is particularly interesting to me because it is related to investigations with which our staff has been occupied for some time. These are concerned with tannins, which are polyphenols that have an affinity for proteins. Some of the tannins are themselves resistant to microbial attack, and they give proteins, with which they combine to produce complexes, considerable resistance to decomposition. The effects of tannins on decomposition of organic compounds are greater in forest soils than in grassland because forest vegetation contains much more tannin than grass.

The plant tissue constituents form insoluble tannin complexes that may coat plant structural constituents and insulate them from microorganisms, as was indicated by Handley some time ago. There is still another prominent effect that reduces the susceptibility of the major plant constituents to decomposition. Exoenzymes, which are proteins, combine with tannins to form complexes and thus are inactivated. Consequently, decomposition of plant substance, whether it is that of succulent plants or mature ones, is affected materially by tannins. Cellulose and hemicelluloses are two of the most abundant plant constituents. Decomposition of these, as well as other polysaccharides, fats and other compounds, whose initial stages of decomposition are hydrolyses by exoenzymes, is vulnerable to inhibition by tannins. Therefore, I would add tannins to the substances that have important effects on decomposition of organic matter in soil. Also I suggest the desirability of thorough study of the tannins, lignins and other polyphenols to establish their roles in the persistence of organic matter in soil and in determining the physical and chemical properties of soil. It is my opinion that the extent of our knowledge of the soil organic matter will closely parallel knowledge of the soil polyphenols.

## *THE PRIMING EFFECT OF ORGANIC MATTER*

The apparent acceleration of decomposition of the soil organic matter by addition to soil of fresh plant material was discussed by Clark (p. 449), together with other phenomena, the interpretations of which are equivocal. There have been various interpretations of the so-called priming effect of added organic matter, but proof is lacking for any of them. Indeed, the effect may be more apparent than real, and there is need for more information to establish the meaning of the results. Might there be exchange of proteins, polysaccharides or other constituents of the adsorbed or otherwise occluded compounds of the soil organic matter for those of the added organic substances? Are there transaminations, or transacetylations or other such reactions between the substances in the soil organic matter and added compounds? If so, decomposition of the substances released from the soil organic matter would provide the basis for a misinterpretation of the results as accelerated decomposition of the soil organic matter. Also, the possible effects of changes in ionic concentration, including pH, following the addition of organic matter are obscure. Various possibilities should be explored to elucidate the phenomenon.

## *LIMITS OF MICROBIAL ACTION*

During the discussion the proposal was made that certain conditions under which there is no evidence that micro-organisms act, should be accepted and thereby removed from further consideration (p. 284). Whereas fundamental laws of physics and thermodynamics establish certain limits for microbial action, the potentialities of micro-organisms are so great that one should be prudent in designating limits of possibility for micro-organisms. I suggest that, in research, we proceed with an open mind, perception and perspicacity. Who would venture the concept of chemolithotrophy now if the principle was unknown? Who would have rationalized the existence of antibiotic-requiring bacteria or of micro-organisms that grow in solutions saturated with copper sulphate at pH zero? He who discloses the impossible frequently establishes the new principles.

## *PESTICIDES*

It is probable that problems related to pesticides will be with us for a long time. Alexander (p. 270) discussed some of the effects of micro-organisms on them and provided evidence that many of the herbicides are decomposed or transformed to non-toxic products. Although certain herbicides are resistant to microbial attack, some of the insecticides are even more stable and seem to be almost completely unaltered by micro-organisms. Although it may be necessary to tolerate the use of pesticides in practical agriculture, is it necessary that use of all pesticides be accepted that meet the requirements for control of the pests? Possibly criteria of acceptability should be established, one criterion of which might be that any compound which is not completely degradable in specified time and under certain conditions, and which is absorbed by plants and persists in the animal, cannot be used! There are probably pesticides that are so resistant that they should not be used. It is my opinion that attention should be devoted, not only to the effectiveness of the compounds as pesticides, but to their effects on man as well. A similar decision was reached about household surfactants, the cross-linked alkyl aryl sulphonates. Their use is being discontinued and biodegradable substances are taking their place.

## *RHIZOSPHERE*

There is justification for increase in concern for the rhizosphere in that the zone is one of the most significant areas in the soil, as regards micro-organisms. It is the region of absorption of plant nutrients and the region where the impact of micro-organisms on the plant are most direct. There is considerable information on the subject but there seem to be more unanswered questions than answered ones. Among the persisting questions are the following. What are the favourable and unfavourable effects of rhizosphere micro-organisms on plant development? To what extent do micro-organisms affect absorption by plants of mineral substances, and, equally important, organic compounds? Assuming organic compounds of microbial origin are absorbed, what effect do they have on plant vigour, rate of growth and the quality of the plant as food and animal feed? What is the possibility of modifying the microbial population of the rhizosphere by inoculation or other means to promote plant development?

Although some answers to the last question have been given by Krasilnikov (p. 422) and others over a period of years, I am not convinced that significant evidence has been provided to justify practical use of inoculation in most soils with most crops by the methods indicated. I have what I hope is a healthy scepticism. It is of my opinion that the evidence is insufficient to justify use now of rhizosphere micro-organisms as inoculants to increase crop yields, improve plant quality or control disease.

It was fortunate that I had the benefit of the suggestive results and ideas presented by Brown and associates before my remarks were made (p. 531). I am now more sympathetic than is indicated by some of my ideas stated in the meeting of the Botanical Congress held in Montreal (Recent Advances in Botany, 1961). If, indeed, inoculation has value, the parameters for use should be established. They should define the cultures that are to be used, the soil and plant conditions under which benefits can be derived from inoculation and the methods of inoculation.

I hope that I have not conveyed the impression that I am opposed to inoculation as such. I will consider it one of the greatest events in soil microbiology and a great boon to practical agriculture when inoculants can be used to solve problems of crop production.

There is still limited knowledge and understanding of the many ways in which micro-organisms and higher plants affect one another in the rhizosphere, but the information that is available is so significant that thorough and detailed study of the interrelations should be made. This might include investigation of the exudation and leakage of organic matter from roots, the organic compounds produced by micro-organisms in the rhizosphere, the kinds and amounts of organic compounds absorbed by plants, their effects on plant development and the quality of the plant as food and feed, and the control of conditions in the rhizosphere by inoculation, fertilization and intensity of plant illumination. Investigations of these subjects have been hampered by lack of suitable methods to obtain the desired information. Therefore, there is need for more sophisticated methods to study the interrelations between micro-organisms and plants. The needs include methods to cultivate normal plants free from micro-organisms for long periods of time, methods for viewing the micro-organisms about roots, methods to isolate the micro-organisms as viable cells and methods to determine the amounts and kinds of organic compounds produced by micro-organisms and by roots of the plants in the rhizosphere.

## *PLANT IMMUNITY*

Related to the development of micro-organisms in the rhizosphere is the subject of plant immunity. One may wonder why tender plant roots resist penetration and attack by soil saprophytes that occur in abundance on the root surfaces. Evidence is accumulating that plants as well as animals contain protective compounds or have systems that keep in check development of all but the small group of micro-organisms known as phytopathogens.

Relatively little is known about the nature and diversity of the compounds involved in protecting the plants but there is evidence that the resistance of plant tissues to microbial attack is due principally to positive factors and not to physical barriers, to lack of microbial food in the tissues or to reaction or redox potential unfavourable to the micro-organisms. Even when saprophytic bacteria are introduced into the tissues they fail to develop. Furthermore, even in symbiosis of micro-organisms and plants, as with legume bacteria and mycorrhizal fungi, penetration of the plant tissues is restricted.

## *NITROGEN FIXATION*

It is fitting that in a discussion of soil bacteriology at least brief remarks should be made of nitrogen fixation and nitrification. Regarding the former, I was impressed by the remark of Russell (p. 82), that non-symbiotic nitrogen fixation is of no practical importance in agricultural soils. I support this idea and would place responsibility on those who claim practical value, for substantial evidence in support of their claim.

The possibility that nitrogen can be fixed by *Azotobacter* from products of anaerobic decomposition of cellulose should not be considered lightly. I refer to the results of Imshenetsky (p. 261), which are similar to those reported by Jensen some time ago. However, from a practical viewpoint, little expense for labour and land to provide cellulose for nitrogen fixation can be justified at the current low price of fertilizer nitrogen (9 to 10 cents per lb. of ammonium nitrogen in the U.S.A.).

The value of symbiotic nitrogen fixation is well established and the fundamentals of its exploitation are known, but there is still need for more information on legume bacteria and inoculation of legumes. This includes need for information on the relationship of bacteria such as *Agrobacterium radiobacter* to the rhizobia, mentioned by Fåhraeus (p. 399). His remarks on transformation among legume bacteria are highly suggestive, but information on the subject is limited. It is even conceivable that transformation may serve as an effective means of modifying many bacteria to obtain types with desirable new characteristics. This subject remains almost completely unexplored for soil bacteria, but progress will depend on more knowledge of the biochemistry of the bacteria and the genetic changes that one wishes to make.

There is also need for methods to preinoculate seeds of legumes that will insure persistence of the bacteria in a viable state. Although the subject has received considerable attention in recent years, the results have been somewhat less satisfactory than desired.

## *NITRIFICATION*

My personal opinion about the necessity and desirability of the process of nitrification for plant growth is the same as that of Chase (p. 608). It is probable that it would be desirable to eliminate the process completely in soils supporting some crop plants if it can be established that the crops can develop well on ammonium nitrogen; the desirability of preventing nitrification will depend on additional knowledge of the utilization of ammonium nitrogen by plants. In any case, it would be desirable to know how to control the nitrification process, how to promote it and how to inhibit it, because one can conceive conditions under which it would be desirable to hold the process in check or to accelerate it. The discovery by Goring of a compound that inhibits oxidation of ammonium nitrogen by nitrifying bacteria provides a tool and a concept with great prospects for practical use.

## *MICRO-ORGANISMS AND MINERAL SUBSTANCES*

I have long been fascinated by the transformations of mineral substances by micro-organisms, their potentialities for altering not only nitrogen but also sulphur, phosphorus, iron, manganese and other elements. These transformations affect the solubility of the compounds of the elements and their oxidation and reduction. Some of the reactions involved are still incompletely known and understood. The reports of Schlegel (p. 234), Holding (p. 516), Chase (p. 593), Zavarzin (p. 612) and others contributed significant information to the subject. Unfortunately, time is lacking to discuss these interesting reports.

## *CONCLUDING REMARKS*

It is probable that soil microbiologists would agree that there are almost unlimited interesting and important potential studies of micro-organisms in soil, their relationships to one another and to plants, and their transformations of the organic and inorganic soil constituents. There would probably be general agreement that the likelihood of making discoveries that would profoundly affect practical agriculture is slight. Still, soil is one of our greatest natural resources, and the soil microbiologist makes an important contribution by explaining the importance of micro-organisms in modifying the organic and mineral substances in the soil environment and in establishing the influence of these changes on plant development. He also becomes involved in the interrelations between the soil saprophytes and phytopathogens in soil and the influence of these relations on parasitism of the plant. Extension of knowledge of the activities of micro-organisms in soils will result in more effective use of soils for plant production and will indicate the potentialities and limits of methods for control of micro-organisms for crop production. The prospects for the future are great, and limited principally by the competence of the soil microbiologist for conjecture and by his knowledge, wisdom, and diligence.

I am grateful to you for this opportunity to speak to you and for your patience. All good things come to an end, and so it is with this symposium. In closing I add an additional word of thanks to the organizing committee for the privilege that they provided us to meet to exchange ideas on the subject of soil microbiology that dominates our professional life and possibly even haunts us at times.

# AUTHOR INDEX

(Contributors to discussions included)

# MICRO-ORGANISM INDEX

# SUBJECT INDEX

The **Ecology** of soil bacteria: an international symposium, edited by T. R. G. Gray and D. Parkinson. [Toronto] University of Toronto Press, 1968.

681 p. illus. 25 cm. $21.75 Can.

(C***)

Includes bibliographies.

1. Soils—Bacteriology—Congresses. 2. Soil micro-organisms—Congresses. I. Gray, Timothy R. G., ed. II. Parkinson, Donald, 1891- ed.

QR111.E25 631.4′6 68–101074

Library of Congress [2]